READINGS IN MATHEMATICAL ECONOMICS

Volume II
CAPITAL AND GROWTH

READINGS IN MATHEMATICAL ECONOMICS

Volume II
CAPITAL AND GROWTH

Edited by
Peter Newman

The Johns Hopkins Press
Baltimore

Manufactured in the United States of America
Library of Congress Catalogue Card Number 68–9695

INTRODUCTION

The purpose of this collection is to bring within easy reach of students and researchers alike some important articles in mathematical economics which are at present scattered over a wide range of sources. It is in the nature of the subject, especially during its formative years, that its major contributions have appeared in an extraordinarily varied set of publications, in mathematical and in economic journals, in various symposia, and in other ad hoc collections. This makes it difficult and expensive to fish for the relatively few items one needs, and it is therefore useful to have the best of them assembled in one place.

I have tried to follow a few principles of selection in choosing the papers that appear in these volumes, although not to the point of avoiding all idiosyncrasy. The chief criterion is that the article be of live interest to current teaching and research in mathematical economics; this has resulted in the inclusion of real classics in the field, for example, the papers by Barone, von Neumann, and Wicksell, even though they were published long ago. On the other hand, papers that were and are gems of analysis but which treat subjects that have been rather well worked over since—almost any article by Edgeworth—have been excluded.

A subsidiary criterion (of this lexical preference structure) is the degree of availability to the average student, and it is on this score alone that the names of Georgescu-Roegen, Morishima, and Samuelson are missing from the list of authors, since each has recently published collections of his articles. Similarly, fundamental papers by Bergson, Frisch, Hicks, Hotelling and Slutsky, to name only a few, are not here only because they are readily available in other books of readings. Two glorious articles, one by Ramsey on optimal savings and the other by Malinvaud on efficient capital accumulation, were originally scheduled to make their appearance but have not done so because they were booked earlier for the American Economic Association's forthcoming *Readings in Welfare Economics,* edited by Kenneth Arrow and Tibor Scitovsky.

This reference reminds us that the boundaries of mathematical economics are not those imposed by subject matter but only by method, and so they change greatly over time. As the "higher mathematics" of one generation becomes standard high-school fare for the next, that part of economic theory designated as "mathematical" retreats to higher and higher ground, until much of what was yesterday the playground of a few blithe spirits becomes today the parade ground for an army of graduate students. And there is no reason to expect this process to converge to any limit, for the application of mathematics has no upper bounds except those on the mathematical economist's own ingenuity and love of adventure.

What is presented here is, very roughly speaking, a composite photograph of some of the best mathematical economics of the last generation that is still alive for us today. If such a photograph had existed thirty-two years ago its subject matter would have looked rather similar but its techniques considerably different; today that collection would probably be called "Readings in Economic Theory" and I believe that precisely the same statement would apply to the relation between the present enterprise and a similar collection edited in the year 2000. The great subjects of value, capital, and growth will still form the central concern of economic theory, but their manner of handling may change in radical and unpredictable ways.

It is now much too late in the day either to argue against the usefulness of mathematics in economic analysis or to claim that the use of mathematical reasoning is by itself a guarantee against lapses of economic logic and rigor. Indeed we have long since reached the stage at which, as Frisch has pointed out, if an economist wants to have his work become popular in the profession he presents it as a coherent model, symbolically expressed. To say this is not to assert that every such model is useful or relevant, or even that it is economics. But taken in conjunction with the rapid growth of econometrics, which is the other half of the triumph of mathematics in economics (and which is not covered here at all), it does imply substantial progress in the evolution of economics as a science.

The ratio between mathematical and economic content varies quite markedly over these two volumes, being high in the comparatively settled parts of the subject where the recent focus has been on tidying up and making rigorous those basic theories which have been with us for some time, as in the theory of general static equilibrium; and rather low in the more recently opened-up sections of the territory, where a natural premium has been placed on rapid reconnaissance as opposed to overconcern about rigor. These are only tendencies, however, and even in the areas of latest exploration, such as the theory of "optimal" growth, there is plenty of difficult and rigorous mathematics.

This latter field, incidentally, is in such a state of ferment that no attempt has been made to include more than a tiny but representative selection of the flood of papers now pouring from the press. Just how large the theoretical literature on economic growth has become may be judged by the bibliography placed at the end of Volume II. The basis for this selection was the bibliography given in Hahn and Matthews' brilliant survey article in the *Economic Journal,* December 1964. Their selection was considerably broadened in scope and extended in time to comprise the period 1946 to early 1967; even so, this long list is not intended to cover the even vaster literature on economic development.

The reader of this collection is assumed to have available to him standard texts on those branches of mathematics normally used by economists, such as analysis, linear algebra, and elementary point-set topology. But there are certain specialized topics in mathematics, peculiarly relevant for economics, that are not as yet normally included in such texts. So Volume I begins with a number of purely mathematical articles which deal with some of these topics. Many of them were written in response to the needs of economic theory, broadly considered, and some of these new mathematical inventions have become almost independent disciplines of their own, of much intrinsic interest and also of wide application to empirical sciences other than economics; this is particularly true of the tools of linear and nonlinear programming. It is good to know that the traffic between mathematics and economics is not all one way.

A book reviewer in *The Economist* once remarked that Sir John Hicks' *Value and Capital* would provide the reader with that "authentic desiccated thrill" which in his view was the mark of a fine piece of abstract, mathematical economic theory. For myself I can testify to the reality of the thrill but not to its aridity. To read for the first time a masterwork like von Neumann's paper on general equilibrium is not merely an exercise in formal aesthetics but also a profoundly exciting experience, like one's first sight of an El Greco or of the soaring symmetry of Kilimanjaro. To reflect at more leisure on the full and deep implications of the paper is a thoroughly satisfying experience, like dinner at a well-ordered restaurant. Indeed the pleasure I have had in editing the whole collection has been much like that of showing hospitality, that sense of well-being which comes from being able to offer one's guests a profusion of refined yet substantial dishes. The pleasure will be complete if the reader shares some of this enjoyment.

Thanks are due to the respective publishers and authors for permission to reproduce the various articles and extracts in this collection. These have been reprinted in their entirety by direct photographic reproduction, a method which is economical and preserves the flavor and pagination of the original but makes correction of misprints rather difficult. A few authors have made such corrections in their papers, but otherwise the articles appear here exactly as originally published.

I am grateful to K. J. Arrow, W. J. Baumol, L. R. Klein, T. C. Koopmans, and E. S. Mills for helpful suggestions, to Takashi Tsushima for doing most of the work on the bibliography in Volume II and to Mr. John Gallman and Mrs. Barbara Miller of The Johns Hopkins Press, who did far more than their share of the editorial chores. The responsibility for selection and arrangement, however, rests with the editor alone.

PETER NEWMAN

The Johns Hopkins University, Baltimore
February, 1968

CONTENTS

Volume II: Capital and Growth

The pagination for this volume is given in brackets at the bottom of each page; the unbracketed page numbers are those of the original publication.

PART I

Capital Theory

1

A MATHEMATICAL ANALYSIS OF DR. ÅKERMAN'S PROBLEM

By K. Wicksell

In the following pages, we shall attempt a mathematical solution of the problem we have just been discussing. We start with the assumption that production is continuous and that capitalization takes place on the basis of the rate of interest for a moment of time. Since machines are in fact discrete and are not therefore capable of being divided into infinitesimal parts, our result will of course only have an approximate validity. But no more can be obtained by any other method of approach.

Using an amount of labour a, a labourer (or group of labourers) produces a capital-good, e.g. an axe, which is instantly taken into employment. If used normally the axe can remain in use for n years after which it is devoid of any value. We assume that the axe is so small (or that the group of labourers required so great) that the *length of time* required for its production compared with its actual life-time need not be taken into account. Our calculations are thus simplified to a considerable extent without, however, losing in force. Naturally it does not follow that a is a negligible quantity.[1] If, however, a labour-year (or else the work of a whole group of labourers for a year) is taken as the unit for the services of labour, a becomes quite small and its reciprocal $\frac{1}{a}$ quite large.

The exchange-value of an axe to the man who buys or employs it naturally depends on its utility for his purposes. We make the additional assumption that this value is known, and that it is estimated to be b (shillings) per annum ; b is therefore the *sum* of the undiscounted value of all its uses for one year. Let us assume that the axe is applied uniformly throughout the year (or years). If Δt is a fraction of time, then the value of the axe's uses for this time is clearly $b.\Delta t$. If we relate the

[1] For example, in modern house-building all the different parts and accessories of the house are manufactured at the same time as the foundations are laid, so that the whole house, even though actually requiring an *amount of labour* corresponding to ten labour-years, is in fact completed in the course of a few months, perhaps only a few weeks, i.e. in a negligibly small period of time as compared with the house's own probable duration.

axe's employment through t years to the present moment and let r be the rate of interest, we obtain its present value by dividing $b\Delta t$ by the binomial expression $(1 + r)$ raised to the power t. Thus—

$$\frac{b.\Delta t}{(1+r)^t} \qquad (1)$$

Let $1 + r = e^\rho$ where $e = 2 \cdot 718 \ldots$ is the base of the natural system of logarithms and ρ is thus the "natural" logarithm of $1 + r$, i.e. the ordinary logarithm divided by $\cdot 434 \ldots$ It can also be expressed in terms of r by means of the logarithmic series, $\rho = \log_e(1+r) = r - \frac{r^2}{2} + \frac{r^3}{3} - \ldots$ which is convergent for $r \leqq 1$. ρ is the instantaneous rate of interest for a moment of time, or what is called in German "Verzinsungsenergie". ρ and r more or less coincide with sufficiently small values for r; otherwise ρ is always less, if only insignificantly, than r (if r is 5 per cent, $\rho = 4 \cdot 88$ per cent, and if ρ is exactly 5 per cent r is $5 \cdot 13$ per cent, and so on). In each case they stand in a definite arithmetical relationship to each other, and it is not very incorrect to assume them to be wholly substitutable for each other.

Substituting in this manner, we obtain for the value of each of the axe's uses discounted to the present—

$$b.e^{-\rho t}\Delta t \qquad (2)$$

Since t is to be taken here as continuously variable, we obtain the present value of all the axe's uses and therefore its own present value by the summation (integration) of the above expression between 0 and n, two points in time

$$b\int_0^n e^{-\rho t}dt = b\frac{(1-e^{-\rho n})}{\rho} \qquad (3)$$

(corresponding to the normal calculations for annuity-loans). If r, and consequently ρ also, were so small that in expanding the series for the exponential function—

$$e^{-\rho n} = 1 - \rho n + \frac{(\rho n)^2}{1.2} - \frac{(\rho n)^3}{1.2.3} + \text{etc.},$$

we need only include the first two terms, the above expression is reduced to $b.n$; in other words, the present value of the axe is equal to the (undiscounted) value of all its uses. If we include the first three terms, we get $bn\left[1 - \frac{\rho n}{2}\right]$, i.e. the total use-value discounted by simple interest on it for half its period of use.

In equilibrium, the value of the axe coincides with its costs of production. Let l be wages per head per annum. Then—

$$b.\frac{1 - e^{-\rho n}}{\rho} = al.^{1} \qquad (4)$$

This equation holds for a, b, l, ρ (or r), and n, as they are determined in an equilibrium situation. If equilibrium is not yet reached, equation (4) describes the following conditions instead. Let us assume that not only is b (the value of the axe's use for a year) given, but also ρ and r, r being taken as the usual rate of interest current at the time. Now if n and a, the life-time of the axe and the amount of labour needed for its production respectively, were also to be technically given (as we often take them to be), the R.H.S. of the equation would represent the sales-value of an axe (l the wages per annum multiplied by a the unit of labour) which is received by the axe-manufacturers. Now although the magnitude of neither n nor a is given, they are *technically related* to each other. By investing more labour on an axe we can increase its durability, all other properties remaining constant; n is thus a function of a and a of n, i.e. of the period for which it is sought to make the axe last while it is being manufactured. Clearly, both increase together, but n must increase *more than* proportionately to a, otherwise, however low the rate of interest, labour could not be employed in producing axes of longer duration, but it would be employed in producing *many* less durable axes instead. We assume therefore that a varies as a fractional power of n, i.e.

$$a = kn^{\nu} \qquad (5)$$

where k is a constant and ν a proper fraction. If, for example, $\nu = \frac{1}{2}$, a would grow proportionately to the numbers 1, 2, 3,

[1] If the yearly services of a whole group of labourers—say of ten men—is taken as the unit, the amount a in terms of this unit falls in proportion as l (in terms of shillings) increases.

4, etc., whilst n grows as the numbers 1, 4, 9, 16, etc. In other words, n increases geometrically in relation to a. Of course the form of this function is too special to reflect the actual relation between a and n when both are undergoing large changes, but with smaller variations which, as a rule, are the only ones likely to occur in practice, it may be as good an approximation formula as any other.[1] If we assume, for example, that it held for axes lasting for 16 to 36 years, and that $\nu = \frac{1}{2}$, then the constant k represents a *quarter* of the amount of labour required to give the axe in question a life-time of 16 years; or else, and it here comes to much the same thing, a *fifth* of the labour needed to produce an axe which is intended to last 25 years, etc.

At this stage, we could, of course, eliminate a from equations (4) and (5), and then l and b would be the only unknowns outstanding. But we prefer to retain both equations in their present form.

For the labourer, or group of labourers, if they themselves are the entrepreneurs, the most advantageous value of n is that which makes the selling price of the axe a maximum in relation to the amount of labour invested, i.e. makes l attain its maximum.[2] Since a variable magnitude at its maxima (or minima) behaves like a constant, we have to differentiate equation (4) as though l were a constant, which gives

$$be^{-\rho n}\Delta n = l\Delta a.^{3} \qquad (6)$$

We have again obviously obtained on the L.H.S. an expression of the form of equation (2), n and Δn taking the place of t and Δt. The obvious implication is that at its maximum $b\Delta n$, the last addition to the value of the axe, when discounted to its present value exactly corresponds to $l\Delta a$, the last increment to the cost of its manufacture.

We get by logarithmic differentiation of (5)

$$\frac{\Delta a}{a} = \nu\frac{\Delta n}{n}. \qquad (7)$$

[1] On the other hand, there is no expression to correspond with Åkerman's i-series, which would describe the condition that the durability of some capital-goods cannot successfully be increased beyond a certain point.

[2] We might also assume that they do not sell their axes but hire them out. Here they must themselves borrow at the rate of interest r or (ρ) for maintaining them—the theoretical result is the same in both cases.

[3] That the remaining condition for the maximization of l, as of ρ in the next case, is here always fulfilled will be shown later.

Substituting in (6)

$$be^{-\rho n}\frac{n}{\nu} = la \qquad (8)$$

and combining with (4), we obtain finally

$$e^{\rho n} = 1 + \frac{\rho n}{\nu} \qquad (9)$$

This result is rather peculiar. The product ρn is here the root of an equation, in which ν is the only variable. In other words once the particular function we have used for extension of life-time is taken as given, it follows that the product of the rate of interest (with continuously compound interest) and the optimal lifetime of the axe is a *constant*, independently of the size of b, as soon as we regard ν as a technical datum. Even with the choice of a less simple function, the connection between n and ρ remains independent of b, provided a is a function of n. (9) is of course a transcendental equation, but we can easily obtain an approximate result for the larger of the real roots.[1] (The other $= 0$ for every value of ν.) If, for example, $\nu = \frac{1}{2}$, ρn is roughly 1·27, so that if ρ is ·05 (and the ordinary rate of interest therefore a little over 5 per cent) the axe's optimum life-time is always *circa* 25 years, however much the value of its uses, calculated per annum, may vary. We shall indicate this root by $\phi(\nu)$ with the proviso that it is a *constant* as soon as ν is taken as a technical datum. The following analysis depends to a great extent on this result.

We have hitherto regarded the rate of interest (r or ρ) as given. Now if we consider capitalists as entrepreneurs, l must be taken as given instead. Those capitalists, who at a given wage manufacture axes to be later applied, are confronted with the problem of making the axes last so long that the capital invested in their manufacture receives the maximum rate of interest. From a mathematical point of view, this problem leads us to exactly the same formula as the first, for when ρ reaches its maximum, it behaves as a constant, and we have therefore to differentiate equation (4) as though l and ρ were constants. We obtain precisely the same equation as before, and also equation (9) in a similar manner.

[1] This can be solved by expanding according to Lagrange's theorem, taking out the root $\rho n = 0$.

$$e^{\rho n} = 1 + \frac{\rho n}{\nu} \tag{9}$$

But it is no longer ρ but l which is the datum. To find n we substitute in (8) the value discovered from (9) for $\rho n = \phi(\nu)$ (e.g. $1{\cdot}27$ if $\nu = \frac{1}{2}$), and eliminate a by means of (5). Thus

$$n^{1-\nu} = \frac{l}{b}\, k\nu e^{\phi(\nu)}, \tag{10}$$

or what comes to the same thing, as $\phi(\nu)$ is the root of (9).

$$n^{1-\nu} = \frac{l}{b}\, k[\nu + \phi(\nu)] \qquad (10\ bis)$$

If $\nu = \frac{1}{2}$ and $\therefore\ \phi(\nu) = 1{\cdot}27$, we get

$$\sqrt{n} = \frac{l}{b}\, 1{\cdot}77k$$

We are here restating the principle with which we were acquainted before, that an increase in wages produces a tendency to increase the durability of a capital-good, in this case in geometric proportion to the rise in wages.[1] This tendency corresponds to the extension of the period of production in the case of "variable real capital" (circulating capital).

Before going any further, we should like to mention an interesting fact with reference to the *average* investment-period of capital tied up in a particular capital-good. Under normal circumstances, the annual yield of a fixed capital-good will afterwards repay as well as yield interest on the costs incurred in making it. As we have maintained in our review of Åkerman, the question of the *order* in which either the former or latter occurs is of merely formal interest. But we should be able to represent the average investment-period of this capital as a period such that if all the uses of the capital-good were finally turned out *at the same time*, they would yield the same interest on the capital as the owner actually obtains. Let this period be m. Since in our example the total value of all the uses is clearly $b.n$, with equation (4) we get

$$bne^{-\rho m} = b\frac{1 - e^{-\rho n}}{\rho} = al \tag{11}$$

[1] We shall later try to show that this result is perfectly general, quite apart from the function for extension of lifetime.

if a is here increased, and therefore according to (5) n too, m must also be increased.[1] Now since n is at its optimal value and we can regard l and ρ as constants (for one is assumed to be an actual constant and the other has attained its maximum), we obtain by logarithmic differentiation of (11) the equation—

$$\frac{\Delta n}{n} - \frac{\Delta a}{a} = \rho \Delta m \qquad (12)$$

describing the relations between the simultaneous increases in n, m, and a. This result is not difficult to interpret. Since a is the amount of labour required to produce one axe, $\frac{1}{a}$ is the number of axes produced by one unit of labour[2] and $\frac{n}{a}$ the number of (potential) yearly uses of $\frac{1}{a}$ axes. Therefore $\frac{bn}{a}$ is the value of all their uses. If for the moment we call this expression P, and retain our assumption that b is a constant we obtain by logarithmic differentiation—

$$\frac{\Delta P}{P} = \frac{\Delta n}{n} - \frac{\Delta a}{a} = \rho \Delta m$$

or

[1] It can easily be shown that if m, the average investment-period, is reckoned on this principle (i.e. of the annuity-loan), it is rather less than half the "amortization period" $\frac{n}{2}$. But the lower the rate of interest, the more closely does it approximate to $\frac{n}{2}$. Since ρ the rate of interest varies inversely with n in our example, m must necessarily increase at the same time as n, perhaps even in a somewhat greater proportion. (We have here another example of the fact that compound interest is superior to simple for purposes of computation; for with the ordinary annuity-loan calculated in the same way, the average amortization period sometimes falls short of half the loan-period and sometimes exceeds it, according to its length and the height of the rate of interest. If, for example, a man has to effect an outlay of £50 at the end of every year for the next twenty years, the best thing for him to do would be to pay the whole lot at once after ten years, if the rate of interest is above 5 per cent, but not otherwise.)

[2] Since a is small, $\frac{1}{a}$ is large. But to make matters more intelligible we can imagine the number of axe-makers to be so large that even this number of axes can be produced almost simultaneously, so that taken together they can be regarded as a single capital-good.

$$\rho = \frac{\dfrac{\Delta P}{\Delta m.}}{P} \tag{13}$$

We might have derived this result directly from (11); it holds, therefore, even if b is not taken as constant, but is allowed to vary in some proportion or other to the lifetime of the axe, as soon as ρ or l attains its maximum. Thus in dealing with fixed capital we obtain a counterpart to the Jevonian principle that interest is "the rate of increase of the produce divided by the whole produce", or is the "marginal productivity of waiting", i.e. with reference to *average waiting* reckoned according to the above principle. At this point we must note that the amount of labour invested is taken as fixed (= 1 unit of labour) so that the average period of waiting becomes capital's only variable dimension. It is also worthy of notice that the principle holds for the *whole* duration of the capital-good, and not merely for the period for which the stock of machines of different ages (= the existing fixed capital) still has to last. On the other hand, it is fairly clear that our principle is completely independent of the assumption we made about the form of the function for extension of lifetime.

We turn now to consider the stock of fixed capital. If the labourer (or group of labourers) continues to produce axes, he (or it) will produce $\frac{1}{a}$ axes in one year and $\frac{n}{a}$ axes in n years.[1] Within this period the number of axes in use will obviously continually increase, but once we get beyond n, it ceases to do so, since the oldest axes are discarded *pari passu* with the manufacture of new ones. Thus we have got here a *fixed* capital consisting of axes, which is "staggered" in structure and which includes $\frac{n}{a}$ axes of various ages, *and as a matter of course the number of uses available is the same at any moment.* The total (undiscounted) value of all the uses available in one year is

[1] The expression $\frac{n}{a}$ has thus a double significance; it is the amount of potential uses of the number of axes produced by one unit of labour in the first place, and the total number produced by a labourer in n years in the second. Because of its second implication it is described in the text as the total number of uses available at one and the same time.

therefore $\frac{b.n.}{a}$. Again, the total value of all the potential uses which the fixed capital, consisting of axes and existing at each moment, represents, is clearly

$$b\frac{n}{a}\,\frac{n}{2} = b\frac{n^2}{2a}$$

For the *time* elapsing during the manufacture of an axe is assumed to be so short that the age of the axe grows continuously from 0 to n years. This proceeds on the assumption that only a single labourer or group of labourers is employed in producing axes. If, however, M labourers or $\frac{M}{10}$ groups of labourers with ten men in each group are occupied in manufacturing axes, all our quantities will naturally have to be multiplied by M; *from now on we take the annual services of one labourer as the unit of labour.*

Now in order to find the value of the capital itself we employ in our calculations that rate of interest which is attained when the best possible line of action is adopted in the use of each individual axe for the *whole* of its life-time. Once equilibrium is finally reached this rate must coincide with the current rate. According to (3) the value of a new axe with n years to live is $b\frac{(1 - e^{-n\rho})}{\rho}$. Therefore the residual value of an axe already used for t years must be

$$\frac{b(1 - e^{-(n-t)\rho})}{\rho} \tag{14}$$

Since Δt is an infinitesimal period of time we regard the axes between the ages $t + \Delta t$ as having the same value. Now since one labourer produces $\frac{1}{a}$ axes per unit of time (one year) and M labourers therefore produce $\frac{M}{a}$ axes; the number of axes in the moment Δt produced t years ago is $\frac{\Delta t M}{a}$ and their total outstanding value is according to (14)

$$M\frac{b}{a}\,\frac{1 - e^{-(n-t)\rho}}{\rho}\,\Delta t.$$

Summing all these values, we obtain the value of all the fixed capital by integrating between $t = 0$ and $t = n$. Thus

$$K = M\frac{b}{a}\frac{1}{\rho}\int_0^n (1 - e^{-(n-t)\rho})dt = M\frac{b}{a}\frac{\rho n - 1 + e^{-\rho n}}{\rho^2} \qquad (15)$$

This equation corresponds to the sums of the recurrent series in Åkerman's analysis, which he does not however summate. It can be checked, for if ρn is so small that we need only consider the first three terms in the exponential series $e^{-\rho n} = 1 - \rho n + \frac{(\rho n)^2}{1.2} - \frac{(\rho n)^3}{1.2.3} + \text{etc.}$, our equation is then reduced to $M\frac{b}{a}\cdot\frac{n^2}{a}$, corresponding to the undiscounted value of all the potential uses of the axes, as we have already seen. Even if the fourth term is included, we obtain the same expression multiplied by the binomial $\left(1 - \frac{\rho n}{3}\right)$, i.e. the value of all the potential uses minus the simple interest on them for a *third* of the *whole* lifetime of each axe—a new but naturally incomplete approximation. The quantity $\frac{n}{3}$ is the distance of the centre of gravity from the base of a triangle, the height of which is n and the base the number of axes in existence. If the potential uses of the whole existing stock of axes are discounted back to the present, the average period of discounting should in fact be $\frac{n}{3}$ (cf. review, p. 270), if we use simple interest.[1]

[1] If a capital-good lasts altogether N *weeks*, and if the same number of capital-goods are all of various ages, the number of remaining weeks' uses of a good already in existence for T weeks is clearly $N-T$, and its average period of discounting, using simple interest, is $\frac{N-T}{2}$ weeks. We obtain the average period of discounting for the whole stock from the formula :—

$$\frac{\sum_{T=0}^{T=N-1} \frac{1}{2}(N-T)^2}{\sum_{T=0}^{T=N-1}(N-T)} = \frac{\frac{1}{2}(N^2 + (N-1)^2 + \ldots + 9 + 4 + 1)}{N + N - 1 + N - 2 + \ldots + 3 + 2 + 1} = \frac{2N+1}{6}$$

or since N is here a large number, $\frac{N}{3}$ weeks approximately. And in the same way, still using simple interest, we get the average *period of investment* for a "staggered variable real capital". (Cf. the relevant passages in my review.)

We can easily prove that at any moment the net value of the uses of the whole of the axe-capital, i.e. the gross value minus the cost of renewal of capital, is the interest on the total value of the capital at the same moment. For it follows from what we have just said that the former is $M\left(\frac{nb}{a} - l\right)\Delta t$, which, using (4), becomes

$$M\frac{b}{a}\frac{\rho n - 1 + e^{-\rho n}}{\rho}\Delta t = \rho K \Delta t. \qquad (16)$$

(16) is of course bound up with the fact that the residual capital-value of the axes already in use is precisely estimated according to this rate of interest, and may therefore be called a truism.

We have not yet made any use of our assumption about the nature of the function of "extension of lifetime", i.e. equation (5). Once (5) is taken into account, K, the amount of capital, becomes a much simpler expression, for in this case ρn is a constant $= \phi(\nu)$, and so the numerator of our fraction also becomes a constant. Further, ρ and a can be simply expressed in terms of n, so that we can express K in terms of M, b, and n. Since according to (10) n is proportional to some power of the ratio $\frac{l}{b}$, we can express K in terms of l and b only, but always with the proviso that it is also a multiple of M and includes a constant factor, which is solely dependent on the value of ν, which is technically given. The significance of this consideration will become apparent later.

In actual fact neither l nor b is given, but the value of both is ultimately determined by the co-operation of free labour with real capital in the production of commodities. For we assume that under free competition wages l are the same for *all* labour, whether it is free labour or "replacement labour" (Åkerman), which is annually invested in machines. To obtain this economic nexus and the data necessary for solving the whole problem, we must now make the further assumption that all the capital of the community consists exclusively of only one kind of capital-good, in this case axes, and that only one kind of product is produced. Since we have previously only been occupied with capitalistic production in its simplest form we are doubtless justified in making an assumption which is rather fantastic if taken by itself.

Let x free labourers co-operate with y units of capital (axes) in a given form. Now with the optimal employment of resources, the product, or the value of the product, will clearly be a *function* of both x and y. We can decide *a priori* that this function must be *homogeneous* and *linear*, i.e. such that a *uniform* increase in x and y produces exactly the same percentage increase in the product. For if two labourers, each having his own axe, could together produce *more* than twice as much as one labourer with one axe, or if the product of three labourers and three axes was proportionately even more, and so on, then we should obviously have to let the labourers co-operate in groups in such a way that the maximum efficiency was reached. But once this maximum has been attained, a further increase in labourers and axes, i.e. an increase in the *number* of such groups, would only produce a proportionate increase in the product. On the whole we can therefore assume that with a constant "stock" of axes per labourer, the product grows in proportion to the number of labourers, but with an increasing or diminishing stock of axes, labour remaining constant, the product certainly increases or diminishes in some degree, although less than proportionately to the change in the number of axes. In other words our productivity function, which we represent by $F(x, y)$, must take the form,

$$F(x, y) = x\Phi\left(\frac{y}{x}\right),$$

where Φ is a function of a *single* variable, i.e. of the ratio $\frac{y}{x}$.

It increases or diminishes simultaneously with its variable, but to a lesser extent. For if it increased in the same proportion, the whole expression could be reduced to $cx\frac{y}{x} = cy$, where c is a constant; in other words, we should arrive at the ludicrous result that the product was solely dependent on the number of axes and not at all on the number of workers. We should get a still more ludicrous result if the function Φ increased more than proportionately to its variable.

Since we are chiefly concerned with expressing this relation in as convenient a form as possible for our calculations, we may simply let the Φ-function vary as a root of its variable, i.e. we may put

$$F(x, y) = cx\left(\frac{y}{x}\right)^{\beta} = cx^{\alpha}y^{\beta},$$

where α and β are both positive fractions and their sum $= 1$. P, the value of the product computed for a moment of time,[1] thus becomes

$$P = F(x, y) = cx^{\alpha}y^{\beta}. \qquad (17)$$

If this equation is partially differentiated with respect to x and y, we obtain

$$\frac{\partial P}{\partial x} = c\alpha x^{\alpha-1}y^{\beta} = \alpha\frac{P}{x}$$

and

$$\frac{\partial P}{\partial y} = c\beta x^{\alpha}y^{\beta-1} = \beta\frac{P}{y}$$

Let us postulate a stationary state in which there is perfect competition between employers and labourers. Once equilibrium has been reached, the first partial derivative must necessarily equal or l the wages per head per annum, and the second b, or the payment received for the yearly use of an axe. Thus

$$l = \alpha\frac{P}{x} \text{ and } b = \beta\frac{P}{y}, \qquad (18)$$

from which, among other things, it follows

$$xl + yb = (\alpha + \beta)P = P, \text{ since } \alpha + \beta = 1.$$

In other words payments, so determined, made to the labourers and the owners of the axes, will together absorb the total value of the product; which is as it should be. Similarly, assuming a continuous productivity function, we obtain the simple ratio of b to l—

$$\frac{b}{l} = \frac{\beta x}{\alpha y} \qquad (19)$$

Let A be the total number of labourers or the supply of labour annually available. If M is the number of labourers

[1] We might also have calculated it for an infinitesimal period of *time*, i.e. multiplied both sides of the equation by Δt. But once production is taken as stationary, this procedure would make no difference whatsoever.

always employed in the manufacture of axes in order to renew or maintain the fixed capital consisting of axes, then the amount of free labour is plainly $A - M$. It follows that the number of axes in use at the same time is $\frac{Mn}{a}$ and that in equilibrium just this proportion between free labourers and axes employed must obtain in each firm, as the result of reciprocal supply and demand; otherwise some of the labourers or axes would be unemployed. We can therefore substitute $A - M$ and $\frac{Mn}{a}$ for x and y in our previous formulæ, and replace P by π, the value of the whole social product. Thus we obtain

$$\pi = c(A - M)^{\alpha} M^{\beta} \left(\frac{n}{a}\right)^{\beta} \qquad (17\ bis)$$

and

$$l = \alpha \frac{\pi}{A - M} \text{ and } b = \beta \frac{\pi}{M} \frac{a}{n} \qquad (18\ bis)$$

and

$$\frac{b}{l} = \frac{\beta}{\alpha} \frac{A - M}{M} \frac{a}{n} \qquad (19\ bis)$$

By making a simple change in equation (8) and then combining it with (9), it follows that if the most profitable lifetime is attained for every axe, then

$$\begin{aligned} \frac{b}{l} &= \nu e^{\rho n} \frac{a}{n} \\ &= \nu e^{\phi(\nu)} \frac{a}{n} \\ &= (\nu + \phi(\nu)) \frac{a}{n} \qquad (8\ bis) \end{aligned}$$

where $\phi(\nu)$ is the root of (9).

We finally obtain—

$$\frac{A - M}{M} = \frac{\alpha}{\beta} (\nu + \phi(\nu)) \qquad (20)$$

This result is calculated to create some astonishment. All the magnitudes on the R.H.S. are *constants* irrespective of the *amount* of social capital. These constants reflect the assumptions we made (1) for the technical conditions under which our capital-goods are manufactured, and (2) for their co-operation with free labour in the production of consumption-goods. Our assumptions have thus shown that, however much the amount of capital itself changes, the distribution of the existing supply of labour between free labour co-operating with capital-goods and labour employed in the maintenance or renewal of capital itself [1] remains *unchanged.* And yet only within limits, since the form of our function is too special to be valid beyond a certain field of variation, even if it contains one arbitrary constant.[2] Within these limits, however, capital, when it does grow, grows *exclusively* in height and not at all in breadth. *N.B.*—When capital first increases and there is a consequent disturbance of equilibrium, capital will also—or rather exclusively—grow in breadth, since in the beginning the additional number of new capital-goods will be of the same type as those already in use. If, on the other hand, the amount of labour invested per moment of time is temporarily increased and the amount of free labour diminished, there will be a rise in wages and a fall in the value of the use of capital (axes), more or less in this sequence. Further, according to (10), the new capital-goods now produced will be manufactured to last longer, as this method of investment has become most profitable. But when equilibrium is reached once more the amounts of free labour and of labour engaged in replacing capital resume their former proportion (at the same time the labourers lose part of, but not all, their recent increase in wages and the capital-goods regain part of, but not all, the value they have just lost). Employing this interesting result, we might regard the productivity function and the function for "extension of lifetime", which have been selected, i.e.

$$a = f(n) = kn^{\nu}$$

$$\text{and } P = F(x, y) = cx^{\alpha}y^{\beta} \quad (\alpha + \beta = 1),$$

as typically *normal* functions from which, taking them as the simplest elements in the problem, we must start in the analysis of the more complicated phenomena of the real world.

[1] In a stationary state these quantities will themselves be constant.

[2] The two coefficients k and c refer only to the value of units, and therefore leave no room for varying conditions in other respects.

With these constants, the values of M and A plainly become

$$M = \frac{\beta A}{\alpha(\nu + \phi(\nu)) + \beta} \text{ and } A - M = \frac{\alpha(\nu + \phi(\nu))A}{\alpha(\nu + \phi(\nu)) + \beta} \quad (20 \; bis).$$

Let $\nu = \frac{1}{2}$: then $\phi(\nu) = 1 \cdot 27$. Further, let $\alpha = \beta = \frac{1}{2}$.[1] Then

$$M = \frac{A}{2 \cdot 77}, \quad A - M = \frac{1 \cdot 77}{2 \cdot 77} A.$$

Rather more than a third of the existing supply of labour should therefore be engaged in manufacturing axes, and the remainder —about two-thirds—in the *application* of the existing stock of axes for the delivery of saw-logs. This result we achieve without taking the amount of axe-capital into account, for, with a small supply of capital in the form of axes, as long as our assumptions hold, they must necessarily be manufactured so as to last for a correspondingly short period, and will therefore need renewal all the more often.

M being determined, the whole problem can be solved without any further difficulty. The remaining unknowns are (1) the amount of capital expressed in terms of the product or of money (for the price of the product is taken as fixed on the great staple markets), (2) the product per annum in terms of the same unit, (3) the duration or lifetime of the capital-goods (axes), (4) wages per annum, (5) the value of the yearly uses of an axe, and (6) the rate of interest prevailing in equilibrium and current throughout the economy. It does not matter which of these is taken as the independent variable, for in any case all the other quantities vary as certain powers of this parameter, each being multiplied by its own constant co-efficient. If we choose n as our independent variable, i.e. if we imagine an equilibrium situation where the total period for which the capital-good lasts is n years, and let C_1, C_2, etc., be the constant coefficients, we obtain

$$K = C_1 n^{1 + \beta(1-\nu)}, \qquad \pi = C_2 n^{\beta(1-\nu)},$$
$$l = C_3 n^{\beta(1-\nu)}, \qquad b = C_4 n^{-\alpha(1-\nu)},$$

and, as before,

$$\rho = \phi(\nu) n^{-1}.$$

[1] It follows from this second assumption that capital and labour are equally important in production, so that a percentage increase in one factor has the same *effect* as an equal increase in the other, which of course is only conceivable in a special situation.

It follows immediately that the exponentials are solely dependent on ν and $\beta(=1-\alpha)$. The coefficients depend on k and c, the meaning of which is well understood. In addition, C_1 and C_2, the first two coefficients, contain A as a factor; for by dividing by A we had obtained the capital and product per head (of labourers) of the population.

Thus with the simplifying assumptions we selected the problem is now solved. But we must of course be very careful in drawing general conclusions from the results obtained if only because of the above reservation (and quite apart from the fact that they are no longer applicable as soon as our quantities move in a negative direction, for what is not valid in a special case is still less so in the general). But a few observations may still be permissible.

As ν is < 1, the capital K clearly increases simultaneously with n, and conversely n with K. For the reason mentioned in our review, this interrelation must be general. Similarly, π grows when n (and K) increase, but much less than the latter, since the index is smaller by one whole unit.[1] The conclusion that an increase in fixed capital also produces an increase in the annual product should also be perfectly general, independently of our particular assumption, as we shall immediately attempt to show.

Similarly, l increases when n and K increase, but b diminishes when n and K increase. This conclusion ought also to be general in its validity, as we shall soon show.

Since the expressions for π and l have the same index, the ratio $\frac{\pi}{l}$ remains a constant, in other words, with increasing capital, wages remain an *unvarying* part of the increasing product, which is a necessary consequence of our assumptions. Given our particular productivity function, the *sum* of the wages of free labour in each firm and throughout industry constitutes an unvarying portion of the product, which follows from (18) and (18 *bis*.) And besides since, according to our function for the "extension of lifetime", $A - M$, the total number of free workers remains constant, every free labourer (and therefore

[1] If $\nu = \frac{1}{2}$ and $\beta = \frac{1}{2}$, K becomes proportional to $\sqrt[4]{n^5}$, but π only to $\sqrt[4]{n}$.

all labourers) receives a constant part of the national dividend when capital increases (though of course labour *now* invested is paid in consumption-goods which are ready *now*, and not in the consumption-goods which they themselves help to make). Naturally, this conclusion cannot be general.

If the proportionate share of the labourers in the total national dividend is constant, then the capitalists' share is also constant. But, as we have maintained, this result holds for the interest on all the capital at the moment of time in question, if the rate of interest is ρ.

Hence $\rho \dfrac{K\Delta t}{\pi \Delta t}$ must be a constant. This result is correct, for $\rho \dfrac{K}{\pi} = \phi(\nu)\dfrac{C_1}{C_2}$, since the powers of n cancel out.

It may be added that the number of capital-goods (axes) in use at the same time, which on the above analysis is

$$M\frac{n}{a} = M\frac{1}{k}n^{1-\nu}$$

necessarily increases with n and also with K, although in a smaller proportion than either, since $1 + \beta(1-\nu) = 1 - \alpha(1-\nu) + 1 - \nu > 1 - \nu$. This result *is general* and holds as we shall soon show, even in the exceptional case when *M diminishes* with an increase in K.

Let us turn to the transition from one equilibrium to another. It is now possible to discover to what extent the closely-related proposition originally advanced by von Thünen that the rate of interest corresponds to the "marginal productivity" of capital is corroborated by our formulæ in the modified form put forward by Åkerman. By logarithmic differentiation we obtain directly

$$\frac{\Delta K}{K} = (1 + \beta(1-\nu))\frac{\Delta n}{n} \text{ and } \frac{\Delta \pi}{\pi} = \beta(1-\nu)\frac{\Delta n}{n}.$$

Therefore

$$\frac{\Delta \pi}{\Delta K} = \frac{\beta(1-\nu)}{1 + \beta(1-\nu)}\,\frac{\pi}{K}$$

We can easily express the value of the ratio $\dfrac{\pi}{K}$ without needing to bother about the rather complicated constants C_1 and C_2. Since the share of capital in the product is equal to the interest on all the capital $= \rho K$ (cancelling Δt out), it must clearly be $\pi - Al$, or, if we take (18 *bis*) and (20 *bis*) into account, it is

$$= \pi \frac{\beta(\nu + \phi(\nu) - 1)}{\nu + \phi(\nu)}.$$

Thus we obtain

$$\frac{\pi}{K} = \frac{\nu + \phi(\nu)}{\beta(\nu + \phi(\nu) - 1)} \rho,$$

and finally

$$\frac{\Delta \pi}{\Delta K} = \frac{1 - \nu}{1 + \beta(1 - \nu)} \frac{\nu + \phi(\nu)}{\nu + \phi(\nu) - 1} \rho. \qquad (22)$$

Our ratio is therefore proportionate, but not equal, to ρ. If $\nu = \frac{1}{2}$, $\phi(\nu) = 1{\cdot}27$, and $\beta = \alpha = \frac{1}{2}$, it becomes $\cdot 92\rho$ approximately, i.e. *rather* less than ρ. This discrepancy is only to be expected, when the increase in capital is partly absorbed by the resulting increase in wages and only part of it is effective in raising production. But since this explanation does not hold here, we may infer that the principle is *not* general. If β is quite small, i.e. if the capital-goods have only a minor significance for production as compared with free labour, then as long as $\nu = \frac{1}{2}$, the first fraction approaches $1 - \nu = \frac{1}{2}$ as closely as possible, whilst the other is always $\frac{1{\cdot}77}{\cdot 77}$, i.e. > 2. Strangely enough, this ratio is thus *greater* than ρ.

In these circumstances, it is already obvious *a priori* that von Thünen's thesis is no longer verified, even in the form in which Åkerman proposes to recast it. In his analysis on p. 152, Åkerman starts by replacing the divisor ΔK by $\Delta K - K\frac{\Delta l}{l}$, and thus subtracts that part of the increase in capital absorbed by the rise of wages. This method of approach is perfectly justifiable (cf. my review) for Böhm-Bawerk's thesis, as we can see from a simple inspection of the formulæ on p. 113 of my *Uber Wert*, etc.[1] But in this particular case, it does not hold good.

[1] If ΔK is replaced by $\Delta K - K\frac{\Delta l}{l}$ in the equation at the bottom of the page, p. 113, op. cit.,

$$\frac{Ap'dt}{dK} = \frac{2p'dt}{ldt + tdl} = \frac{2p'}{l - t^2p''},$$

t^2p'' disappears from the denominator in the fraction on the extreme right, which is reduced to $\frac{2p'}{l} = z$ (the rate of interest).

We obtain without any difficulty

$$\Delta K - K\frac{\Delta l}{l} = K\left(\frac{\Delta K}{K} - \frac{\Delta l}{l}\right) = K\frac{\Delta n}{n}$$

and if $\Delta\pi$ is divided by this expression, the new ratio can be written as

$$\left(\frac{\Delta\pi}{\pi} \div \frac{\Delta n}{n}\right)\frac{\pi}{K} = \beta(1-\nu)\frac{\pi}{K} = \frac{(1-\nu)(\nu+\phi(\nu))}{\nu+\phi(\nu)-1}\rho. \quad (23)$$

The new ratio differs from the old only in this respect, that the factor in the denominator depending on β drops out. Since this is always > 1 as also in this case, the new ratio $\frac{\Delta\pi}{\Delta K}$ is always greater than the old one, but it is not therefore equal to ρ. On the contrary, we should be in a position to show that it must always be *greater* than ρ, except in both the limiting cases, where either ν is very small and $n\rho = \phi(\nu)$ is therefore very large, or where ν approaches unity and $\phi(\nu)$ tends to zero. In *both* these cases the R.H.S. of the equation is reduced to the value of ρ; this is self-evident for the first case and can easily be proved for the second by the method of limits.[1] I cannot enter now on the explanation of this very puzzling formula; presumably it belongs to the sphere of "dynamic" theory, where we cannot confine ourselves to the comparison of two different equilibria, but must also study the transition from one to the other.

Finally, I shall tackle the question which really constitutes the starting point for the whole of this fragmentary essay. It is the validity of the principle that an increase in capital (*measured* in units of product, or the value of the product remaining unaltered) must, *as a general rule*, always produce an increase

[1] Let $\nu = 1 - \epsilon$ where ϵ is a small positive fraction. The value of $\phi(\nu)$ then approximates to 2ϵ, and the value of the denominator thus becomes $+\ \epsilon$. The denominator cannot change signs between the limits $\nu = 0$ and $\nu = 1$ since it would be at a minimum between these points, which can easily be proved to be impossible. Therefore it always remains positive. We can now also prove that this quantity $\nu + \phi(\nu) - 1$ always has a sign *opposite* both to the second derivative of l with respect to n, ρ remaining constant, and to the second derivative of ρ, l remaining constant, when their first derivative becomes $= 0$; whence the values of l and ρ respectively, obtained above, always describe a real maximum. This need not hold in the general case (*vide infra*).

in the volume of production. We have already seen that it is valid on our assumptions.

But even this conclusion now appears more complex to me than I had first believed. The proof I shall advance rests on the assumption that a rise in wages relatively to the use-value of the machine, that is to say an increase in $\frac{l}{b}$, always brings about an extension of lifetime whenever such an extension can be profitable (in other words if all the data are taken as continuously variable). According to (10) and (10 *bis*) n varies quite simply as a positive power of $\frac{l}{b}$ and *vice versa*, but this conclusion follows from $a = kn^{\nu}$, our function for 'extension of lifetime'. If instead we take a more general function, $a = f(n)$, of which it is only assumed that it becomes zero when n is zero, and increases more *slowly* than n, then the matter is no longer self-evident. For brevity, substitute x for $\frac{l}{b}$. We now obtain the corresponding changes in x and n by differentiating (4) and (6), which hold simultaneously for a given value of $x = \frac{l}{b}$, when ρ has reached its maximum. Thus—

$$\frac{1 - e^{-\rho n}}{\rho} = \frac{l}{b} f(n) = xf(n), \qquad (4\ bis)$$

and also

$$e^{-\rho n} = xf'(n), \qquad (6\ bis)$$

where $f'(n)$ is the first derivative of $f(n)$. This expression should now be differentiated with respect to n, x, and ρ, for it involves a shifting of the maximum points themselves. Let $f''(n)$ be the *second* derivative of $f(n)$ and let $\frac{f'(n)}{f(n)} = p$ and $\frac{f''(n)}{f'(n)} = q$. Then on eliminating $\Delta\rho$, we obtain

$$\frac{\Delta x}{\Delta n} = x\left(\frac{1}{n} - p\right)\frac{\rho + q}{\rho + p - \frac{1}{n}} \qquad (24)$$

Clearly, on our assumption ($f(n) = 0$ when $n = 0$ and $f'(n)$ diminishing when n increases), p must be $< \frac{1}{n}$ and $q < 0$. The expression $\frac{1}{n} - p$ is therefore always positive, and in the numerator and the denominator of the next fraction q and $p - \frac{1}{n}$ are both *negative*. But we cannot presume without further analysis that they are simultaneously $<$ or simultaneously $> \rho$.[1] It is therefore not *a priori* impossible for Δx and Δn to have opposite signs. Let us return to our function $a = f(n) = kn^{\nu}$. Then clearly $p = \frac{\nu}{n}$ and $q = -\frac{(1-\nu)}{n}$. Consequently, the numerator and denominator are here identical (if multiplied by n they both become $\rho n + \nu - 1 = \nu + \phi(\nu) - 1$) and our equation is simplified thus—

$$\frac{\Delta x}{\Delta n} = (1 - \nu)\frac{x}{n},$$

which can be directly obtained by logarithmic differentiation of (10). Now since $f(n)$, whatever its actual form, has the same *general* form as our special function, we may infer even now that x and n vary approximately to the same degree. But it is not impossible that they might sometimes vary in *different*

[1] But it can easily be proved that the denominator $\rho + p - \frac{1}{n}$ is always > 0. From (6 *bis*) and (4 *bis*) we find that it must here always have the value

$$\frac{e^{-\rho n} + \rho n - 1}{n(1 - e^{-\rho n})}.$$

The denominator of this fraction is certainly > 0, and so is the numerator, since its value becomes $= 0$ for $\rho n = 0$, but later rises continuously, as $-e^{-\rho n} + 1$ its derivative (with respect to ρn) is always > 0.

It is impossible to get any further without knowing something about $\rho + q$. Still we can easily show that the inequality $\rho + q > 0$ (which for $f(n) = kn^{\nu}$ becomes $\phi(\nu) + \nu - 1 > 0$) constitutes the *second* condition necessary for the emergence of a maximum value for l or ρ in the general case. This condition, however, need not be satisfied throughout. As far as I can see, if $\frac{l}{b}$ is given and n is increasing, there is nothing to prevent a sequence in which there first emerges a maximum value for ρ, then a *minimum*, and then a maximum again, and so on. An interesting consequence of this phenomenon will soon be mentioned.

directions, from which it plainly follows that $x(=\frac{l}{b})$ and n are not uniquely determined by each other but that x may have two (or more) values for the same value of n or, conversely, n may have different values for the same value of x.

In actual fact this last possibility may often be reached, but it should not on that account give rise to any serious dilemma. The only practical significance it can have is that an increase of capital is sometimes distributed between two different investments—two types of machine of different durability (though otherwise identical), both yielding the *same* maximum return on capital. We have confined the number of different investments to *two*, because for technical reasons it often does not pay to manufacture capital-goods lasting for intermediate periods.[1]

It would have very much more serious effects on the following proof, if two different values of $x = \frac{l}{b}$ could hold for the same value of n. But fortunately *this can never happen.* If it could, the conditions of our equations (4 *bis*) and (6 *bis*) could simultaneously be satisfied for the same value of n with two different x-values, x_1 and x_2, and with concomitantly different values for ρ, ρ_1 and ρ_2 $(\rho_1 > \rho_2)$. In other words we should obtain at the same time first $\frac{1 - e^{-\rho_1 n}}{\rho_1} = x_1 f(n)$ and $e^{-\rho_1 n} = x_1 f'(n)$, and secondly $\frac{1 - e^{-\rho_2 n}}{\rho_2} = x_2 f(n)$ and $e^{-\rho_2 n} = x_2 f'(n)$, from which dividing we should obtain

[1] If ρ has two maxima (as distinguished from a minimum) for small values of $\frac{l}{b}$ the manufacturer of machines naturally chooses the *larger*, which we shall assume corresponds to the smaller value of n.

Were capital and $\frac{l}{b}$ to increase, the maximum corresponding to the *higher* value of n may become the greater. Now when ρ has two equal maxima (for different values of n), there must be a case in the transition period analogous to that described in my *Lectures*, p. 163. For a time the increase in capital is divided between two different investments, in which l and b and their ratio $\frac{l}{b}$ do not undergo any further change; for since an ever-growing part of the capital is successively transferred to the longer investment, OM is diminished and A–M increased, so that the proportion between free labour and the available uses of the machines remains unchanged. But I have not been able to complete any research into this interesting question in detail.

$$\frac{e^{\rho_1 n} - 1}{\rho_1} = \frac{e^{\rho_2 n} - 1}{\rho_2}$$

or

$$\frac{\rho_1 - \rho_2}{2} + \frac{\rho_1^2 - \rho_2^2}{6} n + \frac{\rho_1^3 - \rho_2^3}{24} n^2 + \ldots\ldots = 0.$$

If the values of n and ρ are positive, all the terms in the series are also positive, and our assumption therefore involves something absurd.

We may, consequently, proceed on the assumption that an increase in $\frac{l}{b}$ always produces an extension of the lifetime of capital-goods, even if this extension does not always occur continuously; at times it may take place in jumps (or more correctly in such a way that capital is distributed among capital-goods of the same profitability but of different durations).

On this hypothesis the proof of the thesis we previously advanced takes more or less the following form.

When real capital increases it must always increase in "height", in so far as an extension of the durability of machines is technically possible. For were it only to increase in "breadth", so that the only effect would be an increase in the number of machines of the old type, the labour permanently engaged in maintaining it would clearly have increased, once equilibrium had been reached. Hence it follows that the amount of free labour would have diminished at the same time as the number of capital-goods had increased. This must clearly result in a shifting *upwards* of $\frac{l}{b}$, in which case we must infer from our conclusion, which we have just shown to possess general validity, that an *extension* of the lifetime of the capital-good becomes profitable. On the other hand there is no need for an inevitable increase in the "breadth" dimension of capital which follows from what we have said above. On our formula, with an increase in capital the amount of labour required for renewing capital should generally remain unaltered. We may therefore summarily assume that an increase in capital may very well occur with an accompanying *fall* in the breadth dimension. None the less even in this case *the number of capital-goods in existence at the same time* will have increased, for if it had diminished, since the amount of free labour has now *increased*, $\frac{l}{b}$ would have shifted *downwards* and we cannot describe the position in which n has a new and higher value as an equilibrium one. It therefore emerges that there will be a larger number of machines simultaneously with a *larger* supply of free labour, which must obviously lead to an increase in the total product.[1]

Let us now take the commonest instance in which machine-capital increases in breadth as well as in height; then the amount of free labour will diminish. We can conceive of this change as occurring in *two* (or more) stages. Let capital grow in breadth to begin with and only later in height also—in other words, we first increase our M, n remaining constant, and afterwards n as well (with M constant).

The first part of this procedure is soon explained. For since the composition of machine-capital remains the same, the whole process can be regarded as though M units of labour invested in a certain way co-operated with $A - M$ free labour in each case. If M is increased, and $A - M$ diminished by one unit, then, ignoring infinitesimal quantities of higher orders, the total product is increased and there is a difference between the marginal productivies of invested and free labour. This difference must be positive, for as we have always regarded the Productivity Function as being homogeneous and linear (or that it has again become so after any change has taken place) the marginal productivity of each group necessarily coincides with its wages. These must clearly be *greater* for invested than for free labour, as the wages of the former also include *some* interest. Now let the lifetime of the same number of capital-goods increase, M remaining constant. Then it follows that the number of machines in existence must increase (for the number of machines per labourer working on machines is $\frac{n}{a} = \frac{n^{1-\nu}}{k}$) and, if the amount of free labour is constant, the total product must increase still more. If the increase in machine-capital is such that as far as the first part of our analysis is concerned the rate of

[1] Similarly, if we abstract from technical discoveries, which change $f(n)$ and $F(x, y)$ the basic functions themselves, wages must always rise with a relative increase in the amount of capital. The general character of the Productivity Function plainly involves the result that l and b always vary *inversely*; if l has increased n must also increase.

interest not only falls but is at the point of becoming zero, we simply stop at this point and allow n to grow until the rate of interest reaches its maximum (and becomes therefore > 0), and using this point as our starting-point we begin again with the same procedure.

Thus the net result is that a growth of capital, as long as it is such as to be profitable, is always accompanied by an increase in the total product. Consequently the paradox of a fall in the national dividend resulting from continued saving and capital accumulation does not apply to perfectly free *competition*, but the possibility of its holding for a situation in which capitalists combine cannot be excluded.

So far we have treated the lifetime of capital-goods as if it were altogether separated from their other property—their " Automatism ", as Åkerman calls it. Actually, these properties are scarcely ever independent, greater durability is normally combined with greater efficiency in other respects. We ought to be able to express this mathematically so that the a-function does not actually have the simple form $f(n)$, but also contains a quantity g as a variable which objectively refers to the efficiency of the capital-good in question. Thus if, for example, g increases from g_1 to g_2, and $g_2 = 2g_1$, *ceteris paribus* we get a machine of a new type, which can replace two of the older machines in all respects. We need only substitute $f(n, g)$ for $f(n)$ in equation (4 *bis*), and partially differentiate with respect to n and g, to obtain a new equation corresponding to this variable. However, I shall not undertake it here, as I have already taken too much space.

2

THE PLACE OF INTEREST IN THE THEORY OF PRODUCTION

By Oskar Lange

1. INTRODUCTORY REMARKS

In view of the confused state in which the theory of interest is at present a thorough and systematic investigation of its foundations does not seem out of place. The aim of the present paper is to clarify the foundation of the theory of interest by attempting to restate some of its fundamental propositions with special reference to the general theory of production. The relation of the theory of interest to the general theory of production, i.e. the theory of pricing of factors of production, is rather obscure. Outside of a rather vague and, as we shall see later, doubtful statement that the relation of the theory of interest to the general theory of production consists in the first taking into account time while the other is " timeless," little positive has been achieved in this field. Also the discussion of the problem whether there exists a *net* productivity of capital is bound to be rather confused unless the problem of interest is brought into closer connection with the general theory of production. The present paper tries, therefore, to elucidate in a systematic way the place of interest in the general theory of production.

Reasons of exposition and of space require a certain simplification and a limitation of our subject. The simplification consists in the assumption that only one finished commodity is produced in the economic system studied and that only one original factor of production, i.e. labour, and only one real capital good is used. This assumption allows a considerable simplification of the exposition while a generalisation of the theory to the case of production of many commodities with many original factors and many real capital goods does not encounter any logical difficulty. More numerous are the limitations of our study. First of all our investigation is restricted to the case of circulating capital and the delay period at which factors are applied in production is regarded as fixed.[1] Further, our investigation is limited to free competition and to the case where all factors of production are substitutable (the case of limitational factors thus being disregarded). Also the special influence of money creation is ruled out. To do this we need not assume an actual barter economy. We may well assume that commodities are actually bought and sold for money. All we need to know is that money behaves only like a " numéraire," or in other words that it is " neutral." What the actual conditions for money to be " neutral " are, whether they mean a constant amount of money or a constant level of average prices, or even whether " neutral " money is possible at all, need not concern us here. The study of those conditions is a matter for monetary theory. As terms like " money capital " and " monetary saving " are used in this paper the reader ought to be warned

[1] As to the concept of the delay period cf. A. Smithies, " The Austrian Theory of Capital in Relation to Partial Equilibrium Theory," *Quarterly Journal of Economics*, October, 1935, p. 127 seq.

that they have nothing to do with money creation. By " money capital " in this paper the purchasing power at the disposal of entrepreneurs is meant and the only way to increase it is, according to our assumptions, through saving, i.e. through refraining from spending purchasing power for consumption and through transferring it to the disposal of entrepreneurs. Though the abstraction from the influence of money creation cripples the theory of interest substantially it is methodologically both perfectly legitimate and also indispensable. For only after the theory of interest has been established independently of the effects of money creation can a satisfactory elucidation of the influence of money creation on interest and production be achieved. Also the element of risk is ruled out from our study and the rate of interest treated here is the rate of net interest.

A fully developed theory of interest must include all the factors neglected here. However, the more fundamental aspects of the theory of interest can be established within the limitations of our study and all the great standard works on the theory of interest and discussions of the subject have also kept usually within these boundaries.

2. CONDITIONS OF MAXIMUM NET OUTPUT

Our first problem is to find the conditions maximising net output with a given amount of resources. We shall assume that only one commodity is produced in our economic system and let x be the output per unit of time. To produce this commodity a certain amount of labour and a certain amount of equipment (tools, machinery, or materials) is necessary. If l and m are the amounts of labour and equipment used per unit of time the production function of our commodity is :

$$x = F(m, l) \qquad (1)$$

As an illustration, let us think of an economic system as consisting of a Robinson Crusoe, or, to make it more realistic, of a communistic settlement of pioneers in a forest. Let wood be the commodity produced and axes be the equipment. The equipment is assumed in our case to be produced with the aid of labour and of a certain amount of equipment of the same kind. Thus it takes both labour and other axes to produce axes. We may express this by saying that equipment is, in this case, a *circular* factor. If l' and m' be the amount of labour and equipment (axes) respectively used per unit of time to produce equipment, the amount of equipment produced per unit of time is a function of l' and m'. Let this function be $\phi(m', l')$. However, the amount of equipment produced per unit of time consists of two parts. One part m is used for producing the finished commodity (wood in our example), while another part is used to reproduce the worn-out equipment. If the equipment is to be maintained, the worn-out pieces have to be replaced by new ones and the amount of equipment used to produce new equipment is exactly equal to the amounts used in producing the equipment in hand, i.e. equals m'. We have, therefore :

$$m + m' = \phi\,(m', l') \qquad (2)$$

We have thus two production functions.[1] The amounts figuring in the formulae (1) and (2) are all understood as per unit of time. We assume also that the equipment is worn out completely during a unit of time. If a year is chosen as the unit of time this means that each axe has to be replaced after a year. There is also a certain delay of time from the application of labour and equipment to the receipt of the product. However, as a first approximation, we assume that this delay period is fixed by technical considerations alone and that it equals exactly one unit of time. We assume also that the production of the finished commodity and of the equipment is perfectly synchronised, so that we have a constant flow of commodities produced and of equipment to replace the worn-out one. During each unit of time exactly the amount of equipment is reproduced which is wearing out.

To our two production functions we add another equation expressing that the sum of labour used in producing the finished commodity (wood) and used in producing the equipment (axes) is a constant. Thus:

$$l + l' = L \qquad (3)$$

where L is a constant. Equation (3) expresses the condition that the amount of original factors[2] at disposal in our economic system is fixed.[3]

We shall call x the *net output* of our economic system. Our problem is to find the method of production which maximises net output, i.e. to determine m, l, m' and l' so as to maximise the production function (1) subjected to the two supplementary conditions expressed by equations (2) and (3). The solution is found immediately by the method of Lagrange multipliers. Let us form the expression:

$$F(m, l) + \lambda_1 [\phi(m', l') - m - m'] + \lambda_2 (l + l' - L)$$

where λ_1 and λ_2 are Lagrange multipliers. Differentiating this expression with respect to m, l, m' and l' and putting the partial derivatives equal to zero we get:

$$F_m - \lambda_1 = 0$$
$$F_l + \lambda_2 = 0$$
$$\lambda_1 (\phi_{m'} - 1) = 0$$
$$\lambda_1 \phi_{l'} + \lambda_2 = 0$$

and eliminating λ_1 and λ_2 we arrive at the two equations:

$$\phi_{m'} = 1 \qquad (4)$$

and $$F_m \phi_{l'} = F_l \qquad (5)$$

[1] The analogy of these two production functions to the famous reproduction schemes of Marx in the second volume of *Das Kapital* may be noticed.

[2] By original factors we mean factors which are not produced, i.e. which enter as variables into production functions but have no production function of their own. In our simplified case labour is the only original factor of production. It ought to be noticed that this definition of original factors does *not* imply that equipment (axes) is produced by original factors (labour in our instance) alone.

[3] Instead of assuming the amount of labour resources in our economic system to be fixed, we might also assume that it depends on the net output x, for instance our settlers may be willing to work more if the reward expected is greater. In such case equation (3) would be replaced by the equation:

$$l + l' = \psi(x) \qquad (3a)$$

where $\psi(x)$ is the supply function of labour.

which, together with equations (2) and (3), serve to determine the four unknowns l, l', m and m'.[1] By substitution of l and m into equation (1) we can determine the maximum output x.[2]

Equations (4) and (5) require an economic interpretation. Equation (4) says that the marginal productivity of equipment used in the production of equipment is a constant. This can be interpreted in the following way. Write the production function (2) in the form :

$$m = \phi(m', l') - m'$$

Then

$$\frac{\partial m}{\partial m'} = \phi_{m'} - 1$$

and equation (4) can be written :

$$\frac{\partial m}{\partial m'} = 0$$

which means that the marginal *net* productivity of the circular factor is zero. This is obvious. The amount of a circular factor engaged in reproducing itself is not a genuine cost factor. Its use will be extended as long as there is any positive marginal *net* productivity.

Even more simple is the economic interpretation of equation (5). The expression $F_m\phi_{l'}$ is the marginal productivity of labour used in producing equipment (axes) in terms of the finished commodity (wood). Indeed, from (1) and (2) we have :

$$\frac{\partial x}{\partial l'} = F_m\phi_{l'}$$

Let us use the terms direct labour and indirect labour to designate the labour used in the production of the finished commodity and of equipment respectively. Thus $F_m\phi_{l'}$ is the marginal productivity of *indirect* labour while F_l is the marginal productivity of *direct* labour, both marginal productivities being conceived in terms of the finished product (wood, in our instance). Equation (5) states that the *maximum net output is obtained when the marginal productivity of indirect labour is equal to the marginal productivity of direct labour.*

3. THE MARGINAL NET PRODUCTIVITY OF INDIRECT LABOUR

We have seen, so far, that the maximum net output is obtained when the marginal productivity of indirect labour equals the marginal productivity of direct labour. This condition implies, of course, an appropriate division

[1] Equations (4) and (5) are obtained also if instead of (3) the equation (3*a*)—cf. the preceding footnote—is used as a supplementary condition. Thus the replacement of the assumption that the amount of labour resources is fixed by the assumption that their supply depends on the "reward" they get in the magnitude of the net output does not change the conclusions obtained. We use, therefore, in the text only the first assumption as the more simple to handle mathematically.

[2] The problem of maximising net output from a given amount of resources has been treated and equations (4) and (5) have been obtained by Griffith C. Evans, "Maximum Production Studied in a Simplified Economic System," *Econometrica*, January, 1934, pp. 37–41.

of the total labour resources between labour used in producing the finished commodity and labour used in producing equipment. If this appropriate division of the labour resources of the economic system is reached there is no motive to change it in either direction, for any change would result in diminishing net output. Together with equation (4), the equality of the marginal productivity of indirect and of direct labour determines the optimum amount of equipment to be used both in the production of the finished commodity and in the production of equipment. Any decrease of this amount, and also any *increase* of it, would diminish the net output of the economic system.

Now let us imagine a situation in which the amount of equipment is less than the optimum amount. Such a situation may have arisen due to a change in data which makes it advantageous to use more equipment than has been used under the old conditions. For instance, the production functions or the amount of labour available in our economic system may have changed. Or it may be due to an unforeseen destruction of a part of the equipment. For example, a part of the axes may have been destroyed by a fire. If the amount of equipment is smaller than the optimum amount this means that not enough labour is used in producing equipment and too much is used in co-operation with the equipment engaged in the production of the finished commodity. The net output of our economic system may be increased by transferring labour from its direct to its indirect use.

In the situation considered, the marginal productivity of indirect labour is greater than the marginal productivity of direct labour. Indeed, let l_0 be the amount of labour initially engaged in the production of the finished commodity and l'_0 the amount of labour initially engaged in the production of equipment. Let s be the amount of labour transferred from the direct to the indirect use. By putting $l = l_0 - s$ and $l' = l'_0 + s$ production function (1) can be written:

$$x = F(m, l_0 - s) \qquad \text{(1a)}$$

and production function (2) becomes correspondingly:

$$m + m' = \phi(m', l'_0 + s) \qquad \text{(2a)}$$

The marginal increase of net output x due to the transfer of the amount s of labour from its direct to its indirect use is $\frac{\partial x}{\partial s}$.

We have from (1a):

$$\frac{\partial x}{\partial s} = F_m \frac{\partial m}{\partial s} - F_l \qquad \text{(6)}$$

and from (2a):

$$\frac{\partial m}{\partial s} = \phi_{l'} \qquad \text{(7)}$$

Hence, by substitution of (7) into (6):

$$\frac{\partial x}{\partial s} = F_m \phi_{l'} - F_l \qquad \text{(8)}$$

and $F_m\phi_{l'} > F_l$ if $\frac{\partial x}{\partial s} > 0$, i.e. if the amount of indirect labour is less than the optimum amount.

If a unit of labour is transferred from the direct to the indirect use there is a decrease of net output due to the withdrawal of a unit of direct labour and an increase due to the addition of a unit of indirect labour. This decrease, which is equal to the marginal product of a unit of direct labour, is the *cost* involved in adding a unit of indirect labour. Therefore, *the marginal productivity of direct labour may be conceived as being the marginal cost of indirect labour.* If the labour resources are distributed so as to maximise net output the marginal productivity of indirect labour equals its marginal cost. We arrive, then, at the same result whether we evaluate the marginal significance of indirect labour by its marginal productivity (in terms of the finished product) or by its marginal cost (conceived as an opportunity lost). But not so if the amount of indirect labour employed differs from the optimum amount. In such case the evaluation by the marginal productivity and by the marginal cost lead to different results. We shall call the difference between the marginal productivity of indirect labour and its marginal cost the marginal *net* productivity of indirect labour. The marginal cost of indirect labour (in terms of lost opportunities) being equal to the marginal productivity of direct labour, the *marginal net productivity of indirect labour is equal to the difference between the marginal productivity of indirect and of direct labour.*[1]

From (8) it follows immediately that the marginal *net* productivity of indirect labour is positive, zero, or negative according to whether the amount of indirect labour employed is less, equal, or more than the optimum amount. From the second order conditions that the net output be a maximum it follows that $\frac{\partial^2 x}{\partial s^2} < 0$ in the neighbourhood of the maximum point.[2] As according to our definition $\frac{\partial x}{\partial s}$ is the marginal *net* productivity of indirect labour this

[1] The marginal *net* productivity of indirect labour corresponds to what is the substitutive marginal productivity of indirect labour, if we follow Pigou in distinguishing between additive and substitutive marginal productivity (cf. *The Economics of Welfare*, Fourth edition, pp. 131–2). We have from (1) and (2) $\frac{\partial x}{\partial l'} = F_m\phi_{l'}$ if l is regarded as independent of l', and $\frac{\partial x}{\partial l'} = F_m\phi_{l'} - F_l$ if the relation $l + l' = \text{const.}$ is imposed while differentiating. The first is the additive and the second is the substitutive marginal productivity of indirect labour. I prefer, however, to use here the term marginal *net* productivity of indirect labour.

[2] The second order condition that the function (1) subjected to the supplementary conditions (2) and (3) be a maximum is :

$$F_{mm}dm^2 + 2F_{ml}dmdl + F_{ll}dl^2 + F_m d^2m < 0 \quad \text{(I)}$$

Differentiating (8) with respect to s and remembering that m is a function of s we have :

$$\frac{\partial^2 x}{\partial s^2} = F_{ms}\phi_{l'} + F_m\phi_{l's} - F_{ls} \quad \text{(II)}$$

However :

$$F_{ms} = F_{mm}\frac{\partial m}{\partial s} + F_{ml}\frac{dl}{ds} = F_{mm}\phi_{l'} - F_{ml}$$

means that in the neighbourhood of the equilibrium point the marginal *net* productivity of indirect labour must decrease as the amount of indirect labour increases.

Strictly, the condition $\frac{\partial^2 x}{\partial s^2} < 0$ holds only in the neighbourhood of the maximum position. However, generally we may expect the production functions to be shaped so that there is a rather large interval in which the condition $\frac{\partial^2 x}{\partial s^2} < 0$ holds.

The discussion of the properties of the marginal *net* productivity of indirect labour is done most conveniently by means of graphs. In Figs. 1, 2, and 3 the line II' represents the marginal productivity of indirect labour and the line DD' represents the marginal productivity of direct labour, both marginal productivities being understood in terms of the finished commodity. The units of

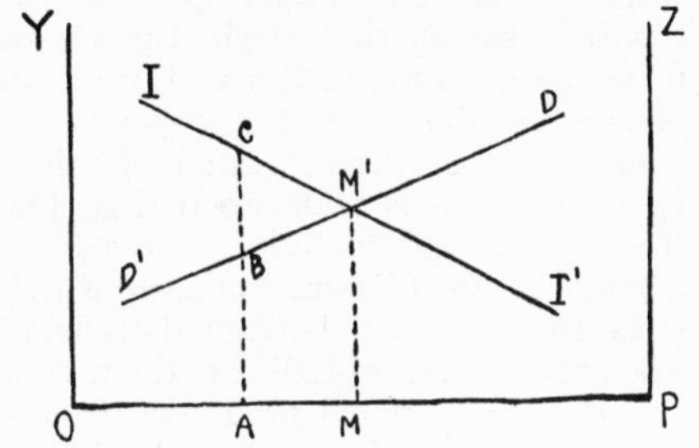

FIGURE 1

$$\phi_{l's} = \phi_{l'l'}\frac{dl'}{ds} + \phi_{l'm'}\frac{\partial m'}{\partial s} = \phi_{l'l'}$$

$$F_{ls} = F_{lm}\frac{\partial m}{\partial s} + F_{ll}\frac{dl}{ds} = F_{ml}\phi_{l'} - F_{ll}$$

Substituting these expressions into (II) we get :

$$\frac{\partial^2 x}{\partial s^2} = F_{mm}\phi^2_{l'} - 2F_{ml}\phi_{l'} + F_{ll} + F_m\phi_{l'l'} \quad \dots\dots \quad \text{(III)}$$

From production function (2) we have :

$$dm = (\phi_{m'} - 1)\, dm' + \phi_{l'}dl'$$

Taking into account that in the maximum position $\phi_{m'} = 1$ (cf. equation (4)) this reduces to :

$$dm = \phi_{l'}dl'$$

or :

$$dm = -\phi_{l'}dl$$

because $dl' = -dl$, resulting from equation (3). Hence :

$$\phi_{l'} = -\frac{dm}{dl}$$

and

$$\phi_{l'l'} = \frac{d^2m}{dl^2}$$

Substituting these relations into (III) and multiplying by dl^2 we arrive at :

$$\frac{\partial^2 x}{\partial s^2}dl^2 = F_{mm}dm^2 + 2F_{ml}dmdl + F_{ll}dl^2 + F_m d^2m \quad \dots\dots \quad \text{(IV)}$$

The right hand side of (IV) is identical with (I) which is negative by the second order maximum condition. Hence :

$$\frac{\partial^2 x}{\partial s^2} < 0 \quad \dots\dots \quad \text{(V)}$$

in the neighbourhood of the maximum position.

indirect labour are measured from the origin O to the right and the units of direct labour are measured from the origin P to the left. The segment OP, which is constant, represents the total amount of labour, direct and indirect. Thus if OA is the amount of indirect labour the corresponding amount of direct labour is PA and $OA+PA=OP$ is the total amount of labour resources available.[1]

The lines II' and DD' need some further explanation. If the marginal productivity of direct and of indirect labour is each a function of one variable (i.e. of the amount of the respective type of labour) alone the lines II′ and DD′ represent simply the marginal productivity of the two types of labour. But if the marginal productivity of direct and of indirect labour is each a function of two variables (i.e. if it depends on the amount of both types of labour employed), the interpretation of the lines II' and DD' needs some qualification. In such case it is understood that, for instance, the ordinate AC represents the marginal productivity of the amount OA of indirect labour when the amount of direct labour employed is PA. Similarly, the ordinate AB is understood to represent the marginal productivity of the amount PA of direct labour when the amount of indirect labour employed is OA.

If both marginal productivities are functions of one variable alone, the curves II' and DD' are both declining, at least in a certain neighbourhood of the maximum position which is determined by their point of intersection. This is obvious as to the marginal productivity of direct labour (as a consequence of the law of diminishing returns). The marginal productivity of indirect labour is the product of the marginal productivity of indirect labour in terms of equipment and of the marginal productivity of equipment in terms of the finished commodity (cf. p. 162). This product diminishes from the point on the two marginal productivities just mentioned diminish both. In this case both curves have, at least in a certain neighbourhood of the maximum position, the shape indicated in Fig. 1. However, if the marginal productivity of direct and of indirect labour is each a function of two variables, one of them may rise while the other declines, but the absolute value of the slope of the rising curve must be smaller than that of the declining curve. This follows from the condition of existence of a maximum position. These conditions are: (i) there must be a point where both curves intersect, i.e. where the marginal productivity of indirect and of direct labour is equal, and (ii) the marginal productivity of indirect labour must be greater than the marginal productivity of direct labour to the left, and smaller to the right of the maximum position.[2] Thus in the neighbourhood of the maximum position

[1] If, instead of assuming the total amount of labour resources to be fixed, we assume it to depend on the amount of net output, the segment OP stretches (or shrinks) as net output increases with the amount of indirect labour approaching its optimum size. However, according to the second order maximum conditions in the neighbourhood of the maximum position the supply of labour resources must increase or decrease at a diminishing rate as net output increases. This prevents the segment OP from stretching (or shrinking) indefinitely and assures a final equilibrium.

[2] This follows from the condition that $\frac{\partial x}{\partial s} = 0$ in the maximum position and $\frac{\partial^2 x}{\partial s^2} < 0$ in the neighbourhood of this position. Recalling that $\frac{\partial x}{\partial s} = F_m \phi_l' - F_l$ we have $F_m \phi_l' - F_l > 0$ to the left and $F_m \phi_l' - F_l < 0$ to the right of the maximum position. The second condition could not be

the two marginal productivity curves must have either the shape indicated in Fig. 1 or one of the shapes indicated in Fig. 2 and Fig. 3.[1]

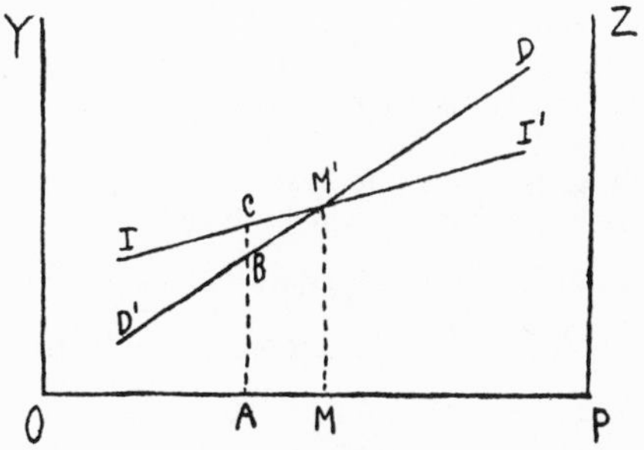

FIGURE 2

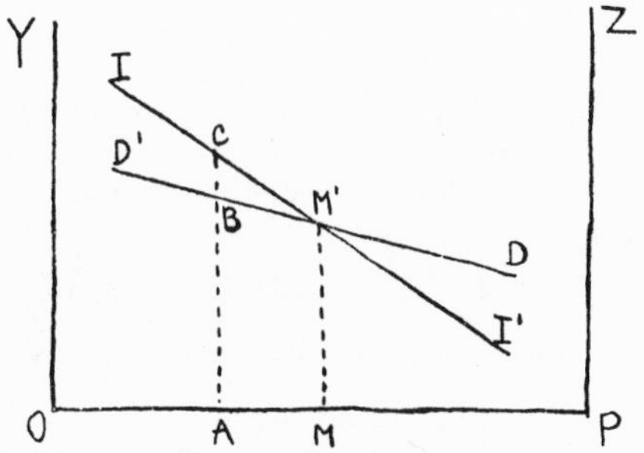

FIGURE 3

If OA is the amount of indirect labour and PA the amount of direct labour actually employed the marginal productivity of indirect and of direct labour is AC and AB respectively. The difference BC between those two marginal productivities is the marginal *net* productivity of indirect labour. By plotting the differences between the ordinates of the curves II' and DD' as ordinates on a separate graph we obtain a curve NN' representing the marginal *net* productivity of indirect labour (cf. Fig. 4). The curve NN' is declining. The marginal *net* productivity of indirect labour is positive to the left of the maximum point M, zero at this point, and negative to the right of it.

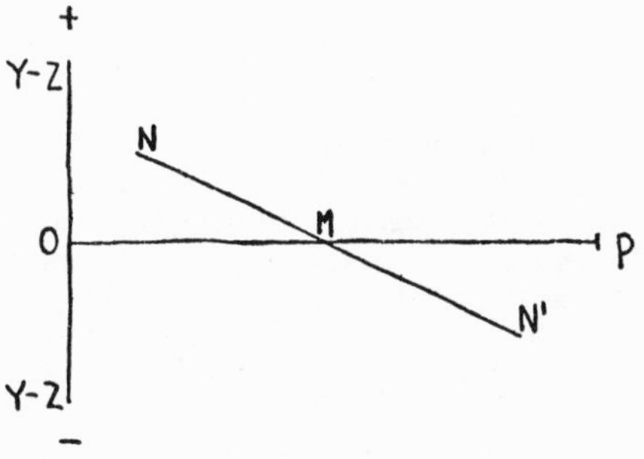

FIGURE 4

4. THE MARGINAL NET PRODUCTIVITY OF REAL CAPITAL

We shall use the term *real capital* to designate the equipment (in our example, the axes) employed in production. For certain purposes it is more

satisfied if both marginal productivity curves were rising and neither the first nor the second condition would be satisfied, if one of the curves being rising and the other declining, the absolute slope of the rising curve were greater than that of the declining curve.

[1] It may be noticed that the marginal productivity curves in Figs. 1, 2, and 3 are drawn only for a certain interval around the maximum position. Outside of this interval their shape may be different; eventually they may intersect again. However, the intersection points next to the maximum position represent unstable equilibria. In any case, the marginal productivity of either direct or indirect labour must be zero in the neighbourhood of the origins O and P, for generally no product can be obtained by using only direct or indirect labour. The transition of the marginal

convenient to consider the marginal *net* productivity of real capital instead of the marginal *net* productivity of indirect labour. The first is derived from the latter in a simple way. The marginal gross productivity of real capital employed in the production of the finished commodity is F_m. To increase the amount of real capital a certain amount of labour must be withdrawn from the production of the finished commodity and transferred to the production of equipment (real capital). This withdrawal leads to a diminution of the output of the finished commodity which constitutes the *cost* of adding an additional amount of real capital. The amount of labour which must be withdrawn to create the additional amount $\triangle m$ of real capital equals $\frac{\partial l'}{\partial m} \triangle m = \frac{\triangle m}{\phi_{l'}}$. Thus the loss of net output involved in withdrawing the amount of labour $\frac{\triangle m}{\phi_{l'}}$ from its direct use is $\frac{F_l}{\phi_{l'}} \triangle m$. This loss is compensated by an increase of net output equal to $F_m \triangle m$. The difference

$$F_m \triangle m - \frac{F_l}{\phi_{l'}} \triangle m$$

is the *net* increment of net output due to an increase $\triangle m$ of the real capital. The rate of increase is then :

$$F_m - \frac{F_l}{\phi_{l'}} \qquad \text{(9)}$$

and is the marginal *net* productivity of real capital. The marginal *net* productivity of real capital is thus the marginal *net* productivity of indirect labour in terms of the finished commodity divided by the marginal gross productivity of indirect labour in terms of equipment (real capital). As the latter is assumed to be always positive the marginal *net* productivity of real capital has always the same sign as the marginal *net* productivity of indirect labour and may be represented by a curve similar in shape to that indicated in Fig. 4.

The increase of the amount of real capital requires a transfer of labour from the production of the finished commodity to the production of equipment. However, such transfer involves a temporary interruption of the synchronisation of production. Immediately after the transfer takes place there is a decrease of the production of the finished commodity and an increase of the amount of labour employed in the production of equipment. Only when the additional equipment is ready and is installed in the production of the finished commodity the synchronisation of production is restored. When this will happen depends on the length of the delay periods in both productions. But from the moment the synchronisation is restored there is an increased perpetual flow of the finished commodity (provided, of course, that the amount of equipment was less than the optimum amount, for otherwise the flow of the finished commodity would be decreased). Thus the transfer of labour from the production of the finished commodity to the production of real capital (equipment) is equivalent to a temporary reduction of the output of the finished

productivity from zero to a positive value can be effected either through a rising branch of the respective marginal productivity curve or through a discontinuous jump. Similarly the transition from a positive value to zero at the other end of the curve may be either continuous or discontinuous.

product recompensated by an increase of the perpetual flow of this product. The said act of transfer of labour is an act of *real saving*.[1] "Real saving" means thus a transfer of labour from its direct use to its indirect use resulting in an increase of real capital.

5. THE RATE OF REAL INTEREST

Following the terminology generally accepted we define the *rate of real interest* as *the ratio of the marginal net productivity of real capital to its marginal cost*. The marginal cost of real capital being $\frac{F_l}{\phi_{l'}}$ (cf. p. 168), the rate of real interest is:

$$i = \frac{F_m - F_l/\phi_{l'}}{F_l/\phi_{l'}} \quad \ldots\ldots \quad (10)$$

This is J. B. Clark's well-known definition of the rate of interest.[2] Formula (10) can also be written in the form:

$$i = \frac{F_m\phi_{l'} - F_l}{F_l} \quad \ldots\ldots \quad (11)$$

which expresses the rate of real interest as *the ratio of the marginal net productivity of indirect labour to its marginal cost*. This is the well-known formula of Wicksell.[3] Both formulae are, of course, equivalent. The first formula refers interest to the marginal *net* productivity of real capital, while the other refers it to the marginal *net* productivity of indirect labour, i.e. to the difference between the marginal productivity of indirect and of direct labour.[4]

The rate of real interest is zero when net output is a maximum. This follows immediately from equation (5) which states a maximum condition. The denominator of formula (10) and (11) being always positive, the rate of real interest is positive or negative according as to whether the amount of real capital (or, what is equivalent, the amount of indirect labour employed) is less or more than the optimum amount, i.e. the amount needed to maximise net output. Writing formula (10) or (11) in the form:

$$i = \frac{F_m\phi_{l'}}{F_l} - 1$$

we observe that the rate of real interest is the nearer zero the nearer the

[1] The term "real" is used here, as in the word "real capital," in distinction to "monetary." The word "saving" means creation of *additional* real capital. It does not include the mere maintenance of the existing real capital.

[2] *The Distribution of Wealth*, New York, 1899, pp. 184–6.

[3] *Lectures on Political Economy*, vol. I, London, 1935, p. 156.

[4] Wicksell gives the definition: "Interest is the difference between the marginal productivity of saved-up labour and land and of current labour and land" (*Lectures*, vol. I, p. 154). We use the expression indirect labour, instead of Wicksell's term "saved-up labour," in order to avoid the appearance as if it were necessary that real capital is produced by labour alone without the co-operation of some quantity of real capital (equipment), too. Production function (2) shows clearly that no such assumption is involved in our analysis.

expression $\frac{F_m \phi_{l'}}{F_l}$ is to unity. Now, this expression approaches unity the more the expression $F_m \phi_{l'} - F_l$, which is the marginal *net* productivity of indirect labour, approaches zero. We have seen that, in a certain neighbourhood of the maximum position, the marginal *net* productivity of indirect labour decreases as the distribution of labour resources between direct and indirect labour approaches the distribution maximising net output. The rate of real interest, or still better the discount factor $1+i$,may thus serve as an index of the distance of the actual allocation of the labour resources from the allocation producing maximum net output.[1]

6. CONDITIONS OF MAXIMUM PROFIT

Having studied the conditions of maximum net output, which are independent of the institutional framework in which production goes on, we now pass to the study of a capitalist enterprise economy.[2] A capitalist enterprise economy works with prices and the producers, who are here called entrepreneurs, do not aim at a maximum net output but at a maximum profit in terms of money instead. By the word profit net profit is understood, of course. If net output is maximised in a capitalist enterprise economy, this is but an incidental result of the profit pursuing activities of the entrepreneurs. We shall restrict our study here to the case where free competition subsists among entrepreneurs. By free competition we mean the fulfilment of the following two conditions: First, the number of entrepreneurs must be large enough, so that no one separately can affect prices appreciably by varying the quantity of his output. Thus the prices given in the market are regarded by each entrepreneur as parameters independent of his behaviour. Second, there must be free entry of new entrepreneurs into the industry, which leads to prices being equal to average cost in long-period equilibrium. It is chiefly the first condition of free competition we shall make use of. The second condition will be needed only for one special purpose.

Let us imagine our enterprise economy as consisting, like the economic system considered, of the production of wood which is carried out with the aid of equipment (axes) and of labour. Further, the equipment is produced with labour and other equipment of the same kind (as axes are produced with labour co-operating with other axes). Finally, the total amount of labour

[1] It may serve as such index, however, only in the interval in which the marginal *net* productivity curve of indirect labour declines monotonously. But as has been already pointed out, the production functions may be generally expected to be shaped so that the marginal productivity curve satisfies this condition for a rather large interval. Outside of this interval, the marginal *net* productivity curve of indirect labour may have a rising branch, and it might be misleading to use the rate of interest as such index.

[2] Strictly speaking, most of our conclusions hold for any economic system working with a price system, and thus hold also for a socialist economy. Only in a socialist economy the price of labour (i.e. the wage rate) appearing in our equations would have to be interpreted as the imputed wages used for purposes of accounting and would not necessarily correspond to an actual share in the personal distribution of income. Therefore, our conclusions concerning the relations between monetary saving and real saving (cf. p. 183) would need some modification if applied to a socialist economy.

resources is assumed to be either constant or to be a function of wages. The system being now an enterprise economy, wood and axes are produced by entrepreneurs whose aim is to obtain a maximum profit. We assume that the finished commodity (wood) and equipment (axes) are produced by different entrepreneurs, the producers of equipment selling the part of their output not needed in their own industry to the producers of the finished commodity. To secure free competition, the number of entrepreneurs must be large, both in the industry producing the finished commodity and in the industry producing equipment. However, in order to simplify the exposition we assume that each of the two industries consists of but one firm which works exactly *as if* under free competition. Thus we have only one firm producing the finished commodity and only one firm producing equipment. We shall call them briefly firm I and firm II. This assumption, though admittedly extremely unrealistic, simplifies the exposition considerably, and a transition to the more realistic case of many firms engaged in each of the two industries presents no difficulty whatever.[1]

We have a production function for firm I which is :

$$x = F(m, l) \quad \dots\dots \quad (1)$$

and a production function for firm II :

$$m+m' = \phi(m', l') \quad \dots\dots \quad (2)$$

all the symbols having the same meaning as before. All the physical quantities involved are understood as per unit of time. The equipment is assumed to wear out completely in a unit of time and the delay period in both firms is assumed to be fixed and equal to one unit of time, too. The production of the finished commodity and of equipment is assumed to be perfectly synchronised.

We have further, either the equation :

$$l+l' = L \quad \dots\dots \quad (3)$$

where L is a constant, or, if the labour resources are not fixed but their supply depends on wages, we have the equation :

$$l+l' = \psi(p_l) \quad \dots\dots \quad (3a)$$

instead, where p_l is the wage rate per unit of time and ψ is the supply function of labour.

As further data we have the price p_x of the finished commodity (wood), the price p_m of equipment (axes), and the price p_l of labour (i.e. the wage rate per unit of time). Free competition being assumed, the price of equipment and the price of labour are the same for the finished commodity producing and for the equipment producing industry. All prices are considered by the entrepreneurs as independent of their individual behaviour.

Our problem is to find for each of our two firms the method of production

[1] We might also do without this assumption by interpreting the production functions (1) and (2) as referring each to a whole industry, instead of to a single firm. These production functions would then have to be interpreted as the sums of the production functions of all the firms in a given industry. But in such case we would have, to avoid unnecessary technical complication, to maximise profit for a whole industry, instead of for a single firm. Though under free competition this leads to the same result, it is equally unrealistic. The reader is free to choose whichever interpretation of our equations he prefers.

which maximises its profit, i.e. we have to determine m and l so as to maximise the profit of firm I and to determine m' and l' so as to maximise the profit of firm II.

The profit π of firm I is:

$$\pi = xp_x - mp_m - lp_l \qquad (4)$$

and similarly the profit π', of firm II is:[1]

$$\pi' = (m+m')p_m - m'p_m - l'p_l \qquad (5)$$

We find the method of production yielding the maximum profit for firm I from the equations:

$$\frac{\partial \pi}{\partial m} = F_m p_x - p_m = 0$$

$$\frac{\partial \pi}{\partial l} = F_l p_x - p_l = 0$$

and similarly for firm II:

$$\frac{\partial \pi'}{\partial m'} = \phi_{m'} p_m - p_m = 0$$

$$\frac{\partial \pi'}{\partial l'} = \phi_{l'} p_m - p_l = 0$$

These equations can be also written in the following form:

$$p_m = F_m p_x \qquad (6)$$

$$p_l = F_l p_x \qquad (7)$$

$$1 = \phi_{m'} \qquad (8)$$

$$p_l = \phi_{l'} p_m \qquad (9)$$

The economic interpretation of equation (8) has been already discussed (cf. p. 162 above). The other equations express the well-known proposition that the price of each factor of production is equal to the value of its marginal product.[2]

We have seven independent equations, i.e. (1), (2), (3) or (3a), (6), (7), (8) and (9), which serve to determine the seven unknowns m, l, m', l', x, p_m and p_l. The price p_x of the finished commodity is determined from outside of the system, for which it is a datum. To determine p_x we need an additional equation, for instance, a demand function connecting p_x and x, or an equation stating that for firm I marginal cost equals average cost.

From equations (6)–(9) the prices p_m and p_l can be eliminated. We have from (7) and (9):

$$\phi_{l'} p_m = F_l p_x$$

Substituting (6) into this expression and dividing both sides by p_x we arrive at:

$$F_m \phi_{l'} = F_l \qquad (10)$$

[1] The profit of firm II may also be written in the form:

$$\pi' = mp_m - l'p_l$$

However, the more explicit cost account indicated in (5) will prove to be of importance later.

[2] Unless explicitly stated otherwise, by marginal product the marginal *physical* product is meant throughout this paper.

If prices are eliminated, the equations (6)–(9) reduce to the two equations (8) and (10) which are identical with the two equations expressing the conditions of maximum net output (cf. equations (4) and (5) on p. 161). Thus the production of the finished commodity is a maximum with the methods of production which maximise the profit of firm I and of firm II simultaneously. It follows especially from (10) that firm I and firm II *obtain simultaneously their maximum profit when the marginal productivity of indirect labour is equal to the maximum productivity of direct labour.*

7. THE FUNCTION OF MONEY CAPITAL

The equations obtained in the preceding paragraph determine the methods of production which maximise the profit of each of our two firms. These methods of production impose on each of the firms to produce a certain optimum output with an optimum combination of the factors of production. To do this each firm must employ a certain optimum amount of factors of production, namely, such amount of each factor as makes the value of its marginal product equal to its price. However, in order to employ such amount of each factor a firm needs a certain amount of money (or, rather, purchasing power). Thus if the optimum method of production imposes the employment of 100 axes and 100 workers per annum, and if the price of an axe is £10 and the yearly wages of a worker are £100, the firm needs a total sum of £11,000 per annum to buy factors of production. Supposing that the wood is sold at the end of the year, the sum of £11,000 is returned, but must be reinvested again. If production is to go on continuously the sum of £11,000 must be kept constantly invested. The fulfilment of the equations of the preceding paragraph presupposes then that the firms are able to procure the sum of money (purchasing power) necessary to purchase the optimum amount of factors of production.

If a firm would not be able to procure the sum of money necessary to purchase the optimum amount of factors of production it could not pursue the best method of production. We shall call the sum of money (i.e. purchasing power) available to a firm for constant investment in (i.e. for the recurrent purchase of) factors of production its *money capital*.[1] The function of money capital is to enable entrepreneurs to purchase factors of production. Money capital is, so to speak, a general " command over means of production." [2] A firm can pursue the best method of production, consisting in employing the amounts of factors of production which equalise the value of the marginal product of a factor and its price, only if it has a sufficient quantity of money capital. If the amount of money capital at the disposal of a firm is not sufficient

[1] It might be better to use the term " numéraire capital " since the specific problems imposed by money creation are ruled out from this investigation. Our term " money capital " corresponds exactly to what is meant by " capital disposal " in the terminology of Cassel, or what might also be called the accumulated savings at the disposal of the entrepreneurs, i.e. the *purchasing power* of which the entrepreneurs dispose to buy factors of production. However, the term " money capital " ought to be more appropriate on account of its direct connotation of the corresponding phenomenon in business practice. It ought only be kept in mind that money is assumed to behave here like a " numéraire," i.e. to be " neutral."

[2] Cf. Schumpeter, *The Theory of Economic Evolution*, Cambridge, Mass., 1934, pp. 116–7.

for this purpose we shall say that the firm suffers from a shortage of money capital.

Our next problem is to investigate the effect of a shortage of money capital on the method of production employed by a firm. For this purpose let us consider firm I and let us assume that the money capital at the disposal of this firm is κ. Thus the firm is not quite free to choose its method of production, for methods of production requiring a money capital larger than κ are not accessible to the firm. Making the best choice it can, the firm will choose the method of production which yields the maximum profit under the provision that the quantity of money invested in the purchase of factors of production is equal to κ, i.e. under the provision :

$$mp_m + lp_l = \kappa \quad \text{.......} \quad (11)$$

where κ is a constant. Our problem is thus to determine the conditions of maximum profit subjected to the supplementary condition (11). Using the method of Lagrange multipliers this reduces to determining the conditions maximising the expression :

$$\pi - \lambda\kappa = xp_x - mp_m - lp_l - \lambda(mp_m + lp_l) \quad \text{.......} \quad (12)$$

where λ is a Lagrange multiplier.

The expression (12) may be written in the more convenient form :

$$\pi - \lambda\kappa = xp_x - mp_m(1+\lambda) - lp_l(1+\lambda) \quad \text{.......} \quad (12a)$$

The method of production maximising the expression (12a) is found from the equations :

$$\frac{\partial(\pi - \lambda\kappa)}{\partial m} = F_m p_x - p_m(1+\lambda) = 0$$

$$\frac{\partial(\pi - \lambda\kappa)}{\partial l} = F_l p_x - p_l(1+\lambda) = 0$$

Similarly, assuming that firm II has but a limited amount κ', of money capital at its disposal the maximisation of its profit is subjected to the supplementary condition :

$$m'p_m + l'p_l = \kappa' \quad \text{.......} \quad (13)$$

where κ' is a constant, and our problem becomes to maximise the expression :

$$\pi' - \lambda'\kappa' = (m+m')p_m - m'p_m(1+\lambda') - l'p_l(1+\lambda') \quad \text{.......} \quad (14)$$

which leads to the equations :

$$\frac{\partial(\pi' - \lambda'\kappa')}{\partial m'} = \phi_{m'} p_m - p_m(1+\lambda') = 0$$

$$\frac{\partial(\pi' - \partial'\kappa')}{\partial l'} = \phi_{l'} p_m - p_l(1+\lambda') = 0$$

where λ' is a Lagrange multiplier.

The equations expressing the maximum conditions may be written in the following form :

$$p_m = \frac{F_m p_x}{1+\lambda} \quad \text{.......} \quad (15)$$

$$p_l = \frac{F_l p_x}{1+\lambda} \qquad (16)$$

$$1 = \frac{\phi_{m'}}{1+\lambda'} \qquad (17)$$

$$p_l = \frac{\phi_{l'} p_m}{1+\lambda'} \qquad (18)$$

The equations (15)–(18), together with the equations (1), (2), (3) or (3a), and with the equations (11) and (13), are nine in number. The number of unknowns is seven, viz. m, l, m', l', x, p_m and p_l. There are thus two equations in excess of the number of unknowns which serve to determine the Lagrange multipliers λ and λ'.

Thus if the choice of the best method of production is restricted by a shortage of money capital the equations (6)–(9) of the preceding paragraph have to be replaced by the equations (15)–(18).

8. THE INTEREST ON MONEY CAPITAL.

The last equations obtained need an economic interpretation. For that purpose the economic meaning of the Lagrange multipliers λ and λ', which are until now mere mathematical symbols, must be found out. To do this we must investigate the effect of a change of the quantity of money capital at the disposal of a firm on the profit obtained by the firm.

Let us first consider firm I. We have from (4) :

$$d\pi = p_x dx - p_m dm - p_l dl \qquad (19)$$

We have also from (1) :

$$dx = F_m dm + F_l dl$$

Substituting this relation into (19) we get :

$$d\pi = (F_m p_x - p_m)dm + (F_l p_x - p_l)dl$$

Equations (15) and 16) yield :

$$F_m p_x = (1+\lambda)p_m$$
$$F_l p_x = (1+\lambda)p_l$$

Taking this into account we arrive at :

$$d\pi = [(1+\lambda)p_m - p_m]dm - [(1+\lambda)p_l - p_l]dl$$

or :

$$d\pi = \lambda(p_m dm + p_l dl)$$

But we have from (11), κ being now assumed as variable :

$$p_m dm + p_l dl = d\kappa \qquad (20)$$

and, therefore :

$$\lambda = \frac{d\pi}{d\kappa} \qquad (21)$$

B

The right-hand side of this expression is the marginal rate of increase of profit due to an increase of the quantity of money capital at the disposal of the firm. An increase of the amount of money capital available to the firm enables the firm to choose a better method of production and $\frac{d\pi}{d\kappa}$ is the rate of increase of profit, it might be called the *marginal profitableness of money capital*. If the firm could borrow an additional amount $\triangle\kappa$ of money capital it would be ready to pay for it any sum up to $\frac{d\pi}{d\kappa}\triangle\kappa$ as interest, for so much is the increase of profit obtained due to an increase $\triangle\kappa$ of the firm's money capital. And if the firm is but one of many competing for the borrowing of additional money capital it must pay as much ; $\frac{d\pi}{d\kappa}$ is then the rate of interest paid for money capital. The Lagrange multiplier λ is thus *the rate of interest on the money capital* employed by firm I.

In a quite similar way it is shown that :

$$\lambda' = \frac{d\pi'}{d\kappa'} \qquad (22)$$

i.e. the marginal profitableness of the money capital invested by firm II. Or in other words : the Lagrange multiplier λ' is the rate of interest on the money capital employed by firm II.

In view of this economic interpretation of the Lagrange multipliers we are going to modify somewhat our assumption concerning the quantity of money capital. Instead of assuming that each firm has a fixed amount of money capital at its disposal we assume now that it is not the quantity of money capital available to each firm separately, but the total amount of money capital in the whole economic system which is fixed and constant. We have, then, in our case the equation :

$$\kappa + \kappa' = K \qquad (23)$$

where K is a constant. Each firm may draw from this total fund of money capital as much as it wants, provided it pays the interest. If free competition subsists both among the firms and among the lenders of money capital the total fund of money capital is distributed among the firms so that each firm pays the same rate of interest and, therefore, the marginal profitableness of money capital is the same for each firm. Thus we have in our case :

$$\lambda = \lambda' \qquad (24)$$

i.e. the rate of interest on money capital is the same for firm I and for firm II. By adding the equations (23) and (24) to our former set of nine equations we can determine the two additional unknowns κ and κ'.

Thus the Lagrange multipliers λ and λ' are equal. The economic interpretation of the formulae (15), (16) and (18) is now obvious. They state the well-known proposition that *the prices of the factors of production are equal to the discounted value of their marginal product.*[1] From formula (17) it will be

[1] Cf. Taussig, *Principles of Economics*, third edition, New York, 1921, Vol. II, p. 217.

observed that the marginal productivity of the circular factor m' is no more constant but depends on the rate of interest. This is explained by the fact that because of the shortage of money capital firm II might, instead of reinvesting the full amount of m', which makes its marginal *net* productivity zero, sell a part of it and by doing so increase its money capital and its profit. This possibility changes the circular factor m' into a genuine cost element with respect to the rate of interest.

We have deduced the interest on money capital from a shortage of money capital which does not permit all firms to engage simultaneously in the best method of production, i.e. in the method which equalises the value of the marginal product of each factor and its price. This way of treating the problem of interest shows clearly the place of interest in the equations of the theory of production. It shows that the equations of the traditional theory of production are based on the tacit assumption that there is always available the money capital necessary to enable all firms to choose the best method of production. If this assumption is replaced by the assumption that the amount of money capital available to a firm, or available in the whole economic system, is short of this requirement, the maximisation of profit is subjected to a restriction and the rate of interest on money capital is a result of this restriction. Our treatment of the problem has the merit of *deducing* the rate of interest on money capital from the equations of the theory of production, instead of introducing it into these equations from outside, as is done by all mathematical economists.

9. INTEREST ON MONEY CAPITAL AND REAL INTEREST.

We have now to analyse the relation between the marginal profitableness of money capital and the marginal *net* productivity of real capital, i.e. the relation between interest on money capital and real interest. There is an obvious analogy between them : as the rate of real interest is an index of the distance of the allocation of the original resources from the allocation maximising net output of the economic system, so the rate of interest on money capital is an index of the distance of the methods of production actually employed from the methods of production which maximise profit for all firms simultaneously. However, this analogy requires some further investigation.

Remembering that $\lambda' = \lambda$, let us eliminate from equations (15), (16) and (18), the prices p_m and p_l. We have from (16) and (18) :

$$\frac{F_l p_x}{1+\lambda} = \frac{\phi_{l'} p_m}{1+\lambda}$$

and substituting (15) into this expression, dividing both sides by p_x and multiplying them both by $1+\lambda$ we get :

$$F_l = \frac{F_m \phi_{l'}}{1+\lambda} \qquad (25)$$

This equation corresponds to equation (10), which holds when there is no shortage of money capital. Equation (25) states that *the marginal productivity of direct labour is equal to the discounted marginal productivity of indirect labour.* From (25) we deduce directly:

$$\lambda = \frac{F_m \phi_{l'} - F_l}{F_l} \quad \ldots\ldots \quad (26)$$

Now, the right-hand side of this expression is nothing else but the rate of real interest (cf. formula (11) on p. 169). We arrive thus to the result that *the rate of interest on money capital is equal to the rate of real interest.* In other words: the marginal profitableness of money capital is equal to the ratio of the marginal net productivity of indirect labour (or of real capital) to its marginal cost.

This rather surprising result shows that a shortage of money capital affects the allocation of labour resources so as to allocate less of them to the indirect use than is required to maximise net output, and more of them into the direct use.

10. MONEY CAPITAL AND REAL CAPITAL.

The equality of the rate of interest on money capital and of the rate of real interest, which in the preceding paragraph has merely been deduced mathematically, needs some further explanation in economic terms. For that purpose we need a more detailed investigation into the mutual relationship between money capital and real capital. The word real capital is used as an alternative name for the equipment co-operating with labour. In our case $m+m'$ is the amount of real capital employed in the economic system. Money capital is the amount of money invested in the purchase of *both* equipment *and* labour. The quantity of money capital is thus larger than the value of real capital employed in production. If $\kappa = mp_m + lp_l$ is the money capital invested by firm I and $\kappa' = m'p_m + l'p_l$ is the money capital invested by firm II the total money capital in our economic system is:

$$K = (m+m')p_m + (l+l')p_l \quad \ldots\ldots \quad (27)$$

while the value of the real capital employed in production is only $(m+m')p_m$.

The distinction between money capital and real capital corresponds to the familiar distinction between capital in terms of "advances" or of "subsistence fund" on one side and capital in terms of "tools and materials" (Marshall's "instrumental capital" [1]) or "intermediate products" on the other side. However, as these terms are somewhat nebulous we prefer to speak simply of money capital as a sum of money invested in the purchase of factors of production and of real capital as a mere alternative term to denote equipment co-operating with labour in production.[2]

Money capital, providing for the entrepreneurs a general "command over means of production," is invested in the purchase of both real capital and

[1] Cf. Marshall, *Principles of Economics*, Eighth edition, London, 1920, p. 75.

[2] For our part we should like to reserve the word capital entirely for the designation of money capital and use for the designation of real capital oniy a word like equipment, means of production, etc. This would avoid much confusion. However, we keep here the term real capital because it is our purpose to study the relationship of two approaches to the interest problem, one of which uses generally the term real capital, while the other uses the term money capital, "advances," etc.

labour. In view of this it seems, at first glance, rather astonishing that a shortage of money capital ought to be accompanied always by a reduction of the employment of real capital which makes the marginal productivity of indirect labour to exceed the marginal productivity of direct labour, and thus to create a positive marginal *net* productivity for real capital. Money capital being used to purchase both real capital and labour it seems strange, indeed, why especially the employment of real capital should be reduced because of a shortage of money capital.[1] And it seems even more astonishing that the rate of interest on money capital should be exactly equal to the rate of real interest, as has been deduced from our equations. However, this coincidence between a shortage of money capital and the reduction of employment of real capital becomes clear upon closer analysis.

In the pricing process of factors of production the marginal productivity of direct labour is discounted only once. We have the equation:

$$p_l = \frac{F_l p_x}{1+\lambda} \qquad (16)$$

But the marginal productivity of indirect labour (in terms of the finished commodity) is discounted twice: once when the labour is used in the production of equipment and another time when equipment is used in the production of the finished commodity. We have:

$$p_l = \frac{\phi_{l'} p_m}{1+\lambda} \qquad (18)$$

and because of:

$$p_m = \frac{F_m p_x}{1+\lambda} \qquad (15)$$

we get finally:

$$p_l = \frac{F_m \phi_{l'} p_x}{(1+\lambda)^2} \qquad (18a)$$

From (16) and (18a) we get:

$$F_l = \frac{F_m \phi_{l'}}{1+\lambda} \qquad (25)$$

i.e. the statement that the marginal productivity of direct labour is equal to the discounted marginal productivity of indirect labour.

What is the economic meaning of the double discounting of the marginal productivity of indirect labour? It is assumed in our study that the production of equipment and the production of the finished commodity take one unit of time each. Thus a shortage of money capital affects the " command over means of production " twice through the production of equipment, while it affects it only once through the production of the finished commodity, for the production of the finished commodity and of equipment, though synchronised,

[1] It may be noted that under our assumption of the real capital wearing out completely in a unit of time this consists entirely of circulating capital. If the real capital were fixed capital it would be clear immediately that a shortage of money capital affects real fixed capital differently than direct labour.

are, so to speak, one on the top of the other in so far as the circular flow of money capital is concerned. A shortage of money capital at the disposal of the firms producing equipment increases the cost (and consequently the prices of equipment) by preventing the firms from using the best method of production. Thus, the firms producing the finished commodity are affected not only by their own shortage of money capital, but also by the shortage of money capital in the equipment producing industry which raises the price of equipment. In our example, the money capital invested in the production of axes bears interest during one year. But the axes used in the production of wood accumulate interest on their value during the year they are used in producing wood. Thus the money capital invested in the production of axes bears interest during two years while the money capital invested in the payment of wages bears interest only during one year. This explains why a shortage in money capital causes a shift of the labour resources towards their direct use and why any decrease of the marginal profitableness of money capital results in a shift of labour resources towards the indirect use, causing a corresponding diminution of the marginal *net* productivity of indirect labour. The equations (16) and (18a) explain the price mechanism through which this shift is effected. At any given moment the amounts of factors, and hence, their marginal productivities, are constant, since it takes some time to change them. Regarding F_l, F_m and $\phi_{l'}$ as constant for the moment, the immediate effect of a change in the rate of interest on money capital is to change the wage-rate paid by the equipment producing industry more than the wage-rate paid by the industry producing the finished commodity. This leads to a shift of labour from one industry to the other, until the wage-rate is the same in both, and causes also a change of the relative prices of equipment and labour.

Let us see what the ultimate effect of a change in the rate of interest on the relative prices of equipment and of labour is. From (15) and (16) we have :

$$\frac{p_l}{p_m} = \frac{F_l}{F_m} \quad \ldots\ldots\ldots\ldots (28)$$

An increase in the rate of interest leads to less labour being invested indirectly and more being invested directly. It follows from (28) :

$$\frac{\partial}{\partial l}\left(\frac{p_l}{p_m}\right) = \frac{F_{ll}F_m - F_{ml}F_l}{F_m^2} \quad \ldots\ldots\ldots\ldots (29)$$

which expression is always negative when $F_{ml} \geqq 0$ and may be positive, in a certain case, when $F_{ml} < 0$, i.e. when both factors are competing. By putting $p_m =$ constant we see that this case is the same as that in which the demand for direct labour is an increasing function of its price. This case being disregarded, *wages fall when the rate of interest increases*, and vice versa. An increase of the rate of interest, by diminishing the demand for indirect labour invested, leads to a decrease of the equipment available. Thus, by a similar procedure, and excluding the case where the demand for equipment is an increasing function of its price, we arrive at the result that *the price of equipment (real capital) varies in the opposite direction from wages.*

Because of $\lambda = \lambda'$ we have:

$$\lambda = \frac{d\pi}{d\kappa} = \frac{d\pi'}{d\kappa'} \qquad (30)$$

From the second order maximum conditions for profit it follows that in a certain neighbourhood of the maximum profit point we have:

$$d^2\pi < 0 \text{ and } d^2\pi' < 0 \qquad (31)$$

and hence:

$$\left.\begin{aligned} &\frac{d\lambda}{d\kappa} = \frac{d^2\pi}{d\kappa^2} < 0 \\ &\text{and} \\ &\frac{d\lambda}{d\kappa'} = \frac{d^2\pi'}{d\kappa'^2} < 0 \end{aligned}\right\} \qquad (31a)$$

From (31a) and from:

$$K = \kappa + \kappa' \qquad (23)$$

we arrive at:

$$\frac{d\lambda}{dK} = \frac{1}{\frac{d\kappa}{d\lambda} + \frac{d\kappa'}{d\lambda}} < 0 \qquad (32)$$

i.e. *the rate of interest decreases as the total amount of money capital increases.*[1] Therefore, in general, *wages increase and the price of equipment decreases when money capital becomes more abundant.*

11. MONEY CAPITAL AND THE SCALE OF OUTPUT

To investigate the function of money capital with respect to the scale of output of a firm we need to make use of the second condition of free competition consisting in the possibility of free entry of new firms into an industry. This possibility leads in the long run to the equality of marginal and average cost. However, as a shortage of money capital brings it about that interest is paid on money capital, it is the *accumulated* marginal and average cost which is to be equal.

The accumulated marginal cost of firm I is:

$$\frac{(p_m dm + p_l dl)(1+\lambda)}{dx} \qquad (33)$$

From (1) we have:

$$dx = F_m dm + F_l dl$$

and from equations (15) and (16):

$$F_m = \frac{p_m(1+\lambda)}{p_x}$$

[1] Generally we may expect the production functions to be shaped so that the relation (31) holds for some larger interval and therefore relation (32) must hold for some larger interval, too.

$$F_l = \frac{p_l\,(1+\lambda)}{p_x}$$

Substituting these two relations into the preceding one we get :

$$dx = \frac{1+\lambda}{p_x}(p_m dm + p_l dl)$$

and by substitution of this into (33) the accumulated marginal cost becomes :

$$\frac{(p_m dm + p_l dl)(1+\lambda)}{dx} = p_x \qquad (34)$$

The equation stating the equality of marginal and of average cost is thus :

$$\frac{(p_m dm + p_l dl)(1+\lambda)}{dx} = \frac{(m p_m + l p_l)(1+\lambda)}{x} = p_x \qquad (35)$$

i.e. *accumulated marginal cost and (in long period equilibrium) average cost are equal to the price of the commodity.*[1]

Similarly the equation stating the equality of (accumulated) marginal and average cost for firm II is obtained :

$$\frac{(p_m dm' + p_l dl')(1+\lambda)}{dm+dm'} = \frac{(m' p_m + l' p_l)(1+\lambda)}{m+m'} = p_m \qquad (36)$$

Remembering that :

$$p_m = \frac{F_m p_x}{1+\lambda} \qquad (15)$$

$$p_l = \frac{F_l p_x}{1+\lambda} \qquad (16)$$

and substituting this into (35) we get for firm I :

$$p_x = \frac{p_x(F_m m + F_l l)}{x}$$

whence the well-known equation :

$$x = F_m m + F_l l \qquad (35a)$$

Similarly, by substitution of (17) and (18) into (36) we get for firm II :

$$m + m' = \phi_{m'} m' + \phi_{l'} l' \qquad (36a)$$

Equations (35) and (36) show that the scale of output does not depend directly on the rate of interest, since the factor $1+\lambda$ on both sides of the equations cancels. However, the scale of output does depend on the rate of interest indirectly. We have seen that the relative shortage or abundance of money capital, of which the rate of interest is an index, affects the price of labour and of equipment, and by doing so it affects the scale of output.

[1] By writing (34) and (35) in the form :

$$\frac{p_m dm + p_l dl}{dx} = \frac{m p_m + l p_l}{x} = \frac{p_x}{1+\lambda}$$

we may also say that simple (not accumulated) marginal and average cost is equal to the *discounted* price of the commodity.

We have from equations (35) and (36):

$$mp_m + lp_l = \frac{xp_x}{1+\lambda}$$

$$m'p_m + l'p_l = \frac{(m+m')p_m}{1+\lambda}$$

Adding these two expressions and taking into account that

$$(m+m')p_m + (l+l')p_l = K \qquad (27)$$

i.e. the total money capital in our economic system, we arrive at:

$$K = \frac{xp_x + (m+m')p_m}{1+\lambda} \qquad (37)$$

The formula obtained states that *the total money capital is equal to the discounted value of the gross product of the economic system.*

From (27) we have:

$$(m+m')p_m = K - (l+l')p_l$$

Taking this into account we can write (37):

$$(1+\lambda)K = xp_x + K - (l+l')p_l$$

whence:

$$(l+l')p_l + \lambda K = xp_x \qquad (38)$$

i.e. *the value of the net product of the economic system is distributed wholly between wage and interest payments.*

12. MONETARY SAVING AND REAL SAVING.

Our discussion of the relation of money capital and real capital showed that an increase of the quantity of money capital is always accompanied by an increase of the amount of real capital employed in production. It was shown that the rate of interest on money capital decreases as money capital becomes more abundant. But as the rate of interest on money capital is equal to the rate of real interest the marginal productivity of indirect labour decreases relatively to the marginal productivity of direct labour, which means an increase of real capital. Money creation being ruled out from our study, the only way to increase the quantity of money capital is through saving. Thus *any monetary saving is accompanied by real saving*, i.e. by an increase in the amount of real capital employed in production. The latter leads to an increase of the net output of the economic system.

It might seem, at first glance, that the amount of monetary saving must be equal to the money value of the real saving performed and that the rate of interest is equal to the value of the marginal increase of the net output due to the increase of money capital. However, this is not so, if we consider the whole economic system. An increase of money capital in the whole economic system changes the prices of real capital goods (equipment) and of labour. As the marginal productivity of direct labour increases relatively to the marginal productivity of indirect labour wages rise.[1] This rise of wages absorbs a part of the monetary saving.

Assuming that wages and the price of equipment change because of the increase of money capital, we have from (27):

$$dK = p_m(dm+dm')+(m+m')dp_m+p_l(dl+dl')+(l+l')dp_l \quad \ldots\ldots \quad (39)$$

Our economic system is subjected to the condition:

$$l+l' = L \quad \ldots\ldots \quad (3)$$

i.e. the total amount of labour resources is constant, or:

$$l+l' = \psi(p_l) \quad \ldots\ldots \quad (3a)$$

i.e. the total amount of labour resources is a function of wages. In the first instance we have:

$$dl+dl' = 0$$

and in the second instance:

$$dl+dl' = \psi'(p_l)dp_l \quad \ldots\ldots \quad (40)$$

where ψ' is the first derivative of the function ψ. The first instance is a particular case of the second when $\psi'(p_l) = 0$. Hence we shall consider the second instance as the more general case.

Substituting (40) into (39) we get:

$$dK = p_m(dm+dm')+(m+m')dp_m+[p_l\psi'(p_l)+(l+l')]dp_l \quad \ldots\ldots \quad (39a)$$

whence:

$$p_m(dm+dm')+(m+m')dp_m = dK-[p_l\psi'(p_l)+(l+l')]dp_l \quad \ldots\ldots \quad (39b)$$

The left-hand side of this formula is the money value of the real saving performed and is equal to the amount of monetary saving minus the part absorbed by an increase of the total wage bill.

From the fact that monetary saving results in an increase of wages and in a decrease of the rate of interest it follows that the rate of interest is *different* from (generally *less* than) the value of the marginal net product of money capital. Indeed, we have from (38):

$$\lambda K = xp_x-(l+l')p_l$$

whence:

$$\lambda dK+Kd\lambda = p_xdx-[p_l\psi'(p_l)+(l+l')]dp_l$$

and finally:

$$\lambda = \frac{dx}{dK}p_x-\frac{[p_l\psi'(p_l)+(l+l')]dp_l}{dK}-\frac{Kd\lambda}{dK} \quad \ldots\ldots \quad (41)$$

According to (32) it is: $\frac{d\lambda}{dK}<0$. Thus the formula obtained states that the rate of interest is equal to the value of the marginal net product of money capital minus the marginal increase in the sum of wages plus the marginal decrease in the sum of interest payments.

[1] As can be seen from formula (29), there may be an exception to this rule. However, the formulae (39) and (41) hold generally, dp_l being the *change* in the wage-rate, whatever the sign of this change is.

The result that the rate of interest is smaller than the value of the marginal net product of money capital has been obtained substantially already by Wicksell.[1] This result throws some light on the relation of money capital to real capital. The rate of interest was found to be equal to the marginal *net* productivity of *real* capital, which is equal to the marginal *profitableness* of money capital. Both these quantities differ, however, from the value of the marginal net *product* of *money* capital.[2] The explanation of this divergence is simple. An increase of money capital increases the net product of the economic system only in so far as it leads to an increase of real capital. However, money capital is used to purchase not only real capital goods (equipment) but also labour. The increase in wages resulting from a transfer of labour from the direct to the indirect use absorbs a part of the money capital saved and causes real saving to be smaller than monetary saving. This effect is counteracted by the fall in the rate of interest releasing some money capital which has been hitherto used for interest payments and which can be now invested in the purchase of real capital.

13. THE PERIOD OF TURNOVER OF MONEY CAPITAL.

Up to now it has been assumed that the production of both the finished commodity and of equipment takes one unit of time each. Thus the money capital invested by each entrepreneur is returned after a unit of time and must be reinvested again. After a unit of time (a year, for instance) the commodity produced by the firm is ready and sold and the money capital invested is returned to the entrepreneur. We call the period after which the money capital is returned its *period of turnover*. Hitherto the period of turnover was assumed to be equal to one unit of time. This can be achieved always by a proper choice of the unit in which time is measured. However, in view of the fact that different industries may have periods of turnover of money capital of different duration, it will prove important to generalise our formulas so as to be valid for any choice of time units.

Let the period of turnover of the money capital invested by firm I be Δt units of time (Δt may also be a proper fraction), and let m and l be the amount of equipment and labour used *per unit of time* and p_m and p_l the prices of equipment and labour. The firm needs now a money capital equal to $\Delta t(mp_m+lp_l)$ to be able to use the quantities mentioned of the factors of production, for a sum of money equal to mp_m+lp_l must be spent during each

[1] Cf. *Über Wert, Kapital und Rente*, reprinted London, 1933, p. 111 seq., and *Lectures*, vol. I, pp. 148, 150 and 180. Formula (41) corresponds to the formula given by Wicksell on p. 180. Cf. also Wicksell's paper on *Real Capital and Interest* (reprinted as an appendix to *Lectures*, Vol. I) p. 268 and pp. 291–93, and Gustaf Åkerman, *Realkapital und Kapitalzins*, fasc. I, Stockholm, 1923, pp. 152–3.

[2] Thus Wicksell's criticism of Thünen's statement that the rate of interest is equal to the marginal net product of a unit of capital (cf. the places quoted in the preceding note) suffers from some confusion. Thünen seems to have meant real capital (cf. *Der isolierte Staat*, Part II, Rostock, 1850, pp. 79 and 97–102) and the rate of interest, as we have seen, equals exactly the marginal *net* productivity of real capital. However, it does not equal the value of the marginal product of *money* capital, and Wicksell was the first to see this discrepancy, though his explanation is somewhat obscure.

unit of time to purchase factors of production, and as this sum will be returned only after a period of Δt units of time, Δt times that sum must be at the disposal of the firm in order to enable it to carry on production. Let x be the output per unit of time and κ be the money capital available to the firm. Firm I maximises its profit (per unit of time) now subject to the supplementary condition :

$$\Delta t(mp_m+lp_l) = \kappa \qquad (42)$$

where κ is a constant.

Using the method of Lagrange multipliers this is equivalent to maximising the expression :

$$\pi-\lambda\kappa = xp_x-mp_m-lp_l-\lambda\Delta t(mp_m+lp_l)$$

where λ is the Lagrange multiplier. Hence the equations :

$$p_m = \frac{F_m p_x}{1+\lambda\Delta t} \qquad (43)$$

$$p_l = \frac{F_l p_x}{1+\lambda\Delta t} \qquad (44)$$

Similarly for firm II, if $\Delta t'$ is its period of turnover of money capital, we get the equations :

$$\phi_{m'} = 1+\lambda'\Delta t' \qquad (45)$$

$$p_l = \frac{\phi_{l'} p_m}{1+\lambda'\Delta t'} \qquad (46)$$

From (43) and (44), together with equations (1) and (42) we derive :

$$\lambda = \frac{d\pi}{d\kappa} \qquad (47)$$

and similarly the relationship :

$$\lambda' = \frac{d\pi'}{d\kappa'} \qquad (48)$$

is obtained. Thus λ and λ' is the rate of interest *per unit of time* on the money capital invested by firm I and firm II respectively. Free competition being assumed as well among the lenders as among the borrowers of money capital we have $\lambda=\lambda'$. Remembering this, we have from (43), (44) and (46) :

$$F_l = \frac{F_m\phi_{l'}}{1+\lambda\Delta t'}$$

whence :

$$\lambda\Delta t' = \frac{F_m\phi_{l'}-F_l}{F_l} \qquad (49)$$

Taking into account formulae (43)–(46) the formulas of the preceding paragraphs can be adjusted so as to make them independent of the unit of time chosen. In consequence of equation (42) and of a similar equation for firm II, equation (37) turns into :

$$\frac{K}{\Delta t}+\frac{K'}{\Delta t'} = \frac{xp_x}{1+\lambda\Delta t}+\frac{(m+m')p_m}{1+\lambda\Delta t'} \qquad (37a)$$

The left-hand side of this equation can be interpreted as the amortisation quota per unit of time of the total money capital. Thus the discounted value of the gross output per unit of time is equal to the amortisation quota per unit of time of the total money capital. For $\Delta t = \Delta t'$ equations (38) and (41) are deduced from (37a). If $\Delta t = \Delta t'$ equations (38) and (41) have to be replaced by some more complicated ones.

14. THE TIME DIMENSION OF INTEREST

The treatment of the problem of interest given here may seem rather paradoxical. We have deduced all the fundamental propositions of the theory of interest from the ordinary equations of the theory of production which are generally regarded as being "timeless" or "instantaneous."[1] It is, however, a commonplace that interest has a time dimension. How, then, could a quantity having a time dimension be deduced from equations which are timeless in character? The solution of the apparent paradox is simple. Our result simply shows that it is fallacious to consider the ordinary equations of the theory of production as timeless. The equations of the theory of production, as well as the other equations of the theory of economic equilibrium, are by no means timeless as a widespread opinion wants to have it. They all include time, though only implicitly, for all the physical quantities, and also profit and utility, entering into those equations are understood to be *per unit of time*. This has been shown already by Jevons' dimensional analysis[2] and has been repeated explicitly by Pareto.[3] The possibility of obtaining the fundamental propositions of the theory of interest from these equations shows clearly that they cannot be timeless.

Let T be the dimension of time and M be the dimension of a quantity of money. It can be shown immediately that the dimension of λ as deduced from our equations is T^{-1} which is the proper dimension of the rate of interest as already established by Jevons.[4] The definition of λ as the rate of interest on money capital is:

$$\lambda = \frac{d\pi}{d\kappa} \qquad (21)$$

i.e. the marginal profitableness of money capital. The dimension of $d\pi$ is the same as the dimension of profit π, i.e. a quantity of money per a certain period of time. The dimension of $d\pi$ is thus MT^{-1}. The dimension of $d\kappa$ is the same as the dimension of money capital κ, i.e. M, money capital being simply an amount of money.[5] The dimension of $\frac{d\pi}{d\kappa}$ is, therefore, $MT^{-1}M^{-1} = T^{-1}$.

[1] Cf. for instance, Schneider, *Theorie der Produktion*, Wien, 1934, p. III and p. 2.

[2] Cf. *The Theory of Political Economy*, fourth edition, London, 1924, pp. 61–9. Cf. also Wicksteed's article on dimensions in *Palgrave's Dictionary of Political Economy*, vol. I, and a paper by the same writer: "On Certain Passages in Jevons' Theory of Political Economy," *Quarterly Journal of Economics*, Vol. III, 1889, p. 307 seq. Both papers of Wicksteed are reprinted in the second edition of *The Commonsense of Political Economy*, Vol. II, London, 1933.

[3] *Manuel d'économie politique*, second edition, Paris, 1927, p. 148.

[4] Loc. cit. p. 247–53.

[5] See Jevons, loc. cit. p. 233–5.

Similarly we obtain T^{-1} as the dimension of the rate of real interest. The definition of the rate of real interest is :

$$\lambda = \frac{F_m\phi_{l'} - F_l}{F_l} \qquad \text{(26)}$$

and by transforming our equations so as to make them independent of the unit of time chosen we get, according to (49) :

$$\lambda = \frac{1}{\Delta t'} \cdot \frac{F_m\phi_{l'} - F_l}{F_l} \qquad \text{(49a)}$$

where $\Delta t'$ is the period turnover of the money capital. Let Q be the dimension of the finished commodity and R the dimension of labour. The marginal productivity of labour (direct or indirect) in terms of the finished commodity has the dimension QR^{-1}. Therefore, the expression $\frac{F_m\phi_{l'} - F_l}{F_l}$ has the dimension $QR^{-1}\,Q^{-1}\,R = 1$. And from (49a) we deduce that the dimension of λ, i.e. the rate of interest per unit of time, is T^{-1}. This proper time dimension of the rate of interest is obscured in formula (26) in which time does not appear explicitly. However, recalling that formula (26) is but a particular case of formula (49a) if the unit of time is chosen so that $\Delta t' = 1$, it becomes clear that T^{-1} is the dimension of the rate of interest also according to formula (26).

The fact that the equations of the theory of production enable us to deduce a rate of interest of the dimension T^{-1} and all the fundamental propositions concerning interest, proves that those equations cannot possibly be timeless in the literal sense of the word. However, the general equations of the theory of production may justly be called " timeless " in another sense. Though time certainly enters implicitly into those equations[1] it does not enter into them *as a variable*. The delay period from the application of the factors of production to the receipt of the product, which is the technological basis determining the period of turnover of money capital, has been assumed as fixed and determined by technological considerations alone and the equipment used in production has been assumed to wear out completely during this delay period. Therefore, time, although it enters implicitly into our equations, does not enter into them as a variable, and in this sense, but only in this sense, they may be regarded as " timeless." [2]

[1] While discussing the period of turnover of money capital time was also introduced explicitly into our equations. However, this might have been avoided by choosing a unit of time equal to the period of turnover of money capital. Thus all the propositions deduced in this paper may be stated so as not to make time appear explicitly in the equations.

[2] This is true, however, only as far as the theory of interest is limited to the consideration of circulating capital. When fixed capital is considered time must be introduced explicitly as a variable into the equations of the theory of production. Similarly by assuming the delay period between the application of factors and the receipt of the product to be variable a generalisation of the equations of the theory of interest can be obtained. (Cf. the paper of Smithies quoted above on p. 159). But this does not change the fact that all the fundamental propositions of the theory of interest can be obtained without introducing time *as a variable* into our theory. Therefore, it is not possible to develop the *whole* theory of interest (with fixed capital and variable delay periods) without introducing time explicitly as a variable. But the fundamental propositions of the theory of interest with respect to circulating capital and the very concept of interest can be obtained without doing so.

The fundamental propositions of the theory of interest being obtained from a theory of production into which time does not enter *as a variable*, it follows that interest is not connected with time in any different way from the way in which the general theory of production is connected with time. Our deduction of the fundamental propositions of the theory of interest has shown that those propositions can be established without introducing time explicitly *as a variable* into our equations.[1] Not the introduction of time as a variable into the equations of the theory of production, but a *shortage of capital*, which affects the distribution of original resources (of labour in our case) between their direct and their indirect uses, is at the basis of the theory of interest. In a capitalist enterprise economy the shortage of capital is a shortage of money capital which is, as we have seen, always associated with a shortage of real capital. A shortage of money capital prevents entrepreneurs from carrying through the optimum scale and the optimum combination of factors of production and the shortage of real capital (equipment), which accompanies the former, prevents the marginal productivity of indirect labour from becoming equal to the marginal productivity of direct labour (or in other words: the marginal *net* productivity of real capital from being zero). The problem of interest is thus essentially a problem of allocation of resources between different uses. The maldistribution of resources consequent upon a shortage of capital arises also, as we have seen, when time does not enter *as a variable* into our problem. Time enters into the dimension of the rate of interest through the fact that the quantities entering into the production functions are conceived as per unit of time and that a delay period is supposed to exist between the application of factors of production and the receipt of the product. Thus time, though associated inseparably with the theory of interest, as with the whole theory of production, is not its outstanding feature. This rôle is reserved to the shortage of capital. When the shortage of capital disappears, so that the marginal productivity of indirect labour becomes equal to the marginal productivity of direct labour, interest vanishes, however much time the production process may take.

15. SHORT PERIOD AND LONG PERIOD EQUILIBRIUM IN THE THEORY OF INTEREST

Our treatment of the interest problem in connection with a shortage of capital shows the real relationship between the theory of interest and the general theory of production. The general theory of production (called also, rather strangely, the theory of " non-capitalistic " production) presupposes that there is always available the amount of capital necessary to choose the

[1] Professor Robbins in his preface to the English translation of Wicksell's *Lectures on Political Economy*, vol. I, p. xiv, says: " The work of Pareto, valuable as it is in other respects . . . it would certainly be correct to say that there is no *time*. Now time is the essence of capital theory." That this sentence overlooks the time dimension contained implicitly in Pareto's theory of economic equilibrium follows not only from what has been said above, but can also be shown from quotations of Pareto himself. Cf. his *Manuel*, p. 148. That interest is not due to introducing time *as a variable* into the equations of the theory of production is established by the results obtained in this paper.

best method of production, i.e. the method which equalises the value of the marginal product of a factor and its price, and consequently equalises also the marginal productivity of indirect and of direct labour. It is a theory of production in a state of perfect *saturation* with capital. The theory of interest, on the other side, is a theory of production subject to a shortage of capital.

The existence of a possibility of saturation of production with capital follows from the maximum conditions. If the production functions are shaped so that a maximum of net output, or of profit, is possible at all, and only under such circumstances equilibrium is possible, the possibility of a saturation of production with capital follows directly. It follows from the existence of a position in which the marginal productivity of indirect labour is equal to the marginal productivity of direct labour. In this position the marginal *net* productivity of real capital is zero. It has been shown that in an enterprise economy a saturation with real capital is equivalent to a saturation with money capital. In such a situation all entrepreneurs use the best method of production possible at all, and have no use for further money capital. As the method of production cannot be improved (i.e. average unit costs cannot be lowered) by investing more money capital the only use entrepreneurs could make of it would be to build parallel establishments. But this would lead to an over-expansion of the industry. Since no reduction of costs can be obtained any more[1] and the industry is confronted with a given demand function, building new establishments would involve the industry in losses. These considerations expose the fallacy of the superstitious belief current among many economists, that there would be an infinite demand for money capital if the rate of interest were zero, or that a saturation with capital could be attained only when all commodities were to become free goods. It follows clearly from the theory of production that a saturation with capital is attained when the marginal productivity of indirect labour becomes equal to the marginal productivity of direct labour.

The relation between the general theory of production, which presupposes a saturation with capital, and the theory of interest, which is based on the assumption of a shortage of capital, is that between a theory of long-period equilibrium and a theory of short-period equilibrium. In the latter the amount of capital is assumed as fixed and interest is deduced from the assumption that this amount is less than the amount required to saturate production with capital. In the former the amount of capital is itself a variable to be determined by all the equations of economic equilibrium. In long-period equilibrium all adjustments are accomplished and the economic system becomes stationary. The rate of interest, being an index of the shortage of capital, is also an index of the distance of the actual state from a long-period equilibrium. There must be certainly always a tendency to approach that long-period equilibrium, for as long as the marginal productivity of indirect labour is greater than the marginal

[1] However, a reduction of average unit costs might be possible if external economies dependent on the total output of the industry existed. The existence of external economies would not move private entrepreneurs to enlarge their output, unless as a result of State intervention. But an appropriate State intervention might create, in such case, additional opportunities for profitable investment of capital. Then, at the point at which external economies cease, investment opportunities reach their definite limit.

productivity of direct labour an advantage is gained from a transfer of labour resources from the direct to the indirect use. In a capitalist enterprise economy this advantage consists in the possibility of increasing profit by investment of additional money capital. But an increase of capital, whether money capital or real capital, involves capital accumulation. *The accumulation of capital provides the bridge between short-period equilibrium and long-period equilibrium in the theory of interest.*[1]

The way towards a long-period equilibrium with regard to interest is necessarily a slow one. For capital accumulation adds per annum but a small fraction to the existing stock of capital. In a monetary system consisting of actual gold circulation any fall in the general price level is counteracted by the inducement it gives to an increase of gold production. But as the annual output of gold is but a small fraction of the existing stock of gold, any adjustment movements working through the mechanism just mentioned must be of a secular character. Similarly with capital accumulation. As the annual accumulation is but a small fraction of the existing stock of capital the movements towards a long-period equilibrium in interest must be of a secular character, too.[2] There may be also some checks (a positive time preference, e.g.) preventing capital accumulation from going on till a perfect equality of the marginal productivity of indirect and of direct labour (and thus a zero rate of interest) is attained. The study of the course of adaptation of interest to a long-period equilibrium is the subject of the theory of capital accumulation. Of the forces governing the accumulation of capital it depends whether the rate of interest reduces in long-period equilibrium actually to zero. However, the tendency towards saturation of production with capital is slowed down by the possibility of extending the durability of fixed real capital (equipment) used in production and of affecting output by varying the delay period between the application of factors of production and the receipt of the product.

[1] In order to avoid the possibility of terminological confusion the possible different signification of the distinction between short-period and long-period equilibrium ought to be kept in mind. (i) First, we have the original Marshallian distinction between short-period and long-period equilibrium with respect to the existence or non-existence of fixed cost items. This is the distinction at the basis of the difference of short-period and long-period cost curves (and supply curves) of a single firm. (ii) The second distinction between short-period and long-period equilibrium refers to whether the number of firms in an industry is regarded as fixed or whether it may be varied by the entry (or exodus) of firms into (or from) the industry. It is this type of long-period equilibrium we have in mind when maintaining that marginal cost must be equal to average cost. With this connotation the term long-period equilibrium was used above, where the equality of marginal and average cost was discussed. The cost curves we had then in mind were long-period cost curves in the meaning of the term as defined sub. (i). Mrs. Robinson proposes to use the words quasi-long-period and long-period equilibrium in the case sub. (ii). Cf. *The Economics of Imperfect Competition*, London, 1933, p. 47 and p. 85. (iii) Finally, we may distinguish between short-period and long-period equilibrium according to whether the amount of capital (money capital and real capital) is regarded as fixed or dependent on all the equations of economic equilibrium. We may call this type of long-period equilibrium, which is the long-period equilibrium fundamental for the theory of interest, the Ricardian long-period equilibrium. It is obvious that it is the Ricardian long-period equilibrium the adjustment to which takes the longest time. Though it is probable that generally the long-period equilibrium sub. (ii) requires a longer adjustment time than the long-period equilibrium sub. (i) it does not seem that such statement would hold always.

[2] It seems to us that the adjustment movements towards a long-period equilibrium with respect to capital accumulation and interest are closely related to the secular wavelike movements in the evolution of the capitalist system known under the name of Kondratief cycles, or " trend " cycles. However, an investigation of this relationship is a topic for a separate study.

C

If the extension of the durability of fixed real capital (i.e. durable equipment) follows a law of diminishing returns, as is only natural to assume, the point of saturation of production with capital is only farther removed, but still existent. For at a certain point the marginal advantage gained by extending the durability of the equipment must become equal to that gained by increasing the quantity of equipment while keeping its lifetime constant. This is the final saturation point, because a further extension of the durability of equipment does not pay. A saturation of production with capital might never be reached only if output could be increased indefinitely by lengthening the delay period, but this does not seem very probable. It is in the study of the effects of fixed capital and of the variability of the delay period that time has to be introduced explicitly as a variable into the equations of the theory of production.

Ann Arbor, Michigan. OSKAR LANGE.

3

PROFESSOR KNIGHT'S NOTE ON INTEREST THEORY

By Oskar Lange

When writing my article on the theory of interest I believed myself fairly near to Professor Knight's position, and I believe myself even nearer to-day when my ideas on the subject have considerably matured. The systematic introduction of circular factors into the theory, the emphasis laid upon the synchronisation of production, the view that time is not the fundamental factor in the theory of interest, the refraining from the use of the concept of the period of production, the view on the place of capital accumulation in the formulation of the theory—all are on the line of Professor Knight's theory. I should like, therefore, to begin my reply to Professor Knight's note with an acknowledgment for his important contributions, which I have tried to incorporate into my treatment of the subject. Our difference of opinion concerns only one single point, where, unfortunately, I find myself unable to agree with Professor Knight. This is the relation between capital and the physical factors of production. But before taking up the issue I want to comment on two minor points where I find myself completely in agreement with Professor Knight.

(i) I did not in my article make any use of the concept of the period of production. Though I believe that, outside of certain exceptions, the most important of which is the construction of permanent equipment, it is possible to define an average period of production of finite length, I regard this concept as utterly useless. Anything it is meant to convey can be said in a much simpler way by using the familiar concepts of cost theory. On this point I find myself in complete agreement with Professor Knight. The " delay period " of which I speak in my article is simply a construction or fabrication period of the product. It refers only to a particular firm and not to the economic system as a whole, and it has nothing whatever to do with the period of production in the Böhm-Bawerk sense.

(ii) There is a point where I accept Professor Knight's criticism wholeheartedly. On p. 229 of his note he mentions that, although I recognise that labour and equipment collaborate in the production of equipment, I do not make full use of this insight. Whenever I come to consider the process of increasing the amount of equipment it is exclusively labour that is transferred from making the product to making the equipment. I am really grateful to Professor Knight for having pointed out this shortcoming of my treatment of the problem.[1] The presentation of the subject in my article had only half outgrown the Wicksellian heritage. Of course, it is *both* labour *and* equipment that is transferred from making the product to making the additional equipment. Therefore also my presentation of interest as the difference between the marginal productivity of indirect and of direct labour does not tell the whole

[1] This shortcoming occurred to me shortly after my article was published. Dr. Zassenhaus also pointed it out to me independently.

story. Interest is *also* the difference between the marginal productivity of an indirect and a direct use of equipment. This is, indeed, contained in my equations—*vide* equation (17) on p. 175—but I failed to draw all the economic conclusions. In consequence my formulation has to be modified as follows: Interest is the difference between the marginal productivity of an indirect and a direct use not only of the original factors but of *any* factor. Any factor which can be used both directly in producing a commodity and indirectly in producing equipment which is used in the production of that commodity has an indirect and a direct marginal productivity in terms of the product. The rate of interest is equal to the ratio of the difference between the indirect and the direct marginal productivity to the direct marginal productivity of *any* factor in *any* two immediately adjacent stages of production.[1] The Wicksellian formulation of the theory is just a special case which holds when equipment is produced by original factors alone.

(iii) The real difference of opinion between Professor Knight and myself concerns the relations of capital to the physical factors of production. In Professor Knight's theory capital is a factor of production co-ordinate with labour and the natural resources. In my theory, however, it is, so to speak, super-ordinate to the physical factors. It is, as Professor Knight rightly interprets (p. 226 of his note), a *method* of employing the physical factors of production. The factors of production which enter into my production functions are only the *physical* factors: labour and capital *goods*, i.e. equipment (natural resources being left out for the sake of simplicity). Capital is a fund of purchasing power at the disposal of the entrepreneurs the scarcity of which limits the possible uses which can be made of the physical factors. It is, to use the excellent phrase of Professor Schumpeter, " a command over means of production." [2] Capital is used for the purchase of *both* capital goods *and* labour (or natural resources)—*vide* p. 178 of my article. Now the difference between capital goods (equipment) and original factors is (as indicated in footnote 2 on p. 161 of my article) that original factors " are not produced," i.e. are given in *fixed* quantities. Original factors are those factors the quantity of which is a *datum* and not a variable to be determined by the theory. Their quantity may vary (the increase of population, for instance), but such variation is not a response to changes in the price system. For the purposes of equilibrium analysis they must be regarded as unaugmentable. Original factors being thus defined, an increase in capital must necessarily lead to a substitution of capital goods for original factors. For although an increase in capital increases the demand for *all* factors of production, the quantity of original factors cannot, by definition, be increased (their full employment being assumed, of course). The resulting increase of their prices leads to a substitution for them of capital goods the quantity of which can be increased by production.

[1] It is assumed here that the delay period is the same in both stages of production and in all industries. Otherwise the formulation becomes more complicated (cf. pp. 187–8 of my article).

[2] Cf. *The Theory of Economic Development*, Cambridge, Mass., 1934, pp. 116–17. *Vide* also Schumpeter, "Das Kapital im wirtschaftlichen Kreislauf und in der wirtschaftlichen Entwicklung" (in *Kapital und Kapitalismus*, edited by B. Harms, vol. I, Berlin, 1931), p. 206 : " Es [i.e. capital] steht nicht als besonderes Produktionsmittel neben Arbeit und Boden. . . . Es steht das Kapital zwischen Unternehmer und Produktionsmitteln."

This theory of capital, however, can be generalised *by dropping the very concept of original factors.* Indeed (here again I believe myself in line with Professor's Knight's theory), it seems rather doubtful whether original factors as defined above really exist. For instance, labour ceases to be an original factor according to my definition when its supply depends on the wage-rate. But, as can be seen from the equations in my article, the theory is not affected at all if the equation stating that the total amount of labour in the economic system is fixed—equation (3) on p. 171—is replaced by an equation stating that it depends on the wage-rate—*ibid.*, equation (3a)—or even by a production function expressing the technical conditions of producing labour (slave-breeding, for instance). In such case all factors are capital goods. An increase in capital increases the demand for all factors, but if their elasticity of supply is different, *factors with a greater elasticity of supply are substituted for factors whose elasticity of supply is smaller.* Thus factors may be regarded as capital goods in a greater or smaller *degree* according to their elasticity of supply. Original factors are only the special limiting case in which the elasticity of supply of certain factors equals zero. This is the most general formulation of the capital theory propounded, in an admittedly imperfect way, in my article, and I hope to present it in the near future in a more elaborate form.

(iv) Treating capital as a factor co-ordinate to the physical factors of production, Professor Knight concludes that its marginal net productivity can never be zero by endowing capital, without further examination, with all the properties we usually ascribe to the physical factors.[1] Now it is true that it is highly improbable that the marginal productivity of capital *goods* (equipment) should ever become zero. But the marginal *net* productivity of *capital* can be zero even when the marginal gross productivity of capital goods is positive. For the marginal *net* productivity of capital is equal to the difference between the marginal productivity of the physical factors and their marginal *cost*, the latter being determined by the marginal productivity of those factors (or of the resources required to produce them) in an alternative use. This alternative use is the direct use in producing the product instead of the indirect use in producing equipment which collaborates in making the product. The marginal *net* productivity of capital becomes zero when the marginal productivity of resources in all possible uses is equal. Whether such a situation can occur depends on the shape of the production functions. What is the actual shape of these functions is a matter for empirical investigation. All I do maintain is that the possibility of such a situation follows from the familiar shape of those functions assumed in the chapters on production of our textbooks of economics.

If the durability of the equipment and the delay period are given, and if if the law of diminishing returns holds for the physical factors of production, an increase in capital, by causing factors to be shifted from the direct to the indirect use, diminishes relatively the marginal productivity in the indirect use and increases relatively the marginal productivity in the direct use of each factor. Under the familiar assumptions concerning the shape of the production functions there exists a point where both marginal productivities mentioned

[1] Cf. Knight, "The Quantity of Capital and the Rate of Interest," Part II (*Journal of Political Economy*, October, 1936), p. 623.

become equal.[1] If we assume, further, that the durability of equipment can be increased, then capital can be absorbed also in extending the lifetime of equipment.[2] But here there exists, too, a limit if, from a certain point on, the extension of durability of equipment is either subject to a law of diminishing returns, or even if the marginal returns only increase less than the marginal productivity of the factors withdrawn from other uses. For the factors used to increase the durability of equipment have to be withdrawn from other uses where their marginal productivity increases in consequence. The limit is reached when the marginal productivity in those other uses becomes equal to the marginal productivity in the extension of the durability of equipment. Finally, additional capital may be used, as Professor Knight is quite right in observing (*vide* p. 224 of his note), to make new forms of final products. But under static conditions, and only those are discussed here, the value of the marginal product of factors used to make new types of goods must be smaller, for otherwise those new types of goods would have been produced before the amount of capital has increased. Since to produce new types of goods factors have to be withdrawn from other uses where their marginal productivity increases in consequence, we reach a limit again.

I am ready, however, to concede to Professor Knight that the reason why the law of diminishing returns, or any other particular law of returns, should hold for the extension of the durability of equipment is much less obvious than in the case of combination of factors of a given durability or of the production of new types of goods. Where *permanent* improvements are possible (*vide* Professor Knight's example of diamond polishing) the (undiscounted) marginal return becomes infinite. In such cases the only limit for the investment of additional capital is when the services of the permanent improvements become free goods, and I accept Professor Knight's argument for these cases. There is, indeed, absolutely no limit for investment if we are bent upon making hundreds of thousands of tunnels through the Rocky Mountains, or any other changes in landscape. The demand may, however, be perfectly saturated, also at a zero rate of interest, with a hundred of them. It is only the services of the permanent improvements, not all services and goods, that have to become free in order to have no further use for additional capital. If, however, the number of permanent improvements for which there would be a demand at a zero rate of interest were infinite, there might really be no limit for the investment of new capital. The other case where no limit for investment exists is when the quantity of product can be increased indefinitely by lengthening the delay period [3] (*vide* p. 192 of my article). For a lengthening of the delay period does not involve any withdrawal of

[1] As pointed out on pp. 166–7 of my article, the condition for it is somewhat more rigorous than the existence of the ordinary law of diminishing returns, because the amounts of the factors used directly are not held constant but decrease with an increase in the indirect use of factors. This imposes certain restrictions on the mixed second order derivatives of the production functions.

[2] This presupposes that the durability of equipment can be varied independently of the method of production (i.e. of the proportion of the different factors). If this is not the case an increase in capital and fall of the rate of interest may lead also to the use of *less* durable equipment.

[3] More generally, this is true for all cases where the amount of the product can be increased by a change of the *time-shape* of the application of factors which requires a larger capital. Anything said in the text about lengthening the delay period holds for this general case, too.

factors from other uses and, consequently, the marginal *net* productivity of capital invested in this way becomes zero only when the amount of product cannot be increased any more by lengthening the delay period. But I doubt whether the cases where the delay period is an *independent* variable in the production function (as in the cases of wine and forests) are frequent or of great importance. They seem to me rather exceptional, and the chief danger of the Austrian *formulation* of the theory of capital is that it elaborates its concepts on the analogy with such exceptional cases.[1] As a rule the delay period depends on the particular method of production adopted and can be varied only together with the proportion of the different factors of production.[2] This, again, imposes a limit to the possibility of investing capital in this way. Concluding, I should like to remark that the difference of opinion between Professor Knight and myself is rather one of degree. I do not state that capital accumulation must lead *necessarily* to a zero marginal net productivity of capital. I quite agree that there may be cases where saturation with capital can never be attained. But I am inclined to be more sceptical about the frequency of their occurrence.

London. OSKAR LANGE.

[1] Needless to say, the Austrian theory, correctly understood, is not limited to these cases. But it is a highly artificial construction which, instead of treating the problem directly, tries to reduce it with the aid of an elaborate apparatus (the period of production !) to an analogy with such exceptional cases. And it is full of pitfalls, too.

[2] This means that the delay period is a function of the proportion of the different factors of production used (cf. Smithies, "The Austrian Theory of Capital in Relation to Partial Equilibrium Theory," *Quarterly Journal of Economics*, October, 1935). In such case an increase in capital and fall of the rate of interest may also *shorten* the delay period.

4

THE NATURE AND IMPLICATIONS OF THE RESWITCHING OF TECHNIQUES *

MICHAEL BRUNO, EDWIN BURMEISTER, AND EYTAN SHESHINSKI

I. INTRODUCTION

By reswitching of techniques we mean the recurrence at different rates of interest of a whole matrix of activities or a "technique of production." The "Ruth Cohen Curiosum" may be considered a special case where only a *single* activity recurs.[1] We have analyzed the conditions under which reswitching can occur, which are perfectly general, the conditions under which it cannot occur, which are quite restrictive, and some of the important implications for capital theory.

In a paper read to the Econometric Society meeting in Rome in September 1965, Luigi Pasinetti [2] was the first to question seriously the validity of Levhari's nonswitching theorem.[3] It is this challenge that gave us the immediate inspiration for our own work. However, Pasinetti's earlier Rome discussion seemed incomplete to us because there was no clear indication whether or not Levhari's

* We are greatly indebted to Paul A. Samuelson and Robert M. Solow for their helpful leads, insights, and numerous discussions. Frank M. Fisher and Robert M. Solow have also given us very helpful comments on an earlier draft.

Likewise we are indebted to the Center for International Affairs, Harvard University, for partial support of M. Bruno's research, to the National Science Foundation for partial support of E. Burmeister's research under Grant GS-571 and to the Irwin Foundation for a Fellowship supporting E. Sheshinski's Ph.D. thesis at Massachusetts Institute of Technology, of which his present contribution forms a part.

1. Joan Robinson, *Accumulation of Capital* (London: Macmillan, 1956); Piero Sraffa, *Production of Commodities by Means of Commodities* (Cambridge: Cambridge University Press, 1960); and M. McManus, "Process Switching in the Theory of Capital," *Economica*, XXX (May 1963). The reswitching phenomenon has also been discussed by Michio Morishima in "Mrs. Robinson's New Book and Professor Leontief's Dynamic System," mimeographed paper, Feb. 1958; "Refutation of the Nonswitching Theorem," this *Journal*, this issue; and *Equilibrium, Stability, and Growth* (Oxford: Clarendon Press, 1964), p. 126.

2. Luigi L. Pasinetti's present paper "Changes in the Rate of Profit and Switches of Techniques," this *Journal*, this issue, is a revised version of the paper he presented in Rome.

3. David Levhari, "A Nonsubstitution Theorem and Switching of Techniques," this *Journal*, LXXIX (Feb. 1965), 98–105.

theorem was in fact wrong and therefore the primary issue was still unresolved.[4] In our subsequent work we have individually and jointly discovered in various ways that the theorem is indeed wrong; the credit, however, goes to Pasinetti's lead. Pasinetti's present paper is a considerable modification and revision of his earlier analysis and now touches on a number of aspects which we have ourselves analyzed in the meantime. We shall nonetheless risk minor repetition for the sake of clarification and proceed with our own discussion as originally envisaged.

Numerical examples and the realization that switching points are roots of n-th degree polynomials (and therefore numerous) have convinced us that reswitching may well occur in a general capital model. A seemingly small alteration in the fundamental lemma can be shown to make Levhari's theorem and its original proof formally correct, but unfortunately the class of cases for which it would remain valid is thereby restricted quite heavily. We have analyzed some alternative sufficiency conditions for non-switching which are of interest in themselves, especially for the two-sector case, but such analyses only help to convince one of their highly restrictive nature.

Two points must be clarified at the outset: (1) There is no essential difference between the circulating-capital and fixed-capital models as far as the important capital-theoretic issues are concerned. One, in fact, includes the other as a special case. (2) Indecomposability of the technique matrix is essentially irrelevant for the reswitching discussion. A short digression on the various capital models and a clarification of their relationships follows in Section II of this paper.

In Section III we use Samuelson's two-sector canonical model of capital to show that there are simple classes of cases in which both reswitching and no reswitching can occur, and we give simple sufficiency conditions for either to take place. It is also shown that in any n-sector model having only one capital good, reswitching cannot occur; difficulties arise with two capital goods. There follows a simple two-sector numerical example to serve as a definite proof that reswitching can occur.

In Section IV we discuss the n-sector model, showing that in general there can be n switching points between any two techniques. We then use Descartes' rule of signs to formulate and interpret a

4. E.g., the modified numerical counterexample produced by Pasinetti in his Rome paper did not satisfy the indecomposability on the whole technique matrix as required by the conditions of Levhari's theorem.

sufficiency condition for nonswitching, which turns out to be extremely restrictive in nature.

Once the reswitching phenomenon is acknowledged, it is important to realize its implications for capital theory. As is often the case after the fact, one finds it hard to differentiate between reswitching and another well-known phenomenon, namely the existence of multiple rates of return to investment in present value calculations.

Perhaps the most interesting and most important finding of our analysis concerns the behavior of consumption and the rate of interest (profit) in steady states. The reswitching phenomenon implies the existence of "perverse behavior" where it is *not* true that steady-state consumption *always rises* as the rate of interest *falls*.[5] Rather for certain ranges of the interest rate, steady-state consumption may *rise* when the rate of interest rises. Moreover, although the reswitching phenomenon alerted us to this possibility, we find that such "perverse behavior" can exist *even when no reswitching occurs on the factor-price frontier*. The latter and related issues form the subject of Section V.

II. Alternative Discrete Capital Models

Various discussions of the reswitching phenomenon employ a great variety of capital models differing with respect to such assumptions as depreciation, timing of wage payments, and the time structure of inputs in the production of capital goods. Pasinetti has illustrated his arguments with a Sraffa model in which capital goods essentially consist of "maturing" labor inputs at different time periods; Levhari considered another Sraffa model with one-period circulating capital.[6] Naturally, one prefers to think in terms of more general fixed-capital models which include the former as special cases. Since all of these alternative models basically lead to the same theoretical conclusions, it seems useful to begin our discussion with a short classification. We try to minimize confusion by indicating how they all relate to each other and how the present issue can be discussed in terms of any of the models and therefore is best analyzed in greatest generality. An issue somewhat related to the same question is the irrelevance of decomposability or indecomposability of the technology matrix.

5. The possibility of such "perverse behavior" was pointed out without proof by Professor Morishima in *Equilibrium, Stability, and Growth, op. cit.*, p. 126.

6. Pasinetti, *op. cit.*, Levhari, *op. cit.*, and Sraffa, *op. cit.*

1. Consider an n-sector fixed-proportions technology (a_{ij}) using and producing n capital goods (prices P_j) and using one primary factor, labor (a_{oj}) commanding a nominal wage w.

Denoting the depreciation rate for the j-th capital good by μ_j and the rate of interest by r, and supposing wages are paid during the production period, we have:

(II.1) $$P_j = wa_{oj} + \sum_{i=1}^{n} (\mu_i + r) P_i a_{ij}; \quad j = 1, \ldots, n,$$

or in vector notation

(II.2) $$p = a_o [\mathrm{I} - \rho a]^{-1}$$

where $p = \left(\frac{P_j}{w}\right)$ and $\rho = [\mu + r]$, a diagonal matrix whose i-th diagonal entry is $(\mu_i + r)$. We must assume that the maximal interest rate, r^*_a, is positive and that $a_{oj} \geqq 0$ to have $p_j \geqq 0$.

There are some obvious special cases of this model which are used often and which we shall at times mention. All of these involve the assumption of a uniform depreciation rate:

$$\mu_i = \mu \text{ and } \rho = r + \mu, \text{ a scalar.}$$

The two extreme subcases here are:

(i) $\mu = 0, \quad \rho = r$ (capital is infinitely durable),

and

(ii) $\mu = 1, \quad \rho = r + 1$ (there is only circulating capital).

2. Next suppose we slightly alter our above assumptions and have wages paid at the *beginning* of the production period. The only change required in equations (II.2) is that a factor $(1 + r)$ now must multiply a_o, i.e., we have

(II.3) $$p = (1 + r)\, a_o\, [I - \rho a]^{-1}.$$

Now if we consider the special case $\mu = 1$ $(\rho = r + 1)$, we get the Sraffa circulating-capital model used by Levhari, i.e.,

(II.4) $$p = a_o[\lambda I - a]^{-1} \text{ where } \lambda \equiv \frac{1}{1+r}.$$

Other than a factor $(1 + r)$ due to a different assumption about wage payments, there is no real difference between the two models except that (II.1) is more general. Clearly the nonsubstitution theorem as well as the discussion of the switching problem could be conducted equally well in terms of the fixed-capital model.

3. Now suppose there are some goods that take more than one period to produce. One can either treat goods-in-process of different ages as different goods (with different activities) or else calculate directly the implied price relationships. For example, if a commodity available at present requires an input a_{oj} of labor t periods

earlier, then that input's contribution to present cost must be $w\, a_{oj}\, (1 + r)^t$. The Pasinetti-Sraffa numerical example uses precisely the latter type of capital model. Clearly a further generalization would have not only labor but also capital inputs required in earlier periods. All of these ideas could be incorporated without difficulty in a modified expression for (II.1) or (II.2). For simplicity we shall confine our discussion to the models that can be derived from (II.2) or (II.3).

There is one general common characteristic of all these models from which reswitching and other properties can be shown to follow. Under some quite unrestrictive assumptions,[7] we can always expand the price vector (in terms of labor units) as a convergent power series in r, i.e.,

(II.5) $$p = g_o + g_1 r + g_2 r^2 + \ldots + g_n r^n + \ldots$$

where g_i are nonnegative vectors whose elements eventually approach zero as n increases. (II.5) is the equation of the factor-price frontier (FPF) in terms of p instead of $1/p$. In Section IV we shall have occasion to examine (II.5) for the general fixed-capital model (II.1) and to provide the economic interpretation of the g_i's. Let us only note here that these vectors can be interpreted in terms of the direct and indirect use of labor in production. The price of any product is thus positive if it uses directly or indirectly some of the primary factor labor.[8] As long as one of these vectors (for $i \geqq 1$) is not zero, we obtain a downward sloping factor-price frontier i.e., $\frac{dp}{dr} > 0$, from (II.5). At the same time we cannot generally say whether the FPF when expressed as $1/p(r)$ will be convex or concave unless we know something about the coefficients.[9]

Finally consider another generalization. Suppose that in addition to fixed-capital goods and consumption goods, we have Leontief-type intermediate goods in the system. We propose to show that the formal properties of the system (II.2) remain unchanged.

Suppose that in addition to a fixed-capital matrix a there is an ordinary input-output matrix $\bar{a}$ (assume a and $\bar{a}$ are defined so as

7. Some variant of the Hawkins-Simon conditions.

8. This, incidentally, does not require indecomposability of the technique matrix.

9. $\frac{d^2(1/p)}{dr^2} = -p^{-2}\left(\frac{d^2p}{dr^2}\right) + 2p^{-3}\left(\frac{dp}{dr}\right)^2$. Even though $\frac{d^2p}{dr^2} > 0$ so that $p(r)$ will always be convex to the origin, $\frac{d^2\left(\frac{1}{p}\right)}{dr^2}$ is a difference of two positive terms and may be either positive or negative.

to be conformable).[1] The price equations must now be modified as follows:

(II.2′) $p = a_o [I - \bar{a} - \rho a]^{-1}$.

But this can also be written in the form

$$p = a_o S[I - \rho a S]^{-1} \qquad \text{where } S = [I - \bar{a}]^{-1}.$$

Now define

$$A_o = a_o[I - \bar{a}]^{-1} \qquad (= \text{"total" labor input}),$$
$$A = a[I - \bar{a}]^{-1} \qquad (= \text{"total" capital matrix}),$$

and we have

$$p = A_o[I - \rho A]^{-1}$$

which is formally equivalent to (II.2).

This derivation has two corollaries. First, for purposes of exposition we can ignore the existence of intermediate inputs since they do not alter the formal structure of the capital model. The second, somewhat more interesting, is that there is a sense in which the distinction between decomposable and indecomposable models is artificial. For example, suppose that the "total" capital matrix A is decomposable while the input-output matrix $\bar{a}$ is indecomposable; then it may be misleading to term the model either decomposable or indecomposable. This ambiguity should be an additional indication that decomposability is not an important property in the present context.[2]

III. Reswitching in Two-Good Technologies

Before returning to a more general discussion of n-sector models, it seems helpful to use a simpler two-sector technology to illustrate the switching problem.

Consider a technique a producing two goods, a capital good (subscript 1) and a consumption good (subscript 2). The capital good is assumed to depreciate at a fixed rate μ_a, and labor (subscript 0) is the only primary input. If we denote the fixed coefficients for this technique by a_{ij} ($i = 0, 1$; $j = 1, 2$) and express the wage rate w and price of capital good P_K in terms of the consumption good as *numéraire*, we get the following price equations:[3]

1. See, e.g., Morishima, *Equilibrium, Stability, and Growth, op. cit.*, Chaps. III and IV, and Jacob T. Schwartz, *Lectures on the Mathematical Method in Analytical Economics* (New York: Gordon and Breach, 1961), Chap. I.

2. Samuelson has suggested an alternative argument using the fact that any decomposable capital matrix can be turned into an indecomposable one by adding some arbitrarily small elements in the right places thereby causing only an infinitesimal change in the FPF.

3. This so-called canonical model was introduced by Samuelson, "Parable and Realism in Capital Theory: The Surrogate Production Function," *Review of Economic Studies*, XXIX (June 1962), 193–207.

(III.1) $P_K = a_{01}w + a_{11}(r + \mu_a) P_K$

(III.2) $1 = a_{02}w + a_{12}(r + \mu_a)P_K,$

from which the following equation for the factor-price curve FPC_a (Figure I) can be derived:

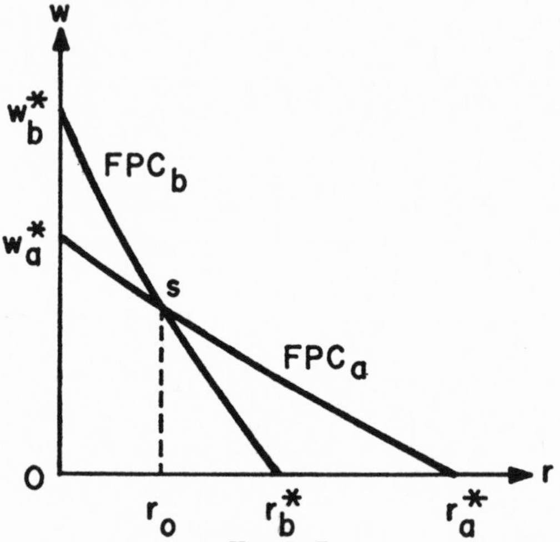

FIGURE I

(III.3) $$w = \frac{1 - (\mu_a + r)a_{11}}{a_{02} + (\mu_a + r)G_a}$$

where

$$G_a = \det \begin{bmatrix} a_{01} & a_{02} \\ a_{11} & a_{12} \end{bmatrix}.$$

This downward sloping FPC will be convex or concave to the origin according to whether $G_a > 0$ or < 0, namely according to whether the consumption good industry is more capital-intensive or more labor-intensive than the capital good industry. For our purposes this distinction is unimportant, and the curve in Figure I is drawn with the assumption $G_a > 0$. Next we note that the FPC intersects both the w and the r axes at w_a^* and r_a^* respectively, where:

$$w_a^* = \frac{1 - \mu_a a_{11}}{a_{02} + \mu_a G_a}$$ = "net" [4] labor productivity in the consumption good sector

4. "Net labor productivity" is the quantity of consumption goods produced per unit of labor after taking into account the indirect labor embodied in the current replacement cost of capital. Perhaps this interpretation can be seen better by rewriting this expression in the form:

$$w_a^* = \frac{1}{a_{02} + \dfrac{a_{01}\mu_a a_{12}}{1 - \mu_a a_{11}}}.$$

and

$$r_a^* = \frac{1}{a_{11}} - \mu_a \quad = \text{"net" capital productivity in the capital good sector.}$$

Consider now an alternative technique b, again producing two goods, the same consumption good as before, but a *different* capital good with depreciation rate μ_b. Technique b is assumed to use only the second type capital good (but the same primary factor labor). Denoting the fixed coefficients for this technique by b_{ij}, we can write analogous expressions leading to the equation for the *FPC* for this case (see FPC_b in Figure I):

(III.4) $$w = \frac{1 - (\mu_b + r)b_{11}}{b_{02} + (\mu_b + r)G_b}.$$

Suppose our hypothetical economy must select one of two alternative techniques. There is one switching point S corresponding to the critical rate of interest r_o. Technique b is more profitable for $0 \leq r < r_o$, and technique a is more profitable for $r_o < r < r_a^*$; thus the factor price frontier is the broken curve $w_b^* S r_a^*$. The techniques are ordered by the rate of interest because as r falls below r_o and the economy switches from technique a to technique b, technique a will never recur if r falls further. But is this feature inherent in the model? The answer turns out to be negative even in this highly simplified model. Figure II illustrates a case where the

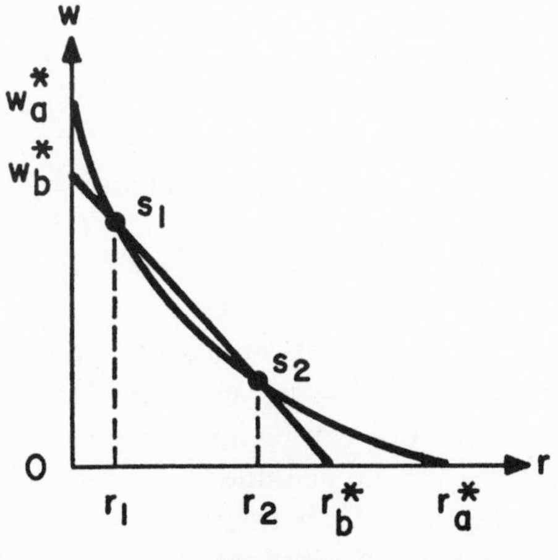

FIGURE II

(When $\mu_a = 0$, $w_a^* = \frac{1}{a_{02}}$). w_a^* will also correspond to the total consumption per capita in a stationary state, a fact that we shall use in subsequent discussion.

two curves cross twice. When r becomes less than r_1, the economy switches back to technique a. Technique a is profitable for two disjoint intervals of r, $0 < r < r_1$ and $r_2 < r < r^*_a$, and the two techniques cannot be ordered. That either one of the cases is in general possible can readily be seen by equating w in equations (III.3) and (III.4) and solving for r. We obtain a quadratic equation for r which, in principle, can easily have two roots in the positive quadrant. A condition for that occurrence can be formulated in terms of the coefficients a_{ij} and b_{ij}. Similarly we can use some known method, such as Descartes' rule of signs, to determine a sufficiency condition which prevents that occurrence. In the next section we shall take the latter approach in the discussion of the general n-sector case. Here a more straightforward and economically meaningful condition can be formulated. (The latter does not, unfortunately, hold in the n-sector case.)

Since we know that there are at most two switching points in this simplified model, we can state the following obvious sufficiency condition for unique switching:

Theorem: If either $r^*_a > r^*_b$ and $w^*_a < w^*_b$
or $r^*_a < r^*_b$ and $w^*_a > w^*_b$,
then there exists only one switching point in the positive quadrant.

In other words, whenever the technique which has a higher capital/output ratio in the capital good industry is also more labor-productive in the consumption good industry, then these techniques can be ordered in an unambiguous manner. (See, e.g., Figure I.)

A number of remarks are now in order:

1. The class of cases which are excluded by this sufficiency condition includes:

(a) Cases in which no switching point exists (i.e., where one technique completely dominates the other).

(b) Cases with multiple roots or cases in which the curves cross only at end points (i.e., $w^*_a = w^*_b$ or $r^*_a = r^*_b$). These again are cases in which one technique can be ignored since it is dominated.

Both (a) and (b) can be classified as irrelevant since the FPF (envelope) is unchanged by their exclusion.

(c) Cases which have two separate crossings inside the positive quadrant, as illustrated in Figure II.[5]

5. After we had completed our analysis, we became aware of the recent book by Professor John R. Hicks, *Capital and Growth* (Oxford: Oxford University Press, 1965); there he has discussed this two-sector model and the reswitching phenomenon. The sufficiency condition which Hicks derives for

2. This sufficiency condition applies to an economy with any number of alternative two-sector techniques all using *different* capital goods and having the same properties as a and b, if the condition of the theorem holds for any pair of techniques a and b. It is sufficient for no reswitching that the ordering of techniques by r^* is exactly the reverse of the ordering by w^*.

3. This sufficiency condition is *not a necessary condition* for nonswitching.

Figure III illustrates an example with three techniques (1, 2 and 3) where *each pair* satisfies the sufficiency condition; yet technique 2 is irrelevant since it is dominated by the combination of 1

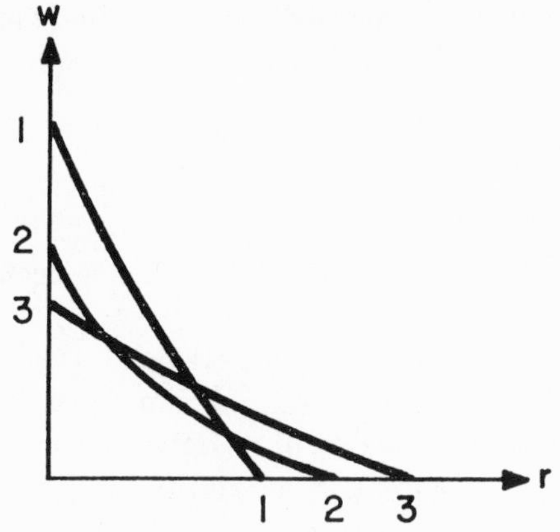

FIGURE III

and 3. Figure VI in Section V illustrates a case where the sufficiency condition is not satisfied, but nevertheless each technique appears only once on the FPF envelope. This case is particularly interesting because we can use it to show that behavior which is "perverse" from the point of view of classical capital theory can occur even when there is no reswitching. We shall return to this point later.[6]

4. We have thus far assumed that $G \neq 0$ for all techniques. Obviously reswitching can also occur when $G = 0$ for some but not all techniques. When $G = 0$ for *all* techniques, factor proportions in the two industries are equal. Then the *FPC*'s are straight lines and the system degenerates to Samuelson's simple surrogate capital model[7] in which reswitching obviously cannot occur.

---

nonswitching is that the ratio of factor intensities must be the same for all techniques (see p. 154). However, this condition is overly strong since it also includes cases of complete dominance which are irrelevant.

6. See Sec. V below and Pasinetti, *op. cit.*, fn. 14.

7. Samuelson, *op. cit.*

5. It should be stressed that the model discussed above is extremely simplified and that the sufficiency condition given does not lend itself to easy generalization if activities use more than one capital good. The latter fact can be seen by considering a case with one consumption good and two capital goods where prices are clearly equations of the third degree. Thus in general there may be three switching points and we can no longer formulate any simple sufficiency condition for nonswitching. We shall return to this problem in the next section.

An interesting question arises at this point. How crucial is the assumption that the two (or more) capital goods in our simplified model are *different*, i.e., nontransferable between activities? Can we get reswitching if all activities use the *same* capital good? The answer to this question turns out to be negative, and we have the following theorem:

Theorem: In a two-sector economy with many alternative independent techniques for producing the two goods, if there is *only one* capital good in the system, reswitching cannot occur.

Proof: Since there is only one capital good (let it be of type a), there is only one P_K in the system. From equation (III.1) we can see that for any given r, there will be only one most efficient activity for producing the one capital good and it cannot recur. Looking at the factor-price frontier in the $\frac{w}{P_K} - r$ plane, we find an envelope of straight line segments. We now need only show that within the range of r *for any one* such segment, an activity for the production of the consumption good cannot recur. This problem, however, is equivalent to that of finding switching points in the previous model for the case in which there is only one way of producing the capital good. From previous considerations we can immediately deduce that for any two *FPC*'s in the $w - r$ plane, there can be at most one switching point in the range $0 < r < r_a^*$ (because there is already one common intersection at $r_a^* = \frac{1}{a_{11}} - \mu_a$). Thus even though a single activity for producing the consumption good may recur, in this case we cannot have the *simultaneous* recurrence of two activities (for the two goods). Thus reswitching in the sense of Levhari cannot occur. Q.E.D.

The above theorem also holds for a multisector economy producing many intermediate (or consumption) goods as long as there is only *one capital good* (i.e., only one interest earning asset).[8]

All the above examples fail to meet Levhari's indecomposability assumption and thus may be deemed irrelevant for his nonswitching theorem. (Note that our examples are decomposable because the consumption good uses capital goods in its production but is not itself used in the production of capital goods.)[9]

For the sake of completeness, we end this section with a numerical example as a definite proof that reswitching can occur despite indecomposability. Although we do not think that indecomposability has any relevance to the switching problem, it is pedagogically preferable and logically crucial to choose an example which satisfies *every* assumption of the theorem to be disproved.[1] The following is a two-sector indecomposable example with circulating capital (i.e., $\mu = 1$) in full conformity with Levhari's model:

The economy produces two goods labeled 1 and 2. Good 1 has two alternative activities while good 2 can be produced by only one available activity:

	Sector 1		Sector 2
	Activity 1	Activity 2	
Labor	0.66	0.01	1.0
Good 1	0.3	0	0.1
Good 2	0.02	0.71	0

Thus there are two possible techniques of production:

$$\text{technique } a = \begin{bmatrix} a_o \\ \hline a \end{bmatrix} = \begin{bmatrix} 0.66 & 1.0 \\ \hline 0.3 & 0.1 \\ 0.02 & 0 \end{bmatrix}$$

and

$$\text{technique } b = \begin{bmatrix} b_o \\ \hline b \end{bmatrix} = \begin{bmatrix} 0.01 & 0.1 \\ \hline 0 & 0.1 \\ 0.71 & 0 \end{bmatrix}.$$

Notice that both techniques are indecomposable.

Some values of $\frac{P_1}{w}$ and $\frac{P_2}{w}$ for both techniques are computed in Table I.

8. This is the obvious case in which the concept of "capital-intensity" can be defined unambiguously.

9. Nothing, however, is changed in our analysis if the consumption good is also used as an intermediate good in the Leontief sense; then the technique matrix may *appear* indecomposable. But this is obviously not the kind of indecomposability that Levhari had in mind.

1. Pasinetti's numerical example is thus, strictly speaking, not a valid counterexample to Levhari's theorem.

TABLE I

$\lambda = \frac{1}{1+r}$	r	Technique a		Technique b	
		$\frac{P_1}{w}$	$\frac{P_2}{w}$	$\frac{P_1}{w}$	$\frac{P_2}{w}$
1.	0.	0.9742	1.0974	0.7750	1.0775
0.95	0.053	1.0512	1.1633	0.8653	1.1437
0.90	0.111	1.1413	1.2379	0.9729	1.2192
0.85	0.176	1.2481	1.3233	1.1028	1.3062
0.80	0.250	1.3769	1.4221	1.2619	1.4077
0.75	0.333	1.5350	1.5380	1.4598	1.5279
0.70	0.429	1.7338	1.6763	1.7112	1.6730
0.65	0.538	1.9911	1.8448	2.0384	1.8521
0.60	0.667	2.3371	2.0562	2.4775	2.0796
0.55	0.818	2.8266	2.3321	3.0907	2.3801
0.50	1.000	3.5714	2.7143	3.9944	2.7989
0.45	1.222	4.8397	3.2977	5.4335	3.4296
0.40	1.500	7.4737	4.3684	8.0225	4.5056
0.35	1.857	16.1936	7.4839	13.8544	6.8155

It is seen that technique b is selected for very low and for very high rates of interest, while for interest rates in the interval (approximately) $r = 0.45$ to $r = 1.79$, technique a is optimal.

IV. Reswitching in a General Capital Model

We now focus our attention on a general model with n capital goods and examine the reswitching phenomenon for this case. Obviously, if reswitching can occur in special two-sector technologies, it will be the rule rather than the exception with any larger number of sectors. We have investigated reswitching where there are a number of alternative activities to produce each good. Subsequently we discuss a general sufficiency condition for nonswitching which, as expected, is very restrictive and is most probably not a realistic assumption in any practical situation.

Consider, as in Levhari's analysis, a general model of an economy using one primary good, labor, and producing n (capital) goods, each one of which can be produced by k_i alternative activities ($i = 1, 2, \ldots, n$). We thus have $\prod_{i=1}^{n} k_i$ alternative technique matrixes $\begin{bmatrix} \cdot & a_o & \cdot \\ & \vdots & \\ & a & \end{bmatrix}$, $\begin{bmatrix} \cdot & b_o & \cdot \\ & \vdots & \\ & b & \end{bmatrix}$, . . . , which constitute the economy's "book of blue prints" or its technology. To make our discussion sufficiently general, suppose these n goods can be fixed-capital goods. Then, for example, prices using technique a are given by the vector equation

(IV.1) $\dfrac{P}{w} = a_o\,[\mathrm{I} - (\mu + r)a]^{-1} = p_a(r)$, where $(\mu + r)$ is a diagonal matrix with the element in the i-th row and i-th column equal to $(\mu_i + r)$.[2] From the subsequent analysis it will be clear that everything discussed for this general model is *a fortiori* applicable to the Levhari-Sraffa model with circulating capital.[3]

We will find it convenient to express the price vector in the following form:

$$\text{(IV.2)}\qquad p_a(r) = \frac{T_a(r)}{Q_a(r)}$$

where $T_a(r)$ is a *vector* of polynomials, each of degree at most $(n-1)$, and $Q_a(r) > 0$ is a polynomial of degree n.[4]

Suppose that technique a is preferred to any other technique b for $r_1 < r < r_o$, and suppose that $r = r_1$ is a genuine switching point (i.e., ties are excluded). For the open interval $r_1 < r < r_o$, we must have

$$p_a(r) \leqq p_b\,(r),$$

from which it follows that

$$\text{(IV.3)}\qquad p_a(r)\,(\mu + r)\,[a - b] + (a_o - b_o) \leqq 0.^5$$

Now define

$$\text{(IV.4)}\qquad G(r) \equiv T_a(r)\,(\mu + r)\,[a - b] + Q_a(r)\,(a_o - b_o) \leqq 0.$$

Note that $G(r)$ is a vector of polynomials whose elements denoted by $G_i(r)$ are linear combinations of the polynomials $T_a(r)$ and $Q_a(r)$; thus $G_i(r)$ is in general a polynomial of degree n.

We next observe that the i-th column of $[a - b]$ will consist of either zeros or a *mixture* of both positive and negative (and possibly zero) elements. The same applies to the augmented matrix when labor inputs are included.[6] It follows that for all r such that

2. We note that if, as in the two-sector model, there is also an $(n+1)$th good which uses all other inputs but is not used by any other activity, its price equation will be $\dfrac{P_{n+1}}{w} = a_{o,\,n+1} + (\mu + r)p_a(r)a_{n+1}$.

3. Observe that $\mu_i = 1$, $i = 1, 2, \ldots, n$, is simply a special case.

4. (IV.2) may be easily derived from (IV.1) by using the familiar adjoint method to calculate the inverse of $[I - (\mu + r)a]$. $Q_a(r)$ is equal to det $[I - (\mu + r)a]$. Since $[I - (\mu + r)a]$ has rank n, it is a polynomial of degree n. Every $(n-1) \times (n-1)$ minor of $[I - (\mu + r)a]$ is a polynomial of degree at most $(n-1)$, and every component of the vector $T_a(r)$ is a linear combination of the latter polynomials and hence also of degree at most $(n-1)$. $Q_a(r) > 0$ by the Hawkins-Simon condition.

5. If there were only circulating capital, $(\mu + r)$ would be replaced by $(1 + r)$ in (IV.3), an inequality obtained by Levhari, *op. cit.*, p. 104.

6. The case of an *all* (semi) positive or *all* (semi) negative column can be excluded since it would indicate that one of the matrixes has been chosen inefficiently, i.e., it is dominated by some other matrix for all r.

$r_1 < r < r_o$ and for each i, we must have *either* $G_i(r) \equiv 0$ or $G_i(r) < 0$. An intermediate case in which $G_i(r) \leqslant 0$ (e.g., a multiple root inside the interval) can be ruled out by making the interval $r_1 < r < r_o$ small enough. A candidate for switching must obviously come from an activity (or activities) for which $G_i(r) < 0$.

Since r_1 is defined as a switching point, there exists at least one index, say $i = q$, and a vector $\begin{bmatrix} b_o \\ \cdot \; \vdots \; \cdot \\ b \end{bmatrix}_q$ for which

(IV.5) $\quad G_q(r_1) = 0$ and $G_q(r) > 0$

for some interval $r_2 < r < r_1$. (The latter follows from the polynomial property of G.) [7]

If q is the only index for which (IV.5) holds, we can readily see that our choice of the new technique b (at least for the interval $r_2 < r < r_1$) will be a change of q-th activity from $\begin{bmatrix} a_o \\ \cdot \; \vdots \; \cdot \\ a \end{bmatrix}_q$ to $\begin{bmatrix} b_o \\ \cdot \; \vdots \; \cdot \\ b \end{bmatrix}_q$, while all other activities remain the same as those in $\begin{bmatrix} a_o \\ \cdot \; \vdots \; \cdot \\ a \end{bmatrix}$. Without loss of generality we can assume $q = 1$ and write

$$\begin{bmatrix} a_o \\ \cdot \; \vdots \; \cdot \\ a \end{bmatrix} - \begin{bmatrix} b_o \\ \cdot \; \vdots \; \cdot \\ b \end{bmatrix} = \begin{bmatrix} d_o \\ \cdot \; \vdots \; \cdot \\ d \end{bmatrix}$$

$$= \begin{bmatrix} d_{o1} & 0 & 0 & & 0 \\ \cdots\cdots & \cdot\,\cdot\,\cdot & \cdot\,\cdot\,\cdot & & \cdot\,\cdot\,\cdot \\ d_1 \;, & 0 \;, & 0 \;, & \ldots \;, & 0 \end{bmatrix}.$$

Thus for all r such that $r_2 < r < r_1$ we have

(IV.6) $\quad G_1(r) > 0$ and $G_i(r) \equiv 0$ for all $i > 1$.

Consider the new price vector $p_b(r)$ given by

$$\begin{aligned} p_b(r) &= b_o[I - (\mu + r)b]^{-1} \\ &= (a_1 - d_o)\,[I - (\mu + r)\,(a - d)\,]^{-1} \\ &= (a_o - d_o)R_a[I + (\mu + r)dR_a]^{-1} \end{aligned}$$

where $R_a \equiv [I - (\mu + r)a]^{-1}$.

Expanding in a power series we get:

(IV.7) $\quad p_b(r) = [p_a(r) - d_oR_a]\,\{I - (\mu + r)dR_a + [(\mu + r)\; dR_a]^2 - \ldots\}.$

7. $G_q(r)$, being an n-th degree polynomial, will have up to n roots and thus in principle there *will be up to n switching points*. By assumption r_1 is the root closest to r_o. It may be noted that here is a case where one recurring activity is synonymous with the recurrence of the entire technique matrix (suppose these are the only two matrixes available). Thus the existence of a "Ruth Cohen Curiosum" for one activity also implies the reswitching phenomenon.

Ignoring second order terms we obtain

$$\text{(IV.8)} \qquad p_b(r) = p_a(r) - [p_a(r)(\mu + r)d + d_o]R_a$$
$$= p_a(r) - \frac{G(r)}{Qa} R_a.$$

Since (1) $G_1(r) > 0$, (2) $G_i(r) = 0$ for $i > 1$, and (3) $R_a > 0$, we have

$$p_b(r) < p_a(r) \text{ for } r_2 < r < r_1,$$

as we would expect. At the same time $(r_1 - r_2)$ can be made sufficiently small so that the constructed matrix b is preferable to any other matrix in that interval.

Clearly if $G_i(r) = 0$ for more than one index i, say for $i = 1, \ldots, m$, then we switch m activities and keep the other $(n\text{-}m)$ fixed; i.e., we take

$$\begin{bmatrix} d \\ \cdots \\ d_o \end{bmatrix} = \begin{bmatrix} d_1 \\ \cdots \\ d_o \end{bmatrix}, \begin{bmatrix} 0 \\ \cdots \\ 0 \end{bmatrix}, \ldots, \begin{bmatrix} 0 \\ \cdots \\ 0 \end{bmatrix} + \cdots + \begin{bmatrix} 0 \\ \cdots \\ 0 \end{bmatrix}, \ldots, \begin{bmatrix} d_m \\ \cdots \\ d_{om} \end{bmatrix}, \begin{bmatrix} 0 \\ \cdots \\ 0 \end{bmatrix}, \ldots, \begin{bmatrix} 0 \\ \cdots \\ 0 \end{bmatrix}.$$

From previous considerations we find that minimizing $p_b(r)$ in the same interval $r_2 < r < r_1$ would necessitate bringing *all* m new activities into the matrix.

Since $[p_a(r)(\mu + r)d + d_oR_a] > 0$ for $d_1, d_2, \ldots, d_m$, $p_b(r)$ in (IV.8) will be smallest if all m activities are introduced simultaneously.

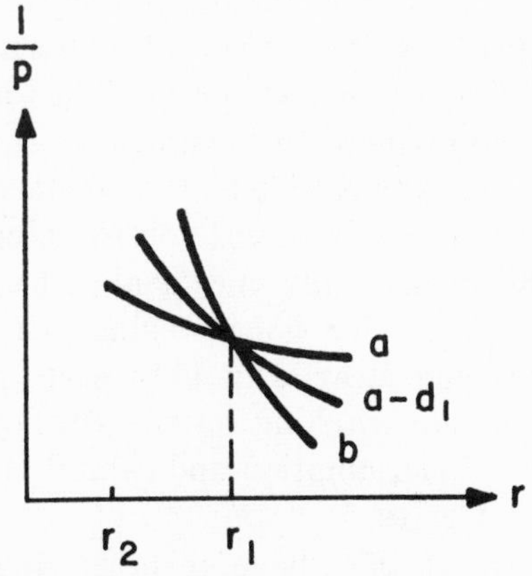

FIGURE IV

r_1 is a common switching point for m activities when the m polynomials $G_i(r)$, $i = 1, 2, \ldots, m$, all happen to have a root at $r = r_1$. If by coincidence *all* n polynomials $G_i(r)$, $i = 1, \ldots, n$, vanish at r_1, then and only then can we say that matrixes a and b which are "adjacent" on the factor-price frontier have no common column, i.e., $(a - b)$ will not contain a zero column vector. For completeness we consider the special case where $G_s(r) \equiv 0$ and

$$\begin{bmatrix} a_o \\ \cdot \; \vdots \; \cdot \\ a \end{bmatrix}_s - \begin{bmatrix} b_o \\ \cdot \; \vdots \; \cdot \\ b \end{bmatrix}_s \neq 0$$

for some index $i = s$. In this case prices are left unaltered by keeping $\begin{bmatrix} a_o \\ \cdot \; \cdot \; \cdot \\ a \end{bmatrix}_s$ in the matrix or by switching to $\begin{bmatrix} b_o \\ \cdot \; \cdot \; \cdot \\ b \end{bmatrix}_s$ i.e., $p_a(r)(\mu + r)d + d_o \equiv 0$ and $p_b(r) = p_a(r)$. Clearly, the above cannot hold for *all* $s = 1, 2, \ldots, n$.

Our results may be summarized by the following theorem:

Theorem: (1) In the general n-sector capital model there may be up to n switching points between any two techniques, and thus a technique may recur up to $(n - 1)$ times. (2) "Adjacent" techniques on two sides of a switching point will usually differ from each other only with respect to *one activity*.[8] Techniques in general may differ with respect to *m activities* $(n \geq m > 1)$ only if certain m independent n-th degree polynomials happen to have a common root at that switching point.

It should be noted that we have confined our discussion to reswitching between pairs of techniques, although the problem of reswitching as originally stated involved only intersection points which lie on the FPF *envelope.* It is clear that there may be no reswitching even if two or more curves intersect several times *below* the envelope.[9] It is important to keep this distinction in mind when discussing sufficiency conditions for nonswitching; assuming that *any two FPC*'s can intersect only once is almost certainly an overly strong sufficient condition for nonswitching. In the next section, however, it will become clear why only such strong restrictions (rather than merely nonswitching on the envelope) might ensure "classical behavior" of consumption and capital across steady states with different interest rates.

The second part of the above theorem helps to clarify discussions about the wrong step in Levhari's proof, namely his funda-

8. This particular result is also stated without proof by Pasinetti, *op. cit.*
9. See Figure VI in Section V below.

mental lemma.[1] His lemma is wrong, but some of the criticism about it is also wrong.

Solow has rightly pointed out that one cannot in general find a semipositive vector x such that either $[a - b]x \geqq 0$, $[a - b]x \leqq 0$, or $[a - b]x = 0$.[2] The second part of our above theorem shows that the lemma will "almost" always work, but only trivially. In other words, we can "almost" always find $x \geqq 0$ such that $[a - b]x = 0$.[3] We agree with Pasinetti[4] that despite this fact, Levhari's proof is incorrect because we could always select a vector x with zeros that correspond precisely to those activities in which switching had taken place. Suppose, however, that we were to *assume* that there exists a vector x (it can be *any* vector!) such that either $[a - b]x \geqq 0$ or $[a - b]x \leqq 0$ for *any* pair of matrices a and b with associated positive price vectors. Strangely enough, Levhari's nonswitching theorem would *then be correct*!

Proof: Suppose there exist two distinct switch points r_1 and r_2. Define the vector function $f(r) \equiv p_a(r)(\mu + r)[a - b] + (a_o - b_o)$. By assumption, $f(r_1) = f(r_2) = 0$ where $r_1 \neq r_2$. Also $p_a'(r) > 0$. Now define the *scalar function*

$$\phi(r) \equiv f(r)x$$

where $\phi(r_1) = \phi(r_2) = 0$. Differentiating $\phi(r)$ we obtain

$$\phi'(r) = [p_a(r) + p_a'(r)(\mu + r)]\,[a - b]x.$$

Thus *for all* r $\phi'(r) > 0$ *if* $[a - b]x \geqq 0$ and $\phi'(r) < 0$ *if* $[a - b]x \leqq 0$. Thus we cannot have $\phi(r_1) = \phi(r_2) = 0$ unless $r_1 = r_2$, which provides a contradiction, and hence two (or more) distinct switch points cannot exist. Q.E.D.

At first glance one might mistakenly conclude that the assumption (that there exists a vector x such that $[a - b]x$ semipositive or seminegative) is only a minor restriction. However, it is a *very* restrictive assumption: it rules out (at least) all switches which involve only one activity and which we considered the "normal" case.[5] Economically the sufficiency condition implies (after some

1. Levhari, *op. cit.*, pp. 104–5.
2. Any (2×2) numerical example in which one row of $[a - b]$ is positive and the other is negative will suffice.
3. If $m < n$, we can always choose an x with zeros in the first m columns and positive elements in the remaining n-m columns; thus $[a - b]x = 0$. Even if $m = n$, there may be cases where the lemma is valid and thus we could claim that it is indeed valid except for extreme coincidences.
4. Pasinetti, *op. cit.*
5. If $[a - b]$ has one column of mixed positive and negative elements and $(n - 1)$ zero columns, then there does not exist *any* vector x such that either $[a - b]x \geqq 0$ or $[a - b]x \leqq 0$. This sufficiency condition can apply

manipulation) that there exists one level of operation for which one technique uses at least as much of all inputs as the other technique and definitely more of at least one input; moreover, the latter must hold for *any* pair of techniques that appear on the factor-price frontier.

We end this section by presenting an alternative sufficiency condition which is again highly restrictive. The price vector for technique a is given by (IV.1). For simplicity we assume that all goods depreciate at the same rate and define the scalar $\rho \equiv \mu + r$. Then

(IV.9) $p_a(\rho) = a_o[I - \rho a]^{-1}.$

Likewise

(IV.10) $p_b(\rho) = b_o[I - \rho b]^{-1}$

gives the price vector when technique b is used. If $\rho = \rho_1$ is a switching point, it follows that

(IV.11) $p_a(\rho_1) - p_b(\rho_1) = a_o[I - \rho_1 a]^{-1} - b_o[I - \rho_1 b]^{-1} = 0.$

(IV.11) is a polynomial of degree at most n, and a simple condition for the existence of at most one positive root can be provided by Descartes' rule of signs. The latter states that the number of positive real roots is equal to the number of variations in sign of the coefficients of the polynomial or is less than this number by a positive integer.[6]

We can obtain the economic interpretation of an analogous sufficiency condition by expanding (IV.9) and (IV.10) in a (convergent) vector power series:

(IV.12) $p_a(\rho) = \alpha_o + \alpha_1\rho + \alpha_2\rho^2 + \ldots$

where $\alpha_o = a_o$, $\alpha_1 = a_o a$, $\alpha_2 = a_o a^2$, . . . ; likewise

(IV.13) $p_b(\rho) = \beta_o + \beta_1\rho + \beta_2\rho^2 + \ldots$

where $\beta_o = b_o$, $\beta_1 = b_o b$, $\beta_2 = b_o b^2$, ... Thus (IV.11) becomes

(IV.14) $p_a(\rho_1) - p_b(\rho_1) = (\alpha_o - \beta_o) + (\alpha_1 - \beta_1)\rho_1 + (\alpha_2 - \beta_2)\rho_1^2 + \ldots = 0.$

Note that α_o is the vector of direct labor inputs; α_1 is the first round of indirect labor; and α_2 is the second round of indirect labor, etc. The β's have the same interpretation in terms of technique b.

Assume that there is only one sign variation in (IV.14). Assume, for example that the first term in (IV.14) is negative for the i-th good ($\alpha_{oi} \leqq \beta_{oi}$), while all the other coefficients are positive

only when there are at least two nonzero columns in $[a - b]$, which in the present model, as we have seen, is not a general case. This might, however, be relevant in an 'Austrian'-type capital model, in which activities are not chosen independently.

6. See, for example, L.E. Dickson, *New First Course in the Theory of Equations* (New York: Wiley, 1939), p. 76.

($a_{ji} \geqq \beta_{ji}$ for $j = 1, 2, \ldots, n$). The first derivative of $p_a(\rho) - p_b(\rho)$ will then be positive for $\rho > 0$, and therefore (IV.14) can have at most one root. This condition on the coefficients has a simple economic interpretation. Recall that a_{oi} and β_{oi} are the *direct* labor inputs per unit of the i-th good, that a_{1i} and β_{1i} are the first round of indirect labor needed to produce a unit of the i-th good, and that a_{2i} and β_{2i} are the second round of indirect labor needed to produce the i-th good, etc.[7] Hence, while activity a_i uses less direct labor than activity b_i, it embodies more indirect labor than activity b_i. If it is desired, one can substitute the word "capital" for "indirect labor," and conclude that activity a_i is more "capital-intensive" than activity b_i.[8]

We conclude that if for any pair of relevant techniques a and b, all pairs of corresponding activities a_i and b_i can be ranked in terms of "capital intensity" (in the above sense, which is independent of the rate of interest), then reswitching cannot occur.[9]

Although the latter sufficiency condition is again highly restrictive, it may be somewhat less restrictive than the former one: note the latter allows changes of single activities while the former does not. We might also observe that the latter condition seems to be the most natural extension of our previous two-sector nonswitching theorem (see Section III). Let us again stress that, except for highly exceptional circumstances, techniques cannot be ranked in order of capital intensity.[1] We thus conclude that reswitching is, at least theoretically, a perfectly acceptable case in the discrete capital model.[2]

Finally, let us note the crucial role of discreteness of activities

7. In the general case where the μ_i are unequal, the price vectors p_a is a polynomial in r. One can show that the first coefficient in that polynomial will be $a_o' = a_o\,[I - \mu_a]^{-1}$ = direct "embodied" labor input. The next terms have somewhat more complicated coefficients but have an analogous interpretation in terms of direct and indirect labor costs.

8. One can show that if we measure aggregate capital in each activity in value (or labor unit) terms, then this interpretation is precise.

The fact that the variations in signs of the input streams are related to the possibility of reswitchings (multiple roots) suggests that reswitching is similar to the problem of an investment option having more than one internal rate of return. (See also Section V below.) That any number of zeros can occur in the present value function was pointed out by Samuelson, "Some Aspects of the Pure Theory of Capital," this *Journal*, LI (May 1937), 469–96.

9. Note that we do not require pairs of activities to be ordered in the *same* way across the two matrixes, i.e., we need not have $a_{oi} \geqq b_{oi}$ or $a_{oi} \leqq b_{oi}$ for all i.

1. We are thus in agreement with Morishima, *Equilibrium, Stability, and Growth*, *op. cit.*, and Pasinetti, *op. cit.*

2. There is an open empirical question as to whether or not reswitching is likely to be observed in an actual economy for reasonable changes in the interest rate.

for obtaining the reswitching result. This is best exhibited by the following interesting theorem due to both M. Weitzman and Solow: In a general n capital good economy, suppose there is at least one capital good that is produced by a smooth neoclassical production function. In such an economy reswitching cannot occur provided that labor and each good are inputs in one or more of the goods produced neoclasically.

Setting the various marginal productivity conditions and supposing that at two different rates of interest the *same* set of input-output coefficients holds, the proof follows by contradiction.

V. Some Additional Implications for Economic Theory

A. *Expressions for National Product*

In order to facilitate the exposition, we assume a circulating-capital technology, although the results can be generalized to include the fixed-capital case without difficulty. Let $X = (X_1, \ldots, X_n)$ denote the output vector. The dynamics of the model are described by

(V.1) $\quad X(t) - C(t) = aX(t+1),$

a difference equation with the interpretation that the part of *this* period's output which *is not* consumed must be equal to the input requirements for *next* period. We also assume that the labor supply is exogenously given, does not grow, and is fully employed.[3] A steady-state solution $X(t) = X(t+1) = X$ must satisfy the balance relationship

(V.2) $\quad X = aX + C$

or

(V.2a) $\quad X = [I - a]^{-1}C$

where the labor constraint is

(V.2b) $\quad L = a_0X.$

The price vector now is (as in Levhari):

(V.3) $\quad P(r) = (1 + r)wa_0[I - (1 + r)a]^{-1}.$

Manipulation of (V.2a), V.2b), and (V.3) yields the following expressions for gross national product and net national product:

(V.4a) $\quad GNP \equiv P(r)X = (1 + r)wL + (1 + r)P(r)aX$

and

(V.4b) $\quad NNP \equiv P(r)C = wL + r[wL + P(r)aX].$

Since labor and circulating capital are paid for at the beginning of

3. We could also generalize the results to the case where L grows according to $\dot{L}/L = n$, an exogenous constant. Here we take $n = 0$, and consider steady states which are in fact stationary states.

the production period, capitalists must advance an amount equal to $[wL + P(r)aX]$, on which they earn a net profit equal to $r[wL + P(r)aX]$ where r is the one-period rate of interest or the profit rate.

Under the simplifying assumption that all wage income is consumed, the quantity $[wL + P(r)aX]$ has a simple interpretation. Then all saving is done by capitalists who must save-invest enough to maintain the value of circulating capital required for the steady state, namely $P(r)aX$.

Let C^* and C^- denote capitalists' and workers' consumption, respectively. Capitalists and workers are faced with their respective budget constraints: [4]

(V.5) $\quad P(r)C^* = r[wL + P(r)aX]$

and

(V.6) $\quad P(r)C^- = wL = \text{constant}.$

The latter is what Samuelson has called net-net national product; it is that part of net national product left over for the primary factor (labor) after the other factors have been paid.[5] Note that $C \equiv C^* + C^-$.

It is easily seen from (V.2a), (V.2b), and (V.3) that there exists a *technical* constraint

(V.7) $\quad L = P(0)C$

where $P(0) = a_0[I - a]^{-1}$. Thus for a given technique $\left[\begin{matrix} & a_0 & \\ \cdot & \cdot\ \cdot & \cdot \\ & a & \end{matrix}\right]$, an equilibrium consumption vector C must satisfy (V.7), the equation of a hyperplane; such a C also satisfies (V.4b), and vice versa.

$P(r)C^-$ does *not* depend on tastes because wL is a fixed number and workers are free to choose any point C^- which satisfies their budget constraint (V.6); thus (V.6) is indeed the consumption possibility schedule for workers. But $P(r)C^*$ *does* depend on tastes. Suppose, for example, that C^- is fixed and equilibrium is established with $C^* = \hat{C}^*$. At first glance, one might think that capitalists are free to move to another point C^* (remember that r is fixed) provided that

$$P(r)\hat{C}^* = P(r)\tilde{C}^*.$$

4. As we will see, it is misleading to call both (V.5) and (V.6) consumption possibility schedules. Note also that the interpretation of C^* and C^- must change if the saving assumption is dropped. In fact, C^- is the *maximum* steady-state consumption for workers, and C^* is the *minimum* steady-state consumption for capitalists. It would be an easy matter to alter the discussion which follows to include any case.

5. Paul A. Samuelson, "A New Theorem on Nonsubstitution," in H. Hegeland (ed.), *Money, Growth, and Methodology; and Other Essays in Economics in Honor of Johan Akerman* (Lund: C. W. K. Gleerup, 1961).

But such a movement is in general impossible because the budget equation for capitalists (V.5) depends on X, and X depends on $C \equiv C^* + C^-$ via (V.2a). Hence (V.5) must be interpreted as a *virtual* consumption possibility schedule. Capitalists are *actually* constrained to a choice of C^* which satisfies

$$\text{(V.8)} \qquad \{P(r) - rP(r)a[I-a]^{-1}\}C^* = r\{wL + P(r)a[I-a]^{-1}C^-\}.$$

With r fixed, we conclude that $P(r)C^*$ and thus $P(r)C$ are not invariant to a change in tastes of *either* workers *or* capitalists, even though $P(r)C^- = wL = constant$ is obviously invariant.[6]

B. Steady-state Consumption Patterns

We now wish to consider a finite set of alternative techniques $\begin{bmatrix} a_0 \\ \cdots \\ a \end{bmatrix}$, $\alpha = a, b, c, \ldots$. The fact that a technique can recur now alerts us to the existence of a "perverse case" in which a low rate of interest is not always associated with high consumption.[7]

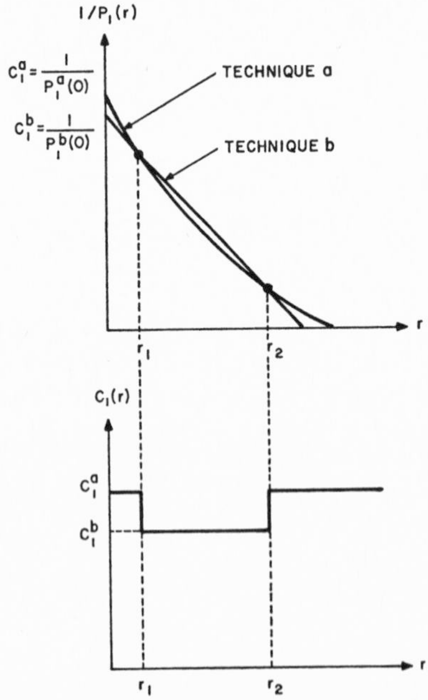

FIGURE V

This fact may be seen most easily by setting $C_2 = \cdots = C_n = 0$ and observing the behavior of C_1 in different steady states. We may

6. *Ibid.*

7. This fact was pointed out by Morishima, *Equilibrium, Stability, and Growth, op. cit.*, p. 126.

solve (V.7) for

$$C_1{}^a = \frac{L}{P_1{}^a(0)} \quad \text{(V.9)}$$

where $P_1{}^a$ (0) is the price of good 1 when $r = 0$ and technique a is employed. We lose no generality by setting $w = L = 1$; then the height at $r = 0$ of the factor-price frontier *for technique* a is equal to $C_1{}^a$. A "perverse case" is illustrated in Figure V.

It is crucial to realize that while reswitching tells us that such behavior exists, the phenomenon illustrated in Figure V exists *without* reswitching, as shown in Figure VI. The cause of the "per-

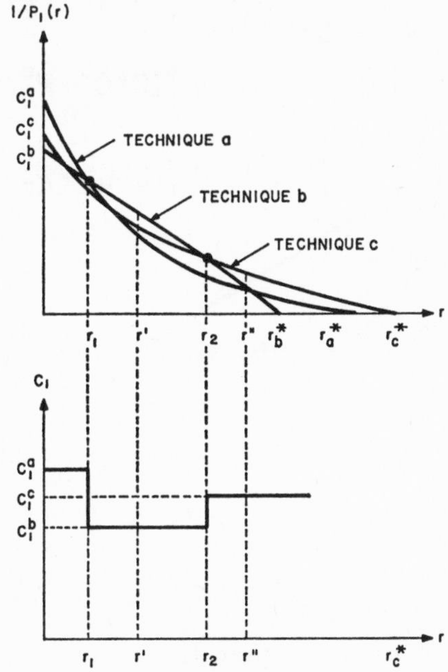

FIGURE VI

verse behavior" in Figure VI can be traced to the fact that the factor-price curves for alternative techniques cross *below* the outer envelope. Thus even though there are no multiple crossings on the outer envelope (the economy's factor-price frontier) and reswitching does not occur, we still find that C_1 *rises* when r is increased from r' to r'' where $r_1 < r' < r_2$ and $r_2 < r'' < r^*_c$.

We note that the sufficiency conditions for nonswitching which we have stated and proved in Sections III and IV may be, in general, overly strong to preclude reswitching on the FPF envelope. However, these same conditions may be *necessary* if the monotonicity of $C(r)$ is to be preserved.

The problem is a bit harder to analyze when there is positive consumption of more than one good, but the same qualitative behavior is possible. With alternative techniques the hyperplane equation (V.7) becomes a set of equations:

(V.10) $L = P^{\alpha}(0)c^{\alpha}, \alpha = a, b, c, \ldots$.

For a two-good economy (V.10) become the equations of straight lines in the $C_1 - C_2$ plane, as illustrated in Figure VII for alter-

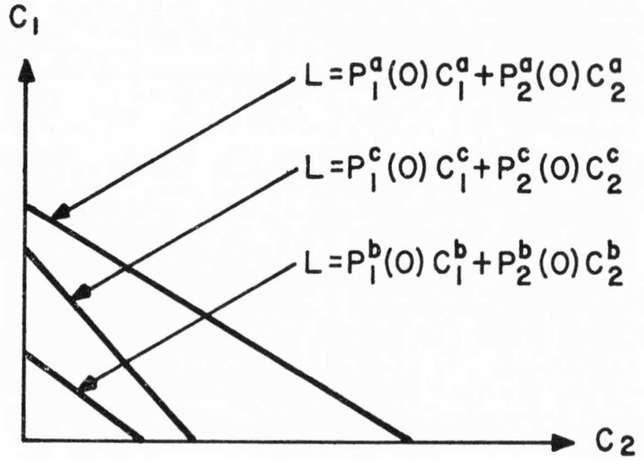

FIGURE VII

native techniques a, b, and c.[8] If, as in Figure VI, technique a is used for $0 \leq r \leq r_1$, b for $r_1 \leq r \leq r_2$, and c for $r_2 \leq r \leq r^*_c$ where $r_1 < r_2$, we can unambiguously say that steady-state consumption is high for low r, then lower for higher r, but higher again for still higher r.

Other conclusions follow from the above analysis. First, since (1) the nonsubstitution theorem tells us that the real wage in terms of every good is always maximized for a given r, and (2) the economy's factor-price frontier is downward sloping, it follows that consumption is maximized when $r = 0$, although that maximum may not be unique.[9] Second, workers' consumption *is* always higher for lower r, a conclusion which follows immediately from (V.6) and the fact that prices *always* increase when r is increased. Finally, the steady-state *value* of circulating capital $P(r)aX$ is not a

8. The three lines in Figure VII are parallel if we have the Marx case of "equal organic composition of capital." The nonsubstitution theorem guarantees that the lines can never cross because *all* prices are simultaneously minimized.

9. If we were to assume $\dot{L}/L = n > 0$, per capita consumption would be maximized when the Golden Rule condition $r = n$ is satisfied.

monotonic function of r, a fact also stated by Pasinetti, Morishima, and others.[1]

C. Transitions between Steady States

We have completely ignored how the economy moves from one steady state to another. It is as if there were different planets possessing the same book of blueprints (set of techniques) but which were in different steady states that correspond to different exogenously given r's. We then would observe each planet and compare their steady-state equilibriums. To discuss a movement from one steady state to another would in general require a theory of interest rate determination. Moreover, we would need to examine dynamic motions of the system and stability problems might become important.

There is, however, a special case which is illuminating and which we can easily discuss. Suppose that the exogenously given interest rate is a switch point between techniques a and b; then both techniques are viable at the given interest rate and $P^a(r) = P^b(r)$. The economy can usually move from consumption vector C^a to C^b, although we shall ignore the exact mechanism by which the movement is in fact accomplished. The above problem has been discussed by Solow, and he has proved that the social rate of return to saving, ρ, is equal to the switch-point interest rate r; a brief discussion of Solow's proof follows.

Suppose that the economy initially uses only technique a and has a corresponding consumption vector C^a. If the economy is able to move in one period to an equilibrium where only technique b is used, there must exist a consumption vector $\bar{C} \geqq 0$ which satisfies

$$\text{(V.11)} \qquad X = \bar{C} + bY$$

where bY is the vector of input requirements using technique b.[2] If such a $\bar{C}$ can be found, the economy may consume $\bar{C}$ for one period and then move into steady-state equilibrium with technique b and consumption C^b. Defining the social rate of return

$$\rho \equiv \frac{P(C^b - C^a)}{P(C^a - \bar{C})},$$

Solow proved that $\rho = r$.[3]

1. Morishima, *Equilibrium, Stability, and Growth, op. cit.*, and Pasinetti, *op cit.*

2. Solow has also considered a more complicated case in which a one-period transition is impossible because there does not exist a solution to $X = \bar{C} + bY$ with $\bar{C} \geqq 0$. The conclusion $\rho = r$ may remain valid even when more than one period is required to complete the transition.

3. From (V.4a) and (V.4b) we have $PC^a = (1 + r)wL + rPaX$, $PC^b =$

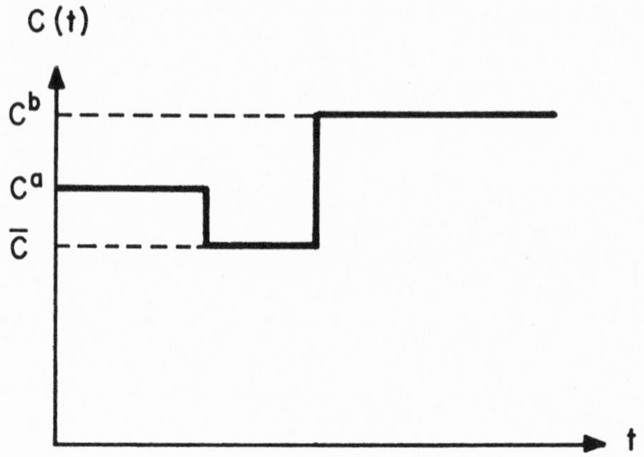

FIGURE VIII

In a well-behaved case $C^a > \bar{C}$ and $C^b > C^a$, and the time path of consumption appears as in Figure VIII. But in a "perverse" case, $C^a < \bar{C}$ and $C^b < C^a$ as illustrated in Figure IX.

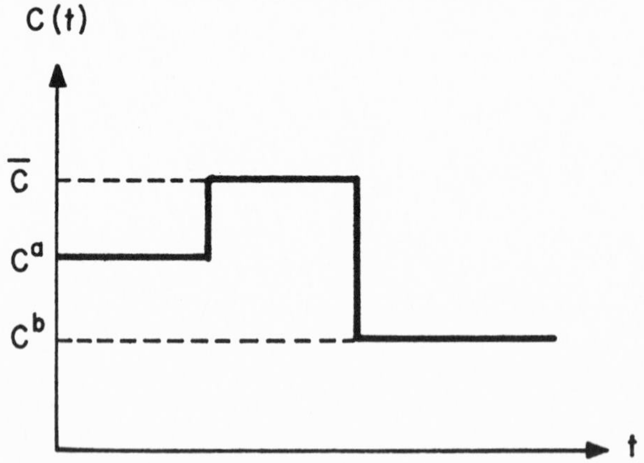

FIGURE IX

What can be concluded?

Since $P^a(r) = P^b(r)$, workers are not affected by the change: they may still consume C^- where $PC^- = wL$. But the story is not the same for capitalists. As $C \equiv C^* + C^-$, it is C^* which changes when the economy moves from technique a to b. If $C^{*b} < C^{*a}$, can we conclude that capitalists have been hurt? The answer is most

$(1+r)wL + rPbY$, and $PX = (1+r)wL + (1+r)PaX$. Then from (V.11) we obtain $PC^a - P\bar{C} = PbY - PaX$. Likewise, $PC^b - PC^a = r(PbY - PaX)$, and the conclusion $\rho = r$ follows immediately.

certainly "no," for it is the capitalists who enjoyed a splash of consumption $\bar{C}^* > C^{*a}$, and the extra consumption in which they indulged for one period is exactly equal to the value of their forever-lower consumption stream $C^{*b} < C^{*a}$ discounted at the social rate of return.[4]

Finally let us point out a corollary of Solow's theorem. If there are a number of switching points, then at all of them the rate of interest (usually) equals the rate of return to saving. The *physical acts* of moving back and forth from one consumption "plateau" to the other as the rate of interest changes will be identical at every switch point, but the interest rate is different at each switch point. In other words, here is a clear illustration of the analogy between the reswitching problem and the existence of multiple rates of return in investment profitability calculations.

One may recall that we have been warned long ago that "there is no new thing under the sun."[5]

MASSACHUSETTS INSTITUTE OF TECHNOLOGY
AND HEBREW UNIVERSITY, JERUSALEM

UNIVERSITY OF PENNSYLVANIA

MASSACHUSETTS INSTITUTE OF TECHNOLOGY AND
HARVARD UNIVERSITY

4. The above argument depends on keeping r fixed. As pointed out by Samuelson, *op. cit.*, when $r = 0$, workers get all of NNP with $P(O)C- = P(O)C$ and $C^* = 0$; and when $r = r^*$, the maximum rate of interest where $w = 0$, $P(0)C^* = PC$ and $C- = 0$.

5. *Bible*, Ecclesiastes 1.9 (about B.C. 977).

5

STATIONARY ORDINAL UTILITY AND IMPATIENCE[1]

By Tjalling C. Koopmans[2]

This paper investigates Böhm-Bawerk's idea of a preference for advancing the timing of future satisfactions from a somewhat different point of view. It is shown that simple postulates about the utility function of a consumption program for an *infinite* future logically imply impatience at least for certain broad classes of programs. The postulates assert continuity, sensitivity, stationarity of the utility function, the absence of intertemporal complementarity, and the existence of a best and a worst program. The more technical parts of the proof are set off in starred sections.

1. INTRODUCTION

Ever since the appearance of Böhm-Bawerk's *Positive Theorie des Kapitals*, the idea of a preference for advancing the timing of future satisfaction has been widely used in economic theory. The question of how to define this idea precisely has, however, been given insufficient attention. If the idea of preference for early timing is to be applicable also to a world of changing prices, money expenditure on consumption is not a suitable measure of "satisfaction level," and money expenditure divided by a consumers' goods price index is at best an approximate measure, useful for econometric work but not providing the sharp distinctions that theory requires. It seems better, therefore, to try to define preference for advanced timing entirely in terms of a *utility function*. Moreover, if the idea of preference for early timing is to be expressed independently of assumptions that have made the construction of cardinal utility possible[3] (such as choice between uncertain prospects, or stochastic choice, or independence of commodity groups in the preference structure) it will be necessary to express it in terms of an *ordinal* utility function, that is, a function that retains its meaning under a monotonic (increasing) transformation. It would seem that this can be done only if one postulates a certain persistency over time in the structure of preference.

This study started out as an attempt to formulate postulates permitting a sharp definition of *impatience*, the short term Irving Fisher has introduced for preference for advanced timing of satisfaction. To avoid complications connected with the advancing age and finite life span of the individual consumer, these postulates were set up for a (continuous) utility function of a consumption program extending over an infinite future period. The

[1] This study was carried out in part under a grant from the National Science Foundation.

[2] I am indebted to Gerard Debreu and Herbert Scarf for extremely valuable comments and suggestions on the subject and methods of this paper.

[3] For a recent discussion, see Debreu [**2**].

surprising result was that only a slight strengthening of the continuity postulate (incorporated in Postulate 1 below) permits one to conclude from the existence of a utility function satisfying the postulates, that impatience prevails at least in certain areas of the program space. In other words, conditions hardly stronger than those that appear needed to *define* impatience in a meaningful way are sufficient to *prove* that there are zones of impatience. Intuitively, the reason is that if there is in all circumstances a preference for postponing satisfaction—or even neutrality toward timing—then there is not enough room in the set of real numbers to accommodate and label numerically all the different satisfaction levels that may occur in relation to consumption programs for an infinite future.

This paper thus has become a study of some implications of a continuous and stationary (see Postulate 3) ordering of infinite programs. Flexibility of interpretation remains as to whether this ordering may serve as a first approximation to the preferences of an individual consumer, or may perhaps be an "impersonal" result of the aggregation of somewhat similar individual preferences (interpreting "consumption" as "consumption per head" in the case of a growing population), or finally may guide choices in a centrally planned economy. In each of these interpretations further modifications and refinements may be called for.

The first paper in the literature basing the study of utility on a set of behavior axioms (or postulates), known to this author, was by Professor Frisch [**5**]. Since then this method has been widely applied to establish utility concepts appropriate to a variety of choice problems. In most cases the postulates have been in terms of preferences rather than of a utility function. To limit the mathematical difficulties, the postulates of the present study are in terms of a utility function, with the understanding that an alternative with higher utility is always preferred over one with lower utility, and indifference exists between alternatives of equal utility. Studies deriving the existence of an ordinal utility function from postulates about preferences have been made by Wold [**10**] and by Debreu [**3**].

Two levels of discussion are separated in what follows. The contents and findings of each section are first stated in general terms. Then, where needed, the more technical stipulations, proofs and discussions are given in a starred section bearing the same number. The starred sections can be passed up by readers interested primarily in the results and in the less technical phases of the reasoning.

2. THE PROGRAM SPACE — NOTATION

A program for an infinite future will be denoted

$$(1) \qquad {}_1x = (x_1, x_2, x_3, \ldots, x_t, \ldots) = (x_1, {}_2x) = \text{etc.}$$

Each symbol x_t, $t = 1, 2, \ldots$, represents a vector (bundle)

$$x_t = (x_{t1}, x_{t2}, \ldots, x_{tn}) \tag{2}$$

of the nonnegative amounts of n listed commodities to be consumed in the period t. Subvectors of (1) consisting of several consecutive vectors (2) will be denoted

$${}_tx_{t'} = (x_t, x_{t+1}, \ldots, x_{t'}), \tag{3}$$

where omission of the right subscript t' of ${}_tx_{t'}$ indicates that $t' = \infty$.The subscript t of x_t is called the *timing* of the consumption vector x_t, the subscript s of ${}_sx = (x_s, x_{s+1}, \ldots)$ the *time* of choice between ${}_sx$ and its alternatives ${}_sx'$, ${}_sx''$, ... A constant program is denoted

$${}_{\text{con}}x = (x, x, x, \ldots). \tag{4}$$

Finally, $\equiv$ denotes equality by definition.

2*. Each consumption vector x_t is to be selected from a connected subset X of the n-dimensional commodity space, which we take to be the same for all t. Hence ${}_tx = (x_t, x_{t+1}, \ldots)$ belongs to the cartesian product ${}_1X$ of an infinite sequence of identical sets X. Expressions such as "for some x_t," "for all ${}_tx$," etc., will in what follows always mean "for some $x_t \in X$," "for all ${}_tx \in {}_1X$," etc., and all functions of x_t or ${}_tx$ are to be thought of as defined on X or on ${}_1X$, respectively.

3. EXISTENCE OF A CONTINUOUS UTILITY FUNCTION

Before stating the basic postulate asserting this existence, the meaning of continuity needs to be clarified. Continuity of a function $f(y)$ of a vector y means that, for every y, one can make the absolute difference $|f(y') - f(y)|$ as small as desired by making the distance $d(y', y)$ between y' and y sufficiently small, regardless of the direction of approach of y' to y. For vectors $y = (y_1, \ldots, y_n)$ with a finite number n of components there is a wide choice of definitions of the distance function $d(y', y)$, all of which establish the same continuity concept, and the maximum absolute difference for any component,

$$d(y', y) = |y' - y| \equiv \max_k |y_k' - y_k| \tag{5}$$

is as suitable as any of a large class of alternatives. But in an infinite-dimensional space the continuity concept is sensitive to the choice of the distance function used. In what follows we shall employ as a "distance" between two programs ${}_1x'$, ${}_1x$, the function

$$d({}_1x', {}_1x) \equiv \sup_t |x_t' - x_t|. \tag{6}$$

This is the maximum distance in the sense of (5) between any two corresponding one-period consumption vectors x_t', x_t, whenever such a maximum exists.[4] This definition treats all future periods alike, and, if anything, has a bias toward neutrality with regard to the timing of satisfaction.

POSTULATE 1. *There exists a utility function* $U({}_1x)$, *which is defined for all* ${}_1x = (x_1, x_2, \ldots)$ *such that, for all t,* x_t *is a point of a connected subset X of the n-dimensional commodity space. The function* $U({}_1x)$ *has the continuity property that, if U is any of the values assumed by that function, and if U' and U'' are numbers such that* $U' < U < U''$, *then there exists a positive number* δ *such that the utility* $U({}_1x')$ *of every program* ${}_1x'$ *having a distance* $d({}_1x', {}_1x) \leqq \delta$ *from some program* ${}_1x$ *with utility* $U({}_1x) = U$ *satisfies* $U' \leqq U({}_1x') \leqq U''$.

Comparison with the above definition of continuity of a function $f(y)$ will show that we are here making a slightly stronger requirement (which obviously implies ordinary continuity). For any U' and U'' bracketing the given U, we want *the same* maximum distance δ between ${}_1x'$ and ${}_1x$ to guarantee that $U' \leqq U({}_1x') \leqq U''$ regardless of which is the member ${}_1x$ of the class of all programs with utility equal to U, to which the program ${}_1x'$ has a distance $\leqq \delta$.

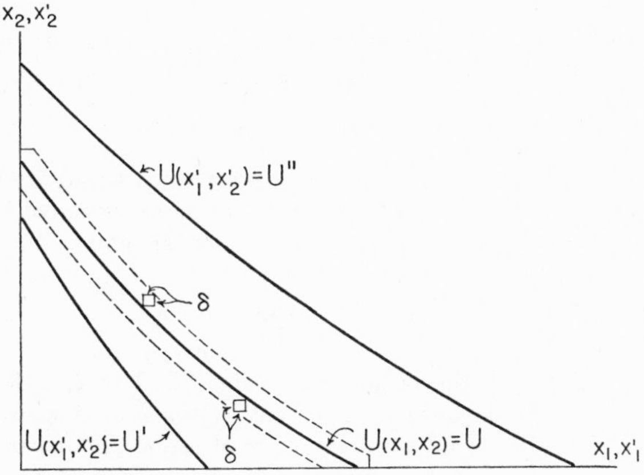

FIGURE 1

Figure 1 shows a simplified case where ${}_1x$ has only two scalar components x_1 and x_2. We then require that there be a band consisting of all points no further than δ away from some point of the indifference curve $U(x_1, x_2) = U$,

[4] If no largest $|x' - x_t|$ exists, but if there is a number exceeding $|x'_t - x_t|$ for all t, then there exists a smallest number with that property, and $\sup_t |x'_t - x_t|$ denotes that number. If no number exceeding $|x'_t - x_t|$ for all t exists, $\sup_t |x'_t - x_t| = \infty$.

which band is to fall entirely within the zone $U' \leqq U(x_1', x_2') \leqq U''$. Essentially, then, we are requiring that the utility function not be infinitely more sensitive to changes in the quantities of one program than it is to any such changes in another *equivalent* program.

3*. If we call the set $\{_1x \in {}_1X \mid U(_1x) = U\}$ the *equivalence class* defined by U, then the continuity property defined by Postulate 1 may be called *uniform continuity on each equivalence class.*[5]

Since $U(_1x)$ is continuous on a connected set $_1X$, the set of values assumed by $U(_1x)$ is an interval I_U.

4. SENSITIVITY

There would not be much interest in a utility function that assumes the same value for all programs. Such a utility function would not discriminate among any alternatives. In fact, we shall need a somewhat stronger sensitivity postulate than just a statement that the utility function is not a constant. We shall require that utility can be changed by changing the consumption vector in some designated period. The use of the first period for this purpose in the following postulate is a matter of convenience, not of necessity.

POSTULATE 2. *There exist first-period consumption vectors x_1, x_1' and a program $_2x$ from-the-second-period-on, such that*

$$U(x_1, {}_2x) > U(x_1', {}_2x).$$

4*. The need for placing the program change for which sensitivity is postulated in a designated period can be illustrated by an example suggested by Scarf. Let there be only one commodity (hence x_t is a scalar, amount of bread, say) and consider

$$U(_1x) \equiv \lim_{T \to \infty} \sup_{t \geqq T} x_t .$$

This function satisfies all the postulates except Postulate 2. A decision-maker guided by it has a heroic unconcern for any (upward or downward) changes in the program that affect only a finite number of periods, no matter how many. His eyes are only on the highest consumption level that is repeated or approximat-

[5] It has been pointed out to me by Debreu that the postulates of this paper do not precisely fit those of his study [**3**] of the existence of a utility function cited above. Since in the topology generated by the distance function (6) the space $_1X$ is not separable, Debreu's theorems do not apply to the present case. Neither can we say, in the topology generated by (6), that, if we specify that X is a compact set, mere continuity of $U(_1x)$ implies the stronger continuity of Postulate 1. Both statements would become valid if the so-called *product topology* were substituted for that used here. For a definition of the product topology, see, for instance, Taylor [**9**, § 2.5, p. 79].

ed infinitely often, no matter how long the wait for the first occurrence of a level close to that top, or the waits between successive occurrences. Postulate 2 excludes him.

5. AGGREGATION BY PERIODS

Having rejected expenditure on consumption as a measure for the satisfaction levels reached in particular periods, we must find another means of labeling such levels. This can be done if we are willing to postulate that the particular bundle of commodities to be consumed in the first period has no effect on the preference between alternative sequences of bundles in the remaining future, and conversely. One cannot claim a high degree of realism for such a postulate, because there is no clear reason why complementarity of goods could not extend over more than one time period. It may be surmised, however, that weaker forms of this postulate would still allow similar results to be reached. The purpose of the present form is to set the simplest possible stage for a study of the effect of timing alone on preference.

POSTULATE 3 (3a *and* 3b). *For all* $x_1, x_1', {}_2x, {}_2x'$,

$$U(x_1, {}_2x) \geqq U(x_1', {}_2x) \text{ implies } U(x_1, {}_2x') \geqq U(x_1', {}_2x')\,, \tag{3a}$$

$$U(x_1, {}_2x) \geqq U(x_1, {}_2x') \text{ implies } U(x_1', {}_2x) \geqq U(x_1', {}_2x')\,. \tag{3b}$$

We shall show that, as a consequence of Postulate 3, the utility function can be written in the form

$$U({}_1x) = V(u_1(x_1), U_2({}_2x))\,, \tag{7}$$

where $V(u_1, U_2)$ is a continuous and increasing function of its two variables u_1, U_2, and where both $u_1(x_1)$ and $U_2({}_2x)$ have the stronger continuity property attributed to $U({}_1x)$ in Postulate 1. We shall call $u_1(x_1)$ *immediate utility* or *one-period utility* (at time $t = 1$), interpreting it as a numerical indicator of the satisfaction level associated with the consumption vector x_1 in period 1. $U_2({}_2x)$ will be called *prospective utility* (as from time $t = 2$), with a similar interpretation with regard to the remaining future. Whereas this suggests calling $U({}_1x)$ prospective utility as from time 1, we shall for contrast call it *aggregate utility* (aggregated, that is, over *all* future time periods). Finally, the function $V(u_1, U_2)$, to be called the *aggregator*, indicates how any given pair of utility levels, immediate (u_1) and prospective (U_2) stacks up against any other pair in making choices for the entire future.

5*. Since x_1 and x_1' as well as ${}_2x$ and ${}_2x'$ can be interchanged in Postulate 3a, and since "$>$" means "$\geqq$ and not $\leqq$" and "$=$" means "$\geqq$ and $\leqq$," Postulate 3a implies that, for all $x_1, x_1', {}_2x, {}_2x'$,

(8>) $\quad U(x_1, {}_2x) > U(x_1', {}_2x)$ implies $U(x_1, {}_2x') > U(x_1', {}_2x')$,

(8=) $\quad U(x_1, {}_2x) = U(x_1', {}_2x)$ implies $U(x_1, {}_2x') = U(x_1', {}_2x')$.

We assign to ${}_2x$ a particular value ${}_2x^0$ for which the statement made in Postulate 2 is valid, and define

(9) $$u_1(x_1) \equiv U(x_1, {}_2x^0) .$$

We then read from (8=) that

$$u_1(x_1) = u_1(x_1') \text{ implies } U(x_1, {}_2x') = U(x_1', {}_2x') \text{ for all } {}_2x' .$$

Again writing ${}_2x$ for ${}_2x'$, this means that

$$U(x_1, {}_2x) = F(u_1(x_1), {}_2x) .$$

Applying a similar argument to Postulate 3b and defining

(10) $$U_2({}_2x) \equiv U(\overset{0}{x_1}, {}_2x) ,$$

we obtain for $U({}_1x)$ the form (7). It follows from the definitions (9) and (10) that $u_1(x_1)$ and $U_2({}_2x)$ have the same continuity property as $U({}_1x)$.

Since $u_1(x_1)$ is defined on a connected set X, its continuity implies that the set of values assumed by $u_1(x_1)$ on X is an interval I_{u_1}. By Postulate 2, I_{u_1} has more than one point. By (8>) and (9) we see that $V(u_1, U_2)$ is increasing in u_1 on I_{u_1}, for all U_2. Moreover, since for any ${}_2x \in {}_1X$ the function $U(x_1, {}_2x)$ is continuous with regard to x_1 on X, the set of values assumed by $V(u_1, U_2)$ for all u_1 in I_{u_1} and any given U_2 is also an interval. Since an increasing function that assumes all values in an interval must be continuous, it follows that $V(u_1, U_2)$ is continuous with regard to u_1, for all U_2.

By similar reasoning, the set of values assumed by $U_2({}_2x)$ on ${}_1X$ is an interval I_{U_2}, and *if* I_{U_2} contains more than one point, $V(u_1, U_2)$ is increasing and continuous with regard to U_2 on I_{U_2}, for all u_1. It is easily seen that, in this case, $V(u_1, U_2)$ is continuous in (u_1, U_2) jointly on $I_{u_1} \times I_{U_2}$.

It may be anticipated here that Postulate 4 of the next section will ensure that I_{U_2} contains more than one point. To see this, let $x_2, x_2', {}_3x$ be vectors satisfying Postulate 2, hence

$$U(x_2, {}_3x) > U(x_2', {}_3x) .$$

We insert ${}_2x \equiv (x_2, {}_3x)$, ${}_2x' \equiv (x_2', {}_3x)$ in the implication,

$$U({}_2x) > U({}_2x') \text{ implies } U(x_1, {}_2x) > U(x_1, {}_2x') ,$$

of Postulate 4, and find that

$$V(u_1(x_1), U_2({}_2x)) > V(u_1(x_1), U_2({}_2x')) ,$$

which is possible only if $U_2({}_2x)$ assumes more than one value.

6. STATIONARITY

Postulate 3b says that the preference ordering within a class of programs ${}_1x$ with a common first-period consumption vector x_1 does not depend on what that vector x_1 is. We now go a step further and require that that preference ordering be the same as the ordering of corresponding programs obtained by advancing the timing of each future consumption vector by one period (and, of course, forgetting about the common first-period vector originally stipulated). This expresses the idea that the passage of time does not have an effect on preferences.

POSTULATE 4. *For some* x_1 *and all* ${}_2x$, ${}_2x'$,

$$U(x_1, {}_2x) \geqq U(x_1, {}_2x') \text{ if and only if } U({}_2x) \geqq U({}_2x') .$$

In the light of (7) and the fact that $V(u_1, U_2)$ increases with U_2, this is equivalent to

$$U_2({}_2x) \geqq U_2({}_2x') \text{ if and only if } U({}_2x) \geqq U({}_2x') .$$

By reasoning similar to that in Section 5*, it follows that

$$U_2({}_2x) = G(U({}_2x)) ,$$

where $G(U)$ is a continuous increasing function of U. If $U = G^{-1}(U_2)$ denotes its inverse,[6] the monotonic transformation

$$U^*({}_1x) \equiv U({}_1x) , \quad u_1^*(x_1) \equiv u_1(x_1) ,$$

$$U_2^*({}_2x) \equiv G^{-1}(U_2({}_2x)) , \quad V^*(u_1^*, U_2^*) \equiv V(u_1^*, G(U_2^*({}_2x)))$$

preserves the preference ordering defined by $U({}_1x)$, and makes the functions $U_2^*({}_2x)$ and $U^*({}_2x)$ identical. We can therefore hereafter drop the time subscripts from the symbols u_1^*, $u_1^*(\ )$, U_2^*, $U_2^*(\ )$. If, now that the reasoning has been completed, we also drop all the asterisks, we have, instead of (7), the simpler relation

$$U({}_1x) = V(u(x_1), U({}_2x)) . \tag{11}$$

This relation will be the point of departure for all further reasoning. It says that the ordering of pairs of utility levels—immediate, $u(x_1)$, and prospective, $U({}_2x)$—defined by the aggregator $V(u, U)$ is such as to produce an ordering of programs for all future time, identical but for a shift in time with the ordering of programs that start with the second period. Of course, ${}_2x$ can again be substituted for ${}_1x$ in (11), giving $U({}_2x) = V(u(x_2), U({}_3x))$ and so on. The function $V(u, U)$ is again continuous and increasing in its arguments u, U.

Since both $u(x_1)$ and $U({}_2x)$ are continuous, the arguments u, U of $V(u, U)$ can take any value in an interval I_u, I_U, respectively, and the values attained by $V(u, U)$ fill the interval I_U. Since we are dealing with ordinal utility, there is still freedom to apply separate increasing transformations to $u(x_1)$ and to $U({}_2x)$, with corresponding transformations of $V(u, U)$, so as to make both I_u and I_U coincide with the unit interval extending from

6 That is, a function such that $G(G^{-1}(U_2)) = U_2$ for all U_2.

0 to 1. The aggregator $V(u, U)$ can then be represented, though incompletely, by its niveau lines in the unit square, which are descending to the right, as shown in Figure 2.

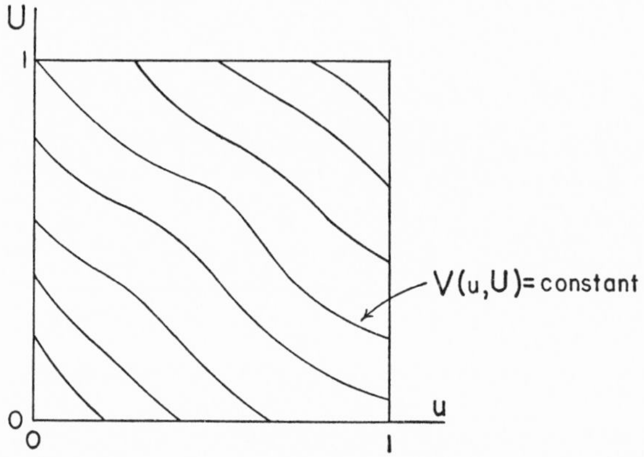

FIGURE 2

The representation is incomplete in that one still has to associate with each niveau line a numerical value of the function, which is to be referred to the vertical scale. It is also somewhat arbitrary in that separate increasing transformations of u and U that preserve the common end points 0, 1 of I_u and I_U are still permitted. The information conveyed by $V(u, U)$ is therefore as yet somewhat hidden in those interrelations between the niveau lines, the verticals, the horizontals, and the numerical niveaus themselves, which are invariant under such transformations.

6*. The question whether I_u or I_U or both include one or both end points, 0 and 1, of the unit interval, still left open by the preceding postulates, will be answered by the next postulate.

7. EXTREME PROGRAMS

In order to sidestep a mathematical complication, we shall only consider the case in which there exist a best program ${}_1\bar{x}$ and a worst program ${}_1\underline{x}$.

POSTULATE 5. *There exist* ${}_1\underline{x}$, ${}_1\bar{x}$ *such that*

$$U({}_1\underline{x}) \leqq U({}_1x) \leqq U({}_1\bar{x}) \text{ for all } {}_1x\,.$$

As a result of the transformations already applied, we must then have

$$U({}_1\underline{x}) = 0, \quad U({}_1\bar{x}) = 1\,. \tag{12}$$

Furthermore, if ${}_1\bar{x} = (\bar{x}_1, \bar{x}_2, \ldots)$, we must also have

$$u(\bar{x}_t) = 1 \text{ for all } t,$$

because, if we had $u(\bar{x}_\tau) < 1$ for some τ, there would exist a program $\bar{x}'$ with $u(\bar{x}'_\tau) > u(\bar{x}_\tau)$ and $\bar{x}'_t = \bar{x}_t$ for all $t \neq \tau$, which would be a better one, in view of (11) and the monotonicity of $V(u, U)$. From this and similar reasoning for the worst program ${}_1\underline{x}$ we have

$$0 = u(\underline{x}_1) \leqq u(x) \leqq u(\bar{x}_1) = 1 \quad \text{for all } x. \tag{13}$$

It follows that in the present case the intervals $I_u = I_U$ contain both end points 0, 1. Finally, if ${}_1\bar{x}$ is a best (${}_1\underline{x}$ a worst) program, it follows from (11) and the monotonicity of $V(u, U)$ that ${}_2\bar{x}$ (or ${}_2\underline{x}$) is likewise a best (worst) program. Hence, by inserting ${}_1\underline{x}$ and ${}_1\bar{x}$ successively into (11) and using (12) and (13), we find that

$$V(0, 0) = 0, \quad V(1, 1) = 1\,. \tag{14}$$

8. A DEFINITION OF IMPATIENCE

Now that we have succeeded in associating with each period's consumption vector x_t a utility level $u_t = u(x_t)$ *derived from the same function* $u(\ )$ *for each period*, we are in a position to define impatience as an attribute of a program ${}_1x$.

DEFINITION 1. *A program* ${}_1x$ *with first- and second-period utility levels* $u_1 \equiv u(x_1)$, $u_2 \equiv u(x_2)$ *and prospective utility* $U_3 \equiv U({}_3x)$ *from-the-third-period-on will be said to meet the impatience condition if*

$$V(u_1, V(u_2, U_3)) \begin{Bmatrix} \geq \\ = \\ < \end{Bmatrix} V(u_2, V(u_1, U_3)) \quad \textit{when} \quad u_1 \begin{Bmatrix} \geq \\ = \\ < \end{Bmatrix} u_2\,.$$

Obviously, any program with $u_1 = u_2$ meets this condition. If $u_1 > u_2$, the condition says that interchange of the first-period consumption vector x_1 with the *less desirable* second-period vector x_2 *decreases* aggregate utility. Clearly, if ${}_1x = (x_1, x_2, {}_3x)$ meets this condition with $u_1 > u_2$, then ${}_1x' \equiv (x_2, x_1, {}_3x)$ meets the condition with $u_1' \equiv u(x_2) < u_2' \equiv u(x_1)$.

Although impatience is here defined as an attribute of a program ${}_1x$, we shall also say that impatience prevails in the point (u_1, u_2, U_3) in a three-dimensional utility space if the above condition is met.

In Sections 9—12 we shall study some preliminary problems in order to turn in Section 13 to the main problem of finding areas in the program space (or in the utility space of u_1, u_2, U_3) where impatience prevails.

9. CORRESPONDING LEVELS OF IMMEDIATE AND PROSPECTIVE UTILITY

In this section we contrast only the first period with the remaining future. Again omitting time subscripts from the corresponding utility variables

u_1 and U_2, we shall study the question whether, if one of the two utilities, immediate (u) or prospective (U) is given, one can find for the other one a value that equates prospective and aggregate utility,

$$V(u, U) = U\,. \tag{15}$$

A pair (u, U) that satisfies this condition will be called a pair of *corresponding* (immediate and prospective) utility levels. One interpretation of this correspondence is that the immediate utility level u just compensates for the postponement of a program with aggregate utility U by one period. Another still simpler interpretation will be given in Section 10.

The existence of a prospective utility U corresponding to a given immediate utility u is readily established. Let u be a point of I_u. Then there exists a one-period consumption vector x such that $u(x) = u$. The aggregate utility $U({}_{\text{con}}x)$ of the constant program in which x is repeated indefinitely then satisfies, by (11),

$$U({}_{\text{con}}x) = V(u(x), U({}_{\text{con}}x))\,, \tag{16}$$

because a shift in time does not modify the program. Hence $U = U({}_{\text{con}}x)$ meets the condition (15) in conjunction with the given u.

We shall now prove that for each u there is only one corresponding U, which represents a continuous increasing function

$$U = W(u), \text{ with } W(0) = 0, \quad W(1) = 1, \tag{17}$$

of u, to be called the *correspondence function*. It follows from this that, conversely, to each U there is one and only one corresponding u. Figure 3 illustrates the connection between $V(u, U)$ and $W(u)$.

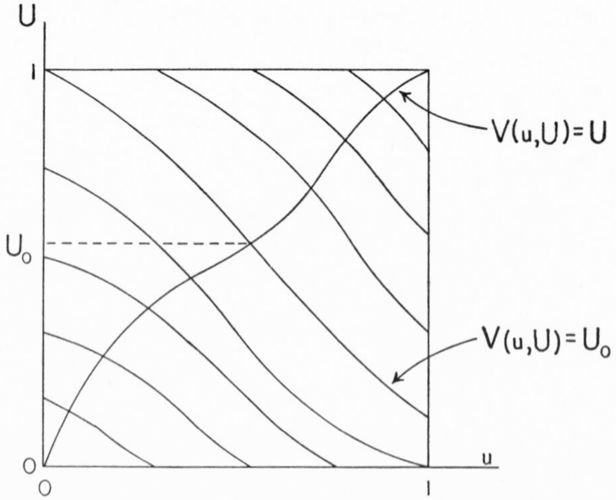

FIGURE 3

9*. We proceed by a sequence of lemmas. With a view to possible later study of the case where no best or worst program exists, Postulate 5 is not assumed in this section 9* (unless otherwise stated).

LEMMA 1a. *Let* $u \in I_u$, $U \in I_U$ *satisfy* (15) *with* $u < 1$. *Then there exists no* $U' \in I_U$ *such that* $U' > U$ *and*

$$V(u, U'') - U'' \geqq 0 \text{ for all } U'' \text{ such that } U < U'' \leqq U' .$$

PROOF. Suppose there were such a U'. There exist a vector x and a program ${}_1x$ such that

$$u(x) = u, \quad U({}_1x) = U.$$

Since $u < 1$, and since $u(x)$ is continuous on the connected set X, we can in particular choose x in such a way that every neighborhood of x in X contains points x' with $u(x') > u$. Consider the programs

$$(18) \qquad \begin{cases} {}_1x^{(\tau)} \equiv (\overbrace{x, x, \ldots, x}^{\tau \text{ components}}, {}_1x) , \\ {}_1x'^{(\tau)} \equiv (x', x', \ldots, x', {}_1x) . \end{cases}$$

Because of (15),

$$U({}_1x^{(\tau)}) = U({}_1x^{(\tau-1)}) = \ldots = U({}_1x) = U \text{ for all } \tau.$$

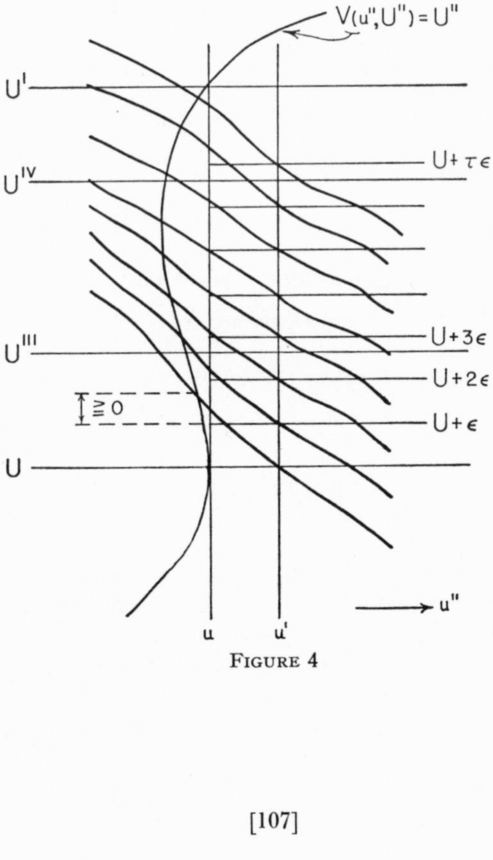

FIGURE 4

Choosing U''', U^{IV} such that $U < U''' < U^{IV} < U'$, we can therefore, because of Postulate 1, choose $\delta > 0$ such that, for all τ,

$$\sup_t |x_t' - x_t^{(\tau)}| \leqq \delta \quad \text{implies} \quad U({}_1x') \leqq U''' .$$

Choosing next x' such that $|x' - x| \leqq \delta$ and $u' \equiv u(x') > u$, we have in particular

(19) $$U({}_1x'^{(\tau)}) \leqq U''' \text{ for all } \tau.$$

Since $u' > u$ the function $V(u', U'') - V(u, U'')$ is positive. As it is also continuous, we have

$$\varepsilon' \equiv \min_{U \leqq U'' \leqq U'} (V(u', U'') - V(u, U'')) > 0 ,$$

and

$$\varepsilon \equiv \min \{\varepsilon', U' - U^{IV}\} > 0 .$$

Using, with regard to any program ${}_1x$, the notation

(20) $$\begin{cases} {}_1u \equiv u({}_1x) \equiv (u(x_1), u(x_2), \ldots) \equiv (u_1, u_2, \ldots) \\ V_\tau({}_1u; U) \equiv V(u_1, V(u_2, \ldots, V(u_\tau, U) \ldots)), \end{cases}$$

we then have, as long as $\tau\varepsilon \leqq U' - U$, and if ${}_{\text{con}}u' \equiv (u', u', \ldots)$,

$$\begin{aligned} U({}_1x'^{(\tau)}) &= V_\tau({}_{\text{con}}u'; U) = V_{\tau-1}({}_{\text{con}}u'; V(u', U)) \geqq V_{\tau-1}({}_{\text{con}}u'; V(u, U) + \varepsilon) \\ &= V_{\tau-1}({}_{\text{con}}u'; U + \varepsilon) = V_{\tau-2}({}_{\text{con}}u'; V(u', U + \varepsilon)) \geqq V_{\tau-2}({}_{\text{con}}u'; V(u, U + \varepsilon) + \varepsilon) \\ &\geqq V_{\tau-2}({}_{\text{con}}u'; U + 2\varepsilon) \geqq \ldots \geqq V(u', U + (\tau - 1)\varepsilon) \geqq U + \tau\varepsilon. \end{aligned}$$

But then we can choose τ such that $U + \tau\varepsilon \leqq U'$ but

$$U({}_1x'^{(\tau)}) \geqq U + \tau\varepsilon \geqq U^{IV} ,$$

a contradiction of (19) which thereby proves Lemma 1. The reasoning is illustrated in Figure 4, where the locus $\{(u'', U'') \mid V(u'', U'') = U''\}$ is drawn in a manner proved impossible in Lemma 1.

Symmetrically, we have

LEMMA 1b. *Let $u \in I_u$, $U \in I_U$ satisfy* (15) *with $u > 0$. Then there exists no $U' \in I_U$ such that $U' < U$ and*

$$V(u, U'') - U'' \leqq 0 \textit{ for all } U'' \textit{ such that } U' \leqq U'' < U .$$

We can now prove, if $\bar{I}_u$ denotes the closure of I_u,

LEMMA 2. *Let $u \in I_u$, $U \in I_U$ satisfy* (15) *with* $0 < u < 1$. *Then*

(21) $V(u', U') - U' < 0$ *for all* $u' \in \bar{I}_u$, $U' \in I_U$ *with* $u' \leqq u$, $U' \geqq U$, *except* $(u', U') = (u, U)$.

(22) $V(u', U') - U' > 0$ *for all* $u' \in \bar{I}_u$, $U' \in I_U$ *with* $u' \geqq u$, $U' \leqq U$, *except* $(u', U') = (u, U)$.

PROOF (see Figure 5). We first prove (21) with $u' = u$ by considering its negation. This says that there exists $U'' \in I_U$ with $U'' > U$ such that $V(u, U'') - U'' \geqq 0$. But this implies by Lemma 1a that there exists U''' with $U < U''' < U''$ such that $V(u, U''') - U''' < 0$, and by the continuity of $V(u, U') - U'$ with respect to U' that there exists a U^{IV} with $U''' < U^{IV} \leqq U''$ such that $V(u, U^{IV}) - U^{IV} = 0$ and $V(u, U') - U' < 0$ for $U''' \leqq U' < U^{IV}$. Inserting U^{IV} for U and U''' for U' in Lemma 1b we find these statements in contradiction with Lemma 1b. This proves (21) with $u' = u$. The remaining cases with $u' < u$, $U' \geqq U$ follow from the increasing property of $V(u', U')$ with respect to u'. The proof of (22) is symmetric to that of (21).

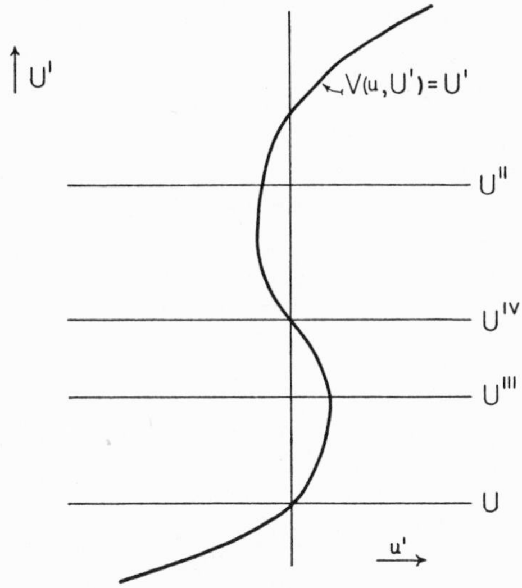

FIGURE 5

Since we know already that there exists for each $u \in I_u$ at least one corresponding U, it follows from Lemma 2 that if $0 < u < 1$ there exists precisely one, to be denoted $W(u)$, and that $W(u)$ increases with u. Moreover, if for $0 < u < 1$ we had

$$W(u) < \lim_{u' \to u+0} W(u') \equiv W(u+0)$$

the continuity of $V(u, U)$ would entail the existence of two different prospective utility levels, $W(u)$ and $W(u+0)$, corresponding to the immediate utility level u, contrary to Lemma 2. Hence $W(u)$ is continuous for $0 < u < 1$, and, since $0 \leqq W(u) \leqq 1$, can be extended by

$$W(0) \equiv \lim_{u \to 0} W(u), \quad W(1) \equiv \lim_{u \to 1} W(u)$$

so as to make $W(u)$ continuous and increasing for $0 \leqq u \leqq 1$.

Now if $0 \in I_U$ and hence $0 \in I_u$, we must have $W(0) = 0$, because $W(0) > 0$ would create a contradiction between (14) and Lemma 1a (with 0 substituted for U, and $W(0)$ for U'), since $V(0, U'') - U'' < 0$ for any U'' such that $0 < U'' \leqq W(0)$ is precluded by Lemma 2 and the continuity of $V(u, U'')$ with respect to u. Similar reasoning for the case $1 \in I_u$ completes the proof of (17).

10. EQUIVALENT CONSTANT PROGRAM

Now that the correspondence of utility levels u, U has been shown to be one-to-one and reversible, another interpretation is available. Given an aggregate utility level U, find the corresponding immediate utility u, and a one-period consumption vector x for which it is attained, $u(x) = u$. Then we can reinterpret (16) to mean that the program ${}_{\text{con}}x$ obtained by indefinite repetition of the vector x again has the given aggregate utility $U({}_{\text{con}}x) = U$. The correspondence (17) therefore gives us a means to associate with any program a constant program of the same aggregate utility.

10*. If Postulate 5 is not assumed, the possibility exists of a program ${}_1x$ with successive one-period utility levels $u(x_t)$ increasing (or decreasing) with t in such a way that no equivalent constant program and no compensation for a postponement of ${}_1x$ by one period exist.

11. EQUATING CORRESPONDING UTILITY LEVELS

The correspondence function $W(u)$ can be used to change the scale of one of the two utility types, for instance of u, in such a way as to equate corresponding utility levels. The appropriate increasing transformation is defined by

$$u^*(x) \equiv W(u(x)), \quad U^*({}_1x) \equiv U({}_1x), \qquad (23)$$
$$V^*(u^*, U^*) \equiv V(W^{-1}(u^*), U^*),$$

where $u = W^{-1}(u^*)$ is the inverse of $u^* = W(u)$. If now u^* and U^* represent corresponding utility levels on the new scales, we have

$$0 = V^*(u^*, U^*) - U^* = V(W^{-1}(u^*), U) - U,$$

and hence, by the definition of $W(u)$,

$$U^* = U = W(W^{-1}(u^*)) = u^*.$$

Hence the new correspondence function $U^* = W^*(u^*)$ is simply the identity $U^* = u^*$, represented in the new form of Figure 3 by the diagonal connecting (0,0) with (1,1). Although this change of scale is not essential for any of the reasoning that follows, we shall make it in order to simplify formulae and diagrams. Dropping asterisks again, the correspondence relation (15) now takes the form

$$V(U, U) = U. \qquad (24)$$

12. REPEATING PROGRAMS

A program in which a given sequence ${}_1x_\tau$ of τ one-period vectors $x_1, x_2, \ldots, x_\tau$ is repeated indefinitely will be called a *repeating program*, to be denoted

$${}_{\text{rep}}x_\tau \equiv ({}_1x_\tau, {}_1x_\tau, \ldots).$$

The sequence ${}_1x_\tau$ will be called the *pattern* of the repeating program, τ its *span*, provided no $\tau' < \tau$ exists permitting the same form. We shall use the notation

$$_{\text{rep}}u_\tau \equiv ({}_1u_\tau, {}_1u_\tau, \ldots),$$
$$_1u_\tau \equiv u_\tau\,({}_1x_\tau) \equiv (u(x_1), \ldots, u(x_\tau)) \equiv (u_1, \ldots, u_\tau)$$

for the corresponding sequences of one-period utility levels, and call ${}_1u_\tau$ the *utility pattern* corresponding to ${}_1x_\tau$. The function

(25) $$V_\tau({}_1u_\tau; U) \equiv V(u_1, V(u_2, \ldots, V(u_\tau, U) \ldots))$$

then indicates how the utility level U of any program is modified if that program is postponed by τ periods and a pattern with the corresponding utility pattern ${}_1u_\tau$ is inserted to precede it.

Given a utility pattern ${}_1u_\tau = u_\tau({}_1x_\tau)$, we can now ask whether there is a utility level U which is not affected by such a postponement,

(26) $$V_\tau({}_1u_\tau; U) = U.$$

Obviously, the utility level

(27) $$U = U({}_{\text{rep}}x_\tau)$$

meets this requirement, because the program ${}_{\text{rep}}x_\tau$ itself is not modified by such postponement. By an analysis entirely analogous to that already given for the case $\tau = 1$, one can show that this utility level is unique and hence is a function

(28) $$U = W_\tau({}_1u_\tau)$$

of the utility pattern. This function is a *generalized correspondence function.* One can interpret it either as the aggregate utility of any program, the postponement of which by τ periods can just be compensated by insertion of a sequence ${}_1x_\tau$ with $u_\tau({}_1x_\tau) = {}_1u_\tau$, or as the aggregate utility of the repeating program ${}_{\text{rep}}({}_1x_\tau)$, where again $u_\tau({}_1x_\tau) = {}_1u_\tau$. As before, one can show that $W({}_1u_\tau)$ is continuous and increasing with respect to each of the variables $u_1, \ldots, u_\tau$. Finally, as before in the case $\tau = 1$,

(29) $$U \begin{Bmatrix} < \\ = \\ > \end{Bmatrix} V_\tau({}_1u_\tau; U) \begin{Bmatrix} < \\ = \\ > \end{Bmatrix} W_\tau({}_1u_\tau) \text{ if } U \begin{Bmatrix} < \\ = \\ > \end{Bmatrix} W_\tau({}_1u_\tau).$$

12*. The uniqueness of the solution of (26) and the first set of inequalities in (29) are proved by having an arbitrary one of the variables $u_1, \ldots, u_\tau$ play the role performed by u in Section 9*. To prove continuity and monotonicity of $W_\tau({}_1u_\tau)$, that role is assigned successively to each of these variables. The second set of inequalities in (29) then follows from (26), (28) and the fact that $V_\tau(u_\tau; U)$ increases with U.

To obtain one further interesting result we revert to the notation (20). By repeated application of (29) we have, for $n = 1, 2, \ldots,$

(30) $$U'' < U = W_\tau({}_1u_\tau) < U' \text{ implies}$$
$$V_{n\tau}({}_{\text{rep}}u_\tau; U'') < V_{n\tau}({}_{\text{rep}}u_\tau; U) = U < V_{n\tau}({}_{\text{rep}}u_\tau; U'),$$

where $V_{n\tau}({}_{\text{rep}}u_\tau,\ U''')$ is increasing with n if $U''' < U$, decreasing if $U''' > U$. It follows that

(31) $$\lim_{n\to\infty} V_{n\tau}({}_{\text{rep}}u_\tau;\ U''')$$

exists for all $U''' \in I_U$. But for any such U''' insertion of (31) for U in (26) satisfies that condition, which we know to be satisfied by U only. Hence, by (28),

(32) $$\lim_{n\to\infty} V_{n\tau}({}_{\text{rep}}u_\tau;\ U''') \equiv V_\infty({}_{\text{rep}}u_\tau) = W_\tau({}_1u_\tau) \quad \text{for all} \quad U''' \in I_U.$$

13. ALTERNATING PROGRAMS AND IMPATIENCE

A repeating program with a span $\tau = 2$ will be called an *alternating program*. Its one-period utility sequence alternates between two different levels, u' and u'', say, which we shall always choose such that

(33) $$u' > u''.$$

If we write $w' \equiv (u', u'')$, $w'' \equiv (u'', u')$ for the two possible utility patterns, the two possible alternating programs have the respective utility sequences

(34) $$\begin{cases} (34') & {}_{\text{rep}}w' \equiv (u', u'', u', u'', \ldots), \\ (34'') & {}_{\text{rep}}w'' \equiv (u'', u', u'', u', \ldots). \end{cases}$$

The implications of the preceding analysis for this type of program are illustrated in Figure 6. The aggregate utility level U' corresponding to (34′),

(35) $$U' \equiv W_2(w'),$$

satisfies the condition

(36) $$\Phi'(U') \equiv V(u', V(u'', U')) - U' = 0.$$

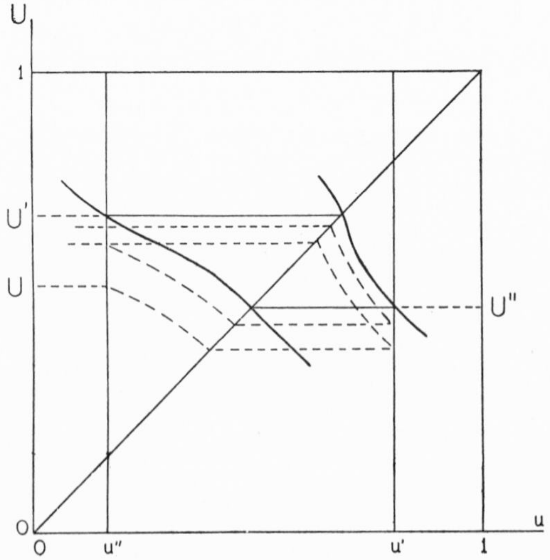

FIGURE 6

Hence U' can be read off, as indicated in Figure 6, from a quadrilateral consisting of two horizontals and two niveau lines (drawn solid), with two vertices on the diagonal of the unit square, the other two vertices on the verticals at $u = u'$ and $u = u''$, respectively. Enlarging on (36), we also have from (29)

$$(37)\qquad 0\begin{Bmatrix}\leq\\=\\>\end{Bmatrix}\Phi'(U) \equiv V(u', V(u'', U)) - U\begin{Bmatrix}\leq\\=\\>\end{Bmatrix}U' - U \text{ if } U\begin{Bmatrix}\geqq\\\leqq\\=\end{Bmatrix}U' .$$

Hence, for any program with an aggregate utility $U \neq U'$, postponement by two periods with insertion of the utility pattern (u', u'') in the first two periods thereby vacated will bring the aggregate utility closer to U', without overshooting. By (32), indefinite repetition of this operation will make the aggregate utility approach U' as a limit (see dotted lines for a case with $U < U'$). Symmetrically to (37), we have

$$(38)\qquad 0\begin{Bmatrix}\leq\\=\\>\end{Bmatrix}\Phi''(U) \equiv V(u'', V(u', U)) - U\begin{Bmatrix}\leq\\=\\>\end{Bmatrix}U'' - U \text{ if } U\begin{Bmatrix}\leq\\=\\>\end{Bmatrix}U'' ,$$

with similar interpretations, and where U'' is related to U', u'' and u' by

$$(39)\qquad u'' < U'' = V(u'', U') < U' = V(u', U'') < u' ,$$

as indicated in Figure 6, and proved in detail below.

We are now ready to draw inferences about the presence of impatience in certain parts of the utility space. The functions $\Phi'(U)$ and $\Phi''(U)$ introduced in (37) and (38) are related to the criterion of impatience by

$$(40)\qquad \Phi(U) \equiv \Phi'(U) - \Phi''(U) = V(u', V(u'', U)) - V(u'', V(u', U)) .$$

Since $u' > u''$, impatience is present whenever $\Phi(U) > 0$. Reference to (37) and (38), or to Figure 7 in which the implications of (37) and (38)

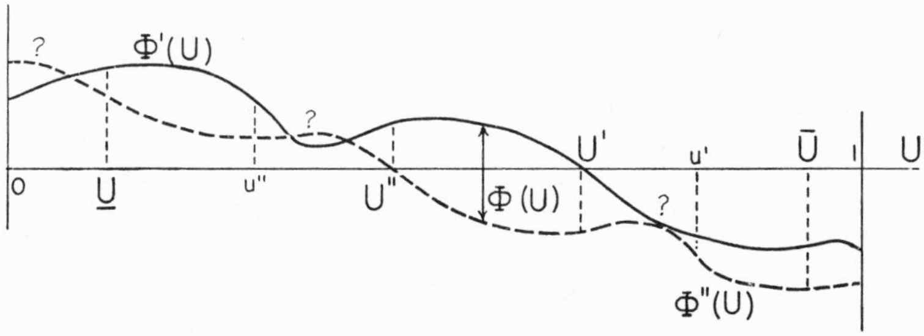

FIGURE 7

are exhibited, shows that, since $\Phi'(U) > 0$ for $0 \leqq U < U'$ and $\Phi''(U) < 0$ for $U'' < U \leqq 1$, we have

$$(41)\qquad \Phi(U) > 0 \text{ for } U'' \leqq U \leqq U'.$$

This proves the presence of impatience in a central zone of the space of the utility triples (u', u'', U), as illustrated in Figure 8. It is to be noted that the result (41) is obtained as long as the two marked points do not fall on the same side of the horizontal at U. This is the case precisely if $U'' \leqq U \leqq U'$.

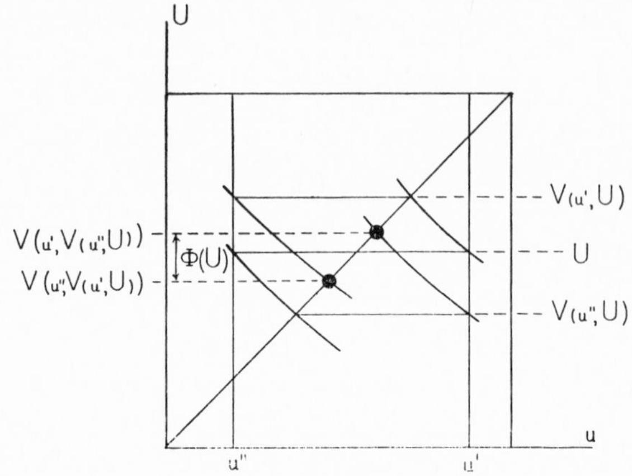

FIGURE 8

Two other zones can be added to this one, on the basis of the monotonicity of $V(u, U)$ with respect to U. If we define $\underline{U}$, $\bar{U}$ by

(42) $$V(u', \underline{U}) = u'', \quad V(u'', \bar{U}) = u',$$

if solutions of these equations exist, and by $\underline{U} = 0$, and/or $\bar{U} = 1$ otherwise, Figure 9 suggests that

(43) $$\Phi(U) > 0 \text{ for } \underline{U} \leqq U \leqq u'' \text{ and for } u' \leqq U \leqq \bar{U}.$$

A detailed proof is given below.

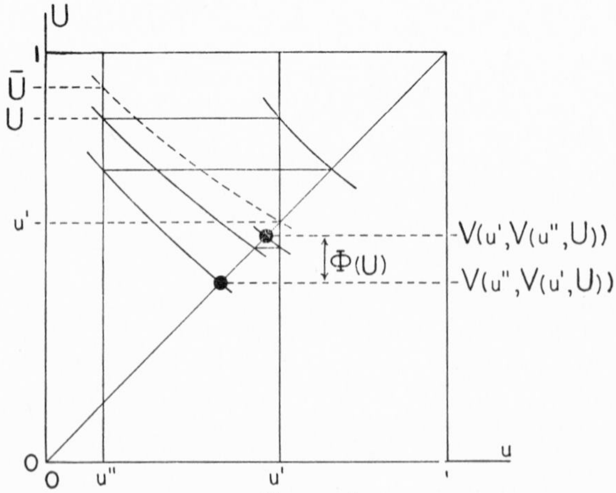

FIGURE 9

There are indications that in the intermediate zones, $u'' < U < U''$ and $U' < U < u'$, impatience is the general rule, neutrality toward timing a conceivable exception. The behavior of $\Phi(U)$ in these zones will not be analyzed further in this paper, in the hope that an argument simpler than that which has furnished these indications may still be found.

For the sake of generality of expression, we shall state the present results in a form that does not presuppose the, convenient but inessential, transformation introduced in Section 11 to equate corresponding utility levels.

THEOREM 1. *If Postulates* 1, 2, 3, 4, *and* 5 *are satisfied, a program* ${}_1x$ *with first- and second-period utilities* $u_1 = u(x_1)$ *and* $u_2 = u(x_2)$ *such that* $u_1 > u_2$ *and with prospective utility as-from-the-third-period* $U_3 = U({}_3x)$ *meets the condition* (40) *of impatience in each of the following three zones:*

(*a*) *If* U_3 *equals or exceeds the utility of a constant program indefinitely repeating the vector* x_1, *provided* U_3 *is not so high (if that should be possible) that the utility of the program* $(x_2, {}_3x)$ *exceeds that of the constant program* $(x_1, x_1, x_1, \ldots)$;

(*b*) *If* U_3 *equals the utility of either of the alternating programs*

$$(x_1, x_2, x_1, x_2, \ldots)$$
$$(x_2, x_1, x_2, x_1, \ldots)$$

or falls between these two utility levels;

(*c*) *If* U_3 *equals or falls below the utility of the constant program* $(x_2, x_2, x_2, \ldots)$, *provided* U_3 *is not so low (if that should be possible) that the utility of the program* $(x_1, {}_3x)$ *falls below that of the constant program* $(x_2, x_2, x_2, \ldots)$.

This is, in a way, a surprising result. The phenomenon of impatience was introduced by Böhm-Bawerk as a psychological characteristic of human economic preference in decisions concerning (presumably) a *finite* time horizon. It now appears that impatience, at least in one central and two outlying zones of the space of programs, is also a necessary logical consequence of more elementary properties of a utility function of programs with an *infinite* time horizon: continuity (uniform on each equivalence class), sensitivity, aggregation by periods, independence of calendar time (stationarity), and the existence of extreme programs.

13*. PROOF. In order to prove relations (39) and (43) on which Theorem 1 depends, without reference to a diagram, we lift from the already proved state ments (37) and (38) the defining relations

(44″) and (44′) $\quad V(u'', V(u', U'')) = U'', \quad V(u', V(u'', U')) = U',$

of U'' and U', respectively. From (44′) we read that $V(u'', V(u', V(u'', U'))) = V(u'', U')$, showing that $V(u'', U')$ satisfies the defining relation (44″) of U''.

This, and an argument symmetric to it, establish the equalities in (39). Now assume first that $U'' < U'$. In that case, because $V(u, U)$ increases with U,

$$0 = V(u', U'') - U' < V(u', U') - U' ,$$

whence $U' < u'$ by Lemma 2, since $V(u', u') - u' = 0$. By similar reasoning, $U'' > u''$, establishing the inequalities in (39) for the present case. But the same reasoning applied to the assumption $U'' \geqq U'$ would entail $u'' \geqq U'' \geqq U' \geqq u'$, which is contradicted by the datum that $u' > u''$. This completes the proof of (39).

To prove (43) we note that, given u', u'' with $u' > u''$,

$$\text{if} \begin{Bmatrix} U = u' \\ u' < U < \bar{U} \\ U = \bar{U} \end{Bmatrix} \text{then } V(u', U) \begin{Bmatrix} = \\ < \\ < \end{Bmatrix} U, \text{and } V(u'', V(u', U)) \begin{Bmatrix} = \\ < \\ < \end{Bmatrix} V(u'', U) \begin{Bmatrix} < \\ < \\ = \end{Bmatrix} u' ,$$

using in succession (24), Lemma 2, the monotonicity of $V(u, U)$ with respect to U, and (42). But then also

$$V(u', V(u'', U)) \begin{Bmatrix} > \\ > \\ = \end{Bmatrix} V(u'', U) ,$$

using again (24) and Lemma 2. A comparison of these results establishes (43).

The forms here given to the proofs of (39) and (43) have been chosen so that they may carry over by mere reinterpretation to a more general case to be considered in a later paper.

14. PERIOD INDEPENDENCE

It might seem only a small additional step if to Postulate 3 we add[7]

POSTULATE 3′ (3′a *and* 3′b). *For all* $x_1, x_2, {}_3x, x_1', x_2', {}_3x'$,

(3′a) $U(x_1, x_2, {}_3x) \geqq U(x_1', x_2', {}_3x)$ *implies* $U(x_1, x_2, {}_3x') \geqq U(x_1', x_2', {}_3x')$,

(3′b) $U(x_1, x_2, {}_3x) \geqq U(x_1', x_2, {}_3x')$ *implies* $U(x_1, x_2', {}_3x) \geqq U(x_1', x_2', {}_3x')$.

In fact, it follows from a result of Debreu [**2**], that this would have quite drastic implications. Postulates 1—5 and 3′ together satisfy the premises of a theorem[8] which, translated in our notation and terminology, says that one can find a monotonic transformation of $U({}_1x)$ such that

$$U({}_1x) = u_1(x_1) + u_2(x_2) + U_3({}_3x) . \tag{46}$$

Taken in combination with the stationarity Postulate 4, this would leave only the possibility that

$$U({}_1x) = \sum_{t=1}^{\infty} \alpha^{t-1} u(x_t), \quad 0 < \alpha < 1 , \tag{47}$$

[7] A postulate very similar to Postulate 3′ is contained in an unpublished memorandum, kindly made available to me by Robert Strotz in 1958.

[8] l.c., Section 3.

that is, aggregate utility is a discounted sum of all future one-period utilities, with a constant discount factor α. This form has been used extensively in the literature.[9] Since the form (47) is destroyed by any other transformations than increasing linear ones, one can look on Postulate 3′ (as Debreu does) as a basis (in conjunction with the other postulates) for defining a *cardinal* utility function (47). While this in itself is not objectionable, the constant discount rate seems too rigid to describe important aspects of choice over time. If for the sake of argument we assume that the aggregator function $V(u, U)$ is differentiable, it is shown below that the *discount factor*

$$\left(\frac{\partial V(u, U)}{\partial U}\right)_{U=u} \tag{48}$$

is invariant for differentiable monotonic transformations. Obviously, it can take different values for different common values of $U = u$. The main purpose of the system of postulates of this paper therefore is to clarify behavior assumptions that will permit the relative weight given to the future as against the present to vary with the level of all-over satisfaction attained —a consideration which can already be found in the work of Irving Fisher [**4**].

14*. To prove the invariance of (48), we observe that the increasing transformations of V, u, U that preserve (24) are of the type

$$u^*(x_1) \equiv f(u(x_1)), \quad U^*({}_2x) \equiv f(U({}_2x)), \quad f(0) = 0, \quad f(1) = 1,$$
$$V^*(u^*, U^*) = f(V(f^{-1}(u^*), f^{-1}(U^*))).$$

But then, for so related values of u^*, U^*, u, U,

$$\frac{\partial V^*(u^*, U^*)}{\partial U^*} = \left(\frac{df(U')}{dU'}\right)_{U'=V(u,U)} \cdot \frac{\partial V(u, U)}{\partial U} \cdot \left(\frac{df^{-1}(U^*)}{dU^*}\right)_{U^*=f(U)}$$

If $u = U$, then, $U' = U$, and the first and third factors of the right hand member are reciprocals, hence cancel.

It should finally be noted that Postulates 3′a and 3′b are not counterparts to each other in the way in which Postulates 3a and 3b are counterparts. The respective counterparts, in that sense, to Postulates 3′a and 3′b are implied in Postulates 1—5, and hence do not need restatement.

Cowles Foundation for Research in Economics at Yale University

[9] See, for instance, Ramsay [**6**], Samuelson and Solow [**7**], Strotz [**8**]. The first two publications find a way to make $\alpha = 1$.

REFERENCES

[1] Böhm-Bawerk, E. von: *Positive Theorie des Kapitals*, Dritte Auflage, 1912, especially Buch IV, Abschnitt I, Gegenwart und Zukunft in der Wirtschaft, pp. 426–486, English Translation in *Capital and Interest*, Vol. II, *Positive Theory of Capital*, Book IV, Section I, pp. 257-289, South Holland, Illinois, 1959.

[2] Debreu, G.: "Topological Methods in Cardinal Utility Theory," Cowles Foundation Discussion Paper No. 76, to appear in *Mathematical Methods in the Social Sciences*, Stanford: Stanford University Press, 1960.

[3] ———: "Representation of a Preference Ordering by a Numerical Function," Chapter XI of Thrall, Coombs and Davis, eds., *Decision Processes*, New York: Wiley, 1954, pp. 159–165.

[4] Fisher, Irving: *The Theory of Interest*, New York: Macmillan, 1930, Chapter IV, especially §§ 3 and 6.

[5] Frisch, R.: *Sur un problème d'économie pure*, Norsk Matematisk Forenings Skrifter, Serie I, No. 16, Oslo, 1926, 40 pp.

[6] Ramsay, F. P.: "A Mathematical Theory of Saving," *Economic Journal*, December, 1928, pp. 543–559.

[7] Samuelson, P. A., and Solow, R.: "A Complete Capital Model Involving Heterogeneous Capital Goods," *Quarterly Journal of Economics*, November, 1956, pp. 537–562.

[8] Strotz, R. H. : "Myopia and Inconsistency in Dynamic Utility Maximization," *Review of Economic Studies*, XXIII, 3 (1957), pp. 165–180.

[9] Taylor, A. E.: *Functional Analysis*, New York, 1958.

[10] Wold, H.: "A Synthesis of Pure Demand Analysis, Part II," *Skandinavisk Aktuaritidskrift*, 26, 1943, pp. 220–263.

Note added in reprinting: The findings of the present paper have been extended by Koopmans, Diamond and Williamson in "Stationary Utility and Time Perspective," *Econometrica*, Jan.-April 1964, by means of the following "time perspective" property: There exist utility scales in which $U' > U$ implies $V(u,U') - V(u,U) \leqq U' - U$. This "quasicardinal" property of the utility function was used to prove a weak impatience inequality ($\Phi(U) \geqq 0$) for the intervals $u'' < U < U''$ and $U' < U < u'$, filling the gaps in Theorem 1. In that paper the space X in Postulate 1 was required to be convex and bounded, to make up for an error in the paragraph in Section 5* above beginning with "By similar reasoning," pointed out by R. Levitan.

PART II

Classical and Neo-Classical Growth Models

6

A MATHEMATICAL FORMULATION OF THE RICARDIAN SYSTEM*

By L. L. Pasinetti

Since his own time, David Ricardo has always occupied a privileged place among economists, even in periods when economic analysis has been developing along paths very different from the ones he pursued. It has never been easy, however, for Ricardo's many interpreters, to state his complete system in a rigorous and concise form, and the reason lies in the peculiarity of some of the concepts he used which are not always defined in an unambiguous way. These concepts have encountered strong criticisms almost at any time, while—on the other hand—the bold analyses they made possible were exerting a sort of fascinating attraction.

In this paper, criticism is left aside and the more constructive approach is taken of stating explicitly the assumptions needed in order to eliminate the ambiguities. Then, the Ricardian system is shown to be very neat and even suitable for a mathematical formulation, with all the well-known advantages of conciseness, rigour and clarity. The task is undertaken in sections 4 to 9, which form the main part of the paper (part II). To avoid digressions and lengthy references there, the difficulties Ricardo was faced with, and the basic features of his theories, are briefly reviewed in the first three introductory sections (part I).

I

1. Theory of Value

The theory of value represents the most toilsome part of Ricardo's theoretical system and in our mathematical formulation it will entail the crudest assumptions. At the time it was put forward, the theory soon became the main target of the criticisms, which Ricardo tried to answer by re-writing twice (in the second and in the third edition) the chapter 'on value' of his *Principles*.[1] No fundamental change was introduced, however, and the three versions represent different ways of framing (in the light of the criticisms) a theory of value which remains essentially the same[2].

* I am grateful to Mr. Kaldor, Prof. Modigliani and Mr. Sraffa for comments and criticism, and to Dr. James Message for a most helpful suggestion in the third section of the appendix.

[1] David Ricardo, *On the Principles of Political Economy and Taxation* (cit. as *Principles*). All references to Ricardo's works in this paper refer to the edition prepared by Piero Sraffa, *The Works and Correspondence of David Ricardo*, in 10 volumes, Cambridge University Press, 1951, (cit. as *Works*).

[2] This is a view to which recently Mr. Sraffa has given full support (*Works*, vol. I, Introduction, pp. XXXVII and ff.). Fragments of an early version of the Ricardian theory of value can be traced in Ricardo's early writings and in some letters (see the evidence given by Mr. Sraffa, *Works*, p. XXXI). It seems that Ricardo tried at the beginning to measure the relevant variables of his system in terms of a main agricultural commodity, namely corn, claiming that this commodity has the property of being both the capital and the product and, therefore, makes it possible to determine the ratio of profit to capital in physical terms without any question of evaluation. This position was, however, very vulnerable and will not be considered in this paper, as Ricardo abandoned it long before writing the *Principles.*

The theory is fundamentally based on the cost of production measured in terms of quantity of labour. Utility[1] is considered to be absolutely essential to, but not a measure of, exchangeable value. To commodities which derive their value from " scarcity alone "[2] (e.g., rare paintings) only a few words are devoted—they are not considered relevant for economic analysis ; Ricardo is concerned only with commodities which are the outcome of a process of production. He begins by restating Adam Smith's proposition that " in the early stages of society, the exchangeable value of commodities . . . depends . . . on the comparative quantity of labour expended on each ".[3] Then, he takes a new and striking step by asserting that *the mentioned proposition is valid in general* and not only in the early stages of society, as Smith claimed. His argument may be roughly expressed in the following way. Suppose two commodities, *A* and *B*, the first of which requires the work of one worker for one year to be produced and the second the work of two workers for one year (the capital employed being just the amount of wages to be anticipated to the workers). Whatever the rate of profit may be, either 10% or 20% or 30%, its amount on the second commodity always is twice as much as on the first commodity ; hence the relative price of the two goods always comes out as equal to the ratio of the quantities of labour required to obtain each of them.[4] If a " commodity could be found, which now and at all times required precisely the same quantity of labour to produce it, that commodity would be of an unvarying value "[5]: it would be an *invariable standard* in terms of which the value of all commodities could be expressed.

This formulation of the theory, of course, did not remain unchallenged. Strong objections were immediately raised (by Malthus, McCulloch, Torrens and others) which may be summarised as follows. Let us suppose, returning to the mentioned example, that the production of commodity *B* requires the work of one worker for two years instead of the work of two workers for one year. In this case, Ricardo's principle no longer applies because, owing to the profits becoming themselves capital at the end of the first year, a change in the rate of profit *does* imply a change in the relative price of the two commodities, even though the relative quantities of labour required by them remain the same. Ricardo could not ignore these objections and already in the first edition of the *Principles* he allowed for some exceptions to his general rule. All exceptions—as he later explained in a letter—" come under one of time ",[6] but he preferred discussing them, in the third edition of the *Principles*, under three groups (i. different proportions of fixed and circulating capital, ii. unequal durability of fixed capital, iii. unequal rapidity with which the circulating capital returns to its employer). However, while allowing for exceptions, Ricardo kept the fundamentals of his theory and tried to overcome the objections by appealing to the order of magnitude of the deviations caused by the exceptions, which he considered as responsible only for minor departures from his general rule. In the previous example, for instance, the modification introduced by the possibility that the same quantity of labour on *B* might be employed in one year or in two different years amounts simply to the effects caused by the amount of profit to be calculated on the wages of the first year. Ricardo holds that this is a difference of minor importance.[7] Therefore, the conclusion is,

[1] Needless to say, the term " utility " has for Ricardo, and in general for the Classics, a different meaning than for us to-day. It simply refers to the " value in use " of a commodity as opposed to its " value in exchange ". See *Principles*, p. 11.

[2] *Principles*, p. 12.

[3] *Principles*, p. 12.

[4] *Principles*, pp. 24 and ff.

[5] *Principles*, version of editions 1 and 2, see p. 17, footnote 3.

[6] Letter to McCulloch, *Works*, vol. VIII, p. 193.

[7] *Principles*, pp. 36 and ff.

the theory of value as stated in terms of quantities of labour, and independently of the distribution of commodities among the classes of the society, does hold, if not exactly, at least as a very good approximation.[1] With this premise, Ricardo considers as " the principal problem of Political Economy " that of determining " the laws which regulate the distribution ".[2]

2. Theory of Distribution

The participants in the process of production are grouped by Ricardo in three classes: landlords who provide land, capitalists[3] who provide capital and workers who provide labour. Total production is entirely determined by technical conditions but its division among the three classes—under the form of rent, profit and wages—is determined by the inter-action of many technical, economic and demographic factors. All Ricardo's analysis on this subject refers to what he calls the *natural* prices of rent, profits and wages. Divergencies of market prices from their natural level are considered only as temporary and unimportant deviations.

Rent, namely " that portion of the produce of the earth which is paid to the landlords for the use of the original and indistructible power of the soil "[4] is determined by technical factors. The technical property that different pieces of land have different fertility and that successive applications of labour to the same quantity of land yield smaller and smaller amounts of product (law of diminishing marginal returns) makes of rent a *net gain* for the landlords. Therefore, rent does not enter Ricardo's theory of value—it is a deduction from the total product. The value of commodities is determined by the quantity of labour employed on the marginal portion of land—that portion of land which yields no rent.

Wages are not related to the contribution of labour to the process of production, as in the modern theories they normally are. Like all economists of his time, Ricardo relates the level of wages to the physiological necessity of workers and their families to live and reproduce themselves. He is convinced that in any particular state of society there exists a *real* wage-rate (so to speak, a certain *basket of goods*) which can be considered as the " natural price of labour ". It need not necessarily be at a strict *subsistence level*[5] (the minimum physiological necessities of life) ; but at that level which in a given country and in a given state of society, besides allowing workers to live, induces them to perpetuate themselves " without either increase or diminution ".[6] When capitalists

[1] With the acceptance of criticisms between the first and the third edition of the Principles, also the choice of a " standard of value " became more difficult. Ricardo reacted to the complication by changing his definitions. In the first edition of the *Principles* he regarded as " standard " a commodity which would require at any time the same amount of unassisted labour (unassisted by capital) ; in the third edition he mentions a " commodity produced with such proportions of the two kinds of capital (fixed and circulating) as approach nearest to the average quantity employed in the production of most commodities ". (*Principles*, p. 63 and p. 45; see also *Works*, Introduction by Mr. Sraffa, vol. I, p. XLII and ff.). Ricardo considered one year a good average and thought that perhaps gold could be the commodity that most closely approaches the requirement of an *invariable standard.* (*Principles*, p. 45.)

[2] *Principles*, p. 5.

[3] Ricardo calls them alternatively " farmers " or " manufacturers " according as he refers to agricultural or to industrial capitalists.

[4] *Principles*, p. 67.

[5] " The natural price of labour—Ricardo says—varies at different times, in the same country, and very materially differs in different countries . . . it essentially depends on the habits and customs of the people . . . Many of the conveniences—Ricardo adds—now enjoyed in an English cottage would have been thought luxuries in an earlier period of our history ". (*Principles*, pp. 96-97).

[6] *Principles*, p. 93.

accumulate capital, demand for labour increases and the market wage-rate rises above its natural level. However, Ricardo believes that such a situation cannot be other than a temporary one because, as the conditions of workers become " flourishing and happy ", they " rear a healthy and numerous family "[1] and the growth of population again brings back the real wage-rate to its *natural* level. It is very impressive to notice how strongly Ricardo is convinced of the operation of this mechanism. To be precise, he always speaks of a process which will operate " ultimately " but the emphasis on it is so strong that his analysis is always carried on *as if* the response were almost immediate.

Profits, finally, represent a residual. Rent being determined by the produce of the marginal land put into cultivation, and the wage rate by non-economic factors, what remains of the total production is retained, under the form of profit, by the capitalists, who are the organizers of the process of production. The capitalists are assumed to be always intent on moving their capital towards any sector of the economy that shows a tendency to yield a rate of profit above the average. This behaviour ensures the equalization of the rate of profit (after risk) all over the economy.

3. Theory of Economic Growth

Economic growth is brought about essentially by the capitalists. The three classes in which Ricardo divides the society have different peculiar characteristics. Landlords are considered as an " unproductive class "[2] of wealthy people who become richer and richer, and consume almost all their incomes in *luxury goods*. Workers also consume everything they get but in a different kind of goods—" necessaries "—in order to live. Capitalists, on the other hand, are the *entrepreneurs* of the system. They represent the " productive class "[2] of the society. Very thrifty, they consume a small amount of what they obtain and devote their profits to capital accumulation.

The process of transforming profits into capital, however, cannot go on indefinitely. Owing to the decreasing marginal returns of new capital (and labour) applied to the same quantity of land, or to less fertile lands, rent increases over time, in real and in money terms, the *money* wage-rate increases too[3], and consequently the profit rate continuously falls.[4] When the rate of profit has fallen to zero, capitalists are prevented from accumulating any more ; the growth process stops and the system reaches a *stationary state*. As a matter of fact—Ricardo adds—the stationary state will be reached *before* the extreme point where all profits have disappeared because, at a certain minimum rate of profit, the capitalists will lose any inducement to accumulate. The final outcome (the stationary state) is postponed in time by new inventions and discoveries which increase the productivity of labour, but it is Ricardo's opinion that it will eventually be attained.

II

4. The " Natural " Equilibrium in a Two-Commodities System

It has been mentioned that Ricardo distinguishes two groups of commodities produced in the economy : " necessaries "—or, we may call them wage-goods—and " luxuries ". The most simple Ricardian system we can conceive of is, therefore, one where each of the two groups is reduced to one commodity. Let us begin with this case and make the following assumptions :

[1] *Principles*, p. 94.
[2] *Principles*, p. 270.
[3] How this happens will appear very clearly in the mathematical treatment of the following sections.
[4] *Principles*, especially chapters VI and XXI.

(i) the system produces only one type of wage-good, let us call it corn ;

(ii) to produce corn, it takes exactly one year ;

(iii) capital consists entirely of the wage bill ; in other words, it is only circulating capital, which takes one year to be re-integrated ;

(iv) there does exist an invariable standard of value, namely a commodity, let us call it gold—a luxury-good—,which at any time and place always requires the same quantity of labour to be produced. Its process of production also takes one year. Prices are expressed in terms of such a commodity and the monetary unit is that quantity of gold which is produced by the labour of one worker in one year.

The Ricardian system can now be stated in terms of equations. Taking the quantity of land in existence as given and supposing that its technical characteristics (fertility and possibilities of intensive exploitation) are known, the production of corn can be expressed by a technical production function, which we may assume to be continuously differentiable :

(1) $X_1 = f(N_1)$ where : X_1 = physical quantity of corn produced in one year ;

N_1 = number of workers employed in the corn production ;

with the following properties:

(1*a*) $f(0) \geqslant 0$

(1*b*) $f'(0) > \bar{x}$ where : $\bar{x}$ = natural wage-rate in terms of corn ;

(1*c*) $f''(N_1) < 0.$

The first inequality means that when no labour is employed, land is supposed to produce either something or nothing at all (negative production is excluded). The meaning of (1*b*) is that, at least when the economic system begins to operate and workers are employed on the most fertile piece of land, they must produce more than what is strictly necessary for their support, otherwise the whole economic system would never come into existence. Finally, (1*c*) expresses the law of decreasing marginal returns.

The production function for gold is much simpler :

(2) $X_2 = \alpha N_2$ where : X_2 = physical quantity of gold produced in one year ;

N_2 = number of workers employed in the production of gold ;

α = physical quantity of gold produced by one worker in one year ($\alpha > 0$).

The following equations are self-explanatory :[1]

(3) $N = N_1 + N_2$ where : N = total number of workers ; N_1 = agricultural workers ; N_2 = workers in the gold industry ;

(4) $W = N x$ — W = total wage-bill, in terms of physical units of corn ; x = real wage-rate (corn) ;

(5) $K = W$ — K = physical stock of capital (corn) ;

(6) $R = f(N_1) - N_1 f'(N_1)$ — R = yearly rent, in real terms (corn) ;

(7) $P_1 = X_1 - R - N_1 x$ — P_1 = yearly total profits, in real terms (corn), in the corn producing sector.

All variables introduced so far are in physical terms. Turning now to the determination of values, we have

(8) $p_1 X_1 - p_1 R = N_1$ where : p_1 = price of corn ;

(9) $p_2 X_2 = N_2$ — p_2 = price of gold.

Equations (8) and (9) are very important in the Ricardian system. They state that the value of the yearly product, *after deduction of rent*, is determined by the quantity of labour required to produce it. In our case, owing to the definition of the monetary unit, the value of the product, after paying rent, is exactly equal to the number of workers employed. From (1), (2) and (6), equations (8) and (9) may be also written

$$(8a) \qquad p_1 = \frac{N_1}{X_1 - R} = \frac{1}{f'(N_1)}$$

$$(9a) \qquad p_2 = \frac{1}{\alpha}.$$

Profits in the gold industry and total profits in the economy emerge as

(10) $p_2 P_2 = p_2 X_2 - N_2 p_1 x$ where : P_2 = profits, in terms of physical units of gold, in the gold industry ;

(11) $\pi = p_1 X_1 + p_2 X_2 - p_1 R - p_1 W$ — π = total profits, in terms of the standard of value.

After substituting from (1)-(10), equation (11) may be also written

$$(11a) \quad \pi = (N_1 + N_2)(1 - x p_1).$$

[1] Equation (6) may not appear so evident as the other equations. Let me state, therefore, an alternative way of writing it. As explained in section 2, rent represents for Ricardo a *surplus*, a net gain for the owners of the more fertile lands with respect to the owners of the marginal land (the land which yields no rent). Therefore, when N_1 workers are employed on land, the resulting total rent can be expressed as a sum of all the *net gains* of the non-marginal land-owners. In analytical terms :

$$(6a) \qquad R = f(0) + \int_0^{N_1} [f'(y) - f'(N_1)]\, dy$$

where $f(0)$, from (1*a*), is the produce that the land-owners can get from land without renting it, i.e. without any labour being employed. By solving the integral appearing in (6*a*), we obtain

$$R = f(0) + f(N_1) - f(0) - N_1 f'(N_1)$$

which is exactly equation (6).

At this point, the equations contain a theory of value and a theory of distribution but not yet a theory of expenditure. Since Ricardo assumes that all incomes are spent (Say's law), to determine the composition of total expenditure only one equation is necessary in the present model, specifying the production of one of the two commodities. Then the quantity produced of the other commodity turns out to be implicitly determined, as *total* production has already been functionally specified. The Ricardian theory is very primitive on this point. Workers are supposed to spend their income on necessities (corn, in our case) capitalists on capital accumulation (corn again, in our case) and land-owners on luxuries. Hence the determining equation is [1]

(12) $p_2 X_2 = p_1 R.$

Let us also write

(13) $w = p_1 x$ where : w = monetary wage-rate ;

(14) $r = \dfrac{\pi}{p_1 K}$ r = rate of profit.

So far 16 variables have appeared : $X_1, X_2, N_1, N_2, N, W, x, K, R, P_1, P_2, \pi, p_1, p_2, w, r$, but only 14 equations. Two more equations are needed in order to determine the system. In a situation which Ricardo considers as *natural*, the following two data have to be added:

(15) $x = \bar{x} > 0$ where : $\bar{x}$ = *natural* real wage-rate, defined as that wage-rate which keeps population constant ;

(16) $K = \bar{K} > 0$ $\bar{K}$ = given stock of capital at the beginning of the year.

The system is now complete and determinate.[2] It can be easily demonstrated (see the appendix) that properties (1*a*), (1*b*), (1*c*) and the inequalities put on (15)-(16) are sufficient conditions to ensure the existence and uniqueness of non-negative solutions. We may consider, therefore, the system of equations (1)-(16) as defining the *natural* equilibrium of the Ricardian system.[3]

5. Some Characteristics of the Ricardian System

Already at this stage, the system of the previous section clearly shows some of the most peculiar characteristics of the Ricardian model. First of all, it contains a theory of value which is completely and (owing to our explicit assumptions) rigorously independent

[1] To be precise, we should allow for a minimum of necessities to be bought by the land-owners. This *minimum*, however, introduces only a constant into the analysis without modifying its essential features. For simplicity, therefore, the procedure is followed of neglecting the constant, which amounts to considering the minimum as negligible and supposing that the whole rent is spent on luxuries. Similarly, a minimum of luxuries might be allowed to be bought by the capitalists. This *minimum* also will be considered as negligible.

[2] It may be interesting to notice that equations (1), (4), (5), (6), (7), (15) and (16), taken by themselves, form an extremely simplified but determined Ricardian system expressed in terms of corn, where any question of evaluation has not yet arisen, corn being the single commodity produced. This is the system which has been used by Mr. Kaldor in his article " Alternative Theories of Distribution," *Review of Economic Studies*, 1955-56.

[3] To justify the terminology, let me mention that in his article " On the Notion of Equilibrium and Disequilibrium " (*Review of Economic Studies*, 1935-36), Professor Ragnar Frisch distinguishes two types of equilibria : *stationary* and *moving*. The *natural* equilibrium of the Ricardian system is not a stationary one, as will be seen in a moment ; it belongs to the *moving* type. Professor Frisch, in that article, describes a somewhat similar situation for the Wicksellian *normal* rate of interest.

of distribution. From equations (8*a*) and (9*a*), it appears that the value of commodities depends exclusively on technical factors (the quantity of labour required to produce them) and on nothing else.

Moreover, the system shows that wage-goods and luxury-goods play two different roles in the system. The production function for the wage commodity turns out to be of fundamental importance, while the conditions of production of the luxury-goods, expressed by α, have in the system a very limited influence. As can be easily found out (see also the appendix), the solutions for *all* variables, except p_2, depend on the function $f(N_1)$ or on its first derivative, while the constant α only enters the solutions for X_2 and p_2. As a consequence, the rate of profit and the money wage-rate are determined by the conditions of production of wage-goods and are entirely independent of the conditions of production of luxury goods.[1] It follows, for example—to mention one problem of concern to Ricardo—that a tax on wage-goods would affect all the participants in the process of production by changing both the money wage-rate and the rate of profit (as can be inferred from equations (13*a*) and (14*a*)), while a tax on luxury-goods would affect only the purchasers of these goods because it leaves the rates of profit and of wages entirely unaffected.[2]

6. The Market Solutions and the Attainment of the " Natural " Equilibrium

Ricardo admits that the market outcomes may not necessarily coincide with those of his " natural " equilibrium, but he considers two types of mechanisms which make the former converge towards the latter. First, he mentions the behaviour of the capitalists, whose readiness to move their capital towards the most profitable sectors of the economy always cause the rates of profit to equalize in all sectors. Secondly, he considers the increase of the working population in response to increases in wages. About the first of these two processes, Ricardo does not really say much more than what is said above. He does not find it useful to enter into complicated details (and in this case they would have been very complicated indeed for him, who did not possess a demand theory). Simply he allows for the process and carries on his analysis (the system (1)-(16)) on the assumption that the equalization of the rates of profit has already been permanently achieved. On the other hand, his analysis is more explicit, and can be clearly formulated, on the second type of mechanism.

At the beginning of our hypothetical year, what is really given (besides capital) is not the wage-rate but the number of workers. Therefore, the solutions determined by the market (supposing the rates of profit already equalized) are given by the system (1)-(14), (16) plus the following equality (replacing (15)):

[1] This can be seen more clearly by re-writing (13) and (14) after substitution from (4), (8*a*), (11*a*) (15). We obtain:

$$(13a) \qquad w = \frac{\bar{x}}{f'(N_1)}\,; \qquad\qquad (14a) \qquad r = \frac{f'(N_1)}{\bar{x}} - 1.$$

[2] The independence of the rate of profit from the conditions of production of luxury-goods is a property of all the theoretical models which use the distinction between wage- and luxury-goods. In plain words, it is due to the peculiarity that wage-goods are necessary to produce any type of goods, while luxury-goods are not. Mr. Sraffa pointed out to me that the property was first discovered by Ladislaus von Bortkiewicz (*Zur Berichtigung der Grundlegenden theoretischen Konstruktion von Marx im dritten Band des ' Kapital '*, in " Jahrbücher für Nationalökonomie und Statistik," July 1907. An English translation can be found as an appendix to the volume *Karl Marx and the Close of his System*, by E. Böhm-Bawerk and *Böhm-Bawerk's Criticism of Marx*, by R. Hilferding, translated and edited by P. M. Sweezy, New York 1949). From our mathematical formulation, the property comes out very simply and clearly.

(15*a*) $N = \bar{N}$ where : $\bar{N}$ = number of workers at the beginning of the year.

The system is again complete and determinate but the wage-rate has now become a variable and has a solution (the market solution). Ricardo is firmly convinced that this solution can only be a temporary and unstable one because, if it comes out different from the *natural* wage-rate ($\bar{x}$), the population will adjust itself in such a way as to bring the two rates together. Analytically, the mechanism may be expressed as follows:

$$(17) \qquad \frac{dN}{dt} = F(x - \bar{x})$$

where : t denotes time and x the wage-rate resulting from the system (1)-(14), (15), (16),

with the properties[1]:

$$(17a) \qquad \begin{array}{l} F(0) = 0 \\ F' > 0 \end{array}$$

which mean that population is stable when $x = \bar{x}$, and it increases (or decreases) when $x > \bar{x}$ (or $x < \bar{x}$).

The differential equation (17) with the properties (17*a*) is of a type which has been extensively studied by Professor Samuelson in connection with what he calls the *correspondence principle* between comparative statics and dynamics.[2] In our case, it can be easily demonstrated[3] that the dynamic movement for $x(t)$ generated by (17) is convergent towards $\bar{x}$ (the natural wage-rate), provided that $\frac{dx}{dN} < 0$, a condition which the system fulfils.[3] Hence, for x, only the *natural* solution $x = \bar{x}$ is a stable solution.

7. The Equilibrium of the Stationary State

The *natural* equilibrium examined in the previous sections is still not a stable state of affairs. Two other types of change are in operation in a Ricardian system as time goes on : (i) the improvements which take place in the technical conditions of production—in our terms, the shifts in time of the production function $f(N_1)$—, and (ii) the accumulation of capital by the capitalists, who add each year a substantial part of their profits to capital. Here again, Ricardo does not consider the first type of change—technical progress—in a systematic way (a characteristic which only to-day can be found in models of economic growth). He only points out that improvements in the technical conditions postpone in time the effects of the changes of type (ii). Since he thinks that these changes (capital accumulation) are—in order of magnitude—the more relevant ones, he concentrates his analysis on them, with the qualification that the effects he shows might be delayed, though not modified, by technical progress.

In analytical terms, capital accumulation represents another dynamic mechanism, in operation on the system already described, of the following type :

[1] The function F and the similar function Φ of the following section are supposed to be continuously differentiable.

[2] P. A. Samuelson, " The Stability of Equilibrium : Comparative Statics and Dynamics," *Econometrica*, April 1941, also *Foundations of Economic Analysis*, Harvard University Press, 1948, especially Chapter IX.

[3] A proof is given in the appendix,

(18) $$\frac{dK}{dt} = \Phi\left(\frac{1}{p_1}\pi\right)$$

or, from (8*a*) and (11*a*),

(19) $$\frac{dK}{dt} = \Phi\left(N[f'(N_1) - x] \right)$$

with the properties :[1]

(19*a*) $$\Phi(0) = 0$$
$$\Phi' > 0.$$

The differential equation (19) is of the same type as (17) and has now to be considered jointly with it. From mere inspection of the two equations, it can be seen that the solutions of the system at which the two dynamic mechanisms cease to operate (the stationary solutions) emerge when $x = \bar{x}$ and $\pi = 0$. Therefore, for any given state of technical knowledge, represented by the technical function $f(N_1)$, the stationary equilibrium is given by equations (1)-(14) plus the following two:

(15) $$x = \bar{x} > 0$$

(16*a*) $$\pi = 0.$$

In order to ensure the existence of non-negative solutions for this system, a somewhat stronger condition than (1*b*) is required, namely

(20) $f'(0) > \bar{x} > f'(\infty)$ where : $f'(\infty) = \lim_{N_1 \to \infty} f'(N_1)$.

The meaning is that there must be a certain point, as population increases, at which the product of the last worker put to work descends below the *natural* wage-rate (a condition which is implicit in Ricardo's arguments). If this condition were not satisfied, the system would expand indefinitely and the stationary state would never be reached. When (20) is satisfied, it is shown in the appendix that two types of solutions exist—one of them corresponds to the equality $f'(N_1) = \bar{x}$ and the other to the equality $N = 0$. The solutions of the second type, however, so called *trivial* (they mean that there is no economic system at all) are uninteresting and moreover they are *unstable*. On the other hand, the solutions corresponding to $f'(N_1) = \bar{x}$ are unique and perfectly *stable*. Therefore, the system necessarily converge towards them. When the situation they represent is attained, all dynamic mechanisms come to a standstill. The wage-rate is at its natural level (no longer disturbed by capital accumulation) and the rate of profit has fallen to zero. The system has reached a stable equilibrium—the Ricardian equilibrium of the stationary state.

8. The Process of Economic Growth

It has been shown in the foregoing sections that the Ricardian system contains many dynamic processes, although some of them are not systematically analysed. The two dynamic processes which are explicitly taken into consideration are convergent and lead to a stationary and stable state. Ricardo, however, investigates the properties of his system at a very particular stage of the whole movement, which he considers the relevant one. Most of his analysis is carried on *as if* the demographic mechanism has already fully worked through, while the capital accumulation process has not yet been completed. In other

[1] If a minimum rate of profit (let us call it $\bar{r}$) is considered necessary in order to induce capital accumulation, equation (18) has to be modified as follows $\frac{dK}{dt} = \Phi\left(\frac{1}{p_1}\pi - \bar{r}K\right)$. However, the conclusions drawn in the text remain the same, with the single modification that the stationary and stable point of convergency of the system instead of being at $\pi = 0$, is at $\pi = \bar{r}p_1K$.

words, he concentrates on describing the changing characteristics of his system in terms of *natural* behaviour of the variables in a process of capital accumulation.

In mathematical notations, this task becomes very easy. It is enough to consider the system (1)-(16) (in which the *natural* wage-rate has been permanently achieved) and to take the derivatives of each variable with respect to capital, which represents the datum—in the *natural* equilibrium—whose variation in time brings about economic growth. A substantial part of the Ricardian analysis is simply expressed by the signs of these derivatives. Let us consider them:

$$\frac{dN}{dK} = \frac{1}{\bar{x}} > 0 \tag{21}$$

$$\frac{dN_1}{dK} = \frac{1}{\bar{x}}\left\{1 - \frac{f(N_1)\,f''(N_1)}{[f'(N_1)]^2}\right\}^{-1} > 0 \tag{22}$$

$$\frac{dN_2}{dK} = \frac{1}{\bar{x}}\left\{1 - \frac{[f'(N_1)]^2}{f(N_1)\,f''(N_1)}\right\}^{-1} > 0 \tag{23}$$

$$\frac{dX_1}{dK} = f'(N_1) \cdot \frac{dN_1}{dK} > 0 \tag{24}$$

$$\frac{dX_2}{dK} = \alpha\,\frac{dN_2}{dK} > 0 \tag{25}$$

$$\frac{dW}{dK} = 1 > 0 \tag{26}$$

$$\frac{dR}{dK} = -N_1 \cdot f''(N_1) \cdot \frac{dN_1}{dK} > 0 \tag{27}$$

$$\frac{dp_1}{dK} = \frac{-f''(N_1)}{[f'(N_1)]^2} \cdot \frac{dN_1}{dK} > 0 \tag{28}$$

$$\frac{dp_2}{dK} = 0 \tag{29}$$

$$\frac{dw}{dK} = \bar{x} \cdot \frac{dp_1}{dK} > 0 \tag{30}$$

$$\frac{dr}{dK} = \frac{f''(N_1)}{\bar{x}} \cdot \frac{dN_1}{dK} < 0. \tag{31}$$

The derivatives have been obtained from the system (1)-(16) and the inequality signs follow from (1*b*), (1*c*), (15), (16), and from other previous inequalities among (21)-(31) themselves. Their economic meaning may be stated as follows. The number of workers (employment), all physical productions, the wage bill, total rent, the price of corn and the natural *money* wage-rate : all increase as long as the process of capital accumulation is going on. As an effect of the same process, the rate of profit constantly decreases. For Ricardo, it took, of course, a much longer process to show what here is demonstrated merely by the sign of a derivative.

Another variable whose response to capital accumulation particularly requires a long analysis in the *Principles*[1] is total profit. For this variable too, let us consider its derivative with respect to capital. From (11*a*) we obtain

[1] *Principles*, chapter VI.

$$(32) \qquad \frac{d\pi}{dK} = \frac{1}{f'(N_1)}\left[\frac{f'(N_1)}{\bar{x}} - 1 + K \cdot \frac{f''(N_1)}{f'(N_1)} \cdot \frac{dN_1}{dK}\right].$$

Now, from (1*c*) and (22), $f''(N_1) < 0$ and $\frac{dN_1}{dK} > 0$. Moreover $f'(N_1) > \bar{x}$ as long as the stationary state has not yet been attained. (At the stationary state $f'(N_1) = \bar{x}$). Therefore, the sign of (32), unlike all the others, is not independent of the amount of K. At the beginning of the process of capital accumulation, where $K = 0$, the third term into brackets vanishes and therefore $\frac{d\pi}{dK} > 0$. At the stationary state, where $f'(N_1) = \bar{x}$, the first two terms into brackets cancel out, and the third is negative, so that $\frac{d\pi}{dK} < 0$. In between, there must be at least one point of maximum total profits $\left(\text{where } \frac{f'(N_1) - \bar{x}}{\bar{x}} = -K \cdot \frac{f''(N_1)}{f'(N_1)} \cdot \frac{dN_1}{dK}\right)$ at which (32) changes its sign from positive to negative as capital accumulates.[1] Hence

$$\frac{d\pi}{dK} \gtreqless 0 \qquad \text{according as to whether } \frac{f'(N_1)}{\bar{x}} - 1 \gtreqless -K \cdot \frac{f''(N_1)}{f'(N_1)} \cdot \frac{dN_1}{dK}$$

which may also be written $\frac{f'(N_1)}{\bar{x}} - 1 \gtreqless -\frac{E[f'(N_1)]}{E\,K}$,

where the first member of the inequality represents the rate of profit (see equation (14*a*)) and the second member represents the *elasticity* of the marginal product from land with respect to capital.

Analytically, the possibility cannot be excluded of more than one point of maximum, in the sense that π might alternatively increase and decrease many times as capital accumulates. For such a possibility to realize, however, the third derivative of $f(N_1)$ must behave in a very peculiar way. Ricardo, of course, did not consider these complications; he explained the process by a long numerical and obviously non-rigorous example which allowed him to consider the normal case in which, as capital accumulation goes on, total profits increase up to a certain point and then decrease.[2] [3]

[1] The reader may easily verify that, as capital accumulates, profits in sector 1 and in sector 2 (namely the variables P_1 and P_2) behave exactly in the same way as total profit (π).

[2] *Principles*, pp. 110 and ff.

[3] While correcting the proofs, I was pointed out a recent paper by H. Barkai where a very simplified one-commodity Ricardian model is worked out in mathematical terms in order to analyse the movements of *relative shares* as capital accumulates (H. Barkai, " Ricardo on Factor Prices and Income Distribution in a Growing Economy," *Economica*, August 1959). Dr. Barkai uses a procedure which has some similarities with the one I have adopted in this section. His analysis, however, seems to me rather inaccurate. Without going into details here (among other things, his conclusions about the behaviour of the share of profits are not altogether correct) I shall only mention that Dr. Barkai's main contention is that the relative share of total wages in total product increases as an effect of capital accumulation (which is obvious, as the real wage-rate is constant and the production function is at diminishing returns) and that this result contradicts what Ricardo said on page 112 of his *Principles*, namely that as capital accumulates, " the labourer's . . . real share will be diminished " (Barkai's quotation). But where is the contradiction? Dr. Barkai's proof refers to the *relative share of total wages* in total product, while Ricardo is talking about the single *labourer's real share*, which is evidently a different thing.

This is a case where the interpretation of Ricardo is quite straightforward. However, as it is always so easy to be misled by particular passages in Ricardo's writings, let me recall the advice of Alfred Marshall: " If we seek to understand him [Ricardo] rightly, we must interpret him generously, more generously than he himself interpreted Adam Smith. When his words are ambiguous, we must give them that interpretation which other passages in his writings indicate that he would have wished us to give them. If we do this with the desire to ascertain what he really meant, his doctrines, though far from complete, are free from many of the errors that are commonly attributed to them ". (Alfred Marshall, *Principles of Economics*, Macmillan London, 8th ed. reset, page 670.)

9. Multi-Commodity Production

We are now in a position to drop the two-commodity assumption and extend our system of equations to the general case of multi-commodity production. As far as the wage-goods are concerned, the extension does not present particular difficulties, although it does emphasize the crudeness of Ricardo's assumptions. The economic theory of demand had not yet been developed, at that time, and there is no question of substitution among wage-goods in the Ricardian model. The *natural* wage-rate is represented by a fixed *basket of goods*, to be accepted as given by factors lying outside economic investigation. With this specification, the introduction in our system of any wage-good i, besides corn, introduces 8 more variables: X_i, N_i, W_i, R_i, P_i, K_i, p_i, x_i, but also 8 more equations of the types (1), (4), (5), (6), (7), (8), (15), (16). The system is again determinate and maintains its basic features already analysed in the previous sections. As a matter of fact, when the *natural* wage-rate is accepted as a fixed basket of goods, there is no gain at all, from an analytical point of view, in extending the system to include any number of wage-goods more than one. The whole structural character of the model is already given by the system of equations (1)-(16), provided that our interpretation of the single wage-commodity is modified in the sense of considering it as a composite commodity, made up of a fixed mixture of wage-goods.[1] The dynamic characteristics of the model also remain unchanged as they depend exclusively on the wage-goods part of the economy.

The problem becomes much more complicated when the extension to multi-commodity production is made for luxury-goods. Here, the introduction of each commodity l_j, besides the one which is used as a standard, introduces 4 more variables : X_{lj}, N_{lj}, p_{lj} P_{lj}, but only 3 more equations of the types (2), (9) and (10). Moreover, it changes equation (12) into the following one:

$$(12a) \qquad p_{l_1} X_{l_1} + p_{l_2} X_{l_2} + \ldots p_{lj} X_{lj} + \ldots p_{ln} X_{ln} = p_w R$$

where the subscript w stands for the composite wage-commodity and the subscripts l_j's stand for the luxury-goods.

Hence, for each luxury-commodity introduced besides the first, one more relation is needed in order to keep the system determinate. Ricardo *does not* provide this relation. Again the difficulty is that he does not have a theory of demand. The assumption of a natural wage-rate solves the problem for the workers (and by consequence for the capitalists) but leaves it still open for the landlords, whose possibilities of substituting one luxury-good for another and whose changes of tastes cannot be ruled out; and Ricardo does not rule them out. Have we to conclude, therefore, that the Ricardian system is indeterminate with respect to the luxury goods? It certainly is, but—interestingly enough—only for the particular variables X_{lj}'s. N_{lj}'s, P_{lj}'s, which are not really of much interest to an economist like Ricardo, *once their totals are determined.*

[1] Professor Samuelson, in his recent " Modern Treatment of the Ricardian Economy, (*The Quarterly Journal of Economics*, February and May, 1959), has been unable to grasp these properties of the Ricardian model. The reason seems to me that he has treated a Ricardian economy with a production function of the neo-classical type (see especially his appendix), which is inappropriate and is responsible for the conclusions he then criticises. Professor Samuelson argues that the classification of lands in order of fertility—namely, in our terms, the technical function $f(N_1)$ — is not an unambiguously determined one because, according to the type of produce which is considered, the classification, i.e. the function $f(N_1)$, may be different. This argument is valid in a neo-classical theoretical framework, where substitution among goods (in consumption and in production) is the main feature of the theory, but is irrelevant in a Ricardian type of analysis, which excludes substitution. When the proportion of the different produces is fixed, the classification of lands in order of fertility is a perfectly determined one.

To see this surprising property of the Ricardian system, let us suppose that n luxury-goods are pıoduced. Then $4(n—1)$ new variables of the types X_{lj}, N_{lj}, P_{lj}, p_{lj}, and $3(n—1)$ new equations of the types (2), (9) and (10) are introduced in the already analysed system. Provisionally, let us write down n demand equations for the lüxury goods :

(33)
$$\begin{aligned} X_{l1} &= \varphi_1 (p_w, p_{l1}, p_{l2} \ldots\ldots p_{ln}, R) \\ X_{l2} &= \varphi_2 (p_w, p_{l1}, p_{l2}, \ldots\ldots p_{ln}, R) \\ &\cdot \\ &\cdot \\ &\cdot \\ X_{ln} &= \varphi_n (p_w, p_{l1}, p_{l2}, \ldots\ldots p_{ln}, R). \end{aligned}$$

Equation (12a), which represents Say's law (namely, landlords spend all their income—no more and no less—on luxury goods), puts a restriction on the (33), so that one of the equations may be dropped. We are left with $(n—1)$ equations, which is the number necessary to determine the system. It is very interesting to notice now that the solutions for all the variables of the system, except the X_{lj}'s, P_{lj}'s, N_{lj}'s, are independent of the (33). In other words, the (33) are required only to determine the single physical productions, employments and profits in each particular luxury-goods sector but not to determine all other variables. *Whatever the demand equations for luxury-goods may be*, i.e., independently of them, all the variables referring to the wage-goods part of the economy, all prices, the rate of profit, and all the macro-economic variables of the system—like total employment, national income, total profits, total rent, total wages, total capital—are already determined by the system.

This is perhaps the most interesting outcome of the whole mathematical formulation attempted in this paper and it will be useful to remind the reader of the assumptions under which it has been reached : (i) perfect mobility of capital ; (ii) Say's law ; (iii) the assumption of circulating capital only, and of a one-year period for *all* processes of production. The last assumption, so stated, is too restrictive. As a matter of fact, it may be dropped and fixed capital introduced into the analysis without affecting the already attained conclusions, provided that the somewhat more general restriction is kept of supposing that all the sectors of the economy use fixed and circulating capital of the same durability and in the same proportions. *This is indeed the crucial assumption* : the determinateness of the whole Ricardian system itself depends on it, in an essential way.

Ricardo himself became aware of this limitation of his theoretical model in connection with the problem of the determination of total employment in the economy. He was disturbed by the discovery and, as a result, in the third edition of the *Principles*, he added the well-known chapter " on machinery ". The problem is that, when the mentioned crucial assumption holds, total employment in the economy, for any given amount of capital, is determined independently of the (33). But when the conditions of the assumption are not realized, total employment comes out different according to the way in which demand (and therefore capital) is distributed among the luxury goods sectors. Having realized this, Ricardo declared explicitly, in the added chapter, that he was mistaken earlier when he extended to the introduction of machinery (i.e., to the case where the proportions of fixed and circulating capital change) his general conclusions about total employment depending on total capital alone and not on how and where this capital is employed. This proposition, in the light of our formulation, appears quite obvious, but it has not appeared so to many of Ricardo's interpreters. Indeed, becaụse of the assertions it contains, which seem to be in contradiction with the general conclusions following from the whole previous analysis, the chapter " on machinery " has always puzzled Ricardo's readers. The mathematical formulation of the present paper helps to clarify the issue. It shows that the entire Ricardian model stands on the assumption of a uniform composition of capital all over the economy. The problem of introduction of machinery exactly hypothesizes a violation of this assumption. Therefore, the general conclusions cannot be extended to this case. Looked at in these terms, the chapter " on machinery " appears, rather than a contradiction, an honest acknowledgement by Ricardo of the limitations of his theory.

10. Concluding Remarks

A few remarks may be drawn as a way of conclusion.

Ricardo's model is built on very crude assumptions. The most crucial of them is that all sectors of the economy use—we might say in more modern terms—the same period of production. This was just the point against which his contemporary critics (especially Malthus) threw their most violent attacks. In their function as critics, they were right. The limits entailed by the assumption are relevant not only for the Ricardian theory of value—as has always been thought—but also for the determinateness itself of the whole system, as soon as the simple case of two-commodity production is departed from.

On the other hand, once the assumptions underlying the whole analysis have been explicitly defined, the system appears to be logically consistent and determinate in all its macro-economic features and even in its sectoral details, except for some particular sectoral variables in which Ricardo was not interested. A mathematical formulation of the model is possible, clarifies many issues—among others, those connected with the controversial chapter " on machinery "—and permits a representation of the Ricardian dynamic processes—in particular the process of economic growth—in a few rigorous and concise notations. The solutions of the *natural* system Ricardo was dealing with are shown to exist and to be unique but not stable. They reach a perfect stability only in the equilibrium of the stationary state.

The whole model, in its crudeness and simplicity, appears remarkably complete and synthetic. Ricardo is always looking for fundamentals. Detailed relations are dealt with only in the light of basic tendencies—when they become too complicated and lead to difficulties, those relations which are thought to be less important are *frozen* by crude assumptions. Whether this is a fruitful methodological line to pursue is open to controversy. Later, neo-classical economists preferred a radically different line of approach. They abandoned too ambitious dynamic outlooks and instead started to analyse, in a complete way and in all its functional interrelationships, at least a more simplified (static) version of economic reality. The step which was supposed to follow, however,—that of passing to a dynamic analysis—has not come out as easy and spontaneous as was expected, and, in recent years, it has not been infrequent for economists, faced with urgent problems of economic development, to have second thoughts on the subject. In this light, the Ricardian analysis, with all the naiveté and the limits of its particular theories, appears less primitive now-a-days than it appeared some decades ago.

Harvard University and Cambridge University. Luigi L. Pasinetti

APPENDIX

Existence and Uniqueness of Stable Solutions

It has been a widespread concern among mathematical economists in the last few decades not to be satisfied any longer (as economists used to be) with mere counting the number of equations and unknowns of their theoretical systems and to enquire more rigorously into the conditions for the existence, uniqueness and stability of the solutions. The task has not proved to be an easy one, as it normally entails mathematical notions and manipulations of a fairly highly sophisticated nature. In our case, fortunately, the proofs can be given in a relatively elementary way, except perhaps for the stability conditions.

1. *Existence and uniqueness of non-negative, non-trivial solutions.* The Ricardian system contains one single *functional* relation, the $f(N_1)$. Therefore, the fundamental step to solving it is to find the value of N_1 which satisfies the restrictions put by the system on the $f(N_1)$. In the system (1)-(15), (16*a*), we may start by taking (11*a*), substitute it into (16*a*) and obtain

$$N[f'(N_1) - \bar{x}] = 0.$$

This equation is satisfied either by $f'(N_1) = \bar{x}$ or by $N = 0$. The latter solution means that there is no economic system at all. Any theoretical representation of an economic system has this solution, but it is an uninteresting one—it represents the so-called *trivial* case. Evidently, the *relevant* solution is the other one. Let us prove therefore:

(i) that N_1^*—defined as the solution of the equation $f'(N_1) = \bar{x}$ — exists and is non-negative ;

(ii) that N_1^* is unique ; and finally,

(iii) that $f(N_1^*) \geqslant N_1^* f'(N_1^*)$. (The reason for this proof will appear in a moment.)

Proof (i). From (20), $f'(0)$ exists and is greater than $\bar{x}$; $f'(\infty)$ also exists and is smaller than $\bar{x}$. Since $\bar{x}$ is a positive constant, there must be a value $0 < N_1^* < \infty$, at which $f'(N_1^*) = \bar{x}$. Hence N_1^* exists and is non-negative.

Proof (ii). From (1*c*), $f''(N_1) < 0$, namely $f'(N_1)$ is a monotonic function. Since $\bar{x}$ is a constant, then (by a straightforward application of Rolle's theorem) N_1^* is unique.

Proof (iii). Call $G = f(N_1) - N_1 f'(N_1)$. Then $\dfrac{dG}{dN_1} = -N_1 f''(N_1) > 0$, namely G is a monotonically increasing function. Since $f(0) \geqslant 0$ and $N_1 \geqslant 0$, from (1*a*) and (i), then G is never negative, or $f(N_1) \geqslant N_1 f'(N_1)$ and, in particular, $f(N_1^*) \geqslant N_1^* f'(N_1^*)$.

By substituting now N_1^* into the system of equations (1)-(15), (16*a*), the solutions come out as:

$$\text{(A1)}\quad X_1 = f(N_1^*) \qquad\qquad \text{(A9)}\quad p_1 = \frac{1}{f'(N_1^*)}$$

$$\text{(A2)}\quad X_2 = \alpha\left[\frac{f(N_1^*)}{f'(N_1^*)} - N_1^*\right] \qquad\qquad \text{(A10)}\quad p_2 = \frac{1}{\alpha}$$

$$\text{(A3)}\quad N = \frac{f(N_1^*)}{f'(N_1^*)} \qquad\qquad \text{(A11)}\quad w = \bar{x}\,\frac{1}{f'(N_1^*)}$$

$$\text{(A4)}\quad N_1 = N_1^* \qquad\qquad \text{(A12)}\quad P_1 = 0$$

$$\text{(A5)}\quad N_2 = \frac{f(N_1^*)}{f'(N_1^*)} - N_1^* \qquad\qquad \text{(A13)}\quad P_2 = 0$$

$$\text{(A6)}\quad W = \bar{x}\,\frac{f(N_1^*)}{f'(N_1^*)} \qquad\qquad \text{(A14)}\quad r = 0$$

$$\text{(A7)}\quad K = \bar{x}\,\frac{f(N_1^*)}{f'(N_1^*)} \qquad\qquad \text{(A15)}\quad x = \bar{x}$$

$$\text{(A8)}\quad R = f(N_1^*) - N_1^* f'(N_1^*) \qquad\qquad \text{(A16)}\quad \pi = 0.$$

It follows that, if N_1^* exists is unique and non-negative and, moreover, if $f(N_1^*) \geqslant N_1^* f'(N_1^*)$, then all (A1)-(A16), namely the non-trivial solutions of the system, exist, are unique and are non-negative. The proofs have been given so far with reference to the equations (1)-(15), (16*a*). *A fortiori*, the solutions of any other system of equations (1)-(16), defined by a given $\bar{K}$ between 0 and K^*, exist, are unique and non-negative. For the system (1)-(16) the trivial solutions are even excluded by hypothesis as $\bar{K} > 0$. (The stars * are taken to denote the non-trivial solutions of the stationary equilibrium).

2. *The stability of the stationary equilibrium.* The stationary equilibrium is defined by the solutions of the system of equations (1)-(15), (16*a*). In order to find out whether it is stable, an investigation has to be made into the dynamic behaviour of the system when *displaced* from the equilibrium solutions. That behaviour is represented by the two differential equations (17) and (18). For a rigorous proof of stability, the two equations have to be considered jointly. Such a proof is given below but, as it entails a rather sophisticated mathematical treatment, it may be useful to give first a more simple proof which, although less rigorous, is intuitively easier to grasp and perhaps also more pertinent to the Ricardian logic.

The function (17) depends on the deviation of x from $\bar{x}$ and the function (18) on the deviation of $f'(N_1)$ from x. The two dynamic mechanisms are, so to speak, one on the top of the other. We may begin, therefore, by proving first, for a given $\bar{K}$, the convergency of the first dynamic process towards $\bar{x}$ and then substitute this stable solution into the second process and carry on a similar investigation on it, for a given $\bar{x}$.

Let us take equation (17) and expand it in a Taylor series around a value of N defined as $N+ = \frac{\bar{K}}{\bar{x}}$:

$$\frac{d(N - N+)}{dt} = F(0) + (N - N+)\,F'(0)\,\frac{dx}{dN} + \frac{(N - N+)^2}{2}\left[F''(0)\left(\frac{dx}{dN}\right)^2 + F'(0)\,\frac{d^2x}{dN^2}\right] + \ldots$$

Neglecting the terms of higher order than the first and recalling that $F(0) = 0$, the equation becomes

$$\frac{d(N - N+)}{dt} = (N - N+) \cdot F'(0) \cdot \frac{dx}{dN}.$$

This is a simple differential equation and its solution is[1]

$$N(t) = N+ + [N(0) - N+] \cdot \exp\left[F'(0) \cdot \frac{dx}{dN} \cdot t\right]$$ where $N(0)$ is the value of N at time zero.

Since $F'(0) > 0$ from (17*a*), a necessary condition for $N(t)$ to converge towards $N+$ (and therefore for $x(t)$ to converge towards $\bar{x}$) is $\frac{dx}{dN} < 0$. Now, from the system (1)-(14), (15*a*), (16), we have $\frac{dx}{dN} = -\frac{\bar{K}}{N^2} < 0$. *The condition is fulfilled.* Hence, *the solution $x = \bar{x}$ is stable.*

By substituting now $x = \bar{x}$ into (19) and developing the same type of analysis, the necessary condition for K to converge towards K^*—defined as the stationary equilibrium solution for K—is

$$\frac{d}{dK}\left(\frac{1}{p_1}\pi\right) < 0.$$

Now, from (11*a*) we can write

$$\frac{d}{dK}\left(\frac{1}{p_1}\pi\right) = \frac{f'(N_1)}{\bar{x}} - 1 + N \cdot f''(N_1) \cdot \frac{dN_1}{dK}.$$

Since $f''(N_1)$ is negative and $f'(N_1)$ is greater or equal to $\bar{x}$ according as to whether $N_1 < N_1^*$ or $N_1 = N_1^*$, then condition $\frac{d}{dK}\left(\frac{1}{p_2}\pi\right) < 0$ is not satisfied when $N = 0$, while it is satisfied when $f'(N_1) = \bar{x}$. Hence, *the solutions of the system corresponding to $f'(N_1) = \bar{x}$ are stable, while the trivial solutions are unstable*—the system necessarily converges towards the first ones. As a conclusion, the system (1)-(15), (16*a*) has *stable solutions*. Such stable solutions are also *unique*.

3. *A more rigorous proof of stability.* Consider equations (17) and (18), representing the variations in time of N and of K. Since N_1 is a monotonically increasing function of N, the equations may be equally expressed in terms of N_1 (namely in terms of the wage-goods sector):

(A17) $$\frac{dN_1}{dt} = g(x - \bar{x})\,; \quad g(0) = 0\,; \quad g' > 0;$$

(A18) $$\frac{dK_1}{dt} = \varphi(P_1), \quad \text{where } K_1 = N_1 x\,; \quad \varphi(0) = 0\,; \quad \varphi' > 0.$$

[1] See any elementary treatise on differential equations or also R. G. D. Allen, *Mathematical Economics*, London 1956, chapter 5.

Our purpose is now to investigate the dynamic behaviour of the system in the vicinity of the stationary solutions $x = \bar{x}$ and $f'(N_1) = x$. Let us expand (A17) in a Taylor series around the value $\bar{x}$. Neglecting the terms of higher order than the first the equation may be written

$$\text{(A17}a\text{)} \qquad \frac{d(N_1 - N_1^*)}{dt} = (x - \bar{x})\, g'(0).$$

Equation (A18) is more complex. Let us first write it in terms of the same variables entering (A17),

$$\frac{dK_1}{dt} = \frac{d(N_1 x)}{dt} = \varphi\left(N_1 [f'(N_1) - x]\right).$$

By expanding also this equation in a Taylor series and neglecting the terms of higher order than the first we obtain

$$\text{(A19)} \qquad N_1 \cdot \frac{dx}{dt} + x \cdot \frac{dN_1}{dt} = \varphi'(0) \cdot \left\{N_1[f'(N_1) - x]\right\}.$$

Let us now express the variables in terms of deviations from their stationary solutions and utilize Taylor's theorem for the $f'(N_1)$. We have

$$[N_1^* + (N_1 - N_1^*)]\frac{d(x - \bar{x})}{dt} + [\bar{x} + (x - \bar{x})]\frac{d(N_1 - N_1^*)}{dt} =$$
$$\varphi'(0) \cdot \left\{[N_1^* + (N_1 - N_1^*)] \cdot [(N_1 - N_1^*) \cdot f''(N_1^*) - x + f'(N_1^*)]\right\}.$$

The squares of $(N_1 - N_1^*)$ and of $(x - \bar{x})$, and their products, represent magnitudes of second order and we may neglect them, re-writing the whole expression as

$$\text{(A20)} \quad N_1^* \frac{d(x - \bar{x})}{dt} + \bar{x}\,\frac{d(N_1 - N_1^*)}{dt} = \varphi'(0) \cdot N_1^* \cdot [(N_1 - N_1^*) \cdot f''(N_1^*) - x + \bar{x}] +$$
$$0\left\{(x - \bar{x})^2;\ (N_1 - N_1^*)^2;\ (x - \bar{x})\,(N_1 - N_1^*)\right\}$$

where the last term denotes the order of magnitude of the neglected products. Multiplying now (A17*a*) by $\bar{x}$ and subtracting it from (A20) we can at last write down our equations in a suitable form for an immediate solution

$$\frac{d(N_1 - N_1^*)}{dt} = (x - \bar{x}) \cdot g'(0) + 0\left\{(x - \bar{x})^2\right\}$$

$$\frac{d(x - \bar{x})}{dt} = (N_1 - N_1^*) \cdot \varphi'(0) \cdot f''(N_1^*) - (x - \bar{x}) \cdot \left[\frac{\bar{x}}{N_1^*}\, g'(0) + \varphi'(0)\right] +$$
$$0\left\{(x - \bar{x})^2;\ (N_1 - N_1^*)^2;\ (x - \bar{x})\,(N_1 - N_1^*)\right\}.$$

The solutions of this system of equations—apart from the neglected terms—take the form[1]

[1] See, for example, A. R. Forsyth, *A Treatise on Differential Equations*, London, 1921, pp. 342 and ff. In order to make the procedure easier to follow, I shall take here the same steps as Professor Samuelson in his already mentioned article in *Econometrica.*

$$N_1(t) = N_1^* + k_{11}\, e^{\lambda_1 t} \quad + k_{12}\, e^{\lambda_2 t}$$
$$x(t) = \bar{x} + k_{21}\, e^{\lambda_1 t} \quad + k_{22}\, e^{\lambda_2 t}$$

where the k's depend on the values of N_1 and x at time zero and the λ's are the roots of the characteristic equation

$$\begin{vmatrix} 0 - \lambda & g'(0) \\ \varphi'(0) \cdot f''(N_1^*) & -\dfrac{\bar{x}}{N_1^*}\, g'(0) - \varphi'(0) - \lambda \end{vmatrix} = 0$$

or

(A21) $$\lambda^2 + \lambda \left[\varphi'(0) + \frac{\bar{x}}{N_1^*} \cdot g'(0)\right] - g'(0) \cdot \varphi'(0) \cdot f''(N_1^*) = 0.$$

For the equilibrium to be stable the real part of λ must be necessarily negative, i.e.,

(A22) $$R(\lambda) < 0.$$

Now, since $\varphi'(0) > 0$, $g'(0) > 0$, and $f''(N_1) < 0$, (A21) can be written as

(A23) $$\lambda^2 + 2\,m\lambda + n^2 = 0$$ where:

$$m = \tfrac{1}{2}\left[\varphi'(0) + \frac{\bar{x}}{N_1}\, g'(0)\right];$$

$$n = \sqrt{- g'(0) \cdot \varphi'(0) \cdot f''(N_1^*)}.$$

Hence:

$$\lambda = -\, m \pm (m^2 - n^2)^{\frac{1}{2}}$$

from which it appears that the real part of λ is always negative, namely that condition (A22) is satisfied. Therefore, the *stationary equilibrium defined by the couple of solutions* $x = \bar{x}$ and $f'(N_1) = \bar{x}$ *is stable.*

A proof of the instability of the trivial solutions, characterized by $N_1 = 0$, can be given in an easier way because in this case the products involving N_1 itself—besides those involving $(x - \bar{x})$—are of second order of smallness and equation (A18) may be considered in isolation, as appears by re-writing (A19) as

$$N_1 \frac{d(x - \bar{x})}{dt} + (x - \bar{x} + \bar{x}) \frac{dN_1}{dt} = \varphi'(0)\, N_1[f'(0) - x + \bar{x} - \bar{x}].$$

and then, neglecting the squares of N_1 and of $(x - \bar{x})$ and their products,

$$\frac{1}{N_1}\frac{dN_1}{dt} = \frac{1}{\bar{x}}\, \varphi'(0)\, [f'(0) - \bar{x}] + 0\left\{N_1^2;\ (x - \bar{x})^2;\ N(x - \bar{x})\right\}.$$

This is a simple differential equation whose solution—apart from the neglected terms—take the form

(A24) $$\log_n N_1 = k\,t + \log_n C$$

namely

$$\text{(A25)} \qquad N_1(t) = C\,e^{kt} \qquad \text{where: } k = \frac{1}{\bar{x}}\,\varphi'(0)\,[f'(0) - \bar{x}],$$

$$\text{and} \quad C = N_1(0).$$

Since $\frac{1}{\bar{x}}\,\varphi'(0)\,[f'(0) - \bar{x}] > 0$, then the solution (A25) is explosive, which means that *the stationary equilibrium defined by the solution $N_1 = 0$ is unstable.*

7

A CONTRIBUTION TO THE THEORY OF ECONOMIC GROWTH

By Robert M. Solow

I. Introduction

All theory depends on assumptions which are not quite true. That is what makes it theory. The art of successful theorizing is to make the inevitable simplifying assumptions in such a way that the final results are not very sensitive.[1] A "crucial" assumption is one on which the conclusions do depend sensitively, and it is important that crucial assumptions be reasonably realistic. When the results of a theory seem to flow specifically from a special crucial assumption, then if the assumption is dubious, the results are suspect.

I wish to argue that something like this is true of the Harrod-Domar model of economic growth. The characteristic and powerful conclusion of the Harrod-Domar line of thought is that even for the long run the economic system is at best balanced on a knife-edge of equilibrium growth. Were the magnitudes of the key parameters — the savings ratio, the capital-output ratio, the rate of increase of the labor force — to slip ever so slightly from dead center, the consequence would be either growing unemployment or prolonged inflation. In Harrod's terms the critical question of balance boils down to a comparison between the natural rate of growth which depends, in the absence of technological change, on the increase of the labor force, and the warranted rate of growth which depends on the saving and investing habits of households and firms.

But this fundamental opposition of warranted and natural rates turns out in the end to flow from the crucial assumption that production takes place under conditions of *fixed proportions.* There is no possibility of substituting labor for capital in production. If this assumption is abandoned, the knife-edge notion of unstable balance seems to go with it. Indeed it is hardly surprising that such a gross

1. Thus transport costs were merely a negligible complication to Ricardian trade theory, but a vital characteristic of reality to von Thünen.

rigidity in one part of the system should entail lack of flexibility in another.

A remarkable characteristic of the Harrod-Domar model is that it consistently studies long-run problems with the usual short-run tools. One usually thinks of the long run as the domain of the neoclassical analysis, the land of the margin. Instead Harrod and Domar talk of the long run in terms of the multiplier, the accelerator, "the" capital coefficient. The bulk of this paper is devoted to a model of long-run growth which accepts all the Harrod-Domar assumptions except that of fixed proportions. Instead I suppose that the single composite commodity is produced by labor and capital under the standard neoclassical conditions. The adaptation of the system to an exogenously given rate of increase of the labor force is worked out in some detail, to see if the Harrod instability appears. The price-wage-interest reactions play an important role in this neoclassical adjustment process, so they are analyzed too. Then some of the other rigid assumptions are relaxed slightly to see what qualitative changes result: neutral technological change is allowed, and an interest-elastic savings schedule. Finally the consequences of certain more "Keynesian" relations and rigidities are briefly considered.

II. A Model of Long-Run Growth

There is only one commodity, output as a whole, whose rate of production is designated $Y(t)$. Thus we can speak unambiguously of the community's real income. Part of each instant's output is consumed and the rest is saved and invested. The fraction of output saved is a constant s, so that the rate of saving is $sY(t)$. The community's stock of capital $K(t)$ takes the form of an accumulation of the composite commodity. Net investment is then just the rate of increase of this capital stock dK/dt or $\dot{K}$, so we have the basic identity at every instant of time:

$$\dot{K} = sY. \tag{1}$$

Output is produced with the help of two factors of production, capital and labor, whose rate of input is $L(t)$. Technological possibilities are represented by a production function

$$Y = F(K,L). \tag{2}$$

Output is to be understood as net output after making good the depreciation of capital. About production all we will say at the moment is that it shows constant returns to scale. Hence the production function is homogeneous of first degree. This amounts to assuming that there is no scarce nonaugmentable resource like land. Constant returns to scale seems the natural assumption to make in a theory of growth. The scarce-land case would lead to decreasing returns to scale in capital and labor and the model would become more Ricardian.[2]

Inserting (2) in (1) we get

$$\dot{K} = sF(K,L). \tag{3}$$

This is one equation in two unknowns. One way to close the system would be to add a demand-for-labor equation: marginal physical productivity of labor equals real wage rate; and a supply-of-labor equation. The latter could take the general form of making labor supply a function of the real wage, or more classically of putting the real wage equal to a conventional subsistence level. In any case there would be three equations in the three unknowns K, L, real wage.

Instead we proceed more in the spirit of the Harrod model. As a result of exogenous population growth the labor force increases at a constant relative rate n. In the absence of technological change n is Harrod's natural rate of growth. Thus:

$$L(t) = L_0 e^{nt}. \tag{4}$$

In (3) L stands for total employment; in (4) L stands for the available supply of labor. By identifying the two we are assuming that full employment is perpetually maintained. When we insert (4) in (3) to get

$$\dot{K} = sF(K, L_0 e^{nt}) \tag{5}$$

we have the basic equation which determines the time path of capital accumulation that must be followed if all available labor is to be employed.

Alternatively (4) can be looked at as a supply curve of labor. It says that the exponentially growing labor force is offered for employment completely inelastically. The labor supply curve is a vertical

2. See, for example, Haavelmo: *A Study in the Theory of Economic Evolution* (Amsterdam, 1954), pp. 9–11. Not all "underdeveloped" countries are areas of land shortage. Ethiopia is a counterexample. One can imagine the theory as applying as long as arable land can be hacked out of the wilderness at essentially constant cost.

line which shifts to the right in time as the labor force grows according to (4). Then the real wage rate adjusts so that all available labor is employed, and the marginal productivity equation determines the wage rate which will actually rule.[3]

In summary, (5) is a differential equation in the single variable $K(t)$. Its solution gives the only time profile of the community's capital stock which will fully employ the available labor. Once we know the time path of capital stock and that of the labor force, we can compute from the production function the corresponding time path of real output. The marginal productivity equation determines the time path of the real wage rate. There is also involved an assumption of full employment of the available stock of capital. At any point of time the pre-existing stock of capital (the result of previous accumulation) is inelastically supplied. Hence there is a similar marginal productivity equation for capital which determines the real rental per unit of time for the services of capital stock. The process can be viewed in this way: at any moment of time the available labor supply is given by (4) and the available stock of capital is also a datum. Since the real return to factors will adjust to bring about full employment of labor and capital we can use the production function (2) to find the current rate of output. Then the propensity to save tells us how much of net output will be saved and invested. Hence we know the net accumulation of capital during the current period. Added to the already accumulated stock this gives the capital available for the next period, and the whole process can be repeated.

III. Possible Growth Patterns

To see if there is always a capital accumulation path consistent with any rate of growth of the labor force, we must study the differential equation (5) for the qualitative nature of its solutions. Naturally without specifying the exact shape of the production function we can't hope to find the exact solution. But certain broad properties are surprisingly easy to isolate, even graphically.

To do so we introduce a new variable $r = \frac{K}{L}$, the ratio of capital to labor. Hence we have $K = rL = rL_0e^{nt}$. Differentiating with respect to time we get

$$\dot{K} = L_0e^{nt}\dot{r} + nrL_0e^{nt}.$$

3. The complete set of three equations consists of (3), (4) and $\frac{\partial F(K,L)}{\partial L} = w$.

Substitute this in (5):

$$(\dot{r} + nr)L_0e^{nt} = sF(K, L_0e^{nt}).$$

But because of constant returns to scale we can divide both variables in F by $L = L_0e^{nt}$ provided we multiply F by the same factor. Thus

$$(\dot{r} + nr)L_0e^{nt} = sL_0e^{nt}F\left(\frac{K}{L_0e^{nt}}, 1\right)$$

and dividing out the common factor we arrive finally at

$$\dot{r} = sF(r,1) - nr. \tag{6}$$

Here we have a differential equation involving the capital-labor ratio alone.

This fundamental equation can be reached somewhat less formally. Since $r = \dfrac{K}{L}$, the relative rate of change of r is the difference between the relative rates of change of K and L. That is:

$$\frac{\dot{r}}{r} = \frac{\dot{K}}{K} - \frac{\dot{L}}{L}.$$

Now first of all $\dfrac{\dot{L}}{L} = n$. Secondly $\dot{K} = sF(K,L)$. Making these substitutions:

$$\dot{r} = r\,\frac{sF(K,L)}{K} - nr.$$

Now divide L out of F as before, note that $\dfrac{L}{K} = \dfrac{1}{r}$, and we get (6) again.

The function $F(r,1)$ appearing in (6) is easy to interpret. It is the total product curve as varying amounts r of capital are employed with one unit of labor. Alternatively it gives output per worker as a function of capital per worker. Thus (6) states that the rate of change of the capital-labor ratio is the difference of two terms, one representing the increment of capital and one the increment of labor.

When $\dot{r} = 0$, the capital-labor ratio is a constant, and the capital stock must be expanding at the same rate as the labor force, namely n.

(The warranted rate of growth, warranted by the appropriate real rate of return to capital, equals the natural rate.) In Figure I, the ray through the origin with slope n represents the function nr. The other curve is the function $sF(r,1)$. It is here drawn to pass through the origin and convex upward: no output unless both inputs are positive, and diminishing marginal productivity of capital, as would be the case, for example, with the Cobb-Douglas function. At the point of intersection $nr = sF(r,1)$ and $\dot{r} = 0$. If the capital-labor ratio r^* should ever be established, it will be maintained, and capital and labor will grow thenceforward in proportion. By constant returns to

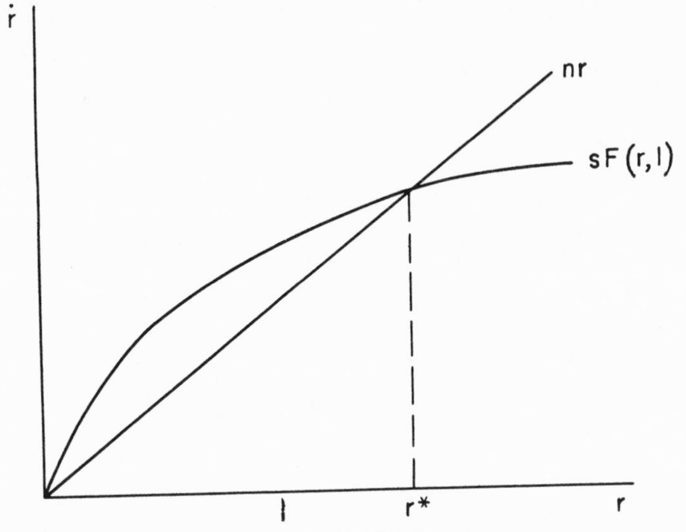

FIGURE I

scale, real output will also grow at the same relative rate n, and output per head of labor force will be constant.

But if $r \neq r^*$, how will the capital-labor ratio develop over time? To the right of the intersection point, when $r > r^*$, $nr > sF(r,1)$ and from (6) we see that r will decrease toward r^*. Conversely if initially $r < r^*$, the graph shows that $nr < sF(r,1)$, $\dot{r} > 0$, and r will increase toward r^*. Thus the equilibrium value r^* is *stable*. Whatever the initial value of the capital-labor ratio, the system will develop *toward* a state of balanced growth at the natural rate. The time path of capital and output will not be exactly exponential except asymptotically.[4] If the initial capital stock is below the equilibrium ratio,

4. There is an exception to this. If $K = 0$, $r = 0$ and the system can't get started; with no capital there is no output and hence no accumulation. But this

capital and output will grow at a faster pace than the labor force until the equilibrium ratio is approached. If the initial ratio is above the equilibrium value, capital and output will grow more slowly than the labor force. The growth of output is always intermediate between those of labor and capital.

Of course the strong stability shown in Figure I is not inevitable. The steady adjustment of capital and output to a state of balanced growth comes about because of the way I have drawn the productivity curve $F(r,1)$. Many other configurations are a priori possible. For example in Figure II there are three intersection points. Inspec-

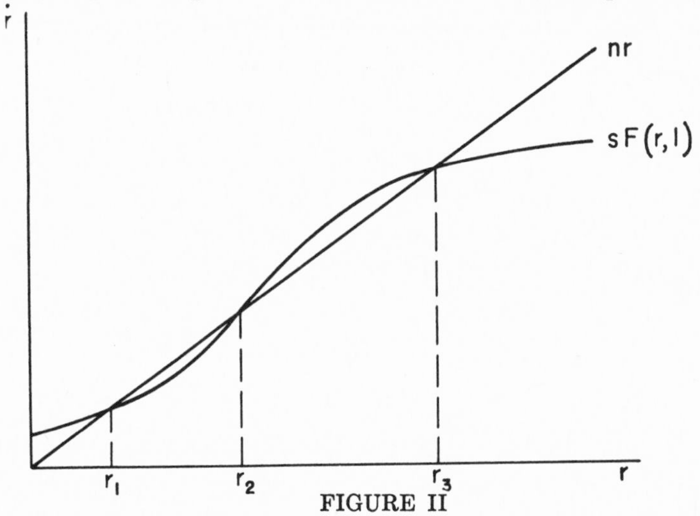

FIGURE II

tion will show that r_1 and r_3 are stable, r_2 is not. Depending on the initially observed capital-labor ratio, the system will develop either to balanced growth at capital-labor ratio r_1 or r_3. In either case labor supply, capital stock and real output will asymptotically expand at rate n, but around r_1 there is less capital than around r_3, hence the level of output per head will be lower in the former case than in the latter. The relevant balanced growth equilibrium is at r_1 for an initial ratio anywhere between 0 and r_2, it is at r_3 for any initial ratio greater than r_2. The ratio r_2 is itself an equilibrium growth ratio, but an unstable one; any accidental disturbance will be magnified over time. Figure II has been drawn so that production is possible without capital; hence the origin is not an equilibrium "growth" configuration.

Even Figure II does not exhaust the possibilities. It is possible

equilibrium is unstable: the slightest windfall capital accumulation will start the system off toward r^*.

that no balanced growth equilibrium might exist.[5] *Any* nondecreasing function $F(r,1)$ can be converted into a constant returns to scale production function simply by multiplying it by L; the reader can construct a wide variety of such curves and examine the resulting solutions to (6). In Figure III are shown two possibilities, together

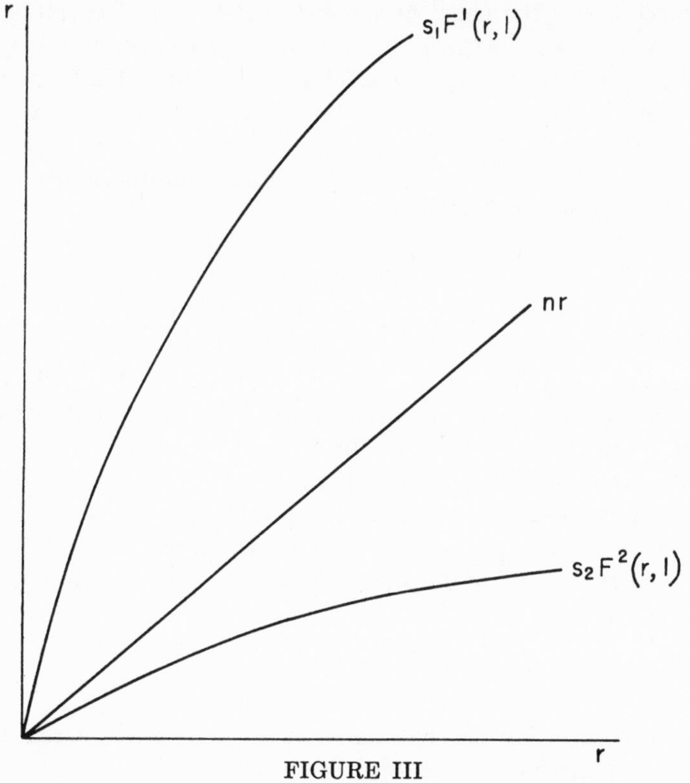

FIGURE III

with a ray nr. Both have diminishing marginal productivity throughout, and one lies wholly above nr while the other lies wholly below.[6] The first system is so productive and saves so much that perpetual full employment will increase the capital-labor ratio (and also the output per head) beyond all limits; capital and income both increase

5. This seems to contradict a theorem in R. M. Solow and P. A. Samuelson: "Balanced Growth under Constant Returns to Scale," *Econometrica*, XXI (1953), 412–24, but the contradiction is only apparent. It was there assumed that every commodity had positive marginal productivity in the production of each commodity. Here capital cannot be used to produce labor.

6. The equation of the first might be $s_1F^1(r,1) = nr + \sqrt{r}$, that of the second $s_2F^2(r,1) = \dfrac{nr}{r+1}$

more rapidly than the labor supply. The second system is so unproductive that the full employment path leads only to forever diminishing income per capita. Since net investment is always positive and labor supply is increasing, aggregate income can only rise.

The basic conclusion of this analysis is that, when production takes place under the usual neoclassical conditions of variable proportions and constant returns to scale, no simple opposition between natural and warranted rates of growth is possible. There may not be — in fact in the case of the Cobb-Douglas function there never can be — any knife-edge. The system can adjust to any given rate of growth of the labor force, and eventually approach a state of steady proportional expansion.

IV. Examples

In this section I propose very briefly to work out three examples, three simple choices of the shape of the production function for which it is possible to solve the basic differential equation (6) explicitly.

Example 1: Fixed Proportions. This is the Harrod-Domar case. It takes a units of capital to produce a unit of output; and b units of labor. Thus a is an acceleration coefficient. Of course, a unit of output can be produced with *more* capital and/or labor than this (the isoquants are right-angled corners); the first bottleneck to be reached limits the rate of output. This can be expressed in the form (2) by saying

$$Y = F(K,L) = \min\left(\frac{K}{a}, \frac{L}{b}\right)$$

where "min (. . .)" means the smaller of the numbers in parentheses. The basic differential equation (6) becomes

$$\dot{r} = s \min\left(\frac{r}{a}, \frac{1}{b}\right) - nr.$$

Evidently for very small r we must have $\frac{r}{a} < \frac{1}{b}$, so that in this range $\dot{r} = \frac{sr}{a} - nr = \left(\frac{s}{a} - n\right)r$. But when $\frac{r}{a} \geqq \frac{1}{b}$, i.e., $r \geqq \frac{a}{b}$, the equation becomes $\dot{r} = \frac{s}{b} - nr$. It is easier to see how this works graphically. In Figure IV the function $s \min\left(\frac{r}{a}, \frac{1}{b}\right)$ is represented by a broken line: the ray from the origin with slope $\frac{s}{a}$ until r reaches the value $\frac{a}{b}$, and then a horizontal line at height $\frac{s}{b}$. In the Harrod model $\frac{s}{a}$ is the warranted rate of growth.

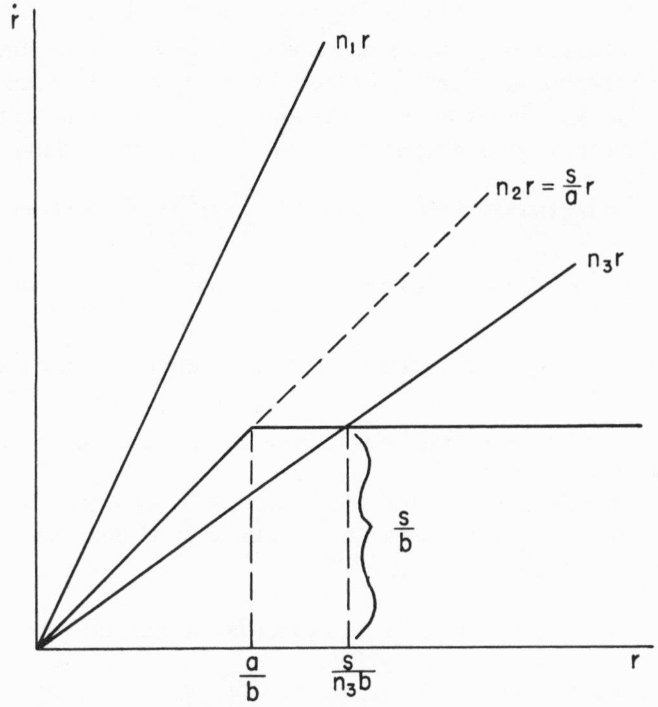

FIGURE IV

There are now three possibilities:

(a) $n_1 > \frac{s}{a}$, the natural rate exceeds the warranted rate. It can be seen from Figure IV that $n_1 r$ is always greater than $s \min\left(\frac{r}{a}, \frac{1}{b}\right)$, so that r always decreases. Suppose the initial value of the capital-labor ratio is $r_0 > \frac{a}{b}$, then $\dot{r} = \frac{s}{b} - n_1 r$, whose solution is $r = \left(r_0 - \frac{s}{n_1 b}\right)e^{-n_1 t} + \frac{s}{n_1 b}$. Thus r decreases toward $\frac{s}{n_1 b}$ which is in turn less than $\frac{a}{b}$. At an easily calculable point of time t_1, r reaches $\frac{a}{b}$. From then on $\dot{r} = \left(\frac{s}{a} - n_1\right) r$, whose solution is $r = \frac{a}{b} e^{\left(\frac{s}{a}-n_1\right)(t-t_1)}$. Since $\frac{s}{a} < n_1$, r will decrease toward zero. At time t_1, when $r = \frac{a}{b}$ the labor supply and capital stock are in balance. From then on as the capital-labor ratio decreases labor becomes redundant, and the extent of the redundancy grows. The amount of unemployment can be calculated from the fact that $K = rL_0e^{nt}$ remembering that, when capital is the bottleneck factor, output is $\frac{K}{a}$ and *employment* is $b\frac{K}{a}$.

(b) $n_2 = \frac{s}{a}$, the warranted and natural rates are equal. If initially $r > \frac{a}{b}$ so that labor is the bottleneck, then r decreases to $\frac{a}{b}$ and stays there. If initially $r < \frac{a}{b}$, then r remains constant over time, in a sort of neutral equilibrium. Capital stock and labor supply grow at a common rate n_2; whatever *percentage* redundancy of labor there was initially is preserved.

(c) $n_3 < \frac{s}{a}$, the warranted rate exceeds the natural rate. Formally the solution is exactly as in case (a) with n_3 replacing n_1. There is a stable equilibrium capital output ratio at $r = \frac{s}{n_3b}$. But here capital is redundant as can be seen from the fact that the marginal productivity of capital has fallen to zero. The proportion of the capital stock actually employed in equilibrium growth is $\frac{an_3}{s}$. But since the capital stock is growing (at a rate asymptotically equal to n_3) the absolute amount of excess capacity is growing, too. This appearance of redundancy independent of any price-wage movements is a consequence of fixed proportions, and lends the Harrod-Domar model its characteristic of rigid balance.

At the very least one can imagine a production function such that if r exceeds a critical value r_{max}, the marginal product of capital falls to zero, and if r falls short of another critical value r_{min}, the marginal product of labor falls to zero. For intermediate capital-labor ratios the isoquants are as usual. Figure IV would begin with a linear portion for $0 \leqq r \leqq r_{min}$, then have a phase like Figure I for $r_{min} \leqq r \leqq r_{max}$, then end with a horizontal stretch for $r > r_{max}$. There would be a whole *zone* of labor-supply growth rates which would lead to an equilibrium like that of Figure I. For values of n below this zone the end result would be redundancy of capital, for values of n above this zone, redundancy of labor. To the extent that in the long run factor proportions are widely variable the intermediate zone of growth rates will be wide.

Example 2: The Cobb-Douglas Function. The properties of the function $Y = K^a L^{1-a}$ are too well known to need comment here. Figure I describes the situation regardless of the choice of the parameters a and n. The marginal productivity of capital rises indefinitely as the capital-labor ratio decreases, so that the curve $sF(r,1)$ must rise above the ray nr. But since $a < 1$, the curve must eventually cross the ray from above and subsequently remain below. Thus the asymptotic behavior of the system is always balanced growth at the natural rate.

The differential equation (6) is in this case $\dot{r} = sr^a - nr$. It is actually easier to go back to the untransformed equation (5), which now reads

$$\dot{K} = sK^a(L_0 e^{nt})^{1-a}. \tag{7}$$

This can be integrated directly and the solution is:

$$K(t) = \left[K_0^b - \frac{s}{n} L_0^b + \frac{s}{n} L_0^b e^{nbt} \right]^{\frac{1}{b}}$$

where $b = 1 - a$, and K_0 is the initial capital stock. It is easily seen that as t becomes large, $K(t)$ grows essentially like $\left(\frac{s}{n}\right)^{1/b} L_0 e^{nt}$, namely at the same rate of growth as the labor force. The equilibrium value of the capital-labor ratio is $r^* = \left(\frac{s}{n}\right)^{1/b}$. This can be verified by putting $\dot{r} = 0$ in (6). Reasonably enough this equilibrium ratio is larger the higher the savings ratio and the lower the rate of increase of the labor supply.

It is easy enough to work out the time path of real output from the production function itself. Obviously asymptotically Y must behave like K and L, that is, grow at relative rate n. Real income per head of labor force, Y/L, tends to the value $(s/n)^{a/b}$. Indeed with the Cobb-Douglas function it is always true that $Y/L = (K/L)^a = r^a$. It follows at once that the equilibrium value of K/Y is s/n. But K/Y is the "capital coefficient" in Harrod's terms, say C. Then in the long-run equilibrium growth we will have $C = s/n$ or $n = s/C$: the natural rate equals "the" warranted rate, not as an odd piece of luck but as a consequence of demand-supply adjustments.

Example 3. A whole family of constant-returns-to-scale production functions is given by $Y = (aK^p + L^p)^{1/p}$. It differs from the Cobb-Douglas family in that production is possible with only one factor. But it shares the property that if $p < 1$, the marginal productivity of capital becomes infinitely great as the capital-labor ratio declines toward zero. If $p > 1$, the isoquants have the "wrong" convexity; when $p = 1$, the isoquants are straight lines, perfect substitutability; I will restrict myself to the case of $0 < p < 1$ which gives the usual diminishing marginal returns. Otherwise it is hardly sensible to insist on full employment of both factors.

In particular consider $p = 1/2$ so that the production function becomes

$$Y = (a\sqrt{K} + \sqrt{L})^2 = a^2K + L + 2a\sqrt{KL}\,.$$

The basic differential equation is

$$\dot{r} = s(a\sqrt{r} + 1)^2 - nr. \tag{8}$$

This can be written:

$$\dot{r} = s\left[(a^2 - n/s)r + 2a\sqrt{r} + 1\right] = s(A\sqrt{r} + 1)(B\sqrt{r} + 1)$$

where $A = a - \sqrt{n/s}$ and $B = a + \sqrt{n/s}$. The solution has to be given implicitly:

$$\left(\frac{A\sqrt{r} + 1}{A\sqrt{r_0} + 1}\right)^{1/A} \left(\frac{B\sqrt{r} + 1}{B\sqrt{r_0} + 1}\right)^{-1/B} = e^{\sqrt{ns}\,t} \tag{9}$$

Once again it is easier to refer to a diagram. There are two possibilities, illustrated in Figure V. The curve $sF(r,1)$ begins at a height s when $r = 0$. If $sa^2 > n$, there is no balanced growth equilibrium: the capital-labor ratio increases indefinitely and so does real output per head. The system is highly productive and saves-invests enough at full employment to expand very rapidly. If $sa^2 < n$, there is a stable balanced growth equilibrium, which is reached according to the solution (9). The equilibrium capital-labor ratio can be found by putting $\dot{r} = 0$ in (8); it is $r^* = (1/\sqrt{n/s} - a)^2$. It can be further calculated that the income per head prevailing in the limiting state of growth is $1/(1 - a\sqrt{s/n})^2$. That is, real income per head of labor force will rise to this value if it starts below, or vice versa.

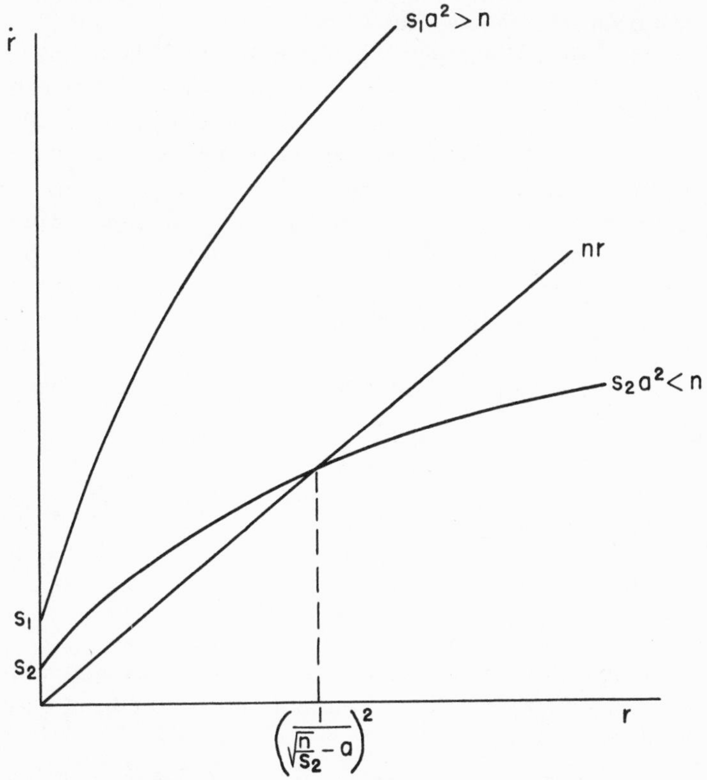

FIGURE V

V. Behavior of Interest and Wage Rates

The growth paths discussed in the previous sections can be looked at in two ways. From one point of view they have no causal significance but simply indicate the course that capital accumulation and real output would have to take if neither unemployment nor excess capacity are to appear. From another point of view, however, we can ask what kind of market behavior will cause the model economy to follow the path of equilibrium growth. In this direction it has already been assumed that both the growing labor force and the existing capital stock are thrown on the market inelastically, with the real wage and the real rental of capital adjusting instantaneously so as to clear the market. If saving and investment decisions are made independently, however, some additional marginal-efficiency-of-capital conditions have to be satisfied. The purpose of this section is to set out the price-wage-interest behavior appropriate to the growth paths sketched earlier.

There are four prices involved in the system: (1) the selling price of a unit of real output (and since real output serves also as capital this is the transfer price of a unit of capital stock) $p(t)$; (2) the money wage rate $w(t)$; (3) the money rental per unit of time of a unit of capital stock $q(t)$; (4) the rate of interest $i(t)$. One of these we can eliminate immediately. In the real system we are working with there is nothing to determine the absolute price level. Hence we can take $p(t)$, the price of real output, as given. Sometimes it will be convenient to imagine p as constant.

In a competitive economy the real wage and real rental are determined by the traditional marginal-productivity equations:

$$\frac{\partial F}{\partial L} = \frac{w}{p} \tag{10}$$

and

$$\frac{\partial F}{\partial K} = \frac{q}{p}. \tag{11}$$

Note in passing that with constant returns to scale the marginal productivities depend only on the capital-labor ratio r, and not on any scale quantities.[7]

7. In the polar case of pure competition, even if the individual firms have U-shaped average cost curves we can imagine changes in aggregate output taking place solely by the entry and exit of identical optimal-size firms. Then aggregate output is produced at constant cost; and in fact, because of the large number of relatively small firms each producing at approximately constant cost for small variations, we can without substantial error define an aggregate production function which will show constant returns to scale. There will be minor deviations since this aggregate production function is not strictly valid for variations in output smaller than the size of an optimal firm. But this lumpiness can for long-run analysis be treated as negligible.

One naturally thinks of adapting the model to the more general assumption of universal monopolistic competition. But the above device fails. If the industry consists of identical firms in identical large-group tangency equilibria then, subject to the restriction that output changes occur only via changes in the number of firms, one can perhaps define a constant-cost aggregate production function. But now this construct is largely irrelevant, for even if we are willing to overlook

The real rental on capital q/p is an own-rate of interest — it is the return on capital in units of capital stock. An owner of capital can by renting and reinvesting increase his holdings like compound interest at the *variable* instantaneous rate q/p, i.e., like $e^{\int_0^t q/p\,dt}$. Under conditions of perfect arbitrage there is a well-known close relationship between the money rate of interest and the commodity own-rate, namely

$$i(t) = \frac{q(t)}{p(t)} + \frac{\dot{p}(t)}{p(t)}. \tag{12}$$

If the price level is in fact constant, the own-rate and the interest rate will coincide. If the price level is falling, the own-rate must exceed the interest rate to induce people to hold commodities. That the exact relation is as in (12) can be seen in several ways. For example, the owner of \$1 at time t has two options: he can lend the money for a short space of time, say until $t + h$ and earn approximately $i(t)h$ in interest, or he can buy $1/p$ units of output, earn rentals of $(q/p)h$ and then sell. In the first case he will own $1 + i(t)h$ at the end of the period; in the second case he will have $(q(t)/p(t))h + p(t + h)/p(t)$. In equilibrium these two amounts must be equal

$$1 + i(t)h = \frac{q(t)}{p(t)}h + \frac{p(t + h)}{p(t)}$$

or

$$i(t)h = \frac{q(t)}{p(t)}h + \frac{p(t + h) - p(t)}{p(t)}.$$

Dividing both sides by h and letting h tend to zero we get (12). Thus this condition equalizes the attractiveness of holding wealth in the form of capital stock or loanable funds.

Another way of deriving (12) and gaining some insight into its role in our model is to note that $p(t)$, the transfer price of a unit of capital, must equal the present value of its future stream of net

its discontinuity and treat it as differentiable, the partial derivatives of such a function will not be the marginal productivities to which the individual firms respond. Each firm is on the falling branch of its unit cost curve, whereas in the competitive case each firm was actually producing at locally constant costs. The difficult problem remains of introducing monopolistic competition into aggregative models. For example, the value-of-marginal-product equations in the text would have to go over into marginal-revenue-product relations, which in turn would require the explicit presence of demand curves. Much further experimentation is needed here, with greater realism the reward.

rentals. Thus with perfect foresight into future rentals and interest rates:

$$p(t) = \int_t^\infty q(u)e^{-\int_t^u i(z)dz}\,du\,.$$

Differentiating with respect to time yields (12). Thus within the narrow confines of our model (in particular, absence of risk, a fixed average propensity to save, and no monetary complications) the money rate of interest and the return to holders of capital will stand in just the relation required to induce the community to hold the

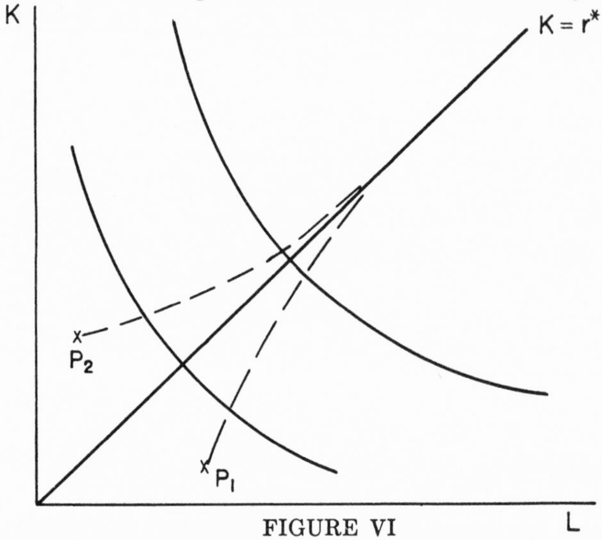

FIGURE VI

capital stock in existence. The absence of risk and uncertainty shows itself particularly in the absence of asset preferences.

Given the absolute price level $p(t)$, equations (10)–(12) determine the other three price variables, whose behavior can thus be calculated once the particular growth path is known.

Before indicating how the calculations would go in the examples of section IV, it is possible to get a general view diagrammatically, particularly when there is a stable balanced growth equilibrium. In Figure VI is drawn the ordinary isoquant map of the production function $F(K,L)$, and some possible kinds of growth paths. A given capital-labor ratio r^* is represented in Figure VI by a ray from the origin, with slope r^*. Suppose there is a stable asymptotic ratio r^*; then all growth paths issuing from arbitrary initial conditions approach the ray in the limit. Two such paths are shown, issuing from initial points P_1 and P_2. Since back in Figure I the approach of r to r^* was monotonic, the paths must look as shown in Figure VI. We see that if the initial capital-labor ratio is higher than the equilibrium value, the ratio falls and vice versa.

Figure VII corresponds to Figure II. There are three "equilibrium" rays, but the inner one is unstable. The inner ray is the dividing line among initial conditions which lead to one of the stable rays and those which lead to the other. All paths, of course, lead upward and to the right, without bending back; K and L always

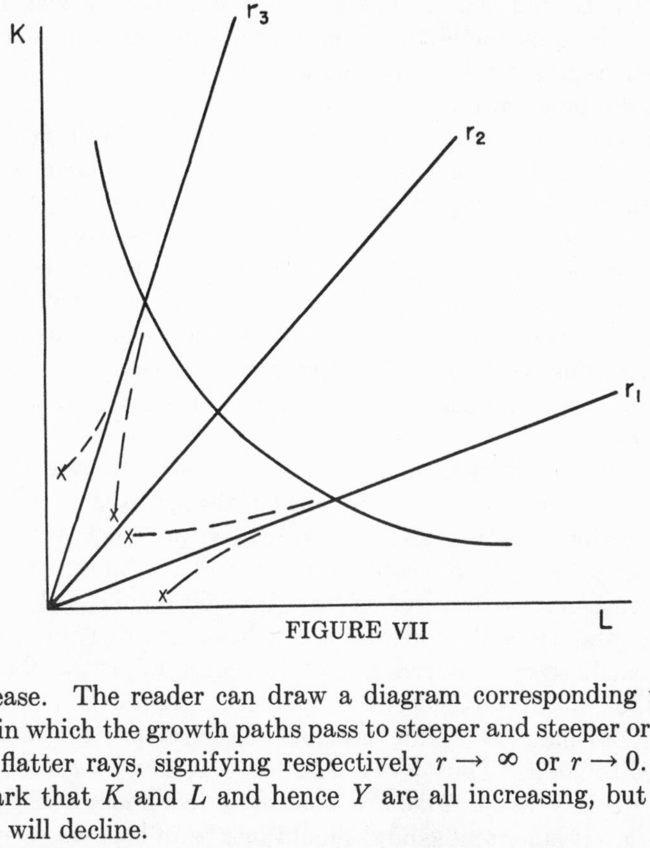

FIGURE VII

increase. The reader can draw a diagram corresponding to Figure III, in which the growth paths pass to steeper and steeper or to flatter and flatter rays, signifying respectively $r \rightarrow \infty$ or $r \rightarrow 0$. Again I remark that K and L and hence Y are all increasing, but if $r \rightarrow 0$, Y/L will decline.

Now because of constant returns to scale we know that along a ray from the origin, the slope of the isoquants is constant. This expresses the fact that marginal products depend only on the factor ratio. But in competition the slope of the isoquant reflects the ratio of the factor prices. Thus to a stable r^* as in Figure VI corresponds an equilibrium ratio w/q. Moreover, if the isoquants have the normal convexity, it is apparent that as r rises to r^*, the ratio w/q rises to its limiting value, and vice versa if r is falling.

In the unstable case, where r tends to infinity or zero it may be that w/q tends to infinity or zero. If, on the other hand, the isoquants reach the axes with slopes intermediate between the vertical and horizontal, the factor price ratio w/q will tend to a finite limit.

It might also be useful to point out that the slope of the curve $F(r,1)$ is the marginal productivity of capital at the corresponding value of r. Thus the course of the real rental q/p can be traced out in Figures I, II, and III. Remember that in those diagrams $F(r,1)$ has been reduced by the factor s, hence so has the slope of the curve. $F(r,1)$ itself represents Y/L, output per unit of labor, as a function of the capital-labor ratio.

In general if a stable growth path exists, the fall in the real wage or real rental needed to get to it may not be catastrophic at all. If there is an initial shortage of labor (compared with the equilibrium ratio) the real wage will have to fall. The higher the rate of increase of the labor force and the lower the propensity to save, the lower the equilibrium ratio and hence the more the real wage will have to fall. But the fall is not indefinite. I owe to John Chipman the remark that this result directly contradicts Harrod's position[8] that a perpetually falling rate of interest would be needed to maintain equilibrium.

Catastrophic changes in factor prices do occur in the Harrod-Domar case, but again as a consequence of the special assumption of fixed proportions. I have elsewhere discussed price behavior in the Harrod model[9] but I there described price level and interest rate and omitted consideration of factor prices. Actually there is little to say. The isoquants in the Harrod case are right-angled corners and this tells the whole story. Referring back to Figure IV, if the observed capital-labor ratio is bigger than a/b, then capital is absolutely redundant, its marginal product is zero, and the whole value of output is imputed to labor. Thus $q = 0$, and $bw = p$, so $w = p/b$. If the observed r is less than a/b labor is absolutely redundant and $w = 0$, so $q = p/a$. If labor and capital should just be in balance, $r = a/b$, then obviously it is not possible to impute any specific fraction of output to labor or capital separately. All we can be sure of is that the total value of a unit of output p will be imputed back to the

8. In his comments on an article by Pilvin, this *Journal*, Nov. 1953, p. 545.

9. R. M. Solow, "A Note on Price Level and Interest Rate in a Growth Model," *Review of Economic Studies*, No. 54 (1953–54), pp. 74–78.

composite dose of a units of capital and b units of labor (both factors are scarce). Hence w and q can have any values subject only to the condition $aq + bw = p$, $aq/p + bw/p = 1$. Thus in Figure IV anywhere but at $r = a/b$ either capital or labor must be redundant, and at a/b factor prices are indeterminate. And it is only in special circumstances that $r = a/b$.

Next consider the Cobb-Douglas case: $Y = K^a L^{1-a}$ and $q/p = a(K/L)^{a-1} = ar^{a-1}$. Hence $w/q = \frac{1-a}{a} r$. The exact time paths of the real factor prices can be calculated without difficulty from the solution to (7), but are of no special interest. We saw earlier, however, that the limiting capital-labor ratio is $(s/n)^{1/1-a}$. Hence the equilibrium real wage rate is $(1 - a)(s/n)^{a/1-a}$, and the equilibrium real rental is an/s. These conclusions are qualitatively just what we should expect. As always with the Cobb-Douglas function the share of labor in real output is constant.

Our third example provides one bit of variety. From $Y = (a\sqrt{K} + \sqrt{L})^2$ we can compute that $\partial Y/\partial L = a\sqrt{\frac{K}{L}} + 1 = a\sqrt{r} + 1$. In the case where a balanced growth equilibrium exists (see end of section IV) $r^* = \left(\frac{1}{\sqrt{n/s} - a}\right)^2$; therefore the limiting real wage is $w/p = \frac{1}{\sqrt{n/s} - a} + 1 = \frac{1}{1 - a\sqrt{s/n}}$. It was calculated earlier that in equilibrium growth $Y/L = \left(\frac{1}{1 - a\sqrt{s/n}}\right)^2$. But the relative share of labor is $(w/p)(L/Y) = 1 - a\sqrt{s/n}$. This is unlike the Cobb-Douglas case, where the relative shares are independent of s and n, depending only on the production function. Here we see that *in equilibrium growth* the relative share of labor is the greater the greater the rate of increase of the labor force and the smaller the propensity to save. In fact as one would expect, the faster the labor force increases the lower is the real wage in the equilibrium state of balanced growth; but the lower real wage still leaves the larger labor force a greater share of real income.

VI. Extensions

Neutral Technological Change. Perfectly arbitrary changes over time in the production function can be contemplated in principle, but are hardly likely to lead to systematic conclusions. An especially easy kind of technological change is that which simply multiplies the production function by an increasing scale factor. Thus we alter (2) to read

$$Y = A(t)F(K,L). \tag{13}$$

The isoquant map remains unchanged but the output number attached to each isoquant is multiplied by $A(t)$. The way in which the (now ever-changing) equilibrium capital-labor ratio is affected can be seen on a diagram like Figure I by "blowing up" the function $sF(r,1)$.

The Cobb-Douglas case works out very simply. Take $A(t) = e^{gt}$ and then the basic differential equation becomes

$$\dot{K} = se^{gt}K^a(L_0e^{nt})^{1-a} = sK^aL_0{}^{1-a}e^{(n(1-a)+g)t},$$

whose solution is

$$K(t) = \left[K_0{}^b - \frac{bs}{nb+g}L_0{}^b + \frac{bs}{nb+g}L_0{}^b e^{(nb+g)t}\right]^{1/b}$$

where again $b = 1 - a$. In the long run the capital stock increases at the relative rate $n + g/b$ (compared with n in the case of no technological change). The eventual rate of increase of real output is $n + ag/b$. This is not only faster than n but (if $a > 1/2$) may even be faster than $n + g$. The reason, of course, is that higher real output means more saving and investment, which compounds the rate of growth still more. Indeed now the capital-labor ratio never reaches an equilibrium value but grows forever. The ever-increasing investment capacity is, of course, not matched by any speeding up of the growth of the labor force. Hence K/L gets bigger, eventually growing at the rate g/b. If the initial capital-labor ratio is very high, it might fall initially, but eventually it turns around and its asymptotic behavior is as described.

Since the capital-labor ratio eventually rises without limit, it follows that the real wage must eventually rise and keep rising. On the other hand, the special property of the Cobb-Douglas function is that the relative share of labor is constant at $1 - a$. The other essential structural facts follow from what has already been said: for example, since Y eventually grows at rate $n + ag/b$ and K at rate $n + g/b$, the capital coefficient K/Y grows at rate $n + g/b - n - ag/b = g$.

The Supply of Labor. In general one would want to make the supply of labor a function of the real wage rate and time (since the labor force is growing). We have made the special assumption that $L = L_0e^{nt}$, i.e., that the labor-supply curve is completely inelastic with respect to the real wage and shifts to the right with the size of the labor force. We could generalize this somewhat by assuming that whatever the size of the labor force the proportion offered depends on the real wage. Specifically

$$L = L_0e^{nt}\left(\frac{w}{p}\right)^h. \tag{14}$$

Another way of describing this assumption is to note that it is a scale blow-up of a constant elasticity curve. In a detailed analysis this particular labor supply pattern would have to be modified at very high real wages, since given the size of the labor force there is an upper limit to the amount of labor that can be supplied, and (14) does not reflect this.

Our old differential equation (6) for the capital-labor ratio now becomes somewhat more complicated. Namely if we make the price level constant, for simplicity:

$$\dot{r} = sF(r,1) - nr - h\frac{\dot{w}}{w}. \tag{6a}$$

To (6a) we must append the marginal productivity condition (10) $\frac{\partial F}{\partial L} = \frac{w}{p}$. Since the marginal product of labor depends only on r, we can eliminate w.

But generality leads to complications, and instead I turn again to the tractable Cobb-Douglas function. For that case (10) becomes

$$\frac{w}{p} = (1 - a)r^a$$

and hence

$$\frac{\dot{w}}{w} = a\frac{\dot{r}}{r}.$$

After a little manipulation (6a) can be written

$$\dot{r} = (sF(r,1) - nr)\left(1 + \frac{ah}{r}\right)^{-1},$$

which gives some insight into how an elastic labor supply changes things. In the first place, an equilibrium state of balanced growth still exists, when the right-hand side becomes zero, and it is still stable, approached from any initial conditions. Moreover, the equilibrium capital-labor ratio is *unchanged;* since $\dot{r}$ becomes zero exactly where it did before. This will not always happen, of course; it is a consequence of the special supply-of-labor schedule (14). Since r behaves in much the same way so will all those quantities which depend only on r, such as the real wage.

The reader who cares to work out the details can show that over the long run capital stock and real output will grow at the same rate n as the labor force.

If we assume quite generally that $L = G(t,w/p)$ then (6) will take the form

$$\text{(6b)} \qquad \dot{r} = sF(r,1) - \frac{r}{G}\left(\frac{\partial G}{\partial t} + \dot{w}\,\frac{\partial G}{\partial\left(\frac{w}{p}\right)}\right).$$

If $\dot{r} = 0$, then $\dot{w} = 0$, and the equilibrium capital-labor ratio is determined by

$$sF(r,1) = \frac{r}{G}\,\frac{\partial G}{\partial t}.$$

Unless $1/G\ \partial G/\partial t$ should happen always to equal n, as in the case with (14), the equilibrium capital-labor ratio *will* be affected by the introduction of an elastic labor supply.

Variable Saving Ratio. Up to now, whatever else has been happening in the model there has always been growth of both labor force and capital stock. The growth of the labor force was exogenously given, while growth in the capital stock was inevitable because the savings ratio was taken as an absolute constant. As long as real income was positive, positive net capital formation must result. This rules out the possibility of a Ricardo-Mill stationary state, and suggests the experiment of letting the rate of saving depend on the yield of capital. If savings can fall to zero when income is positive, it becomes possible for net investment to cease and for the capital stock, at least, to become stationary. There will still be growth of the labor force, however; it would take us too far afield to go wholly classical with a theory of population growth and a fixed supply of land.

The simplest way to let the interest rate or yield on capital influence the volume of savings is to make the fraction of income saved depend on the real return to owners of capital. Thus total savings is $s(q/p)Y$. Under constant returns to scale and competition, the real rental will depend only on the capital-labor ratio, hence we can easily convert the savings ratio into a function of r.

Everyone is familiar with the inconclusive discussions, both abstract and econometrical, as to whether the rate of interest really has any independent effect on the volume of saving, and if so, in what direction. For the purposes of this experiment, however, the natural assumption to make is that the savings ratio depends positively on the yield of capital (and hence inversely on the capital-labor ratio).

For convenience let me skip the step of passing from q/p to r via marginal productivity, and simply write savings as $s(r)Y$. Then the only modification in the theory is that the fundamental equation (6) becomes

$$\dot{r} = s(r)F(r,1) - nr\,. \tag{6c}$$

The graphical treatment is much the same as before, except that we must allow for the variable factor $s(r)$. It may be that for sufficiently large r, $s(r)$ becomes zero. (This will be the case only if, first, there is a real rental so low that saving stops, and second, if the production function is such that a very high capital-labor ratio will drive the real return down to that critical value. The latter condition is not satisfied by all production functions.) If so, $s(r)F(r,1)$ will be zero for all sufficiently large r. If $F(0,1) = 0$, i.e., if no production is possible without capital, then $s(r)F(r,1)$ must come down to zero again at the origin, no matter how high the savings ratio is. But this is not inevitable either. Figure VIII gives a possible picture. As usual r^*, the equilibrium capital-labor ratio, is found by putting $\dot{r} = 0$ in (6c). In Figure VIII the equilibrium is stable and eventually capital and output will grow at the same rate as the labor force.

In general if $s(r)$ does vanish for large r, this eliminates the possibility of a runaway indefinite increase in the capital-labor ratio as in Figure III. The savings ratio *need* not go to zero to do this, but if it should, we are guaranteed that the last intersection with nr is a stable one.

If we compare any particular $s(r)$ with a constant saving ratio, the two curves will cross at the value of r for which $s(r)$ equals the old constant ratio. To the right the new curve will lie below (since I am assuming that $s(r)$ is a decreasing function) and to the left it will lie above the old curve. It is easily seen by example that the equilibrium r^* may be either larger or smaller than it was before. A wide variety of shapes and patterns is possible, but the net effect tends to be stabilizing: when the capital-labor ratio is high, saving is cut down; when it is low, saving is stimulated. There is still no possibility of a stationary state: should r get so high as to choke off

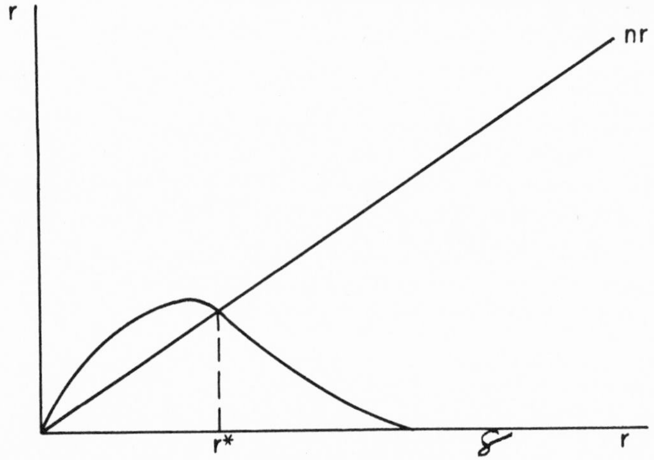

FIGURE VIII

saving and net capital formation, the continual growth of the labor force must eventually reduce it.

Taxation. My colleague, E. C. Brown, points out to me that all the above analysis can be extended to accommodate the effects of a personal income tax. In the simplest case, suppose the state levies a proportional income tax at the rate t. If the revenues are directed wholly into capital formation, the savings-investment identity (1) becomes

$$\dot{K} = s(1 - t)Y + tY = (s(1 - t) + t)Y.$$

That is, the effective savings ratio is *increased* from s to $s + t(1 - s)$. If the proceeds of the tax are directly consumed, the savings ratio is *decreased* from s to $s(1 - t)$. If a fraction v of the tax proceeds is invested and the rest consumed, the savings ratio changes to

$s + (v - s)t$ which is larger or smaller than s according as the state invests a larger or smaller fraction of its income than the private economy. The effects can be traced on diagrams such as Figure I: the curve $sF(r,1)$ is uniformly blown up or contracted and the equilibrium capital-labor ratio is correspondingly shifted. Non-proportional taxes can be incorporated with more difficulty, but would produce more interesting twists in the diagrams. Naturally the presence of an income tax will affect the price-wage relationships in the obvious way.

Variable Population Growth. Instead of treating the relative rate of population increase as a constant, we can more classically make it

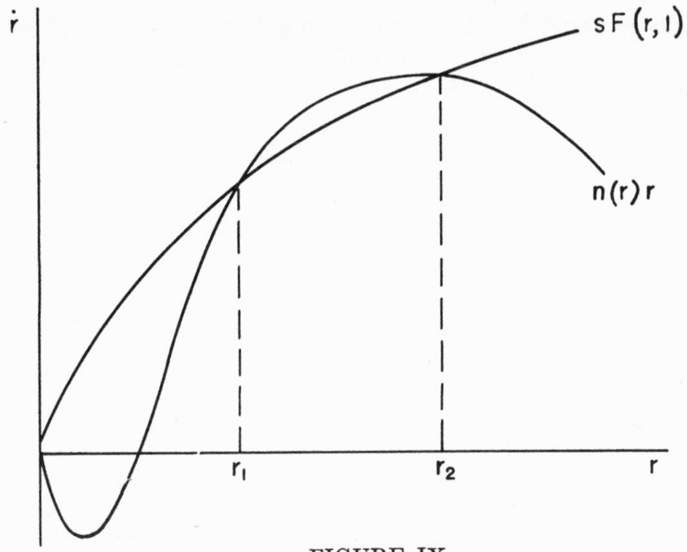

FIGURE IX

an endogenous variable of the system. In particular if we suppose that $\dot{L}/L$ depends only on the level of per capita income or consumption, or for that matter on the real wage rate, the generalization is especially easy to carry out. Since per capita income is given by $Y/L = F(r,1)$ the upshot is that the rate of growth of the labor force becomes $n = n(r)$, a function of the capital-labor ratio alone. The basic differential equation becomes

$$r = sF(r,1) - n(r)r\,.$$

Graphically the only difference is that the ray nr is twisted into a curve, whose shape depends on the exact nature of the dependence between population growth and real income, and between real income and the capital-labor ratio.

Suppose, for example, that for very low levels of income per head or the real wage population tends to decrease; for higher levels of income it begins to increase; and that for still higher levels of income the rate of population growth levels off and starts to decline. The result may be something like Figure IX. The equilibrium capital-labor ratio r_1 is stable, but r_2 is unstable. The accompanying levels of per capita income can be read off from the shape of $F(r,1)$. If the initial capital-labor ratio is less than r_2, the system will of itself tend to return to r_1. If the initial ratio could somehow be boosted above the critical level r_2, a self-sustaining process of increasing per capita income would be set off (and population would still be growing). The interesting thing about this case is that it shows how, in the total absence of indivisibilities or of increasing returns, a situation may still arise in which small-scale capital accumulation only leads back to stagnation but a major burst of investment can lift the system into a self-generating expansion of income and capital per head. The reader can work out still other possibilities.

VII. Qualifications

Everything above is the neoclassical side of the coin. Most especially it is full employment economics — in the dual aspect of equilibrium condition and frictionless, competitive, causal system. All the difficulties and rigidities which go into modern Keynesian income analysis have been shunted aside. It is not my contention that these problems don't exist, nor that they are of no significance in the long run. My purpose was to examine what might be called the tightrope view of economic growth and to see where more flexible assumptions about production would lead a simple model. Underemployment and excess capacity or their opposites can still be attributed to any of the old causes of deficient or excess aggregate demand, but less readily to any deviation from a narrow "balance."

In this concluding section I want merely to mention some of the more elementary obstacles to full employment and indicate how they impinge on the neoclassical model.[1]

Rigid Wages. This assumption about the supply of labor is just the reverse of the one made earlier. The real wage is held at some

1. A much more complete and elegant analysis of these important problems is to be found in a paper by James Tobin in the *Journal of Political Economy*, LXII (1955), 103–15.

arbitrary level $\left(\frac{\overline{w}}{p}\right)$. The level of employment must be such as to keep the marginal product of labor at this level. Since the marginal productivities depend only on the capital-labor ratio, it follows that fixing the real wage fixes r at, say, $\bar{r}$. Thus $K/L = \bar{r}$. Now there is no point in using r as our variable so we go back to (3) which in view of the last sentence becomes

$$\bar{r}\dot{L} = sF(\bar{r}L,L),$$

or

$$\frac{\dot{L}}{L} = \frac{s}{\bar{r}} F(\bar{r},1).$$

This says that *employment* will increase exponentially at the rate $(s/r)F(\bar{r},1)$. If this rate falls short of n, the rate of growth of the labor force, unemployment will develop and increase. If $s/\bar{r}F(\bar{r},1) > n$, labor shortage will be the outcome and presumably the real wage will eventually become flexible upward. What this boils down to is that if $(\overline{w}/p)$ corresponds to a capital-labor ratio that would normally tend to decrease ($\dot{r} < 0$), unemployment develops, and vice versa. In the diagrams, $s/\bar{r}F(\bar{r},1)$ is just the slope of the ray from the origin to the $sF(r,1)$ curve at $\bar{r}$. If this slope is flatter than n, unemployment develops; if steeper, labor shortage develops.

Liquidity Preference. This is much too complicated a subject to be treated carefully here. Moreover the paper by Tobin just mentioned contains a new and penetrating analysis of the dynamics connected with asset preferences. I simply note here, however crudely, the point of contact with the neoclassical model.

Again taking the general price level as constant (which is now an unnatural thing to do), the transactions demand for money will depend on real output Y and the choice between holding cash and holding capital stock will depend on the real rental q/p. With a given quantity of money this provides a relation between Y and q/p or, essentially, between K and L, e.g.,

$$(15) \qquad \overline{M} = Q\left(Y, \frac{q}{p}\right) = Q(F(K,L), F_K(K,L))$$

where now K represents capital *in use*. On the earlier assumption of full employment of labor via flexible wages, we can put $L = L_0e^{nt}$, and solve (15) for $K(t)$, or employed capital equipment. From $K(t)$ and L we can compute $Y(t)$ and hence total saving $sY(t)$. But this represents net investment (wealth not held as cash must be held as capital). The given initial stock of capital and the flow of investment determine the available capital stock which can be compared with $K(t)$ to measure the excess supply or demand for the services of capital.

In the famous "trap" case where the demand for idle balances becomes infinitely elastic at some positive rate of interest, we have a rigid factor price which can be treated much as rigid wages were treated above. The result will be underutilization of capital if the interest rate becomes rigid somewhere above the level corresponding to the equilibrium capital-labor ratio.

But it is exactly here that the futility of trying to describe this situation in terms of a "real" neoclassical model becomes glaringly evident. Because now one can no longer bypass the direct leverage of monetary factors on real consumption and investment. When the issue is the allocation of asset-holdings between cash and capital stock, the price of the composite commodity becomes an important variable and there is no dodging the need for a monetary dynamics.

Policy Implications. This is hardly the place to discuss the bearing of the previous highly abstract analysis on the practical problems of economic stabilization. I have been deliberately as neoclassical as you can get. Some part of this rubs off on the policy side. It may take deliberate action to maintain full employment. But the multiplicity of routes to full employment, via tax, expenditure, and monetary policies, leaves the nation *some* leeway to choose whether it wants high employment with relatively heavy capital formation, low consumption, rapid growth; or the reverse, or some mixture. I do not mean to suggest that this kind of policy (for example: cheap money and a budget surplus) can be carried on without serious strains. But one of the advantages of this more flexible model of growth is that it provides a theoretical counterpart to these practical possibilities.[2]

Uncertainty, etc. No credible theory of investment can be built on the assumption of perfect foresight and arbitrage over time. There are only too many reasons why net investment should be at

2. See the paper by Paul A. Samuelson in *Income Stabilization for a Developing Democracy*, ed. Millikan (New Haven, 1953), p. 577. Similar thoughts have been expressed by William Vickrey in his essay in *Post-Keynesian Economics*, ed. Kurihara (New Brunswick, 1954).

times insensitive to current changes in the real return to capital, at other times oversensitive. All these cobwebs and some others have been brushed aside throughout this essay. In the context, this is perhaps justifiable.

Robert M. Solow.

Massachusetts Institute of Technology

8

ECONOMIC GROWTH AND CAPITAL ACCUMULATION

By T. W. Swan

1. *From Adam Smith to Arthur Lewis.*

"The design of the book is different from that of any treatise on Political Economy which has been produced in England since the work of Adam Smith." "The last great book covering this wide range was John Stuart Mill's *Principles of Political Economy.*" The first sentence is from Mill's preface, the second from the preface to Lewis' *The Theory of Economic Growth.* It would be rash to conclude from this sequence that one might keep up-to-date in economics by reading a new book every century. Lewis' remark is partly a warning that his book is about applications as well as theories, and partly a reminder that he is taking up an old theme of English economic thought. When Keynes solved "the great puzzle of Effective Demand", he made it possible for economists once more to study the progress of society in long-run classical terms—with a clear conscience, "safely ensconced in a Ricardian world."

The aim of this paper is to illustrate with two diagrams a theme common to Adam Smith, Mill, and Lewis, the theory of which is perhaps best seen in Ricardo: namely, the connexion between capital accumulation and the growth of the productive labour force. The neo-classical economists were in favour of productivity and thrift, but never found a way to make much use of them. Earlier views were much more specific: for example, Adam Smith's industry "proportioned to capital", Ricardo's Doctrine of Unbalanced Growth, Mill's "Irish peasantry, only half fed and half employed", now so familiar in the work of Harrod, Nurkse, or Lewis, and in a hundred United Nations reports. Nevertheless, our illustration takes a neo-classical form, and enjoys the neo-classical as well as the Ricardian vice.[1]

2. *An Unclassical Case.*

In the first instance, capital and labour are the only factors of production. In a given state of the arts, the annual output Y depends on the stock of capital K and the labour force N, according to the constant-elasticity production function $Y = K^{\alpha} N^{\beta}$. With constant returns to scale, $\alpha + \beta = 1$. The annual additon to the capital stock is

1. An appendix discusses some of the questions—especially those raised by Joan Robinson—concerning the role of Capital as a factor of production in the neo-classical theory. However, the appendix makes no attempt to discuss or defend the use of this or other concepts in a dynamic analysis, except by indicating some very artificial assumptions by which the main difficulties might be dodged.

the amount saved[2] sY, where s is a given ratio of saving to output (or income.)

Therefore the annual relative rate of growth of capital is $s\frac{Y}{K}$. The symbols y and n stand for the annual relative rates of growth of output and labour respectively. In these terms the production function implies the basic formula for the rate of growth of output[3]:

$$(1)\ y = \alpha s\frac{Y}{K} + \beta n$$

Effective demand is so regulated (*via* the rate of interest or otherwise) that all savings are profitably invested, productive capacity is fully utilized, and the level of employment can never be increased merely by raising the level of spending. The forces of perfect competition drive the rate of profit or interest r and the (real) wage rate w into equality with the marginal productivities of capital and labour, derived from the production function:

$$(2)\quad r = \alpha\frac{Y}{K} \qquad (3)\quad w = \beta\frac{Y}{N}$$

Thus the profit rate is proportional to output per unit of capital, $\frac{Y}{K}$, or the *output-capital ratio;* the wage rate is proportional to output per unit of labour, $\frac{Y}{N}$, or *output per head.* The relative shares of total profits and total wages in income are constants, given by the production elasticities α and β.

In Figure 1, look first at the three heavy lines. The rate of growth of capital $s\frac{Y}{K}$ is shown as a function of the output-capital ratio by a line through the origin with a slope equal to the saving ratio ($s = 10$ per cent).[4]

This may be called the *growth line* of capital. The resulting contribution of capital to the growth of output, $\alpha s\frac{Y}{K}$, is another line through the origin, of slope αs ($\alpha = 0{\cdot}4$), and may be called the *contribution line* of capital.[5]

2. A given amount of saving, in terms of output, has a constant productive equivalent in terms of the capital stock. In Joan Robinson's language, the Wicksell effect is assumed to be zero. Part IV of the appendix argues that Joan Robinson is mistaken in her view that a rule can be laid down regarding the direction of the Wicksell effect.

3. The formula is obtained after logarithmic differentiation of the production function. All variables are treated as continuous functions of time, which is measured in years. For example, "annual output" is the instantaneous rate of output per annum. The words "growth", "rate of growth", etc. always refer to instantaneous relative rates of growth per annum, subject to instantaneous compounding.

4. Numerical plottings are used merely to help fix ideas.

5. According to the marginal productivity formula (2) above, $\alpha s\frac{Y}{K} = sr$. The rate of profit may therefore be read directly from Figure 1 by multiplying the contribution line of capital by 10.

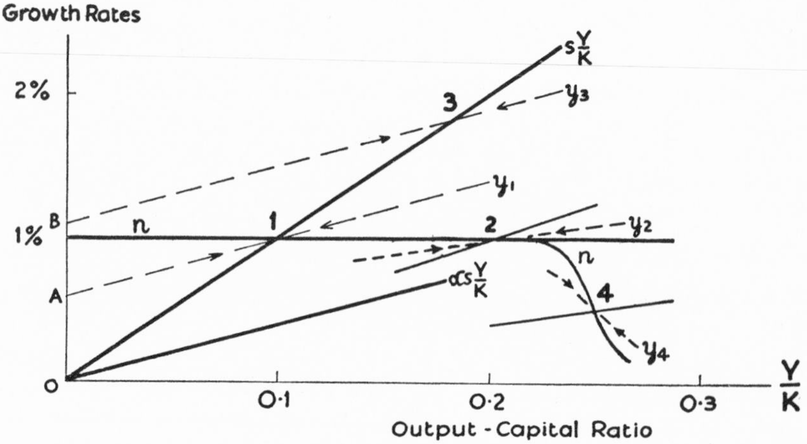

FIGURE 1.

The growth line of labour is horizontal, the rate of growth of the labour force being assumed for the present to be constant ($n = 1$ per cent). The distance OA on the vertical axis is βn ($\beta = 1 - \alpha = 0{\cdot}6$), which is labour's contribution to the growth of output. Adding the contributions of capital and labour gives the growth line of output, y_1. Since $\alpha + \beta = 1$, the geometry of the diagram implies that the three growth lines (of capital, labour, and output) must intersect at the same point (1), where growth in each case is 1 per cent per annum. The growth line of output is intermediate between the growth lines of labour and capital, and divides the vertical distance between them in the proportion $\alpha : \beta$. Anywhere west of (1) output is growing faster than capital, so the output-capital ratio is rising—moving eastward. Anywhere east of (1), capital is growing faster than output, so the movement of the output-capital ratio is westward. Only at (1) is there a resting-place. *At any other point the economy is always in motion towards (1)*,[6] as shown by the arrows on the line y_1.

The point (2) is another equilibrium point like (1), except that it corresponds with a saving ratio of 5 per cent, instead of 10 per cent at (1). The (unlabelled) continuous line is the new growth line of capital, with a slope through the origin of 5 per cent. The line y_2 is the new growth line of output, which if extended would meet the vertical axis at A as before. (The new contribution line of capital is not drawn.) At (2) economic growth is uniformly 1 per cent, just as at (1), because the three growth lines must still intersect somewhere on the horizontal line n. The given rate of growth of labour thus determines the equilibrium growth rate of the whole economy, while the saving ratio determines the output-capital ratio at which equilibrium will occur.

Suppose the economy is at (2), and that a thrift campaign suddenly raises the saving ratio from 5 per cent to 10 per cent. The growth line of output shifts from y_2 to y_1. Output per head begins to improve (as shown by the height of y_1 above n near (2)), and the wage rate rises in the same proportion. The output-capital ratio gradually sinks westward, and the profit rate sinks in the same proportion. The improvement of output per head continues at an ever-slackening pace down the slope of y_1, towards (1). At (1) output per head and the wage rate are higher than at (2), while the output-capital ratio and the profit rate are lower. These are permanent changes, but the rate of economic growth is faster only in the course of transition from (2) to (1).

Suppose next that the state of the arts, hitherto assumed constant, continually improves. "Neutral" technical progress contributes to the growth of output an annual m per cent beyond the contributions of capital and labour. In Figure 1 the distance AB on the vertical axis is m, at an assumed rate of $\frac{1}{2}$ per cent. The new growth line of output y_3 shows this amount added on top of y_1 (for a 10 per cent saving ratio), and it cuts the growth line of capital at the point (3). This will now be the equilibrium point. In some respects the transition from (2) to (1) is reversed by the introduction of technical progress, since the output-capital ratio and the rate of profit are both higher at (3) than at (1). But the main change is that output per head is not only permanently higher, but perpetually rising (as shown by the height of y_3 above n at (3)). Its rate of increase is actually greater than the m per cent contributed directly by technical progress, because the contribution of capital is also sustained by technical progress at a higher level (as shown by the height of y_1 above n at (3)).

The effect of a change in thrift, assuming constant technical progress, is not shown in the diagram. If another situation were depicted, combining the 5 per cent saving ratio of (2) with the

6. Figure 1 is in effect the "phase portrait" of a first-order differential equation in the variable $\frac{Y}{K}$ (cf. Andronow & Chaikin, *Theory of Oscillations,* Chapter IV). A similar device is used by R. M. Solow (*A Contribution to the Theory of Economic Growth,* Quarterly Journal of Economics, February, 1956). The approach to the point (1) along y_1 is asymptotic—i.e., (1) is reached only in infinity, the speed of travel towards it being directly related to the distance remaining to be travelled. (The time taken for $\frac{Y}{K}$ to move any given distance towards equilibrium is not revealed by the diagram, and can be discovered only by integrating the differentiai equation.) A point such as (1) is a *stable* equilibrium point because the growth line of capital cuts the growth line of labour (and so the growth line of output) from below. If over a certain range the saving ratio s were a decreasing function of $\frac{Y}{K}$, the growth line of capital might cut the growth line of labour from above, and this second intersection would be an *unstable* equilibrium point (the arrows would be directed away from it on either side).

½ per cent technical progress of (3), its equilibrium point would be found to lie well to the east of (3), but on exactly the same parallel of economic growth. So long as technical progress and the rate of growth of labour are taken as *data,* they jointly determine the equilibrium growth rate of output and capital.[7] After a transitional phase, the influence of the saving ratio on the rate of growth is ultimately absorbed by a compensating change in the output-capital ratio.

This conclusion is not really surprising. It is in fact the counterpart in our present unclassical model of the classical proposition that capital accumulation leads *ultimately* to the stationary state. A rise in the saving ratio does mean that the level of output per head is permanently higher at any time thereafter than it would have been otherwise. Further, the "transitional phase" is never literally completed; the "transitional" acceleration-deceleration of growth might be visible for centuries, depending entirely on the numerical assumptions. However, only extreme assumptions could produce such a result. It is at first sight disconcerting to find that "plausible" figuring suggests that even the impact effect of a sharp rise in the saving ratio may be of minor importance for the rate of growth: for example, the maximum amount added to the rate of growth, at the beginning of the transition from (2) to (1) in Figure 1, is only 0·4 per cent, though the thrift campaign doubles the saving ratio at a point where the yield on capital is 8 per cent.

To this anti-accumulation, pro-technology line of argument there are at least two possible anwers. First, the rate of technical progress may not be independent of the rate of accumulation, or (what comes to much the same thing) accumulation may give rise to external economies, so that the true social yield of capital is greater than any "plausible" figure based on common private experience.[8] This point would have appealed to Adam Smith, but it will not be pursued here. Second, the rate of growth of labour may

7. Equation (1) on page 335, with the addition of m per cent technical progress, becomes

$$(1') \quad y = \alpha s \frac{Y}{K} + \beta n + m$$

from which it follows that when $y = s\frac{Y}{K}$ (i.e., at an equilibrium point where the output-capital ratio is stationary) $y = \frac{\beta n + m}{1 - \alpha}$. For $\alpha + \beta = 1$ this is simply $y = n + \frac{m}{1 - \alpha}$.

8. In Figure 1, allowing for external economies, $\alpha + \beta$ would exceed unity and so y_1 would cut the growth line of capital above the level of n, just as y_3 does. If the external economies were concentrated on the side of capital (rather than labour), this elevation would take the form of a steeper slope for the contribution line of capital, which of course would no longer correspond with the rate of profit.

not be independent of the rate of accumulation. This is the distinctively classical answer.

In Figure 1 the sloping branch of the growth line of labour represents a situation in which the supply of labour is "elastic" in the vicinity of a certain level of output per head (and wage rate). This situation may be given a Malthusian interpretation, as the response of population to an improvement in the means of subsistence; it may be a situation of "disguised unemployment", with unproductive labour kept in reserve (by sharing with relatives, etc.) at a minimum living standard; it may be the result of Trade Union resistance or some other kind of institutional or conventional barrier, expressed in real terms; or it may reflect a potential supply of migrant labour, available if satisfactory living standards are offered. In any of these situations, "demand for commodities is not demand for labour" (if only Mill had understood his own doctrine): the growth, or productive employment, of the labour force depends directly on the rate of accumulation. In the neighbourhood of the point (4), which is drawn for a saving ratio of 2 per cent, a higher saving ratio will evidently raise the rate of economic growth almost in proportion—and not only "transitionally", but in equilibrium as well. On the other hand, the wage rate and output per head (of *productively employed* labour) will not be much improved; nor will the rate of profit and the output-capital ratio suffer much decline.

This last fact is of course one of the reasons why capital accumulation appears so much more effective in raising the rate of economic growth when faster growth means primarily a faster expansion of productive employment, rather than a faster improvement of output per head. But the main reason is that accumulation is justly credited with the productive contribution of the additional labour that it "sets in motion."

It is now possible to look at Figure 1 in a new light. What is the maximum rate of labour growth consistent with the maintenance of a given standard of output per head? The answer (assuming no technical progress) is that for any such standard—i.e., at any given level of the output-capital ratio—the maximum rate of growth is directly proportional to the saving ratio. In fact, the growth line of capital $s\frac{Y}{K}$, wherever it lies, is the locus of all growth rates at which output per head is constant.

This is a more classical view of the problem, and also, unfortunately, perhaps more relevant to many contemporary problems of population pressure and economic growth. However, to see its implications in either context, it is necessary to introduce a characteristic feature of the classical model—namely, the limited "powers of the soil".

3. *A Classical Case.*

A fixed factor of production, which may be called land, can be introduced very simply. Let its production elasticity be γ. Then, assuming constant returns to scale, $\alpha + \beta + \gamma = 1$. However, since land is fixed in supply, it does not appear in the basic formula for the growth of output, $y = \alpha s \frac{Y}{K} + \beta n$, but makes its presence felt by reducing the sum of α and β below unity. With this interpretation, the former marginal productivity relationships for r and w remain unchanged, and there is now a third, of similar form, to determine the rent of land. α, β, and γ are now the constant relative shares of the three factors in income.

If Figure 1 were drawn for $\alpha + \beta < 1$, the growth line of output would cut the growth line of capital below the horizontal growth line of labour. The only possible equilibrium with constant labour growth (and no technical progress) would be one in which output per head and the wage rate were perpetually falling. However, an answer can be given to the question: what rate of labour growth will maintain constant output per head? This condition can be expressed by putting $y = n$ in the formula repeated in the last paragraph, which gives $n = \frac{\alpha}{1 - \beta} s \frac{Y}{K}$. In Figure 2 the constants are assumed to be $\alpha = 0{\cdot}3$, $\beta = 0{\cdot}5$, $\gamma = 0{\cdot}2$ and $s = 10\%$. The coincident values of y and n that satisfy the condition of constant output per head are shown as a function of the output-capital ratio by the growth line $n_1 = y_1$, and this *locus classicus* is called the Ricardian line.

Along the Ricardian line labour is growing as fast as is compatible with a given living standard—keeping pace with the growth of output. Except at the origin, the growth line of capital lies above the Ricardian line, for capital must always grow faster than labour in order to sustain output per head in the face of continually diminishing returns on the land. But since capital is therefore also growing faster than output, the output-capital ratio is continually falling; the profit rate is falling in the same proportion, the wage rate is stable, while rent per acre is rising in proportion with output. As the output-capital ratio falls, the growth rate of labour and output gradually recedes down the slope of the Ricardian line, retreating from the unequal struggle against niggardly nature. In this manner the natural progress of society continues indefinitely towards the origin, where at last the growth line of capital and the Ricardian line intersect, at the point (1), in a stationary state.

If "long indeed before this period the very low rate of profit" has "arrested all accumulation", the change will have been seen in Figure 2 in the form of a decline in the saving ratio, reducing the

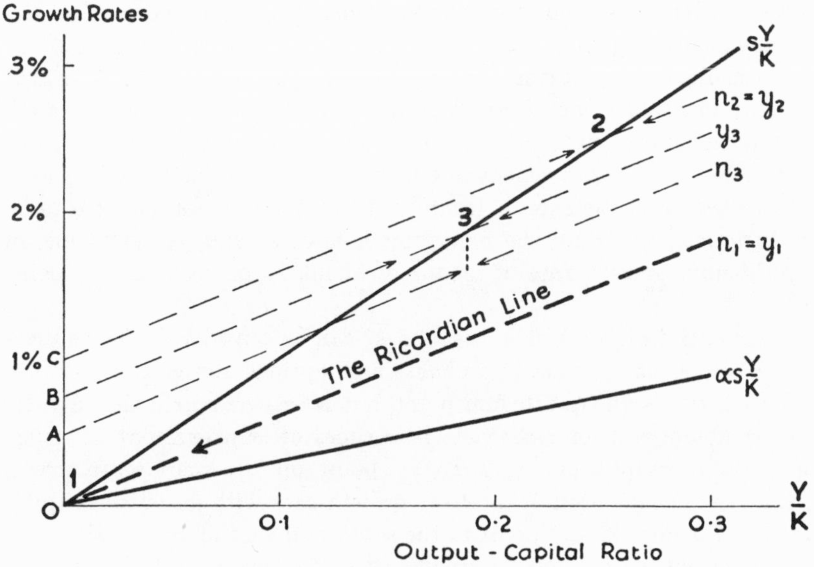

FIGURE 2.

slopes of the growth lines down to zero. On the other hand, a higher saving ratio would proportionally raise the growth rates at every point, but only temporarily interrupt the inevitable progress towards stationariness.

Suppose that this "gravitation . . . is happily checked at repeated intervals" by a constant rate of technical progress ($m = \frac{1}{2}$ per cent, as before). The new version of the Ricardian line $n_2 = y_2$ will lie above the old by the distance OC, which is $\frac{m}{1-\beta}$.[9] At the point (2) where the new line intersects the growth line of capital, technical progress is exactly balanced against diminishing returns, and output per head is constant with a growth rate of about $2\frac{1}{2}$ per cent. So instead of gravitating towards the origin, the economy if necessary levitates to this stable equilibrium point. Ricardo would no doubt object that if population is supposed to grow for ever at $2\frac{1}{2}$ per cent, it is very likely that at some point diminishing returns will set in with a violence not allowed for in our production function.

Given the proposition that at *some* standard of living (for the purpose of the foregoing argument it may be low or high) population will multiply fully in proportion with output, there is perhaps something to be said for the classical "law" of historically diminishing returns. It is in relation to the Malthusian postulate that the classical

9. This is obtained by putting $y = n$ in $y = \alpha s\frac{Y}{K} + \beta n + m$.

vision failed most signally. Suppose then that each generation demands samething better for its children: population is regulated so as to achieve, not a given living standard, but a progressive annual improvement of q per cent. The new element q affects the growth line of labour (now the locus of all labour growth rates consistent with q per cent improvement in output per head) exactly as if q were subtracted from the rate of technical progress, m.[10] Assuming q to be as little as $\frac{1}{4}$ per cent, the new growth lines n_3 and y_3 determine an equilibrium growth rate of labour of about $1\frac{1}{2}$ per cent at the point (3).

Growth lines such as n_1, n_2, and n_3 can be considered, not as time-paths which on various improbable assumptions the economy would follow towards an equilibrium point, but rather as a grid that divides the economic map into characteristic zones of improvement or deterioration in output per head. Every point on the map represents a particular conjunction of a labour growth rate with an output-capital ratio. In Figure 2, any point to the south and east of n_1 is a situation in which output per head is rising even if there is no technical progress. Between n_1 and n_3 output per head in the absence of technical progress would be falling, but with the assumed $\frac{1}{2}$ per cent technical progress it is rising by more than $\frac{1}{4}$ per cent. Between n_3 and n_2 the rise is less than $\frac{1}{4}$ per cent. A labour growth rate that strays to the north and west of n_2 incurs a decline in output per head, unless technical progress is greater than $\frac{1}{2}$ per cent.

A higher saving ratio, even though it does not change the growth rate at any of the so-called equilibrium points, swings the whole grid to the north and west. As a result, there is a larger area of desirable situations to the south and east of any given criterion of improvement, and a smaller area of undesirable situations to the north and west.

4. *The Harrod Model*

The model used above differs from Harrod's model of economic growth only in that it systematizes the relations between the "warranted" and "natural" rates of growth, and introduces land as a fixed factor.

Any point on the growth line of capital, $s\frac{Y}{K}$, is Harrod's warranted rate of growth $G_w = \frac{s}{C_r}$, since the output-capital ratio $\frac{Y}{K}$ at any given level is the reciprocal of Harrod's capital coefficient C_r. The corresponding point on the growth line of output is Harrod's natural rate of growth G_n. At an equilibrium point, where the two growth lines intersect, the warranted and natural rates of growth are equal.

10. This is obtained by putting $y = n + q$ in the formula of the last footnote.

At any other point the wage rate and the profit rate are moving in such a way as to induce entrepreneurs to adjust the output-capital ratio in the direction which will bring the warranted and natural rates of growth together. Specifically, a reduction in the output-capital ratio (an increase in Harrod's C_r) always involves a decline in the rate of profit, and this automatically implies the appropriate movement of the wage rate.

Harrod envisages exactly the same mechanism of adjustment, *via* the "deepening" factor, d, which "may have a positive value because the rate of interest is falling". He argues that natural market forces cannot be expected to achieve the desired results, but does not despair that Keynesian policies may be successful. Nevertheless some of his readers seem to have been misled into the belief that in Harrod's model equality between the warranted and the natural rates of growth can occur only "by a fluke".[11] Harrod's own view is stated very clearly:

"Our aim should be to get such a progressive reduction in the rate of interest that $G_w\ C_r = s - d = G_n\, C_r$. If d is positive, C_r will increase through time, and may eventually become so great as to enable us to dispense with d. At that point interest need fall no further."[12]

The mechanism of Figures 1 and 2 merely makes explicit what this statement implies.

T. W. Swan

Australian National University,
Canberra.

APPENDIX: NOTES ON CAPITAL[1]

I Joan Robinson's Puzzle.
II The Wicksell Effect.
III Åkerman's Problem.
IV The Wicksell Effect in Reverse.

I. *Joan Robinson's Puzzle*

If we had to put up a scarecrow (as Joan Robinson calls it) to keep off the index-number birds and Joan Robinson herself, it would look something like this: Labour and Land are homogeneous man-

11. Joan Robinson, *The Accumulation of Capital,* p. 405.
12. *Towards A Dynamic Economics,* p. 96.

1. These notes are concerned with certain difficulties in the idea of Capital as a factor of production that were first seen by Wicksell and have now been greatly elaborated by Joan Robinson in two articles (*Review of Economic Studies* 1953-54, and *Economic Journal* 1955) and in her book, *The Accumulation of Capital.* See also the articles by D. G. Champernowne and R. F. Kahn, and by D. G. Champernowne, in the same number of *R.E.S.,* and by R. M. Solow in *R.E.S.* 1955-56. The criticism here ventured is in no sense a book review: it touches on only one aspect of a very important book, and in relation to the text above is best regarded as a face-saving gesture.

hours and acres respectively; Capital is made up of a large number of identical meccano sets, which never wear out and can be put together, taken apart, and reassembled with negligible cost or delay in a great variety of models so as to work with various combinations of Labour and Land, to produce various products, and to incorporate the latest technical innovations illustrated in successive issues of the Instruction Book; Output consists of goods (including meccano sets) that are all produced and sold at constant price-ratios amongst themselves, no matter how the rates of wages, rents, and profits may vary—e.g. they are all produced by similar (but continuously variable) combinations of Labour, Land, and Capital, with similar efficiency, and under similar competitive conditions; Saving = Investment = Accumulation is the current output of meccano sets, and can always be measured (by virtues of the constant price-ratios) at a constant value per meccano set in terms of peanuts or any other consumption product forgone: etc. With assumptions of this kind, the basic model of the text could be rigorously established in a form that would deceive nobody.

Fortunately, economists have usually been willing to hope that even very complicated aggregates like Output might somehow still contain, for some purposes, a rough kernel of meaning "in an index-number sense"—a meaning not literally dependent upon the fantastic assumptions required to avoid all index-number ambiguities. Joan Robinson[2] has spoilt this game for us by insisting that the social Capital, considered as a factor of production accumulated by saving, cannot be given *any* operative meaning—not even in the abstract conditions of a stationary state.

2. The following passages are from the first of Joan Robinson's articles (*R.E.S.* 1953-54, pp. 81 and 82):

"The student of economic theory is taught to write $O = f(L, C)$ where L is a quantity of labour, C a quantity of capital and O a rate of output of commodities. He is instructed to assume all workers alike, and to measure L in man-hours of labour; he is told something about the index-number problem involved in choosing a unit of output; and then he is hurried on to the next question, in the hope that he will forget to ask in what units C is measured. Before ever he does ask, he has become a professor, and so sloppy habits of thought are handed on from one generation to the next. . . .

When we are discussing accumulation, it is natural to think of capital as measured in terms of product. The process of accumulation consists in refraining from consuming current output in order to add to the stock of wealth. But when we consider what addition to productive resources a given amount of accumulation makes, we must measure capital in labour units, for the addition to the stock of productive equipment made by adding an increment of capital depends upon how much work is done in constructing it, not upon the cost, in terms of final product, of an hour's labour. Thus, as we move from one point on a production function to another, measuring capital in terms of product, we have to know the product-wage rate in order to see the effect upon production of changing the ratio of capital to labour. Or if we measure in labour units, we have to know the product-wage in order to see how much accumulation would be required to produce a given increment of capital. But the wage rate alters with the ratio of the factors: one symbol, C, cannot stand both for a quantity of product and a quantity of labour time."

That there should be great difficulties in handling the concept of Capital in a process of change is not surprising. A piece of durable equipment or a pipe-line of work-in-progress has dimensions in time that bind together sequences of inputs and outputs jointly-demanded or jointly-supplied at different dates.[3] The aggregation of capital into a single stock at a point of time is thus the correlative of an aggregation of the whole economic process, not only in cross-section (which gives rise to the ordinary index-number problems), but also in time itself: in other words, the reduction of a very high-order system of lagged equations—in which each event, its past origins and its future consequences, could be properly dated and traced backward and forward in time—to a more manageable system with fewer lags. This second kind of aggregation introduces a further set of ambiguities, similar in principle to those of index-numbers, but as yet hardly investigated.[4] Our scarecrow assumptions dodge both sets of ambiguities—the first because all price-ratios within Output are held constant, the second because Capital, in the form of meccano sets, is both infinitely durable and instantaneously adaptable. This is an extreme of aggregation. From the idea of capital as a single stock there is in principle no sudden transition to "the enormous who's who of all the goods in existence"[5]. Between the two extremes lies an ascending scale of nth-order dynamic systems, in which capital like everything else is more and more finely subdivided and dated, with ascending degrees of (potential) realism and (actual) complexity. In fact, most of us are left at ground-level, on ground that moves under our feet.

In a stationary state, all the complexities of dating disappear. Related inputs and outputs, investments and returns, events and expectations, may be generations removed, but what happens at any time

3. Like the wool and mutton of Marshall's sheep (Wicksell, *Lectures,* Vol. 1, p. 260).

4. By what test should the (relative) success of a proposed scheme of aggregation be judged? Probably, by some measure of the degree of preservation of the dominant behaviour patterns which would be represented in the linear case by the larger roots of an appropriate high-order micro-system; surely not by the degree of "realism" of the scarecrow assumptions necessary to give literal validity to the low-order macro-system. In the present context, we are saved the trouble of trying to apply the suggested criterion by the fact that no appropriate micro-system is available (no one has yet set *Value and Capital* in motion, except under assumptions almost as rigidly fantastic as our own scarecrow). The puzzle may actually be easier if there are strong non-linear features (floors, ceilings, thresholds, etc.), since these sometimes lead to a limited number of highly characteristic patterns of behaviour.

If the hands of a clock give a fair approximation to the even flow of time, in spite of the diminishing force exerted by the spring as it unwinds, our thanks are due to the discontinuous, non-linear mechanism of the escapement. This result is achieved at the price of an ambiguity—the finite intervals between ticks. Even the best clock is a mere scarecrow model of Time, and absurdly unrealistic from the viewpoint of the General Theory of Relativity. A bad clock that still ticks, or a good one wrongly set, may mean that its user misses the bus.

5. Joan Robinson, *R.E.S.* 1953-54, pp. 83-85.

is exactly repeated at any other time. No information is lost and no ambiguity created by aggregating all times into an eternal present; the shadows of past and future appear only in the form of profit steadily accruing at the ruling rate of interest on the time-consuming investment processes of which every moment has its share. Joan Robinson still insists that Capital cannot be given a meaning conformable with those neo-classical exercises in comparative statics for which the stationary state is expressly designed. In particular, Capital cannot be put into a production function from which, given the supplies of Labour and Land, under perfect-competition profit-maximization assumptions, the equilibrium rates of real wages, rent, and profit may be deduced in the form of marginal productivities. If this scheme is unworkable in a stationary state, it can hardly be sensible to retain it in a dynamic model (like that of our text).

From the various accounts given by Joan Robinson it is not easy to pick out the "basic fallacy" of the marginal productivity scheme. In the passage already quoted[6] she makes the novel suggestion that the production function itself works only if the stock of capital is measured by its value in wage-units, in which case it becomes useless for explaining the equilibrium factor-rewards. But it soon appears that, whatever may be the defects of the neo-classical production function, one geared to what Champernowne calls J.R. units can produce only mental and diagrammatic contortions. (Are there perhaps signs in *The Accumulation of Capital* of the reluctant beginnings of regret for this aberration?)

Frequently Joan Robinson seems to be explaining the factor-rewards by a widow's cruse type of distribution theory.[7] At first sight, it is not altogether clear whether she puts this forward as an independent explanation, or is merely exhibiting the other side of the double-entry national income accounts, which of course always balance in exact confirmation of the theory.[8] Before long, the reader begins

6. p. 344, note 2.

7. The widow's cruse theory of distribution is set out by Nicholas Kaldor (who calls it the Keynesian theory) in *R.E.S.* 1955-56. p. 94 ff. Briefly, the theory says that, given the ratio of investment to income, and given the propensities to save out of profits and wages respectively, the distribution of income between profits and wages must be such as to make the saving ratio equal the investment ratio. For examples see *The Accumulation of Capital* pp. 48, 75-83, 255, 271, 312, 331.

8. Consider the following example of widow's cruse reasoning (*The Accumulation of Capital,* p. 312):

"The relation of the rate of profit to the marginal product of investment is seen in its simplest form in the imagined state of bliss, where the highest technique known is already in operation throughout the economy and population is constant. The marginal product of investment is then zero. If there is no consumption out of profit (and no saving out of wages or rents) the rate of profit also is zero, and the wages and rent bill absorbs the whole annual output.

But if there is consumption out of profits (and no saving out of rent or wages) the rate of profit remains positive, for the prices of commodities (in

to understand that this profoundly arithmetical organon is not a rival economic calculus, but a subsidiary device that applies, as it were, only in blank spots on the map of economic calculation.[9] In Joan Robinson's world, the blanks are enlarged into great zones marked out by frontier-lines of technical discontinuity. Typically, all products are consumed in fixed proportions and capable of being produced by a single discontinuous "hierarchy of techniques"; each technique has its own fixed factor-proportions, which are rigidly unadaptable; techniques displace each other in profitability across iso-cost "frontiers" defined by well-separated critical sets of factor-rewards; any frontier applies uniformly and simultaneously to every industry throughout the economy.[10] Only at the frontier between two techniques is economic calculation, or the Principle of Substitution, fully effective. Within each zone (i.e. within the limits of the critical sets of factor-rewards along its frontiers) almost anything may happen.

The paradoxes and fabulous histories that enliven *The Accumulation of Capital* have their licence in these extremes of discontinuity. They are not the consequence of any special feature of Joan Robinson's view of capital or of the marginal calculus. When eventually

---

relation to money wages and rents) are such that their total selling value exceeds their total costs by the amount of expenditure out of profits. The total of real wages then falls short of total output by the amount of consumption of rentiers, that is, of purchase of commodities out of profit and rent incomes."

It is possible to clarify the two cases distinguished in these paragraphs. In a state of bliss with constant population investment is zero. Since therefore the amount saved has to be zero, any positive profit-saving propensity, whether unity or less, certainly precludes a positive amount of profits; so the second paragraph must refer only to a zero profit-saving propensity, as in effect its two sentences twice affirm (profits = selling value — (wages + rents) = consumption out of profits). Keeping the assumption of no saving out of wages or rents, the meaning of Joan Robinson's two cases may now be rendered as follows:

(i) If the capitalists save some part of any profits they may get, they get no profit, *either* because the rate of profit on capital employed is zero *or* because their saving propensity "multiplies" output itself down to zero (bliss becomes Nirvana).

(ii) If the capitalists consume the whole of any profits they may get, their profits equal the amount they consume, which is positive if they get any profits to consume. (The reason for this ham and eggs dictum is supplied by Kaldor, *R.E.S.* 1955-56, p. 95.)

The marginal productivity theory, on the other hand, infers that in a state of bliss the rate of profit is zero: capital has become a free good, and full employment output is blissfully consistent with zero profits. The true contribution of Keynesian theory is to point out that in these circumstances any positive saving propensity *out of wages or rents* is inconsistent with full employment output.

9. Just as the multiplier theory (to which the widow's cruse is closely related) applies when aggregative economic calculation is suspended by Keynesian unemployment.

10. Note how "realistic" it seems to allow for technical discontinuities (one thinks of coke-ovens, blast furnaces, etc.). The end-result in Joan Robinson's model is that the opportunities for substitution are limited in any situation to a single, universal choice between two techniques; and this restriction becomes the dominant feature of the economy as a whole. The "neo-classical vice of implicit theorising" has here its counterpart in the vice of *explicit realism.*

she considers a primitive agricultural economy in which continuous factor substitution is for once allowed,[11] her theory runs familiarly in terms of discounted products, following Wicksell. Again, when she indulges in some pronouncements concerning the nature of the factors of production and their marginal products, the substance of her thoughts is recognizable as that of the so-called Austrian view of the rôle of capital and time in production, more especially in the form which it was given by Wicksell.[12]

To find the kernel of Joan Robinson's meaning, it is best to go back to Wicksell,[13] to whose ideas she pays repeated and generous tribute. Part II of this appendix examines the problem from Wicksell's viewpoint. But first look again at the early Joan Robinson polemic against the neo-classical scheme (quoted on p. 344), and consider four comments:

1. The value of a stock of capital "in terms of product" is no more plausible than its value in J.R. units as an input to be fed into a production function. If Capital is to be treated, from a productive viewpoint, on all fours with Labour and Land, it must somehow be measured "in terms of its own technical unit",[14] in spite of the obvious difficulties. (In our scarecrow model, it is the *number* of meccano sets, along with the number of manhours and acres, that directly determines the volume of Output—not their value in terms of anything, although it happens that in our model the value of a meccano set in terms of product is constant.)

Joan Robinson is correct in so far as she is complaining that the neo-classical tradition contains no indication of how a "technical unit" for capital may be devised.

11. *The Accumulation of Capital,* pp. 291-292. "This . . . is purely a repetition of our former argument in a simpler setting."

12. *The Accumulation of Capital,* pp. 310-311. Cf. Wicksell, *Lectures,* p. 150.

13. If I were advising a student on a method of approach to *The Accumulation of Capital,* I would recommend the following preparations: (1) Re-read the whole of Wicksell's *Lectures,* Vol. 1. (2) Concentrate in particular on a full understanding of the discontinuous "exception" described by Wicksell in the last complete paragraph on page 177; this sets the stage for Joan Robinson's book. (3) Read the two articles by D. M. Bensusan-Butt, *Oxford Economic Papers,* September, 1954, and *American Economic Review,* September, 1954, for an analysis which in several respects anticipates Joan Robinson, but in terms of a much simpler, and also more flexible, model.

14. Wicksell, *Lectures,* p. 149. Wicksell rejected the possibility of employing such a unit, partly because he could see no way of combining the different kinds of "tools, machinery, and materials, etc." in a "unified treatment" (though he did not shrink from treating labour, land, and product as if each were homogeneous), and partly because he believed at the time that the Walrasian solution of the pricing of newly-produced capital goods involved "arguing in a circle". This latter problem, he thought, would still have to be solved before the "yield" of particular capital goods could be linked up with the rate of interest. Later (cf. *Lectures,* p. 226) he seems to have realised that this criticism was mistaken. The circularity that worried Wicksell (the fact that the rate of interest enters as a cost in the production of capital goods themselves) is merely another aspect of the mutual inter-dependence of all variables in the Walrasian system. For a similar example, see p. 357, below.

2. On the other hand, there is an ambiguity in her view that capital "measured in terms of product" goes naturally with a discussion of accumulation because "accumulation consists in refraining from consuming current output in order to add to the stock of wealth". What is the addition to the stock of wealth that is made by current accumulation? It is not the *change in the value* of the stock, measured in terms of product, but rather the *value of the change*, measured in terms of product, i.e. the (real) value of the current output not consumed, and so added to the stock. Only the latter element corresponds with the idea of accumulation, unless current output, income, saving, and investment are defined to include current revaluations of the pre-existing stock of capital goods—which is not the conventional usage.[15]

Joan Robinson apparently takes it for granted that the value of the capital stock in terms of product is the same thing as the cumulated value (the time-integral) of investment and saving in terms of product. The two measures may in fact diverge very widely, if there is any change in relative values between "capital goods" and "product": in the first measure, every such change is reflected in an immediate revaluation of the whole capital stock; in the second, the capital stock is recorded as a "perpetual inventory" accumulated by saving at original cost in terms of product. The first measure is certainly Wicksell's. The second is the neo-classical tradition—or rather the tradition of all the economists from Adam Smith to Keynes who have thought of current output as being divided between consumption on the one hand and additions to the capital stock (saving, investment, accumulation) on the other. In a stationary equilibrium, the two measures coincide: but they part company even for infinitesimal variations at the margin of a stationary state, if those variations involve any change in relative values between "capital goods" and "product."

3. A measure of the capital stock in its own technical unit—if that were feasible, as with meccano sets—is of course not the same thing as either of the two measures "in terms of product". When capital is measured in meccano sets, its marginal productivity—the rate of increase of product with respect to the number of meccano sets employed—does not correspond in equilibrium with the ruling rate of profit (the rate of interest), but with that rate multiplied

15. The value changes that accrue as "depreciation" are of course allowed for in the conventional definitions, but we are here concerned with quite a different issue. The relevant distinction is often made explicit in national income statistics in the form of an *inventory revaluation adjustment*. This adjustment is made only in respect of inventories, since revaluations of other capital assets are not included in the figures in the first place.

by the value of a meccano set in terms of product.[16] At the same time, the rate of increase in the number of meccano sets is the current rate of saving divided by the value of a meccano set. Thus for the purpose of any marginal calculation in which the value of a meccano set enters as a constant, Capital may be measured in terms of product (as the accumulation of saving), and its marginal productivity will then correspond with the rate of profit.

This is the *rationale* of the neo-classical procedure. Two elements of calculation are involved, and in both the value of a meccano set is correctly taken as constant: (a) a maximization process in which all prices, including the price of meccano sets, are treated in perfect competition as constant parameters, and (b) a marginal increment of accumulation—the translation of a small amount of product by saving into additional meccano sets—in which the "error" in measuring the capital stock arising from an associated marginal change in the value of a meccano set is confined to the marginal addition being made to the capital stock, and so is of "the second order of smalls". (The revaluation of the pre-existing stock, which occurs in the measure of capital in terms of product that Joan Robinson has in mind, is of a very different order.)

As soon as this point is accepted, it follows that the neo-classical procedure does not, after all, depend on the existence of a "technical unit" of capital—the meccano set—the value of which is in any case cancelled out. For marginal variations about the stationary equilibrium position—i.e. for all the purposes of the neo-classical theory—the natural unit of Capital is simply "an equilibrium dollar's worth" regardless of the physical variety of capital goods, and regardless of marginal value-changes or marginal adaptations of capital towards different physical forms.[17]

4. The foregoing argument is evidently quite symmetrical with respect to every factor and indeed every product: at the margin of a stationary state, Capital, Labour, Land, and Output can each be measured in terms of "an equilibrium dollar's worth". From the "tangency" and "convexity" conditions prevailing at the equilibrium point—by virtue of the first and second-order conditions of the economic maximization process—all valid theorems (as Samuelson might say) can then be deduced. In the given unit, aggregation is

16. To the profit-maximising, cost-minimising entrepreneur, the cost of the annual services of a meccano set, comparable with the real wage in terms of product which is the cost of the annual services of a unit of labour, is the annual interest bill on the price of a meccano set in terms of product.

17. This is essentially the familiar principle which Samuelson calls the Wong-Viner-Harrod envelope theorem (P. A. Samuelson, *The Foundation of Economic Analysis,* pp. 34, 66n, 243; also in *R.E.S.* 1953-54, p. 5). See also Marshall (rebuking J. A. Hobson), *Principles,* p. 409n.

itself quite superficial: the equalities and inequalities that hold for the aggregates at the equilibrium point hold uniformly in terms of "an equilibrium dollar's worth" of every possible subdivision of factor and product right down to the level of the individual firm. That is why the neo-classical theory often appears to be both aggregative and exact.

However, this achievement involves an inherent limitation, against which Joan Robinson has all along been tilting. The theory tells us something about the properties of an equilibrium point, but it gives no information in finite terms about one point in relation to any other point.[18] For instance, it does not enable us to "draw" the hypothetical isoquants of a production function combining (say) Capital and Labour. All we know, from the neo-classical or any similar theory, is certain curvature properties that must hold at any point that is capable of being an equilibrium point. Assuming one such point, we are entitled to draw an invisibly small segment of a curve with the known properties—a grin without a cat. Yet why should we expect a theory to produce even a hypothetical cat? The trouble is that if we were supplied with all the hypotheses or empirical data in the world, we should still be puzzled to draw the rest of the curve, because we should want each point on it to be a potential equilibrium point, whereas our unit—"an equilibrium dollar's worth"—is defined only for a single equilibrium point, and changes its character at any point separated by a finite distance from the first. It may do no harm to sketch in a metaphorical curve, provided the argument touches only a single equilibrium point and its immediate neighbourhood. On these terms, "comparative statics" is a misnomer: not different situations, but only "virtual" displacements at the margin of one situation, can be considered.

For structural comparisons "in the large" (e.g. as between two stationary states with different factor endowments), either the variables must be measurable in naturally homogeneous technical units (like meccano sets and manhours), or else some artificial means must be found to co-ordinate measurements made at different points. For the latter purpose, Champernowne has proposed the use of a *chain index*,[19] an approach which is entirely in keeping with the true character of aggregative analysis. Champernowne's chain index, as presented, looks like a rather *ad hoc* and specialized device to cope with Joan Robinson's difficulties. The next part of these notes is intended to show how a chain index of capital emerges naturally from the analysis of a simple problem considered by Wicksell.

18. In a footnote (*The Accumulation of Capital,* p. 414n.) Joan Robinson says something rather like this.
19. *R.E.S.* 1953-54, p. 112.

II. *The Wicksell Effect*

Joan Robinson finds extraordinary significance in Wicksell's demonstration that an increase in the social capital is partly "absorbed by increased wages (and rent), so that only the residue . . . is really effective as far as a rise in production is concerned".[20] "The amount of employment offered by a given value of capital depends upon the real-wage rate. At a lower wage rate there is a smaller value of a given type of machine."[21] To its discoverer, the *Wicksell effect* seemed mainly important as an obstacle to the acceptance of "von Thünen's thesis", the marginal productivity theory of interest. To Joan Robinson, "this point of Wicksell's is the key to the whole theory of accumulation and of the determination of wages and profits".[22]

To identify the Wicksell effect we may re-work very briefly his "point-input, point-output" case.[23] For Wicksell's grape-juice we substitute labour, imagining a productive process in which the application of an amount of labour N at a point of time results after a "period of production" t in a final output Q which is greater the longer the period of production allowed. Other variables are the real wage rate w, the value of capital in the form of goods-in-process K (both w and K measured in terms of product), and the competitive rate of interest or profit r. Interest is instantaneously compounded; e is the base of natural logarithms. Wicksell's main equations then appear as follows:

$$(1)\quad Q = Nf(t) \qquad (2)\quad w = \frac{Q}{N} e^{-rt} \qquad (3)\quad r = \frac{f'(t)}{f(t)}$$

$$(4a)\quad K = Nw \int_0^t e^{rx}\, dx = Nw \frac{e^{rt} - 1}{r}$$

$$(4b)\quad K = \frac{Q - Nw}{r}$$

Equation (1) is the production function, showing output per unit of labour as an increasing function $f(t)$ of the period of production. Equations (2) and (3) flow from (1) under perfect-competition profit-maximization assumptions: the wage rate is the discounted product per unit of labour, and the interest rate the (relative) "marginal productivity of waiting". Equation (4a) evaluates K from the cost side as the wages bill continuously invested in production and

20. *Lectures,* p. 268.

21. *The Accumulation of Capital,* p. 391.

22. *The Accumulation of Capital,* p. 396.

23. *Lectures,* pp. 172-181, and in particular pp. 178-180. In the following re-formulation, nothing material is changed. The reader is referred to Wicksell for further explanations. Where our symbols differ from his, the equivalents are: $\frac{Q}{N} = W, N_\omega = V_o, r = \rho$. Wicksell's "one hectolitre of grape-juice", which does not appear explicitly, is our N, but the change is only formal. Our numbering of the equations is not the same as Wicksell's. For the mathematics of this case, see R. G. D. Allen, *Mathematical Analysis for Economists,* pp. 248, 362, 403.

cumulated at compound interest over the period t; while (4b), using (1) and (2), shows that K is also the capitalized value of total profits $Q - Nw$. Using the second-order maximization condition upon $f(t)$, Wicksell proved that in equilibrium (for given N) increasing K necessarily means increasing w, decreasing r, and increasing t. In Joan Robinson's language, increasing t represents a higher "degree of mechanization", made profitable as w increases—the *Ricardesque effect.*

Differentiating (1) and (4a) or (4b) while holding N constant, Wicksell next derived a formula for the rate of increase of Q with respect to K. This formula can be expressed in four distinct ways:

$$\text{(5a)} \quad \frac{dQ}{dK} = r - K\left(\frac{r}{w}\frac{dw}{dK} + \left(\frac{rt}{1-e^{-rt}} - 1\right)\frac{dr}{dK}\right)$$

$$\text{(5b)} \quad = r + \left(K\frac{dr}{dK} + N\frac{dw}{dK}\right)$$

$$\text{(5c)} \quad = r + (K - Nwt)\frac{dr}{dK}$$

$$\text{(5d)} \quad = r - \left(\frac{K - Nwt}{wt}\right)\frac{dw}{dK}$$

The second term in these expressions is always negative—i.e. the "marginal productivity of capital" in this sense is always less than the rate of interest, part of the increase in K having been "unproductively absorbed". This is the Wicksell effect. Our four versions suggest that it is somewhat misleading to ascribe the "absorption" simply to increased wages. Version (a) shows the Wicksell effect from the viewpoint of the *cost* of the capital stock (4a), as the consequence of a higher wage rate only partly offset by a lower interest rate. Version (b), from the viewpoint of *capitalized profits* (4b), shows it as the consequence of a lower interest rate only partly offset by a higher wage rate. Versions (c) and (d) use the relation between r and w given in (2) to attribute the whole Wicksell effect on the one hand to a lower interest rate, and on the other hand to a higher wage rate. The multiplicity of explanations shows how treacherous is the idea of causation amongst interdependent variables.

Yet the different versions of the Wicksell effect have one common feature which is itself a complete explanation. To see this, we first write out the logarithmic total differential of (4a) and (4b), giving four alternative expressions for a (proprotional) change in the value of capital to parallel the four versions of (5):

$$\text{(6a)} \quad \frac{dK}{K} = \left[\frac{dN}{N} + \frac{rt}{1-e^{-rt}}\frac{dt}{t}\right] + \left[\frac{dw}{w} + \left(\frac{rt}{1-e^{-rt}} - 1\right)\frac{dr}{r}\right]$$

$$(6b) \qquad = \left[\frac{Q}{Kr}\frac{dQ}{Q} - \frac{Nw}{Kr}\frac{dN}{N}\right] - \left[\frac{Nw}{Kr}\frac{dw}{w} + \frac{dr}{r}\right]$$

$$(6c) \qquad = \left[\;\text{''} \qquad\qquad \text{''}\;\right] - \left[\frac{K - Nwt}{K}\frac{dr}{r}\right]$$

$$(6d) \qquad = \left[\;\text{''} \qquad\qquad \text{''}\;\right] + \left[\frac{K - Nwt}{Krt}\frac{dw}{w}\right]$$

Here the terms are grouped by the square brackets into two columns. The first column shows the component of a change in the value of capital due to "productive" features (more labour, a longer period of production, greater output). The second column shows the component due to "financial" features (changes in the wage and interest rates). It is easy to verify that the different versions in each column are vertically equivalent: i.e. the "productive" component and the "financial" component of a change in K are respectively the same, whether considered (a) in terms of cost or (b) in terms of capitalization, and in the case of the "financial" element whether ascribed (c) to an interest change or (d) to a wage change. Let us make this distinction explicit by defining two synthetic variables, k and p, with the following properties at a certain equilibrium point:

$$(7) \quad kp = K$$

$$(8a) \; \frac{dk}{k} = \frac{dN}{N} + \frac{rt}{1 + e^{-rt}}\frac{dt}{t} \qquad (8b) \; \frac{dp}{p} = \frac{dw}{w} + \left(\frac{rt}{1 - e^{-rt}} - 1\right)\frac{dr}{r}$$

In these definitions, K is broken into two components which may be interpreted as a "quantity" k, and a "price" (in terms of product) p; $\frac{dk}{k}$ is identified with the first column of (6), and $\frac{dp}{p}$ with the second column. The stated properties cannot hold generally, because the product of the integrals of (8a) and (8b) is not, in general, K. Nevertheless the definitions involve no contradiction if they are restricted to a particular set of equilibrium values of w, r, and t—namely, those prevailing at the equilibrium point for which in any particular case the differentials in (5) or (6) are also calculated. We shall return in a moment to the question of integrating (8a) and (8b) so as to define k and p for other points.

Next we can put $dK = K\left(\frac{dk}{k} + \frac{dp}{p}\right) = pdk + kdp$ in (5a), and arrange the result as follows:

$$(5a') \quad \frac{dQ}{pdk} = r + \frac{kr}{dk}\left(\frac{dp}{p} - \frac{dw}{w} - \left(\frac{rt}{1 - e^{-rt}} - 1\right)\frac{dr}{r}\right)$$

According to the definition of $\frac{dp}{p}$ in (8b), the second term—which previously showed the Wicksell effect—is now identically zero: when the increment of capital is taken as $K\frac{dk}{k}$, or pdk ("the value of the change"), its marginal productivity corresponds with the rate of interest. The same result can of course be obtained by a similar substitution in the other three versions of (5). Here is the common feature of all four versions of the Wicksell effect, that the effect disappears when the marginal change in capital is measured so as to exclude $K\frac{dp}{p}$, or kdp, which is the revaluation of the capital stock resulting from an associated marginal change in wage and interest rates. *The Wicksell effect is nothing but an inventory revaluation.*

The wage rate, previously given by (2) as the average product of labour discounted over the period of production, may now also be derived as the marginal productivity of labour. Differentiating (1), using (3), and substituting for dt from (8a), we obtain:

$$(9)\quad \frac{dQ}{Q} = e^{-rt}\frac{dN}{N} + (1 - e^{-rt})\frac{dk}{k}$$

By (1), (2), and (4b), the two coefficients in (9) are the proportional shares of wages and profits in output, $\frac{Nw}{Q}$ and $\frac{Kr}{Q}$, respectively. Therefore:

$$(10)\quad dQ = wdN + rpdk$$

Accordingly, when the quantity of capital k is held constant, $w = \frac{dQ}{dN}$.

The component pdk is the value at ruling prices (in terms of product) of an increment of capital goods, and so corresponds with the usual idea of investment, saving, or accumulation. It may be convenient to call $\frac{dQ}{pdk}$ $(= r)$ the *marginal efficiency of investment,* reserving the term *marginal productivity of capital* for $\frac{dQ}{dk}$ $(= rp)$. In relation to our earlier discussion, dk is an increment of capital measured "in terms of its own technical unit" (like meccano sets), while pdk is an increment measured in terms of "an equilibrium dollar's worth".

But we are now a step forward. The definitions of k and p in (7) and (8) can be recognized in their essential character as the differential definitions of *chain indexes* of quantity and price, by which Divisia provided "an elegant logical justification" of Marshall's original invention of the chain index.[24] Thus although (8a) and (8b) cannot

24. Ragnar Frisch, *Econometrica* 1936, pp. 7-8. The elementary index-number formula used to construct each link of the chain will vary, as Frisch points out, "according as we choose the approximation principle for the steps of the numerical integration".

usually be integrated to give exact measures of k and p, such that $kp = K$ at every point, they can in principle be integrated numerically in successive small "links" (correcting the weights as each link is added) so as to form a consistent pair of chain indexes of the "quantity" and "price" of capital. With these indexes approximate structural comparisons "in the large" between different equilibrium situations may be made. The index k enters with N in the production function, while the index p measures for each point of the production function the amount of accumulation in terms of product necessary to achieve a given addition to k—in effect, converting "an equilibrium dollar's worth" at one point into its productive equivalent at another point.

This operation can most easily be visualized by considering a special case in which (8a) and (8b) lend themselves to exact integration—namely, the case in which the function $f(t)$ is of constant elasticity, and may be written $f(t) = t^{\alpha}$. Then by (3) $rt = \alpha$. The proportional share of profits in output is also now a constant, which it is convenient to write $1 - e^{-rt} = \beta$. Therefore (8a) and (8b) become

$$(8a')\ \frac{dk}{k} = \frac{dN}{N} + \frac{\alpha}{\beta}\frac{dt}{t} \qquad (8b')\ \frac{dp}{p} = \frac{dw}{w} + \left(\frac{\alpha}{\beta} - 1\right)\frac{dr}{r}$$

and in this form they give immediately the integrals

$$(a')\ k = C_1 N t^{\frac{\alpha}{\beta}} \qquad (b')\ p = C_2\, w r^{\left(\frac{\alpha}{\beta} - 1\right)}$$

where C_1 and C_2 are constants of integration.[25] The production function (1) may now be expressed in terms of N and k, and its partial derivatives with respect to these factors of production will appear as w and rp:

$$(1')\ Q = N^{1-\beta} k^{\beta} \qquad (2')\ w = (1-\beta)\frac{Q}{N} \qquad (3')\ rp = \beta\frac{Q}{K}$$

Given the definitions of k and p in (a′) and (b′), the new system is in all respects the equivalent of Wicksell's, as the reader may readily confirm by substitution. Although the wage rate w and the yield (or quasi-rent) of a unit of capital rp are derived from the new production function as the marginal productivities of labour and capital, it seems at first sight that in order to discover r we must know p, and *vice-versa*. However, in (b′) there is another relation between

25 In order that k and p may satisfy (7) and (4), C_1 and C_2 must satisfy

$$C_1 C_2 = (e^{\alpha} - 1)\, \alpha^{-\frac{\alpha}{\beta}}$$

It is convenient to choose units so that $C_1 = 1$. This choice accounts for the absence from (1′) below of any explicit constant of integration.

w, r, and p, which enables r and p to be separately determined once the values of w and rp are given at any point of the production function.[26]

When the elasticity of $f(t)$ is not constant, this exact formulation in terms of k and p is no longer possible "in the large". Nevertheless the chain indexes of k and p are available as approximate measures, and they will play in principle the same role as k and p in the special case just considered.[27]

But why bother to show that with the help of chain indexes the neo-classical scheme can approximately mimic the solution of a highly artificial problem already obtained in an exact form by Wicksell? One answer is that Wicksell's analysis is exact only when K—the *value* of capital in terms of product—is taken as an independent variable. To consider the effect of a given amount of *accumulation*—the forgone consumption of a given amount of product—Wicksell too would have been driven to approximations and index-numbers. Another answer is that the elements which appear in our definitions of the indexes k and p are merely particular illustrations, drawn from Wicksell's model, of the "productive" and the "financial" attributes of capital goods that have to be distinguished in measuring their "quantity" and "price": index-number measurements may still be appropriate when capital does not take those particular forms which enabled Wicksell to specify its productive effect directly in terms of a period of time.

Wicksell himself thought of the period of production or period of investment as no more than a notional index of the time-aspect of capital—"a mathematical concept, without direct physical or psychic significance", but which "should, nevertheless, be retained as a concise general principle, reflecting the essence of productive capital".[28] If Joan Robinson will allow Wicksell in this spirit to draw a production function involving N, t, and (indirectly) K, she ought not to object if others prefer to draw one involving N, k, and (indirectly) p: for there is, as we have seen, a method by which one scheme may be translated into the other.

26. In this special case where the production function is such that the proportional share of each factor in output is constant, there is obviously no difficulty in extending the above analysis to cover any number of different factors of production. As far as I can see, the chain index approach in the general case also extends to any number of factors, provided that continuous adjustments in factor proportions are assumed to be possible. Champernowne (*R.E.S.* 1953-54, pp. 121-125, 132-135) shows that the chain index in general breaks down for more than two factors when techniques are discontinuous.

27. Of course a chain index is not necessarily a "better" approximation than some other kind of index-number. For the present purpose, however, the chain index in its Divisia formulation is very convenient, in that it shows a consistent way of making approximate measurements "in the large", while keeping the advantage of theoretical exactness "in the small".

28. *Lectures,* p. 184.

III. *Åkerman's Problem*

By the same method, Gustaf Åkerman's problem of durable capital equipment—as analysed by Wicksell in a celebrated essay[29]—can also be solved in accordance with the marginal productivity theory. Wicksell's analysis was mainly intended to refute Åkerman's claim that this could be done.

In the model which Wicksell developed for the purpose, capital consists of axes, which can be made more or less durable by putting more or less labour into their manufacture; the optimum life of an axe, n years, is chosen to maximize profits; the stock of axes in the stationary equilibrium is a "balanced equipment" with a uniform age distribution from o to n years; M labourers out of the total labour force A are occupied in replacing the nth part of the stock that wears out each year, while A-M "free labourers" co-operate with the stock of axes to produce a (net) output π. K is the value of the stock of axes (in terms of product), l the wage rate, and ρ the rate of interest.[30]

K is evaluated by Wicksell in equation (15) p. 283. With one substitution from equation (4) p. 276, (15) becomes:

$$(15.1) \quad K = Mnl\left(\frac{1}{1-e^{-\rho n}} - \frac{1}{\rho n}\right)$$

Here Mnl is the replacement cost of the whole stock of axes, while the bracketed expression can be recognized as the Champernowne-Kahn formula for the value of a "balanced equipment" as a proportion of its replacement cost.[31] Differentiating (15.1) as it stands, and

29. First published in Swedish in 1923, then republished in 1934 with the English edition of *Lectures,* Vol. 1, pp. 274-99). Until the Joan Robinson—Kahn-Champernowne papers of 1953-54, this essay seems to have been the only analysis available in English of the specific questions posed for (long-run) capital theory by durable, depreciable, capital equipment.

30. Wicksell's notation is preserved. In this case no attempt will be made to re-formulate Wicksell's model. Assuming that the interested reader will look up the original, we give the essentials of the argument with a minimum of incidental explanation.

31. Wicksell's derivation of (15) is explained by R. G. D. Allen, *Mathematical Analysis for Economists,* p. 405. The Champernowne-Kahn formula is derived by Champernowne and Kahn in four different ways (*R.E.S.* 1953-54, pp. 107-111). Joan Robinson reports in her preface that C. A. Blyth has derived it independently.

The underlying principle can be seen in graphical terms. The cost or value of a "machine" is equal to its future gross earnings discounted to the present moment. Given the prospective earnings at each point of its life, and given the rate of interest at which they are to be discounted, a curve showing the machine's value as a function of its age will fall from its starting-point at age o (replaceplacement cost) down to zero at age n years when it falls to pieces. The average value of the machine *per year of life* is the area under the curve divided by n. A "balanced equipment" of such machines is of uniform age distribution from o to n, and so repeats in cross-section the life-history of a single machine. The average value *per machine* in a "balanced equipment" is therefore also the area under the curve divided by n. In the particular case when the earnings of a machine are at a constant rate throughout its life, the Champernowne-Kahn formula gives the ratio of this average value to the original value at age o.

then making a substitution from Wicksell's equation (9) p. 278, we obtain the logarithmic total differential of K:

$$(15.2)\ \frac{dK}{K}=\left[\frac{dM}{M}+\frac{(1-\nu)\ (\nu+\phi(\nu))}{\nu+\phi(\nu)-1}\frac{dn}{n}\right]$$
$$+\left[\frac{dl}{l}+\left(\frac{1-\nu}{\nu+\phi(\nu)-1}-\nu\right)\frac{d\rho}{\rho}\right]$$

The proportional change in the value of capital is split by the square brackets into a "productive" and a "financial" component, just as in (6a) of Part II. Again we identfy $\frac{dk}{k}$ with the first component, and $\frac{dp}{p}$ with the second. This time the distinction is easier to visualize. The "technical unit" of capital in which k is measured is in effect a *standard axe* (of given durability and age), while p is the value of such an axe, calculated at current wage and interest rates. This follows simply from the fact that the second component of (15.2) is the differential of (15.1) with respect to l and ρ, calculated as of constant M and n. In the present model the definition of a "standard axe" creates no index-number problems: Wicksell's constant elasticity formulae mean that the coefficients in (15.2) are constants, so that k and p can be obtained by direct integration as indexes with correct and constant weights at every point. Moreover, M is a constant proportion of the total labour force A (Wicksell, p. 287), and is therefore determined when A is taken as an independent variable.

The rest follows as in Part II—the Wicksell effect disappears, the production function[32] can be written in terms of A and k, etc. In fact, with an appropriate revision or re-interpretation of the various constants, our earlier equations (a′), (b′), (1′), (2′), and (3′) will now serve as an exact representation in neo-classical form of Wicksell's analysis of Åkerman's problem.

IV. *The Wicksell Effect in Reverse*

One new feature emerges. In the model of Part II increasing K (or k) always means increasing p: the wage rate rises and the interest rate falls, but the net effect is necessarily a rise in the value of a unit of capital in terms of product. Thus the Wicksell effect is an apparent absorption of capital. However, in the model of Part III it turns out that the two components of (15.2) may very well be of

32. With k defined as above, it can be shown that the production function given by Wicksell in equation (17 *bis*) p. 287 is correctly reproduced by the integral of the following expression:

$$\frac{d\pi}{\pi}=\left(1-\beta\frac{\nu+\phi(\nu)-1}{\nu+\phi(\nu)}\right)\frac{dA}{A}+\beta\,\frac{\nu+\phi(\nu)-1}{\nu+\phi(\nu)}\,\frac{dk}{k}$$

By Wicksell's assumptions, the coefficients are constants.

opposite sign. So long as the "convexity" conditions for profit maximization are satisfied, a higher wage rate and a lower interest rate must still accompany increasing K (or k), but the interest effect on p may now outweigh the wage effect.[33] The value of a "standard axe" may fall. *In this event the Wicksell effect goes into reverse.*

When Wicksell calculated $\frac{d\pi}{dK}$ he found again that by this measure Åkerman's and von Thünen's thesis was "not verified", but he found also that in his new model $\frac{d\pi}{dK}$ might actually exceed the rate of interest—i.e. he discovered the Wicksell effect in reverse. This phenomenon left Wicksell very puzzled, and caused him to admit that his previous explanation, in terms of the absorption of capital in increased wages, was "*not* general".[34]

Once it is realized that the Wicksell effect merely reflects a revaluation of the capital stock, it is no longer puzzling that it may go in either direction. When wages rise and interest falls, whether the value of a "standard axe" goes up or down in terms of product may be expected to turn (broadly speaking) on a comparison of the relative importance of the two factors for the axe on the one hand, and for the product on the other. In general, there is no presumption either way. But in Wicksell's previous models, before his analysis of Åkerman's problem, the product typically emerged only at the last and most "capitalistic" stage of production. In such models (as in Part II above) a higher wage rate and a lower interest rate must depress the final product, and elevate the goods-in-process at the earlier stages, in relative value. Hence Wicksell's surprise on finding himself at the age of 72 in a new world of durable capital equipment, in which this rule no longer applies.

33. Here we are looking at capital from the viewpoint of cost, as in (6a). It is possible as before to express $\frac{dp}{p}$ in terms of either the wage rate or the interest rate alone. For instance, corresponding with (6c), the second component of (15.2) may be written:

$$\frac{dp}{p} = -\left[\nu + \beta(1-\nu) - \frac{1-\nu}{\nu + \phi(\nu) - 1}\right]\frac{d\rho}{\rho}$$

The second-order maximization conditions imply that β and ν are each less than unity, and that the denominator of the third term is positive. But the sign of the sum within the brackets (which in (6c) is always positive) depends on the relative magnitudes of β and ν; it can be negative if β is small and ν neither very near unity nor very near zero.

34. pp. 292-293. It is interesting to note that Wicksell in these pages experimented with the possibility of adjusting his measure of the increase in capital, by deducting the effect of the rise in the wage rate, precisely as we have done in defining $\frac{dk}{k}$ and $\frac{dp}{p}$. He failed to reach the same conclusion only because he did not allow for the lower interest rate as well as for the higher wage rate.

What is more puzzling is why Joan Robinson thirty years later should write as if she and Wicksell were both back in the old world where capital was goods-in-process. Her rule that "at a lower wage rate there is a smaller value of a given type of machine" need not hold even for Wicksell's hand-made axe, far less for a typical machine, itself a capitalistic product.[35] The revaluation of a given machine in an opposite direction to the wage rate (in the same direction as the interest rate) is a reverse Wicksell effect, but there is nothing perverse about it[36], and in general it is just as likely to happen as its obverse, the original Wicksell effect.

Most puzzling of all is how the possibility of a shift in relative value between capital good and product *in an unpredictable direction* can become in Joan Robinson's hands "the key to the whole theory of accumulation and of the determination of wages and profits."

35. The influence of interest on the value of an axe is confined in (15.1) and (15.2) to the Champernowne-Kahn term of (15.1)—i.e. to the effect of the interest rate on the value of a "balanced equipment" of axes as a proportion of its replacement cost. The latter consists of labour cost alone. If axes were themselves made with the co-operation of capital, their replacement cost would also contain an interest element, and it would be much easier for the reverse Wicksell effect to occur.

36. The perverse case discussed by Joan Robinson, in which a higher wage rate and a lower interest rate make a *less* mechanized technique relatively profitable, has nothing to do with the direction of the Wicksell effect, though one might easily get the impression that Joan Robinson thinks it does (see *R.E.S.* 1953-54 pp. 95-96, 106, and *The Accumulation of Capital*, pp. 109-110, 147-148, 418). The perversity arises essentially from a failure over a certain range of the second-order ("convexity") conditions for profit maximization, as indeed Wicksell pointed out in his analysis of Åkerman's problem (pp. 294-297, especially the footnote on p. 295). Only in his earlier goods-in-process model would a reverse Wicksell effect imply the failure of those conditions, and so perversity.

9

THE ECONOMIC IMPLICATIONS OF LEARNING BY DOING

By Kenneth J. Arrow

It is by now incontrovertible that increases in per capita income cannot be explained simply by increases in the capital-labor ratio. Though doubtless no economist would ever have denied the role of technological change in economic growth, its overwhelming importance relative to capital formation has perhaps only been fully realized with the important empirical studies of Abramovitz [1] and Solow [11]. These results do not directly contradict the neo-classical view of the production function as an expression of technological knowledge. All that has to be added is the obvious fact that knowledge is growing in time. Nevertheless a view of economic growth that depends so heavily on an exogenous variable, let alone one so difficult to measure as the quantity of knowledge, is hardly intellectually satisfactory. From a quantitative, empirical point of view, we are left with time as an explanatory variable. Now trend projections, however necessary they may be in practice, are basically a confession of ignorance, and, what is worse from a practical viewpoint, are not policy variables.

Further, the concept of knowledge which underlies the production function at any moment needs analysis. Knowledge has to be acquired. We are not surprised, as educators, that even students subject to the same educational experiences have different bodies of knowledge, and we may therefore be prepared to grant, as has been shown empirically (see [2], Part III), that different countries, at the same moment of time, have different production functions even apart from differences in natural resource endowment.

I would like to suggest here an endogenous theory of the changes in knowledge which underlie intertemporal and international shifts in production functions. The acquisition of knowledge is what is usually termed " learning," and we might perhaps pick up some clues from the many psychologists who have studied this phenomenon (for a convenient survey, see Hilgard [5]). I do not think that the picture of technical change as a vast and prolonged process of learning about the environment in which we operate is in any way a far-fetched analogy; exactly the same phenomenon of improvement in performance over time is involved.

Of course, psychologists are no more in agreement than economists, and there are sharp differences of opinion about the processes of learning. But one empirical generalization is so clear that all schools of thought must accept it, although they interpret it in different fashions: Learning is the product of experience. Learning can only take place through the attempt to solve a problem and therefore only takes place during activity. Even the Gestalt and other field theorists, who stress the role of insight in the solution of problems (Köhler's famous apes), have to assign a significant role to previous experiences in modifying the individual's perception.

A second generalization that can be gleaned from many of the classic learning experiments is that learning associated with repetition of essentially the same problem is subject to sharply diminishing returns. There is an equilibrium response pattern for any given stimulus, towards which the behavior of the learner tends with repetition. To have steadily increasing performance, then, implies that the stimulus situations must themselves be steadily evolving rather than merely repeating.

The role of experience in increasing productivity has not gone unobserved, though the relation has yet to be absorbed into the main corpus of economic theory. It was early observed by aeronautical engineers, particularly T. P. Wright [15], that the number of labor-hours expended in the production of an airframe (airplane body without engines) is a decreasing function of the total number of airframes of the same type previously produced. Indeed, the relation is remarkably precise; to produce the Nth airframe of a given type, counting from the inception of production, the amount of labor required is proportional to $N^{-1/3}$. This relation has become basic in the production and cost planning of the United States Air Force; for a full survey, see [3]. Hirsch (see [6] and other work cited there) has shown the existence of the same type of " learning curve " or " progress ratio," as it is variously termed, in the production of other machines, though the rate of learning is not the same as for airframes.

Verdoorn [14, pp. 433-4] has applied the principle of the learning curve to national outputs; however, under the assumption that output is increasing exponentially, current output is proportional to cumulative output, and it is the former variable that he uses to explain labor productivity. The empirical fitting was reported in [13]; the estimated progress ratio for different European countries is about ·5. (In [13], a neo-classical interpretation in terms of increasing capital-labor ratios was offered; see pp. 7-11.)

Lundberg [9, pp. 129-133] has given the name " Horndal effect " to a very similar phenomenon. The Horndal iron works in Sweden had no new investment (and therefore presumably no significant change in its methods of production) for a period of 15 years, yet productivity (output per manhour) rose on the average close to 2% per annum. We find again steadily increasing performance which can only be imputed to learning from experience.

I advance the hypothesis here that technical change in general can be ascribed to experience, that it is the very activity of production which gives rise to problems for which favorable responses are selected over time. The evidence so far cited, whether from psychological or from economic literature is, of course, only suggestive. The aim of this paper is to formulate the hypothesis more precisely and draw from it a number of economic implications. These should enable the hypothesis and its consequences to be confronted more easily with empirical evidence.

The model set forth will be very simplified in some other respects to make clearer the essential role of the major hypothesis; in particular, the possibility of capital-labor substitution is ignored. The theorems about the economic world presented here differ from those in most standard economic theories; profits are the result of technical change; in a free-enterprise system, the rate of investment will be less than the optimum; net investment and the stock of capital become subordinate concepts, with gross investment taking a leading role.

In section 1, the basic assumptions of the model are set forth. In section 2, the implications for wage earners are deduced; in section 3 those for profits, the inducement to invest, and the rate of interest. In section 4, the behavior of the entire system under steady growth with mutually consistent expectations is taken up. In section 5, the divergence between social and private returns is studied in detail for a special case (where the subjective rate of discount of future consumption is a constant). Finally, in section 6, some limitations of the model and needs for further development are noted.

1. The Model

The first question is that of choosing the economic variable which represents " experience ". The economic examples given above suggest the possibility of using cumulative output (the total of output from the beginning of time) as an index of experience, but this does not seem entirely satisfactory. If the rate of output is constant, then the stimulus to learning presented would appear to be constant, and the learning that does take place is a gradual approach to equilibrium behavior. I therefore take instead cumulative gross investment (cumulative production of capital goods) as an index of experience. Each new machine produced and put into use is capable of changing the environment in which production takes place, so that learning is taking place with continually new stimuli. This at least makes plausible the possibility of continued learning in the sense, here, of a steady rate of growth in productivity.

The second question is that of deciding where the learning enters the conditions of production. I follow here the model of Solow [12] and Johansen [7], in which technical change is completely embodied in new capital goods. At any moment of new time, the new capital goods incorporate all the knowledge then available, but once built their productive efficiency cannot be altered by subsequent learning.

To simplify the discussion we shall assume that the production process associated with any given new capital good is characterized by fixed coefficients, so that a fixed amount of labor is used and a fixed amount of output obtained. Further, it will be assumed that new capital goods are better than old ones in the strong sense that, if we compare a unit of capital goods produced at time t_1 with one produced at time $t_2 > t_1$, the first requires the co-operation of at least as much labor as the second, and produces no more product. Under this assumption, a new capital good will always be used in preference to an older one.

Let G be cumulative gross investment. A unit capital good produced when cumulative gross investment has reached G will be said to have *serial number G*. Let

$\lambda(G)$ = amount of labor used in production with a capital good of serial number G,
$\gamma(G)$ = output capacity of a capital good of serial number G,
x = total output,
L = total labor force employed.

It is assumed that $\lambda(G)$ is a non-increasing function, while $\gamma(G)$ is a non-decreasing function. Then, regardless of wages or rental value of capital goods, it always pays to use a capital good of higher serial number before one of lower serial number.

It will further be assumed that capital goods have a fixed lifetime, $\bar{T}$. Then capital goods disappear in the same order as their serial numbers. It follows that at any moment of time, the capital goods in use will be all those with serial numbers from some G' to G, the current cumulative gross investment. Then

$$(1) \qquad x = \int_{G'}^{G} \gamma(G)dG,$$

(2) $$L = \int_{G'}^{G} \lambda(G)dG.$$

The magnitudes x, L, G, and G' are, of course, all functions of time, to be designated by t, and they will be written $x(t)$, $L(t)$, $G(t)$, and $G'(t)$ when necessary to point up the dependence. Then $G(t)$, in particular, is the cumulative gross investment up to time t. The assumption about the lifetime of capital goods implies that

(3) $$G'(t) \geqq G(t - \bar{T}).$$

Since $G(t)$ is given at time t, we can solve for G' from (1) or (2) or the equality in (3). In a growth context, the most natural assumption is that of full employment. The labor force is regarded as a given function of time and is assumed equal to the labor employed, so that $L(t)$ is a given function. Then $G'(t)$ is obtained by solving in (2). If the result is substituted into (1), x can be written as a function of L and G, analogous to the usual production function. To write this, define

(4) $$\Lambda(G) = \int \lambda(G)dG,$$
$$\Gamma(g) = \int \gamma(G)dG.$$

These are to be regarded as indefinite integrals. Since $\lambda(G)$ and $\gamma(G)$ are both positive, $\Lambda(G)$ and $\Gamma(G)$ are strictly increasing and therefore have inverses, $\Lambda^{-1}(u)$ and $\Gamma^{-1}(v)$, respectively. Then (1) and (2) can be written, respectively,

(1′) $$x = \Gamma(G) - \Gamma(G'),$$

(2′) $$L = \Lambda(G) - \Lambda(G').$$

Solve for G' from (2′).

(5) $$G' = \Lambda^{-1}[\Lambda(G) - L].$$

Substitute (5) into (1′).

(6) $$x = \Gamma(G) - \Gamma\{\Lambda^{-1}[\Lambda(G) - L]\},$$

which is thus a production function in a somewhat novel sense. Equation (6) is always valid, but under the full employment assumption we can regard L as the labor force available.

A second assumption, more suitable to a depression situation, is that in which demand for the product is the limiting factor. Then x is taken as given; G' can be derived from (1) or (1′), and employment then found from (2) or (2′). If this is less than the available labor force, we have Keynesian unemployment.

A third possibility, which, like the first, may be appropriate to a growth analysis, is that the solution (5) with L as the labor force, does not satisfy (3). In this case, there is a shortage of capital due to depreciation. There is again unemployment but now due to structural discrepancies rather than to demand deficiency.

In any case, except by accident, there is either unemployed labor or unemployed capital; there could be both in the demand deficiency case. Of course, a more neoclassical model, with substitution between capital and labor for each serial number of capital good, might permit full employment of both capital and labor, but this remains a subject for further study.

In what follows, the full-employment case will be chiefly studied. The capital shortage case, the third one, will be referred to parenthetically. In the full-employment case, the depreciation assumption no longer matters; obsolescence, which occurs for all capital goods with serial numbers below G', becomes the sole reason for the retirement of capital goods from use.

The analysis will be carried through for a special case. To a very rough approximation, the capital-output ratio has been constant, while the labor-output ratio has been declining. It is therefore assumed that

(7) $\gamma(G) = a,$

a constant, while $\lambda(G)$ is a decreasing function of G. To be specific, it will be assumed that $\lambda(G)$ has the form found in the study of learning curves for airframes.

(8) $\lambda(G) = bG^{-n},$

where $n > 0$. Then

$$\Gamma(G) = aG, \ \Lambda(G) = cG^{1-n}, \text{ where } c = b/(1-n) \text{ for } n \neq 1.$$

Then (6) becomes

(9) $$x = aG\left[1 - \left(1 - \frac{L}{cG^{1-n}}\right)^{1/(1-n)}\right] \text{ if } n \neq 1.$$

Equation (9) is always well defined in the relevant ranges, since from (2′),

$$L = \Lambda(G) - \Lambda(G') \leqq \Lambda(G) = cG^{1-n}.$$

When $n = 1$, $\Lambda(G) = b \log G$ (where the natural logarithm is understood), and

(10) $x = aG(1-e^{-L/b})$ if $n = 1$.

Although (9) and (10) are, in a sense, production functions, they show increasing returns to scale in the variables G and L. This is obvious in (10) where an increase in G, with L constant, increases x in the same proportion; a simultaneous increase in L will further increase x. In (9), first suppose that $n < 1$. Then a proportional increase in L and G increases L/G^{1-n} and therefore increases the expression in brackets which multiplies G. A similar argument holds if $n > 1$. It should be noted that x increases more than proportionately to scale changes in G and L in general, not merely for the special case defined by (7) and (8). This would be verified by careful examination of the behavior of (6), when it is recalled that $\lambda(G)$ is non-increasing and $\gamma(G)$ is non-decreasing, with the strict inequality holding in at least one. It is obvious intuitively, since the additional amounts of L and G are used more efficiently than the earlier ones.

The increasing returns do not, however, lead to any difficulty with distribution theory. As we shall see, both capital and labor are paid their marginal products, suitably defined. The explanation is, of course, that the private marginal productivity of capital (more strictly, of new investment) is less than the social marginal productivity since the learning effect is not compensated in the market.

The production assumptions of this section are designed to play the role assigned by Kaldor to his " technical progress function," which relates the rate of growth of output per worker to the rate of growth of capital per worker (see [8], section VIII). I prefer to think of relations between rates of growth as themselves derived from more fundamental relations between the magnitudes involved. Also, the present formulation puts more stress on gross rather than net investment as the basic agent of technical change.

Earlier, Haavelmo ([4], sections 7.1 and 7.2) had suggested a somewhat similar model. Output depended on both capital and the stock of knowledge; investment depended on output, the stock of capital, and the stock of knowledge. The stock of knowledge was either simply a function of time or, in a more sophisticated version, the consequence of investment, the educational effect of each act of investment decreasing exponentially in time.

Verdoorn [14, pp. 436-7] had also developed a similar simple model in which capital and labor needed are non-linear functions of output (since the rate of output is, approximately, a measure of cumulative output and therefore of learning) and investment a constant fraction of output. He notes that under these conditions, full employment of capital and labor simultaneously is in general impossible—a conclusion which also holds for for the present model as we have seen. However, Verdoorn draws the wrong conclusion: that the savings ratio must be fixed by some public mechanism at the uniquely determined level which would insure full employment of both factors; the correct conclusion is that one factor or the other will be unemployed. The social force of this conclusion is much less in the present model since the burden of unemployment may fall on obsolescent capital; Verdoorn assumes his capital to be homogeneous in nature.

2. Wages

Under the full employment assumption the profitability of using the capital good with serial number G' must be zero; for if it were positive it would be profitable to use capital goods with higher serial number and if it were negative capital good G' would not be used contrary to the definition of G'. Let

w = wage rate with output as numéraire.

From (1′) and (7)

$$(11) \qquad G' = G - (x/a)$$

so that

$$(12) \qquad \lambda(G') = b\left(G - \frac{x}{a}\right)^{-n}.$$

The output from capital good G' is $\gamma(G')$ while the cost of operation is $\lambda(G')w$. Hence

$$\gamma(G') = \lambda(G')w$$

or from (7) and (12)

$$(13) \qquad w = a\left(G - \frac{x}{a}\right)^{n}/b.$$

It is interesting to derive labor's share which is wL/x. From (2′) with $\Lambda(g) = cG^{1-n}$ and G' given by (11)

$$L = c\left[G^{1-n} - \left(G - \frac{x}{a}\right)^{1-n} \right],$$

for $n \neq 1$ and therefore

$$(14) \qquad wL/x = a\left[\left(\frac{G}{x} - \frac{1}{a}\right)^{n}\left(\frac{G}{x}\right)^{1-n} - \left(\frac{G}{x} - \frac{1}{a}\right)\right]/(1-n) \text{ for } n \neq 1,$$

where use has been made of the relation, $c = b/(1-n)$. It is interesting to note that labor's share is determined by the ratio G/x.

Since, however, x is determined by G and L, which, at any moment of time, are data, it is also useful to express the wage ratio, w, and labor's share, wL/x, in terms of L and G. First, G' can be found by solving for it from (2′).

$$(15) \qquad G' = \left(G^{1-n} - \frac{L}{c}\right)^{1/(1-n)} \text{ for } n \neq 1.$$

We can then use the same reasoning as above, and derive

$$(16) \qquad w = a\left(G^{1-n} - \frac{L}{c}\right)^{n/(1-n)}/b,$$

$$(17) \qquad \frac{wL}{x} = \frac{\left[\left(\frac{L}{G^{1-n}}\right)^{(1-n)/n} - \frac{1}{c}\left(\frac{L}{G^{1-n}}\right)^{1/n}\right]^{n/(1-n)}}{b\left[1 - \left(1 - \frac{L}{cG^{1-n}}\right)^{1/(1-n)}\right]}.$$

Labor's share thus depends on the ratio L/G^{1-n}; it can be shown to decrease as the ratio increases.

For completeness, I note the corresponding formulas for the case $n = 1$. In terms of G and x, we have

$$(18) \qquad w = (aG - x)/b,$$

$$(19) \qquad wL/x = \left(\frac{aG}{x} - 1\right)\log\frac{G/x}{(G/x) - (1/a)}.$$

In terms of G and L, we have

$$(20) \qquad G' = Ge^{-L/b},$$

$$(21) \qquad w = \frac{aG}{be^{L/b}},$$

$$(22) \qquad wL/x = \frac{L}{b(e^{L/b} - 1)}.$$

In this case, labor's share depends only on L, which is indeed the appropriate special case ($n=1$) of the general dependence on L/G^{1-n}.

The preceding discussion has assumed full employment. In the capital shortage case, there cannot be a competitive equilibrium with positive wage since there is necessarily unemployment. A zero wage is, however, certainly unrealistic. To complete the model, it would be necessary to add some other assumption about the behavior of wages. This case will not be considered in general; for the special case of steady growth, see Section 5.

3. Profits and Investment

The profit at time t from a unit investment made at time $v \leqq t$ is

$$\gamma[G(v)] - w(t)\ \lambda[G(v)].$$

In contemplating an investment at time v, the stream of potential profits depends upon expectations of future wages. We will suppose that looking ahead at any given moment of time each entrepreneur assumes that wages will rise exponentially from the present level. Thus the wage rate expected at time v to prevail at time t is

$$w(v)\ e^{\theta(t-v)},$$

and the profit expected at time v to be received at time t is

$$\gamma[G(v)]\ [1-W(v)\ e^{\theta(t-v)}],$$

where

$$W(v) = w(v)\ \lambda[G(v)]/\gamma[G(v)], \tag{23}$$

the labor cost per unit output at the time the investment is made. The dependence of W on v will be made explicit only when necessary. The profitability of the investment is expected to decrease with time (if $\theta > 0$) and to reach zero at time $T^* + v$, defined by the equation

$$We^{\theta T^*} = 1. \tag{24}$$

Thus T^* is the expected economic lifetime of the investment, provided it does not exceed the physical lifetime, $\bar{T}$. Let

$$T = \min(\bar{T}, T^*). \tag{25}$$

Then the investor plans to derive profits only over an interval of length T, either because the investment wears out or because wages have risen to the point where it is unprofitable to operate. Since the expectation of wage rises which causes this abandonment derives from anticipated investment and the consequent technological progress, T^* represents the expected date of obsolescence. Let

$$\rho = \text{rate of interest.}$$

If the rate of interest is expected to remain constant over the future, then the discounted stream of profits over the effective lifetime, T, of the investment is

$$(26)\qquad S = \int_{o}^{T} e^{-\rho t}\,\gamma[G(v)]\,(1 - W\,e^{\theta t})dt,$$

or

$$(27)\qquad \frac{S}{\gamma[G(v)]} = \frac{1 - e^{-\rho T}}{\rho} + \frac{W(1 - e^{-(\rho-\theta)T})}{\theta - \rho}.$$

Let

$$(28)\qquad V = e^{-\theta T} = \max\,(e^{-\theta \bar{T}}, W),\ \alpha = \rho/\theta.$$

Then

$$(29)\qquad \frac{\theta\,S}{\gamma[G(v)]} = \frac{1 - V^{\alpha}}{\alpha} + \frac{W(1 - V^{\alpha-1})}{1-\alpha} = R(\alpha).$$

The definitions of $R(\alpha)$ for $\alpha = 0$ and $\alpha = 1$ needed to make the function continuous are:

$$R(0) = -\log V + W(1 - V^{-1}),\ R(1) = 1 - V + W\log V.$$

If all the parameters of (26), (27), or (29) are held constant, S is a function of ρ, and, equivalently, R of α. If (26) is differentiated with respect to ρ, we find

$$dS/d\rho = \int_{o}^{T} (-t)e^{-\rho t}\,\gamma[G(v)]\,(1 - W\,e^{\theta t})dt < 0.$$

Also

$$S < \gamma[G(v)] \int_{o}^{T} e^{-\rho t}dt = \gamma[G(v)]\,(1 - e^{-\rho T})/\rho$$

$$< \gamma[G(v)]/\rho.$$

Since obviously $S > 0$, S approaches 0 as ρ approaches infinity. Since R and α differ from S and ρ, respectively, only by positive constant factors, we conclude

$$dR/d\alpha < 0,\quad \lim_{\alpha \to +\infty} R(\alpha) = 0.$$

To examine the behavior of $R(\alpha)$ as α approaches $-\infty$, write

$$R(\alpha) = -\frac{(1/V)^{1-\alpha}}{(1-\alpha)^2}\,[(1-\alpha)V + \alpha\,W]\left(\frac{1-\alpha}{\alpha}\right) + \frac{1}{\alpha} + \frac{W}{1-\alpha}.$$

The last two terms approach zero. As α approaches $-\infty$, $1 - \alpha$ approaches $+\infty$. Since $1/V > 1$, the factor

$$\frac{(1/V)^{1-\alpha}}{(1-\alpha)^2}$$

approaches $+\infty$, since an exponential approaches infinity faster than any power. From (28), $V \geqq W$. If $V = W$, then the factor,

$$(1-\alpha)V - \alpha W = \alpha(W - V) + V,$$

is a positive constant; if $V > W$, then it approaches $+\infty$ as α approaches $-\infty$. Finally,

$$\frac{1-\alpha}{\alpha}$$

necessarily approaches -1. Hence,

(30) $R(\alpha)$ is a strictly decreasing function, approaching $+\infty$ as α approaches $-\infty$ and 0 as α approaches $+\infty$.

The market, however, should adjust the rate of return so that the discounted stream of profits equals the cost of investment, i.e., $S = 1$, or, from (29),

(31) $R(\alpha) = \theta/\gamma[G(v)]$.

Since the right-hand side of (31) is positive, (30) guarantees the existence of an α which satisfies (31). For a given θ, the equilibrium rate of return, ρ, is equal to $\alpha\,\theta$; it may indeed be negative. The rate of return is thus determined by the expected rate of increase in wages, current labor costs per unit output, and the physical lifetime of the investment. Further, if the first two are sufficiently large, the physical lifetime becomes irrelevant, since then $T^* < \bar{T}$, and $T = T^*$.

The discussion of profits and returns has not made any special assumptions as to the form of the production relations.

4. Rational Expectations in a Macroeconomic Growth Model

Assume a one-sector model so that the production relations of the entire economy are described by the model of section 1. In particular, this implies that gross investment at any moment of time is simply a diversion of goods that might otherwise be used for consumption. Output and gross investment can then be measured in the same units.

The question arises, can the expectations assumed to govern investment behavior in the preceding section actually be fulfilled? Specifically, can we have a constant relative increase of wages and a constant rate of interest which, if anticipated, will lead entrepreneurs to invest at a rate which, in conjunction with the exogenously given rate of interest to remain at the given level? Such a state of affairs is frequently referred to as " perfect foresight," but a better term is " rational expectations," a term introduced by J. Muth [10].

We study this question first for the full employment case. For this case to occur, the physical lifetime of investments must not be an effective constraint. If, in the notation of the last section, $T^* > \bar{T}$, and if wage expectations are correct, then investments will disappear through depreciation at a time when they are still yielding positive current profits. As seen in section 2, this is incompatible with competitive equilibrium and full employment. Assume therefore that

(32) $T^* \leqq \bar{T}$;

then from (28), $W = V$, and from (29) and (31), the equilibrium value of ρ is determined by the equation,

(33) $$\frac{1 - W^\alpha}{\alpha} + \frac{W - W^\alpha}{1 - \alpha} = \frac{\theta}{a},$$

where, on the right-hand side, use is made of (7).

From (16), it is seen that for the wage rate to rise at a constant rate θ, it is necessary that the quantity,

$$G^{1-n} - \frac{L}{c},$$

rise at a rate $\theta(1 - n)/n$. For θ constant, it follows from (33) that a constant ρ and therefore a constant α requires that W be constant. For the specific production relations (7) and (8), (23) shows that

$$W = \frac{a\left(G^{1-n} - \frac{L}{c}\right)^{n/(1-n)}}{b} \frac{bG^{-n}}{a} = \left(1 - \frac{L}{cG^{1-n}}\right)^{n/(1-n)},$$

and therefore the constancy of W is equivalent to that of L/G^{1-n}. In combination with the preceding remark, we see that

(34) L increases at rate $\theta(1 - n)/n$, G increases at rate θ/n.

Suppose that

σ = rate of increase of the labor force,

is a given constant. Then

(35) $\theta = n\,\sigma/(1-n)$,

(36) the rate of increase of G is $\sigma/(1-n)$.

Substitution into the production function (9) yields

(37) the rate of increase of x is $\sigma/(1-n)$.

From (36) and (37), the ratio G/x is constant over time. However, the value at which it is constant is not determined by the considerations so far introduced; the savings function is needed to complete the system. Let the constant ratio be

(38) $G(t)/x(t) = \mu$.

Define

$g(t)$ = rate of gross investment at time $t = dG/dt$.

From (36), $g/G = \sigma/(1 - n)$, a constant. Then

$$(39) \qquad g/x = (g/G)(G/x) = \mu\,\sigma/(1 - n).$$

A simple assumption is that the ratio of gross saving (equals gross investment) to income (equals output) is a function of the rate of return, ρ; a special case would be the common assumption of a constant savings-to-income ratio. Then μ is a function of ρ. On the other hand, we can write W as follows, using (23) and (13):

$$(40) \qquad W = a\,\frac{\left(G - \frac{x}{a}\right)^n}{b}\;\frac{bG^{-n}}{a} = \left(1 - \frac{x}{aG}\right)^n = \left(1 - \frac{1}{a\mu}\right)^n.$$

Since θ is given by (35), (33) is a relation between W and ρ, and, by (40) between μ and ρ. We thus have two relations between μ and ρ, so they are determinate.

From (38), μ determines one relation between G and X. If the labor force, L, is given at one moment of time, the production function (9) constitutes a second such relation, and the system is completely determinate.

As in many growth models, the rates of growth of the variables in the system do not depend on savings behavior; however, their levels do.

It should be made clear that all that has been demonstrated is the existence of a solution in which all variables have constant rates of growth, correctly anticipated. The stability of the solution requires further study.

The growth rate for wages implied by the solution has one paradoxical aspect; it increases with the rate of growth of the labor force (provided $n < 1$). The explanation seems to be that under full employment, the increasing labor force permits a more rapid introduction of the newer machinery. It should also be noted that, for a constant saving ratio, g/x, an increase in σ decreases μ, from (39), from which it can be seen that wages at the initial time period would be lower. In this connection it may be noted that since G cannot decrease, it follows from (36) that σ and $1-n$ must have the same sign for the steady growth path to be possible. The most natural case, of course, is $\sigma > 0$, $n < 1$.

This solution is, however, admissible only if the condition (32), that the rate of depreciation not be too rapid, be satisfied. We can find an explicit formula for the economic lifetime, T^*, of new investment. From (24), it satisfies the condition

$$e^{-\theta T^*} = W.$$

If we use (35) and (40) and solve for T^*, we find

$$(41) \qquad T^* = \frac{-(1-n)}{\sigma}\log\left[1 - \frac{1}{a\mu}\right]$$

and this is to be compared with $\bar{T}$; the full employment solution with rational expectations of exponentially increasing wages and constant interest is admissible if $T^* \leqq \bar{T}$.

If $T^* > \bar{T}$, then the full employment solution is inadmissible. One might ask if a constant-growth solution is possible in this case. The answer depends on assumptions about the dynamics of wages under this condition.

We retain the two conditions, that wages rise at a constant rate θ, and that the rate of interest be constant. With constant θ, the rate of interest, ρ, is determined from (31); from (29), this requires that

(42) W is constant over time.

From the definition of W, (23), and the particular form of the production relations, (7) and (8), it follows that the wage rate, w, must rise at the same rate as G^n, or

(43) G rises at a constant rate θ/n.

In the presence of continued unemployment, the most natural wage dynamics in a free market would be a decreasing, or, at best, constant wage level. But since G can never decrease, it follows from (43) that θ can never be negative. Instead of making a specific assumption about wage changes, it will be assumed that any choice of θ can be imposed, perhaps by government or union or social pressure, and it is asked what restrictions on the possible values of θ are set by the other equilibrium conditions.

In the capital shortage case, the serial number of the oldest capital good in use is determined by the physical lifetime of the good, i.e.,

$G' = G(t - T)$. From (43),

$$G(t - T) = e^{-\theta T/n} G.$$

Then, from (1') and (7),

$$x = aG(1 - e^{-\theta T/n}),$$

so that the ratio, G/x, or μ, is a constant,

(44) $\mu = 1/a(1 - e^{-\theta T/n})$.

From (43), $g/G = \theta/n$; hence, by the same argument as that leading to (39),

(45) $g/x = \theta/na(1 - e^{-\theta T/n})$.

There are three unknown constants of the growth process, θ, ρ, and W. If, as before, it is assumed that the gross savings ratio, g/x, is a function of the rate of return, ρ, then, for any given ρ, θ can be determined from (45); note that the right-hand side of (45) is a strictly increasing function of θ for $\theta \geq 0$, so that the determination is unique, and the rate of growth is an increasing function of the gross savings ratio, contrary to the situation in the full employment case. Then W can be solved for from (31) and (29).

Thus the rate of return is a freely disposable parameter whose choice determines the rate of growth and W, which in turn determines the initial wage rate. There are, of course, some inequalities which must be satisfied to insure that the solution corresponds to the capital shortage rather than the full employment case; in particular, $W \leq V$ and also the labor force must be sufficient to permit the expansion. From (2′), this means that the labor force must at all times be at least equal to

$$cG^{1-n} - c(G')^{1-n} = cG^{1-n}(1 - e^{-\theta(1-n)\bar{T}/n});$$

if σ is the growth rate of the labor force, we must then have (46)

$$(46) \qquad \sigma \geqq \theta(1-n)/n,$$

which sets an upper bound on θ (for $n < 1$). Other constraints on ρ are implied by the conditions $\theta \geqq 0$ and $W \geqq 0$ (if it is assumed that wage rates are non-negative). The first condition sets a lower limit on g/x; it can be shown, from (45), that

$$(47) \qquad g/x \geqq 1/a\bar{T};$$

i.e., the gross savings ratio must be at least equal to the amount of capital goods needed to produce one unit of output over their lifetime. The constraint $W > 0$ implies an interval in which ρ must lie. The conditions under which these constraints are consistent (so that at least one solution exists for the capital shortage case) have not been investigated in detail.

5. Divergence of Private and Social Product

As has already been emphasized, the presence of learning means that an act of investment benefits future investors, but this benefit is not paid for by the market. Hence, it is to be expected that the aggregate amount of investment under the competitive model of the last section will fall short of the socially optimum level. This difference will be investigated in detail in the present section under a simple assumption as to the utility function of society. For brevity, I refer to the *competitive solution* of the last section, to be contrasted with the *optimal* solution. Full employment is assumed. It is shown that the socially optimal growth rate is the same as that under competitive conditions, but the socially optimal ratio of gross investment to output is higher than the competitive level.

Utility is taken to be a function of the stream of consumption derived from the productive mechanism. Let

$$c = \text{consumption} = \text{output} - \text{gross investment} = x - g.$$

It is in particular assumed that future consumption is discounted at a constant rate, β, so that utility is

$$(48) \qquad U = \int_0^{+\infty} e^{-\beta t}c(t)dt = \int_0^{+\infty} e^{-\beta t}x(t)dt - \int_0^{+\infty} e^{-\beta t}g(t)dt.$$

Integration by parts yields

$$\int_0^{+\infty} e^{-\beta t}g(t)dt = e^{-\beta t}G(t)\Big|_0^{+\infty} + \beta\int_0^{+\infty} e^{-\beta t}G(t)dt.$$

From (48),

(49) $$U = U_1 - \lim_{t \to +\infty} e^{-\beta t} G(t) + G(0),$$

where

(50) $$U_1 = \int_o^{+\infty} e^{-\beta t}[x(t) - \beta\, G(t)]dt.$$

The policy problem is the choice of the function $G(t)$, with $G'(t) \geq 0$, to maximize (49), where $x(t)$ is determined by the production function (9), and

(51) $$L(t) = L_0 e^{\sigma t}.$$

The second term in (49) is necessarily non-negative. It will be shown that, for sufficiently high discount rate, β, the function $G(t)$ which maximizes U_1 also has the property that the second term in (49) is zero; hence, it also maximizes (49), since $G(0)$ is given.

Substitute (9) and (51) into (50).

$$U_1 = \int_o^{+\infty} e^{-\beta t} G(t) \left[a - \beta - a\left(1 - \frac{L_o e^{\sigma t}}{cG^{1-n}}\right)^{1/(1-n)}\right] dt.$$

Let $\bar{G}(t) = G(t)\, e^{-\sigma t/(1-n)}$.

$$U_1 = \int_o^{+\infty} e^{-\left(\beta - \frac{\sigma}{1-n}\right)t}\, \bar{G}(t)\left[a - \beta - a\left(1 - \frac{L_0}{c\bar{G}^{1-n}}\right)^{1/(1-n)}\right] dt.$$

Assume that

(52) $$\beta > \frac{\sigma}{1-n};$$

otherwise an infinite utility is attainable. Then to maximize U_1 it suffices to choose $\bar{G}(t)$ so as to maximize, for each t,

(53) $$\bar{G}\left[a - \beta - a\left(1 - \frac{L_0}{c\bar{G}^{1-n}}\right)^{1/(1-n)}\right].$$

Before actually determining the maximum, it can be noted that the maximizing value of $\bar{G}$ is independent of t and is therefore a constant. Hence, the optimum policy is

(54) $$G(t) = \bar{G}\, e^{\sigma t/(1-n)},$$

so that, from (36), the growth rate is the same as the competitive. From (52), $e^{-\beta t}G(t) \longrightarrow 0$ as $t \longrightarrow +\infty$.

To determine the optimal $\bar{G}$, it will be convenient to make a change of variables. Define

$$v = \left(1 - \frac{L_o}{c\bar{G}^{1-n}}\right)^{n/(1-n)}.$$

so that

(55) $$\bar{G} = \left[\frac{L_0}{(1 - \nu^{(1-n)/n})}\right]^{1/(1-n)}.$$

The analysis will be carried through primarily for the case where the output per unit capital is sufficiently high, more specifically, where

(56) $$a > \beta.$$

Let

(57) $$\gamma = 1 - \frac{\beta}{a} > 0.$$

The maximizing $\bar{G}$, or ν, is unchanged by multiplying (53), the function to be maximized, by the positive quantity, $(c/L_0)^{1/(1-n)}/a$ and then substituting from (55) and (57). Thus, ν maximizes

$$(1 - \nu^{(1-n)/n})^{-1/(1-n)} (\gamma - \nu^{1/n}).$$

The variable ν ranges from 0 to 1. However, the second factor vanishes when $\nu = \gamma^n < 1$ (since $\gamma < 1$) and becomes negative for larger values of ν; since the first factor is always positive, it can be assumed that $\nu < \gamma^n$ in searching for a maximum, and both factors are positive. Then ν also maximizes the logarithm of the above function, which is

$$f(\nu) = -\frac{\log (1 - \nu^{(1-n)/n})}{1 - n} + \log (\gamma - \nu^{1/n}),$$

so that

$$f'(\nu) = \frac{\nu^{\frac{1}{n} - 2}}{n} \left[\frac{\gamma - \nu}{(1 - \nu^{(1-n)/n})(\gamma - \nu^{1/n})}\right].$$

Clearly, with $n < 1$, $f'(\nu) > 0$ when $0 < \nu < \gamma$ and $f'(\nu) < 0$ when $\gamma < \nu < \gamma^n$, so that the maximum is obtained at

(58) $$\nu = \gamma.$$

The optimum $\bar{G}$ is determined by substituting γ for ν in (55).

From (54), L/G^{1-n} is a constant over time. From the definition of ν and (58), then,

$$\gamma = \left(1 - \frac{L}{cG^{1-n}}\right)^{n/(1-n)}$$

for all t along the optimal path, and, from the production function (9),

(59) $$\gamma = \left(1 - \frac{x}{aG}\right)^n \text{ for all } t \text{ along the optimal path.}$$

This optimal solution will be compared with the competitive solution of steady growth studied in the last section. From (40), we know that

(60) $$W = \left(1 - \frac{x}{aG}\right)^n \text{ for all } t \text{ along the competitive path.}$$

It will be demonstrated that $W < \gamma$; from this it follows that *the ratio G/x is less along the competitive path than along the optimal path.* Since along both paths,

$$g/x = [\sigma/(1 - n)]\ (G/x),$$

it also follows that *the gross savings ratio is smaller along the competitive path than along the optimal path.*

For the particular utility function (48), the supply of capital is infinitely elastic at $\rho = \beta$; i.e., the community will take any investment with a rate of return exceeding β and will take no investment at a rate of return less than β. For an equilibrium in which some, but not all, income is saved, we must have

$$(61) \qquad \rho = \beta.$$

From (35), $\theta = n\sigma/(1 - n)$; hence, by definition (28),

$$(62) \qquad \alpha = (1 - n)\beta/n\sigma.$$

Since $n < 1$, it follows from (62) and the assumption (52) that (63)

$$(63) \qquad \alpha > 1.$$

Equation (33) then becomes the one by which W is determined. The left-hand side will be denoted as $F(W)$.

$$F'(W) = \frac{1 - W^{\alpha - 1}}{1 - \alpha}.$$

From (63), $F'(W) < 0$ for $0 \geqq W < 1$, the relevant range since the investment will never be profitable if $W > 1$. To demonstrate that $W < \gamma$, it suffices to show that $F(W) > F(\gamma)$ for that value of W which satisfies (33), i.e., to show that

$$(64) \qquad F(\gamma) < \theta/a.$$

Finally, to demonstrate (64), note that $\gamma < 1$ and $\alpha > 1$, which imply that $\gamma^{\alpha} < \gamma$, and therefore

$$(1 - \alpha) - \gamma^{\alpha} + \alpha\gamma > (1 - \alpha)(1 - \gamma).$$

Since $\alpha > 1$, $\alpha(1 - \alpha) < 0$. Dividing both sides by this magnitude yields

$$\frac{1 - \gamma^{\alpha}}{\alpha} + \frac{\gamma - \gamma^{\alpha}}{1 - \alpha} < \frac{1 - \gamma}{\alpha} = \frac{\theta}{a}$$

where use is made of (57), (28), and (61); but from (33), the left-hand side is precisely $F(\gamma)$, so that (64) is demonstrated.

The case $a \leqq \beta$, excluded by (56), can be handled similarly; in that case the optimum v is 0. The subsequent reasoning follows in the same way so that the corresponding competitive path would have $W < 0$, which is, however, impossible.

6. Some Comments on the Model

(1) Many writers, such as Theodore Schultz, have stressed the improvement in the quality of the labor force over time as a source of increased productivity. This interpretation can be incorporated in the present model by assuming that σ, the rate of growth of the labor force, incorporates qualitative as well as quantitative increase.

(2) In this model, there is only one efficient capital-labor ratio for new investment at any moment of time. Most other models, on the contrary, have assumed that alternative capital-labor ratios are possible both before the capital good is built and after. A still more plausible model is that of Johansen [7], according to which alternative capital-labor ratios are open to the entrepreneur's choice at the time of investment but are fixed once the investment is congealed into a capital good.

(3) In this model, as in those of Solow [12] and Johansen [7], the learning takes place in effect only in the capital goods industry; no learning takes place in the use of a capital good once built. Lundberg's Horndal effect suggests that this is not realistic. The model should be extended to include this possibility.

(4) It has been assumed here that learning takes place only as a by-product of ordinary production. In fact, society has created institutions, education and research, whose purpose it is to enable learning to take place more rapidly. A fuller model would take account of these as additional variables.

REFERENCES.

[1] Abramovitz, M., " Resource and Output Trends in the United States Since 1870," *American Economic Review, Papers and Proceedings of the American Economic Associations*, 46 (May, 1956): 5-23.

[2] Arrow, K. J., H. B. Chenery, B. S. Minhas, and R. M. Solow, " Capital-Labor Substitution and Economic Efficiency," *Review of Economics and Statistics*, 43 (1961): 225-250.

[3] Asher, H., *Cost-Quantity Relationships in the Airframe Industry*, R-291, Santa Monica, Calif.: The RAND Corporation, 1956.

[4] Haavelmo, T. *A Study in the Theory of Economic Evolution*, Amsterdam: North Holland, 1954.

[5] Hilgard, E. R., *Theories of Learning*, 2nd ed., New York: Appleton-Century-Crofts, 1956.

[6] Hirsch, W. Z., " Firm Progress Radios," *Econometrica*, 24 (1956): 136-143.

[7] Johansen, L., " Substitution vs. Fixed Production Coefficients in the Theory of Economic Growth: A Synthesis," *Econometrica*, 27 (1959): 157-176.

[8] Kaldor, N., " Capital Accumulation and Economic Growth," in F. A. Lutz and D. C. Hague (eds.), *The Theory of Capiatl*, New York: St. Martin's Press, 1961, 177-222.

[9] Lundberg, E., *Produktivitet och räntabilitet*, Stockholm: P. A. Norstedt and Söner, 1961.

[10] Muth, J., " Rational Expectations and the Theory of Price Movements," *Econometrica* (in press).

[11] Solow, R. M., " Technical Change and the Aggregate Production Function," *Review of Economics and Statistics*, 39 (1957): 312-320.

[12] Solow, R. M., " Investment and Technical Progress," in K. J. Arrow, S. Karlin, and P. Suppes (eds.), *Mathematical Methods in the Social Sciences*, 1959, Stanford, Calif.: Stanford University Press, 1960, 89-104.

[13] Verdoorn, P. J., " Fattori che regolano lo sviluppo della produttività del lavoro," *L'Industria*, 1 (1949).

[14] Verdoorn, P. J., " Complementarity and Long-Range Projections," *Econometrica*, 24 (1956): 429-450.

[15] Wright, T. P., " Factors Affecting the Cost of Airplanes," *Journal of the Aeronautical Sciences*, 3 (1936): 122-128.

Stanford. KENNETH J. ARROW.

PART III

Models of Optimal Growth

10

A MODEL OF GENERAL ECONOMIC EQUILIBRIUM[1]

By J. von Neumann

The subject of this paper is the solution of a typical economic equation system. The system has the following properties:

(1) Goods are produced not only from "natural factors of production," but in the first place from each other. These processes of production may be circular, i.e. good G_1 is produced with the aid of good G_2, and G_2 with the aid of G_1.

(2) There may be more technically possible processes of production than goods and for this reason "counting of equations" is of no avail. The problem is rather to establish which processes will actually be used and which not (being "unprofitable").

In order to be able to discuss (1), (2) quite freely we shall idealise other elements of the situation (see paragraphs 1 and 2). Most of these idealisations are irrelevant, but this question will not be discussed here.

The way in which our questions are put leads of necessity to a system of inequalities (3)—(8′) in paragraph 3 the possibility of a solution of which is not evident, i.e. *it cannot be proved by any qualitative argument.* The mathematical proof is possible only by means of a generalisation of Brouwer's Fix-Point Theorem, i.e. by the use of very fundamental *topological* facts. This generalised fix-point theorem (the "lemma" of paragraph 7) is also interesting in itself.

The connection with topology may be very surprising at first, but the author thinks that it is natural in problems of this kind. The immediate reason for this is the occurrence of a certain "minimum-maximum" problem, familiar from the calculus of variations. In our present question, the minimum-maximum problem has been formulated in paragraph 5. It is closely related to another problem occurring in the theory of games (see footnote 1 in paragraph 6).

A direct interpretation of the function $\phi(X, Y)$ would be highly desirable. Its rôle appears to be similar to that of thermodynamic potentials in phenomenological thermodynamics; it can be surmised that the similarity will persist in its full phenomenological generality (independently of our restrictive idealisations).

Another feature of our theory, so far without interpretation, is the remarkable duality (symmetry) of the monetary variables (prices y_j, interest factor β) and the technical variables (intensities of production x_i, coefficient of expansion of the economy α). This is brought out very clearly in paragraph 3 (3)—(8′) as well as in the minimum-maximum formulation of paragraph 5 (7**)—(8**).

Lastly, attention is drawn to the results of paragraph 11 from which follows, among other things, that the normal price mechanism brings about—if our assumptions are valid—the technically most efficient intensities of production. This seems not unreasonable since we have eliminated all monetary complications.

The present paper was read for the first time in the winter of 1932 at the mathematical seminar of Princeton University. The reason for its publication was an invitation from Mr. K. Menger, to whom the author wishes to express his thanks.

1. Consider the following problem: there are n goods $G_1, \ldots, G_n$ which can be produced by m processes $P_1, \ldots, P_m$. Which processes will be used (as "profitable") and what prices of the goods will obtain? The problem is evidently

[1] This paper was first published in German, under the title *Über ein Ökonomisches Gleichungssystem und eine Verallgemeinerung des Brouwerschen Fixpunktsatzes* in the volume entitled *Ergebuisse eines Mathematischen Seminars*, edited by K. Menger (Vienna, 1938). It was translated into English by G. Morgenstern. A commentary note on this article, by D. G. Champernowne, is printed below.

non-trivial since either of its parts can be answered only after the other one has been answered, i.e. its solution is implicit. We observe in particular :

(*a*) Since it is possible that $m > n$ it cannot be solved through the usual counting of equations.

In order to avoid further complications we assume :

(*b*) That there are constant returns (to scale) ;

(*c*) That the natural factors of production, including labour, can be expanded in unlimited quantities.

The essential phenomenon that we wish to grasp is this : goods are produced from each other (see equation (7) below) and we want to determine (*i*) which processes will be used ; (*ii*) what the relative velocity will be with which the total quantity of goods increases ; (*iii*) what prices will obtain ; (*iv*) what the rate of interest will be. In order to isolate this phenomenon completely we assume furthermore :

(*d*) Consumption of goods takes place only through the processes of production which include necessities of life consumed by workers and employees.

In other words we assume that all income in excess of necessities of life will be reinvested.

It is obvious to what kind of theoretical models the above assumptions correspond.

2. In each process P_i $(i = 1, \ldots, m)$ quantities a_{ij} (expressed in some units) are used up, and quantities b_{ij} are produced, of the respective goods G_j $(j = 1, \ldots, n)$. The process can be symbolised in the following way :

$$P_i : \sum_{j=1}^{n} a_{ij} G_j \rightarrow \sum_{j=1}^{n} b_{ij} G_j \qquad (1)$$

It is to be noted :

(*e*) Capital goods are to be inserted on both sides of (1) ; wear and tear of capital goods are to be described by introducing different stages of wear as different goods, using a separate P_i for each of these.

(*f*) Each process to be of unit time duration. Processes of longer duration to be broken down into single processes of unit duration introducing if necessary intermediate products as additional goods.

(*g*) (1) can describe the special case where good G_j can be produced only jointly with certain others, viz. its permanent joint products.

In the actual economy, these processes P_i, $i = 1, \ldots, m$, will be used with certain *intensities* x_i, $i = 1, \ldots, m$. That means that for the total production the quantities of equations (1) must be multiplied by x_i. We write symbolically :

$$E = \sum_{i=1}^{m} x_i P_i \qquad (2)$$

$x_i = 0$ means that process P_i is not used.

We are interested in those states where the whole economy expands without change of structure, i.e. where the ratios of the intensities $x_1 : \ldots : x_m$ remain unchanged, although $x_1, \ldots x_m$ themselves may change. In such a case they are multiplied by a common factor α per unit of time. This factor is the *coefficient of expansion of the whole economy*.

3. The numerical unknowns of our problem are : (*i*) the *intensities* $x_1, \ldots, x_m$ of the processes $P_1, \ldots, P_m$; (*ii*) the *coefficient of expansion* of the whole economy α ; (*iii*) the *prices* $y_1, \ldots, y_n$ of goods $G_1, \ldots, G_n$; (*iv*) the interest factor β $(= 1 + \frac{z}{100}$, z being the rate of interest in % per unit of time. Obviously :

$$x_i \geqq 0, \qquad (3) \qquad\qquad y_j \geqq 0, \qquad (4)$$

and since a solution with $x_1 = \ldots = x_m = 0$, or $y_1 = \ldots = y_n = 0$ would be meaningless :

$$\sum_{i=1}^{m} x_i > 0, \qquad \ldots\ldots (5) \qquad\qquad \sum_{j=1}^{n} y_j > 0, \qquad \ldots\ldots (6)$$

The economic equations are now :

$$\alpha \sum_{i=1}^{m} a_{ij}\, x_i \leqq \sum_{i=1}^{m} b_{ij}\, x_i, \qquad \ldots\ldots (7)$$

and if in (7) $<$ applies, $y_j = 0$ .... (7′)

$$\beta \sum_{j=1}^{n} a_{ij}\, y_j \geqq \sum_{j=1}^{n} b_{ij}\, y_j, \qquad \ldots\ldots (8)$$

and if in (8) $>$ applies, $x_i = 0$................................ (8′)

The meaning of (7), (7′) is : it is impossible to consume more of a good G_j in the total process (2) than is being produced. If, however, less is consumed, i.e. if there is excess production of G_j, G_j becomes a free good and its price $y_j = 0$.

The meaning of (8), (8′) is : in equilibrium no profit can be made on any process P_i (or else prices or the rate of interest would rise—it is clear how this abstraction is to be understood). If there is a loss, however, i.e. if P_i is unprofitable, then P_i will not be used and its intensity $x_i = 0$.

The quantities a_{ij}, b_{ij} are to be taken as given, whereas the x_i, y_j, α, β are unknown. There are, then, $m + n + 2$ unknowns, but since in the case of x_i, y_j only the ratios $x_1 : \ldots : x_m$, $y_1 : \ldots : y_n$ are essential, they are reduced to $m + n$. Against this, there are $m + n$ conditions (7) + (7′) and (8) + (8′). As these, however, are not equations, but rather complicated inequalities, the fact that the number of conditions is equal to the number of unknowns does not constitute a guarantee that the system can be solved.

The dual symmetry of equations (3), (5), (7), (7′) of the variables x_i, α and of the concept " unused process " on the one hand, and of equations (4), (6), (8),)8′) of the variables y_j, β and of the concept " free good " on the other hand seems remarkable.

4. Our task is to solve (3)—(8′). We shall proceed to show :

Solutions of (3)—(8′) *always exist*, although there may be several solutions with different $x_1 : \ldots : x_m$ or with different $y_1 : \ldots : y_n$. The first is possible since we have not even excluded the case where several P_i describe the same process or where several P_i combine to form another. The second is possible since some goods G_j may enter into each process P_i only in a fixed ratio with some others. But even apart from these trivial possibilities there may exist—for less obvious reasons—several solutions $x_1 : \ldots : x_m$, $y_1 : \ldots : y_m$. Against this it is of importance that α, β should have the same value for all solutions ; i.e. α, β *are uniquely determined*.

We shall even find that α and β can be directly characterised in a simple manner (see paragraphs 10 and 11).

To simplify our considerations we shall assume that always :

$$a_{ij} + b_{ij} > 0 \qquad \ldots\ldots (9)$$

(a_{ij}, b_{ij} are clearly always $\geqq 0$). Since the a_{ij}, b_{ij} may be arbitrarily small this restriction is not very far-reaching, although it must be imposed in order to assure uniqueness of α, β as otherwise W might break up into disconnected parts.

Consider now a hypothetical solution x_i, α, y_j, β of (3)—(8′). If we had in (7) always $<$, then we should have always $y_j = 0$ (because of (7′)) in contradiction to (6).

If we had in (8) always $>$ we should have always $x_i = 0$ (because of (8′)) in contradiction to (5). Therefore, in (7) $\leqq$ always applies, but $=$ at least once; in (8) $\geqq$ always applies, but $=$ at least once.

In consequence :

$$\alpha = \underset{j = 1, \ldots, n}{\text{Min.}} \left[\frac{\sum_{i=1}^{m} b_{ij}\ x_i}{\sum_{i=1}^{m} a_{ij}\ x_i} \right] \ldots\ldots\ldots\ldots\ldots\ldots\ldots\ldots (10),$$

$$\beta = \underset{i = 1, \ldots, m}{\text{Max.}} \frac{\sum_{j=1}^{n} b_{ij}\ y_j}{\sum_{j=1}^{n} a_{ij}\ y_j} \ldots\ldots\ldots\ldots\ldots\ldots\ldots\ldots (11).$$

Therefore the x_i, y_j determine uniquely α, β. (The right-hand side of (10), (11) can never assume the meaningless form $\frac{0}{0}$ because of (3)—(6) and (9)). We can therefore state (7) + (7′) and (8) + (8′) as conditions for x_i, y_j only :

$y_j = 0$ for each $j = 1, \ldots, n$, for which :

$$\frac{\sum_{i=1}^{m} b_{ij}\ x_i}{\sum_{i=1}^{m} a_{ij}\ x_i}$$

does not assume its minimum value (for all $j = 1, \ldots, n$) . . . (7*).

$x_i = 0$ for each $i = 1, \ldots, m$, for which :

$$\frac{\sum_{j=1}^{n} b_{ij}\ y_i}{\sum_{j=1}^{n} a_{ij}\ y_i}$$

does not assume its maximum value (for all $i = 1, \ldots, m$) . . . (8*).

The $x_1, \ldots, x_m$ in (7*) and the $y_1, \ldots, y_n$ in (8*) are to be considered as given. We have, therefore, to solve (3)—(6), (7) and (8) for x_i, y_j.

5. Let X' be a set of variables $(x'_1, \ldots, x'_m)$ fulfilling the analoga of (3), (5) :

$$x'_i \geqq 0, \ldots\ldots (3') \qquad \sum_{i=1}^{m} x'_i > 0, \ldots\ldots (5')$$

and let Y' be a series of variables $(y'_i, \ldots, y'_n)$ fulfilling the analoga of (4), (6) :

$$y'_j \geqq 0, \ldots\ldots (4') \qquad \sum_{j=1}^{n} y'_j > 0, \ldots\ldots (6')$$

Let, furthermore,

$$\phi(X'_i, Y'_i) = \frac{\sum_{i=1}^{m} \sum_{j=1}^{n} b_{ij}\ x'_i\ y'_j}{\sum_{i=1}^{m} \sum_{j=1}^{n} a_{ij}\ x'_i\ y'_j} \ldots\ldots\ldots\ldots (12)$$

Let $X = (x_1, \ldots, x_m)$, $Y = (y_1, \ldots, y_n)$ the (hypothetical) solution, $X' = (x'_i, \ldots, x'_m)$, $Y' = (y'_1, \ldots, y'_n)$ to be freely variable, but in such a way that (3)—(6) and (3')—(6') respectively are fulfilled; then it is easy to verify that (7*) and (8*) can be formulated as follows:

$\phi(X, Y')$ assumes its minimum value for Y' if $Y' = Y$ ..... (7**).

$\phi(X', Y)$ assumes its maximum value for X' if $X' = X$ ..... (8**).

The question of a solution of (3)—(8') becomes a question of a solution of (7**), (8**) and can be formulated as follows:

(*) *Consider* (X', Y') *in the domain bounded by* (3')—(6'). *To find a saddle point* $X' = X$, $Y' = Y$, *i.e. where* (X, Y') *assumes its minimum value for* Y', *and at the same time* (X', Y) *its maximum value for* Y'.

From (7), (7*), (10) and (8), (8*), (11) respectively, follows:

$$\alpha = \frac{\sum_{j=1}^{n}\left[\sum_{i=1}^{m} b_{ij}\, x_i\right] y_j}{\sum_{j=1}^{n}\left[\sum_{i=1}^{m} a_{ij}\, x_i\right] y_j} = \phi(x, y) \text{ and } \beta = \frac{\sum_{i=1}^{m}\left[\sum_{j=1}^{n} b_{ij}\, y_j\right] x_i}{\sum_{i=1}^{m}\left[\sum_{j=1}^{n} a_{ij}\, y_j\right] x_i} = \phi(x, y)$$

respectively.

Therefore:

(**) *If our problem can be solved, i.e. if* $\phi(X', Y')$ *has a saddle point* $X' = X$, $Y' = Y$ *(see above), then*:

$\alpha = \beta = \phi\,(X,Y) =$ *the value at the saddle point* .... (13)

6. Because of the homogeneity of $\phi\,(X', Y')$ (in X', Y', i.e. in $x', \ldots, x_m'$ and $y_1', \ldots y_m'$) our problem remains unaffected if we substitute the normalisations

$$\sum_{i=1}^{m} x_i = 1, \ldots\ldots (5^*) \qquad \sum_{j=1}^{n} y_j = 1, \ldots\ldots (6^*)$$

for (5'), (6') and correspondingly for (5), (6). Let S be the X' set described by:

$$x_i' \geqq 0, \ldots\ldots (3') \qquad \sum_{i=1}^{m} x_i' = 1, \ldots\ldots (5^*)$$

and let T be the Y' set described by:

$$y_j' \geqq 0, \ldots\ldots (4') \qquad \sum_{j=1}^{n} y_j' = 1, \ldots\ldots (6^*)$$

(S, T are simplices of, respectively, $m - 1$ and $n - 1$ dimensions).

In order to solve[1] we make use of the simpler formulation (7*), (8*) and combine these with (3), (4), (5*), (6*) expressing the fact that $X = (x_1, \ldots, x_m)$ is in S and $Y = (y_1, \ldots, y_n)$ in T.

7. We shall prove a slightly more general lemma: Let R_m be the m-dimensional

[1] The question whether our problem has a solution is oddly connected with that of a problem occurring in the Theory of Games dealt with elsewhere. (Math. Annalen, 100, 1928, pp. 295–320, particularly pp. 305 and 307–311). The problem there is a special case of (*) and is solved here in a new way through our solution of (*) (see below). In fact, if $a_{ij} \equiv 1$, then $\sum_{i=1}^{m} \sum_{j=1}^{n} a_{ij}\, x'_i\, y'_j = 1$ because of (5*), (6*). Therefore $\phi\,(X', Y') = \sum_{i=1}^{m} \sum_{j=1}^{n} b_{ij}\, x'_i\, y'_j$, and thus our (*) coincides with loc. cit., p. 307. (Our $\phi\,(X', Y')$, b_{ij}, x'_i, y'_j, m, n here correspond to $h\,(\xi, \eta)$, a_{pq}, ξ_p, η_q, $M + 1$, $N + 1$ there).

It is, incidentally, remarkable that (*) does not lead—as usual—to a simple maximum or minimum problem, the possibility of a solution of which would be evident, but to a problem of the saddle point or minimum-maximum type, where the question of a possible solution is far more profound.

space of all points $X = (x_1, \ldots, x_m)$, R_n the n-dimensional space of all points $Y = (y_1, \ldots, y_n)$, R_{m+n} the $m + n$ dimensional space of all points $(X, Y) = (x_1, \ldots x_m, y_1, \ldots, y_n)$.

A set (in R_m or R_n or R_{m+n}) which is *not empty, convex closed and bounded* we call a set C.

Let S°, T° be sets C in R_m and R_n respectively and let $S^\circ \times T^\circ$ be the set of all (X, Y) (in R_{m+n}) where the range of X is S° and the range of Y is T°. Let V, W be two closed subsets of $S^\circ \times T^\circ$. For every X in S° let the set $Q(X)$ of all Y with (X, Y) in V be a set C; for each Y in T° let the set $P(Y)$ of all X with (X, Y) in W be a set C. Then the following lemma applies.

Under the above assumptions, V, W have (at least) one point in common.

Our problem follows by putting $S^\circ = S$, $T^\circ = T$ and $V =$ the set of all $(X, Y) = (x_1, \ldots, x_m, y_1, \ldots, y_n)$ fulfilling (7*), $W =$ the set of all $(X, Y) = (x_1, \ldots, x_m, y_1, \ldots, y_n)$ fulfilling (8*). It can be easily seen that V. W are closed and that the sets $S^\circ = S$, $T^\circ = T$, $Q(X)$, $P(Y)$ are all simplices, i.e. sets C. The common points of these V, W are, of course, our required solutions $(X, Y) = (x_1, \ldots, x_m, y_1, \ldots, y_m)$.

8. To prove the above lemma let S°, T°, V, W be as described before the lemma.

First, consider V. For each X of S° we choose a point $Y^\circ(X)$ out of $Q(X)$ (e.g. the centre of gravity of this set). It will not be possible, generally, to choose $Y^\circ(X)$ as a continuous function of X. Let $\epsilon > 0$; we define:

$$w^\epsilon(X, X') = \text{Max.}\ (0, 1 - \frac{1}{\epsilon}\ \text{distance}\ (X, X')) \quad \ldots\ldots\ldots\ldots \quad (14)$$

Now let $Y^\epsilon(X)$ be the centre of gravity of the $Y^\circ(X')$ with (relative) weight function $w^\epsilon(X, X')$ where the range of X' is S°. I.e. if $Y^\circ(X) = (y_1^\circ(x), \ldots, y_n^\circ(x))$, $Y^\epsilon(X) = (y_1^\epsilon(x), \ldots, y_n^\epsilon(x))$, then:

$$y_j^\epsilon(X) = \int_{S^\circ} w^\epsilon(X, X')\, y_j^\circ(X')\, dX' \Big/ \int_{S^\circ} w^\epsilon(X, X')\, dX', \ldots. \quad (15)$$

We derive now a number of properties of $Y^\epsilon(X)$ (valid for all $\epsilon > 0$):

(*i*) $Y^\epsilon(X)$ is in T°. Proof: $Y^\circ(X')$ is in $Q(X')$ and therefore in T°, and since $Y^\epsilon(X)$ is a centre of gravity of points $Y^\circ(X')$ and T° is convex, $Y^\epsilon(X)$ also is in $T^\bullet$.

(*ii*) $Y^\epsilon(X)$ is a continuous function of X (for the whole range of S°). Proof: it is sufficient to prove this for each $y_j^\epsilon(X)$. Now $w^\epsilon(X, X')$ is a continuous function of X, X' throughout; $\int_{S^\circ} w^\epsilon(X, X')\, dX'$ is always > 0, and all $y_j^\circ(X)$ are bounded (being co-ordinates of the bounded set S°). The continuity of the $y_j^\epsilon(X)$ follows, therefore, from (15).

(*iii*) For each $\delta > 0$ there exists an $\epsilon_0 = \epsilon_0(\delta) > 0$ such that the distance of each point $(X, Y^{\epsilon_0}(X))$ from V is $< \delta$. Proof: assume the contrary. Then there must exist a $\delta > 0$ and a sequence of $\epsilon_\nu > 0$ with $\lim_{\nu \to \infty} \epsilon_\nu = 0$ such that for every $\nu = 1, 2, \ldots$ there exists a X_ν in S° for which the distance $(X_\nu, Y^{\epsilon_\nu}(X_\nu))$ would be $\geqq \delta$. A fortiori $Y^{\epsilon_\nu}(X_\nu)$ is at a distance $\geqq \frac{\delta}{2}$ from every $Q(X')$, with a distance $(X_\nu, X') \leqq \frac{\delta}{2}$.

All X_ν, $\nu = 1, 2, \ldots$, are in S° and have therefore a point of accumulation X^* in S°; from which follows that there exists a subsequence of X_ν, $\nu = 1, 2, \ldots$, converging towards X^* for which distance $(X_\nu, X^*) \leqq \frac{\delta}{2}$ always applies. Substituting this subsequence for the ϵ_ν, X_ν, we see that we are justified in assuming: $\lim X_\nu = X^*$, distance $(X_\nu, X^*) \leqq \frac{\delta}{2}$. Therefore we may put $X' = X^*$ for every $\nu = 1, 2, \ldots$, and in consequence we have always $Y^{\epsilon_\nu}(X_\nu)$ at a distance $\geqq \frac{\delta}{2}$ from $Q(X^*)$.

$Q(X^*)$ being convex, the set of all points with a distance $< \frac{\delta}{2}$ from $(Q(X^*)$ is also convex. Since $Y^{\epsilon_\nu}(X_\nu)$ does not belong to this set, and since it is a centre of gravity of points $Y^\circ(X')$ with distance $(X_\nu, X') \leqq \epsilon_\nu$ (because for distance $(X_\nu, X') > \epsilon_\nu$, $w^{\epsilon_\nu}(X_\nu, X') = 0$ according to (14)), not all of these points belong to the set under discussion. Therefore: there exists a $X' = X_\nu$ for which the distance $(X_\nu, X'_\nu) \leqq \epsilon_\nu$ and where the distance between $Y^\circ(X'_\nu)$ and $Q(X^*)$ is $\geqq \frac{\delta}{2}$.

Lim $X_\nu = X^*$, lim distance $(X_\nu, X'_\nu) = 0$, and therefore lim $X'_\nu = X^*$. All $Y^\circ(Y_\nu)$ belong to T° and have therefore a point of accumulation Y^*. In consequence, (X^*, Y^*) is a point of accumulation of the $(X_\nu, Y^\circ(X_\nu))$ and since they all belong to V, (X^*, Y^*) belongs to V too. Y^* is therefore in $Q(X^*)$. Now the distance of every $Y^\circ(Y_\nu)$ including from $Q(X^*)$ is $\geqq \frac{\delta}{2}$. This is a contradiction, and the proof is complete.

(*i*)—(*iii*) together assert: for every $\delta > 0$ there exists a continuous mapping $Y_\delta(X)$ of S° on to a subset of T° where the distance of every point $(X, Y_\delta(X))$ from V is $< \delta$. (Put $Y_\delta(X) = Y^\epsilon(X)$ with $\epsilon = \epsilon_0 = \epsilon_0(\delta)$).

9. Interchanging S° and T°, and V and W we obtain now: for every $\delta > 0$ there exists a continuous mapping $X_\delta(Y)$ of T° on to a subset of S° where the distance of every point $(X_\delta(Y), Y)$ from W is $< \delta$.

On putting $f_\delta(X) = X_\delta(Y_\delta(X))$, $f_\delta(X)$ is a continuous mapping of S° on to a subset of S°. Since S° is a set C, and therefore topologically a simplex[1] we can use L. E. J. Brouwer's Fix-point Theorem[2]; $f_\delta(X)$ has a fix-point. I.e., there exists a X^δ in S° for which $X^\delta = f_\delta(X^\delta) = X_\delta(Y_\delta(X^\delta))$. Let $Y^\delta = Y_\delta(X^\delta)$, then we have $X^\delta = X_\delta(Y^\delta)$. Consequently, the distances of the point (X^δ, Y^δ) in R_{m+n} both from V and from W are $< \delta$. The distance of V from W is therefore $< 2\delta$. Since this is valid for every $\delta > 0$, the distance between V and W is $= 0$. Since V, W are closed and bounded, they must have at least one common point. This proves our lemma completely.

10. We have solved (7*), (8*) of paragraph 4 as well as the equivalent problem (*) of paragraph 5 and the original task of paragraph 3: the solution of (3)—(8'). If the x_i, y_j (which were called X, Y in paragraphs 7—9) are determined, α, β follow from (13) in (**) of paragraph 5. In particular, $\alpha = \beta$.

We have emphasised in paragraph 4 already that there may be several solutions x_i, y_j (i.e. X, Y); we shall proceed to show that there exists only one value of α (i.e. of β). In fact, let $X_1, Y_1, \alpha_1, \beta_1$ and $X_2, Y_2, \alpha_2, \beta_2$ be two solutions. From (7**), (8**) and (13) follows:

$$\alpha_1 = \beta_1 = \phi(X_1, Y_1) \leqq \phi(X_1, Y_2),$$
$$\alpha_2 = \beta_2 = \phi(X_2, Y_2) \geqq \phi(X_1, Y_2),$$

therefore $\alpha_1 = \beta_1 \leqq \alpha_2 = \beta_2$. For reasons of symmetry $\alpha_2 = \beta_2 \leqq \alpha_1 = \beta_1$, therefore $\alpha_1 = \beta_1 = \alpha_2 = \beta_2$.

[1] Regarding these as well as other properties of convex sets used in this paper, c.f., e.g. Alexandroff and H. Hopf, *Topologie*, vol. I, J. Springer, Berlin, 1935, pp. 598–609.
[2] Cf., e.g. 1 c, footnote 1, p. 480.

We have shown :

At least one solution X, Y, α, β exists. For all solutions :

$$\alpha = \beta = \phi\ (X,\ Y) \qquad (13)$$

and these have the same numerical value for all solutions, in other words : The interest factor and the coefficient of expansion of the economy are equal and uniquely determined by the technically possible processes $P_1, \ldots, P_m$.

Because of (13), $\alpha > 0$, but may be $\gtreqless 1$. One would expect $\alpha > 1$, but $\alpha \leqq 1$ cannot be excluded in view of the generality of our formulation : processes $P_1, \ldots, P_m$ may really be *unproductive*.

11. In addition, we shall characterise α in two independent ways.

Firstly, let us consider a state of the economy possible on purely technical considerations, expanding with factor α' per unit of time. I.e., for the intensities $x_1, \ldots, x_m$ applies :

$$x_i \geqq 0 \qquad (3') \qquad\qquad \sum_{i=1}^{m} x_i' > 0 \qquad (5') \text{ and}$$

$$\alpha' \sum_{i=1}^{m} a_{ij}\ x_i' \leqq \sum_{i=1}^{m} b_{ij}\ x_i' \qquad (7'')$$

We are neglecting prices here altogether. Let $x_i, y_j, \alpha = \beta$ be a solution of our original problem (3)—(8′) in paragraph 3. Multiplying (7″) by y_j and adding $\sum_{j=1}^{n}$ we obtain :

$$\alpha' \sum_{i=1}^{m} \sum_{j=1}^{n} a_{ij}\ x_i'\ y_j \leqq \sum_{i=1}^{m} \sum_{j=1}^{n} b_{ij}\ x_i'\ y_j,$$

and therefore $\alpha' \leqq \phi\ (X', Y)$. Because of (8**) and (13) in paragraph 5, we have :

$$\alpha' \leqq \phi\ (X',\ Y) \leqq \phi\ (X,\ Y) = \alpha = \beta \qquad (15).$$

Secondly, let us consider a system of prices where the interest factor β' allows of no more profits. I.e. for prices $y_1', \ldots y'_n$ applies :

$$y'_j \geqq 0, \qquad (4') \qquad\qquad \sum_{j=1}^{n} y'_j > 0, \qquad (6') \text{ and}$$

$$\beta' \sum_{j=1}^{n} a_{ij}\ y'_j \geqq \sum_{j=1}^{n} b_{ij}\ y'_j \qquad (8'')$$

Hereby we are neglecting intensities of production altogether. Let $x_i, y_j, \alpha = \beta$ as above. Multiplying (8″) by x_i and adding $\sum_{i=1}^{m}$ we obtain :

$$\beta' \sum_{i=1}^{m} \sum_{j=1}^{n} a_{ij}\ x_i\ y'_j \leqq \sum_{i=1}^{m} \sum_{j=1}^{n} b_{ij}\ x_i\ y'_j$$

and therefore $\beta' \geqq \phi\ (X, Y')$. Because of (7**) and (13) in paragraph 5, we have :

$$\beta' \geqq \phi\ (X,\ Y') \geqq \phi\ (X,\ Y) = \alpha = \beta \qquad (16)$$

These two results can be expressed as follows :

The greatest (purely technically possible) factor of expansion α' of the whole economy is $\alpha' = \alpha = \beta$, neglecting prices.

The lowest interest factor β' at which a profitless system of prices is possible is $\beta' = \alpha = \beta$, neglecting intensities of production.

Note that these characterisations are possible only on the basis of our knowledge that solutions of our original problem exist—without themselves directly referring to this problem. Furthermore, the equality of the maximum in the first form and the minimum in the second can be proved only on the basis of the existence of this solution.

Princeton, N.J. J. v. NEUMANN.

11

A NOTE ON J. v. NEUMANN'S ARTICLE ON "A MODEL OF ECONOMIC EQUILIBRIUM"[1]

By D. G. Champernowne

SCOPE OF THE PAPER

The supreme merit of this paper lies in the elegance of the mathematical solution of a highly generalised problem in theoretical economics. But the paper is of considerable interest to economists as well as to mathematicians, because it deals simultaneously with questions on several fields of economics, which until this paper was first read, (in 1932) had seldom been considered together as parts of one problem. For example, in this short paper the author considers which goods will be free goods, and the determination of the prices of goods which are not free : at the same time he examines which productive processes and scales of production will be optimum and which will be unprofitable : he also examines the degree in which each optimum process will be used and the relative amounts of different goods that will be produced. At the same time he demonstrates the mechanism which determines the rate of interest and the rate of expansion of the whole economy.

Approaching these questions as a mathematician, Dr. Neumann places emphasis on rather different aspects of the problem than would an economist. Whereas he takes great care to give an absolutely rigorous mathematical argument and to state his assumptions completely and without ambiguity, he develops his points with the minimum of descriptive explanation. The paper is logically complete and admirably concise. In contrast to the convention among mathematical writers of reducing explanations to a minimum and stating assumptions as concisely as possible, economists more usually provide illustrative examples and repetitions of their argument to ease the reader's task of comprehension. Those accustomed to these less austere conventions may therefore be interested to read the following discursive commentary which develops some of the points of economic interest in Dr. Neumann's classic article.

By adopting extremely artificial assumptions, the author rendered his problem soluble and concentrated attention on some very interesting properties of the actual economic system. But at the same time this process of abstraction inevitably made many of his conclusions inapplicable to the real world : others could be applied only after considerable modifications. It is interesting to enquire how far the properties in his simplified model do correspond to similar phenomena in the real world.

THE APPROACH TO THE PROBLEM

Prof. v. Neumann's method is the familiar one of examining the conditions of equilibrium of his simplified model of the economic world. The first point is to get clear what is meant by equilibrium. The definition of equilibrium is very similar to that of the economist's stationary state : but in v. Neumann's article equilibrium differs from a stationary state's equilibrium in the vital respect that a uniform expansion of the whole system is allowed under equilibrium. Such a state of equilibrium may be called a quasi-stationary state, although v. Neumann does not in fact use this term.

From the point of view of the mathematician, the most important result of the article is the proof that under the simplified conditions there assumed, it will be possible for the model to have any equilibrium position at all, in the sense in which equilibrium

[1] This note is the outcome of conversations with Mr. N. Kaldor, to whom many of the ideas in it are due. I am also indebted to Mr. P. Sraffa of Cambridge and to Mr. Crum of New College, Oxford, for instruction in subjects discussed in this article.

is there defined. This may seem rather surprising, as one is rather apt to investigate conditions of equilibrium without bothering first of all to find out whether any equilibrium position need actually exist at all : one is liable to assume that some equilibrium position is possible. The fact that it is necessary to prove the existence of an equilibrium position before finding out the properties of such a position may be illustrated by the following consideration. Although v. Neumann defines equilibrium to be that of a quasi-stationary state, which may be expanding, he might perhaps have chosen to define equilibrium to be that of a stationary state without expansion or contraction. It so happens that the simplifying assumptions made about his economic model make it impossible in general for it to settle down to a state of stationary equilibrium : if, therefore, he had assumed that such a stationary equilibrium position was possible and had investigated the various conditions which the system must satisfy when in equilibrium, he would evidently have arrived at ridiculous results. For similar reasons, it was therefore necessary for him to prove that there was at least one possible position of quasi-stationary state equilibrium, before it was of any use investigating the properties which the system must have in such an equilibrium position.

Although, to the mathematician, the most interesting part of this paper will be that which proves the existence of at least one equilibrium position ; for the economist the most interesting part is that which analyses the properties of the system when it is in equilibrium. Fortunately, once the existence of an equilibrium position has been demonstrated, the arguments demonstrating the nature of this equilibrium are of quite an elementary nature, and it is possible to translate the rigorous mathematics of this part of the article into a somewhat looser form of words more readily digestible by those who are unused to thinking in terms of symbols.

Before turning to these arguments, it is useful to examine the manner in which v. Neumann approaches the economic problem. As we have seen, he is concerned not with short period problems but with the properties of the economic system when it has settled down to an equilibrium position which may be described as a quasi-stationary state. In such a state, all prices remain constant, the production of all goods remains in the same proportion although a uniform geometric rate of growth is allowed to the whole system. Thus if in any period the output of one particular good doubles, so then does the output of every other good double in that period, and the population and quantity of each kind of capital equipment double also in the same period. Thus in equilibrium there is no progress or change in production per head of population : growth merely consists of replication and the economic system expands like a crystal suspended in a solution of its own salt. The composition of any given volume of the crystal is at all times the same. To describe a system with uniform expansion of this kind we have introduced the term quasi-stationary state.

The model, being concerned only with a quasi-stationary state, can throw no direct light on problems of economic development and changes in the standard of living. The model has only one advantage over the strictly stationary state and that is that the community has an outlet for its savings in providing for the uniform expansion of the community and its stock of equipment.

In order to make it possible for quasi-stationary state equilibrium to exist in the model, several drastic simplifying assumptions had to be introduced. Constant returns were assumed in the sense that any economic process could be carried out at half, double, or in general x times its given scale, without any increase in costs per unit of output. Conditions of perfect competition in the long period were also assumed, and it was supposed that the natural factors of production (including labour) were available in unlimited quantities. One other very important assumption was implied, although it was nowhere very clearly stated : this was that no saving was carried out by the workers whereas the propertied class saved the whole of their income. These various simplifying assumptions, although necessary if a rigorous proof of the existence of equilibrium was to be possible, evidently render the model unsuitable for examining problems connected with monopoly, economies of mass production, technical progress, or with land.[1] Since monetary problems are also assumed away, the reader may begin to wonder in what way the model has interesting relevance to conditions in the real world.

Prof. v. Neumann's model does however exhibit certain features of a competitive capitalist economy which tend to be obscured in the more traditional approach and can deal with the consequences of the circular nature of the production process (*i.e.* that commodities are largely produced out of each other) in a way that is not possible under it. By reducing the role of the worker-consumer to that of a farm animal, he can focus attention on those parts of the mechanism determining prices and the rate of interest, which depend on supply conditions alone and not on the tastes of consumers. This emphasis is important because the orthodox analysis has distributed attention evenly between marginal utility and conditions of supply ; since supply is often more elastic than demand, prices in the long run do over a wide field reflect contrasts in cost rather than conditions of consumers' demands: a price-theory focussing attention on costs can give a very clear and yet an approximately true account. We may first consider v. Neumann's approach to the problem of prices.

Consider a good which may be manufactured out of a lot of other goods : in the simplified conditions of the model the cost price of the good will consist of the values of the goods of which it is composed plus an interest charge on the fixed and working capital involved in the process. If a good is a joint product, then the value of the other products must be subtracted from the cost in arriving at the cost price of the good. Competition will ensure that where a good may be produced by many different processes, its cost price will correspond to the costs in the cheapest process.

Wage costs are not considered as such, for labourers are not separately considered any more than are farm animals. It is supposed that they will do their work in return for rations of shelter, fuel, food and clothing, just as a horse works when it is fed and cared for. The costs of labour thus consist of the goods which maintain the workers, just as the costs of a horse's work consist of his fodder, stabling, etc. The essential point about v. Neumann's theory of prices is that goods are made out of goods alone and that the cost price of any good or collection of goods consists of the value of the goods from which they are made plus an interest charge.

Prof. v. Neumann's approach to the theory of the rate of interest is interesting. He makes no reference to marginal products or to the marginal efficiency of capital : nor does he regard the rate of interest as depending on the relative efficiency of production processes involving different " periods of production " : the rate of interest is not determined as the supply price of waiting, abstinence or saving, for it is assumed that the propertied class save all their income and that the working class consume all theirs. Nor is the rate of interest determined as the measure of liquidity preference, for money as such plays no part in v. Neumann's article. The rate of interest appears as the natural and optimum rate of organic expansion[2] of the system, and depends on the technical processes of production which are available. If these processes enable the system to expand at 5 per cent per annum at most, then 5 per cent per annum will be the rate of interest.

In its concern with a quasi-stationary state, in its theory of prices as determined

[1] By assuming both constant returns and perfect competition, v. Neumann also implies that the division of the total output (by means of a given process) between firms (using that process) is indeterminate.

[2] See pp. 14–15 for a fuller explanation of this concept.

by the minimum cost of goods made from other goods alone, and in its theory of the rate of interest determined by the greatest possible rate of expansion of the economic system, this paper approaches the problems of economics in an extremely original and stimulating fashion : it can claim, quite apart from the beautiful mathematical proof of the existence of an equilibrium position, to make a substantial contribution to the economic theory of interest, prices and production.

THE PROOF OF THE PROPERTIES OF THE SYSTEM IN EQUILIBRIUM

It would not be profitable to comment on the large part of the paper which deals with the proof of the existence of an equilibrium, since the argument is essentially one of advanced mathematics which cannot be economically expressed in words. But those readers who prefer to think in words rather than symbols may be interested in the following comments on v. Neumann's proof of the properties of the economic system in equilibrium.

Prof. v. Neumann defines a process of production as an operation lasting for one unit of time which converts one bundle of goods into another bundle of goods. He includes the fixed capital equipment used both in the bundle of goods which is converted and again in the bundle of goods which emerges from the operation. He supposes that there are available always a very large number of possible production processes, and that constant returns prevail in the sense that any operation can be carried out at any scale without affecting the relation of the output to the input. In any given process of production, the relative quantities of goods put in are absolutely fixed, and so are the relative quantities of the goods emerging from it : thus the only way in which an entrepreneur can alter the proportions between the goods which he uses is to change from one process of production to another : similarly he must do this in order to change the proportion of goods in his output. What would normally be regarded as two different forms of the same process of production, the one involving slightly different proportions of the factors of production than the other, is thus treated by v. Neumann as being two different processes of production.

It is fairly obvious that with given prices, some production processes are likely to be more profitable than others, in the sense that they could afford to pay a higher rate of interest without making losses. One of v. Neumann's conditions for equilibrium is in fact that every process in use should make zero profits : for under perfect competition, positive profits would attract competitors to use the same process and negative profits would deter people from using the process at all. He thus obtains the following rule for equilibrium :

> *Profitability Rule.*—Only those processes will be used which, with the actual prices and rate of interest, yield zero profits after payment of interest. These processes will be the most profitable ones available.

The second part of the rule follows from the fact that if there were any processes which could earn positive profits they would not have continued out of use under competition.

The usual point of view in economic theory is that free goods play no part in the economic system : but part of v. Neumann's problem is to determine which goods will be free goods in equilibrium. It is an essential property of his equilibrium that the physical outputs of all goods, whether free or not, remain in the same proportions to each other throughout time : so do the physical inputs. Suppose that the system in equilibrium is expanding by k per cent per unit of time : then the input of each good at any moment must be exactly k per cent greater than the input for the previous unit of time. Clearly this can only continue indefinitely if the output of every good is at least k per cent greater than the input of every good, since the source of the input at any moment is simply the output of the previous unit of time. But there may be goods for which the output exceeds the input by more than k per cent : there will then be more than enough of these goods to supply the input of the next moment of time, and if the equilibrium continues it is clear that in the case of these goods, larger and larger surplus stocks will be built up. v. Neumann concludes that the prices of these goods can only remain in equilibrium if they have become free goods in the sense that these prices are zero. Hence he obtains his rule about free goods :

> *Free goods rule.*—In an equilibrium production system, those goods whose output exceeds their input by more than the expansion rate of k per cent will be free goods. Only those goods whose output exceeds their input by the minimum, namely k per cent, will have prices (other than zero).

Prof. v. Neumann is also able to tell us quite a lot about the relative intensities with which the various profitable processes will be used. We may refer to the organisation of processes of production in any given proportions as being a system of production. We may define the expansion rate of any given system of production in terms of the relation of the output to the input of the various goods. We may, in short, define the rate of expansion of the system to be equal to the least rate of expansion of any good involved in the system. For instance, if there is a good whose output under the system exceeds its input by 2 per cent, and if there is no good whose output under the system exceeds its input by less than 2 per cent, then we say that the rate of expansion under this system is 2 per cent. Thus defined, the term rate of expansion may be applied to any production system whether it is in equilibrium or not.

Prof. v. Neumann obtains the following remarkable rule :

> *System of production rule.*—In equilibrium, the system of production actually used will have the greatest rate of expansion of all possible productive systems.

It should be noticed that this comprehensive rule does not involve prices at all : it shows that the system of production actually used has a maximum property depending only on what processes of production are in fact available.

A little reflection will confirm the validity of the rule. The reason for it is roughly this : if any system of production with a higher expansion rate were available, then it would pay all entrepreneurs to adopt this other system in place of the processes they are supposed to be using in equilibrium, and in this case the equilibrium could not continue. This point requires further explanation. In the conditions of the model, the input of any process is the same as the capital involved in the process : interest payments have to be made out of the excess of the value of output over the value of input. A little reflection will confirm that the rate of interest which any process can afford to pay per unit of time must therefore be the percentage by which the value of its output exceeds the value of its input. In equilibrium, we know that each process makes zero profits and hence that each process used can just afford to pay the actual rate of interest. It follows that in every process actually used the value of output exceeds the value of input by exactly the rate of interest. From this it follows in turn that the value of output for the system as a whole in equilibrium exceeds the value of input by a proportion equal to the rate of interest : in other words, the rate of expansion of the system is equal to the rate of interest. This equilibrium rate of interest is, as we have seen, the maximum rate of interest which the equilibrium system can afford to pay. Suppose that there were some other system with a larger rate of expansion, then it is clear that it could afford to pay a higher rate of interest : since it is open to any entrepreneur to adopt this other production system, he would be able to make a profit by so doing because he would then be able to afford more than the actual rate of interest : equilibrium would therefore be impossible if there were any other production system with a rate of expansion greater than that of the actual production system. That is why in equilibrium the actual production system must have the greatest possible rate of expansion, as stated in the system-of-production rule.

In the course of this argument we have incidentally demonstrated another of v. Neumann's results which may be summed up in the following rule :

> *Rate of interest rule.*—In equilibrium, the rate of interest equals the rate of expansion.

We still need to obtain a rule for determining the system of prices under equilibrium. The only result about prices which we have so far considered is that which gives the price of one good in terms of the prices of other goods : this in itself is not immediately helpful if we suppose the prices of all goods to be unknown. In order to understand the rule which prices must obey in equilibrium, it is useful to consider a new concept. This concept is the rate of interest possible under a given system of prices. With given prices, any particular production process will be able to pay a rate of interest equal to the percentage excess of the value of its output with those prices over the value of its input. In particular, with these prices, there will be one or more production processes which can afford to pay a rate of interest higher than can any other production processes. This particular rate of interest will be called the rate of interest possible under the given system of prices. The rule for determining prices may be set out in the following terms* :

> *Price system rule.*—The price system in equilibrium will have a possible rate of interest smaller than or as small as that of any other price system.

The reader will notice that this rule is closely analogous to the production system rule. Its validity may be confirmed by the following argument. In equilibrium, we have seen that the production system actually used must have an expansion rate equal to the actual rate of interest : it follows that the actual production system could afford to pay at least the actual rate of interest, whatever system of prices were ruling.[1] *A fortiori*, whatever the price system might be, at least one of the production processes actually used would be able to afford at least the actual rate of interest. This implies that no price system can have a possible rate of interest less than the actual rate of interest ruling in an equilibrium position. This result is embodied in the price system rule given above.

ECONOMIC IMPLICATIONS OF THE RESULTS

Since v. Neumann's results only relate to a quasi-stationary state, the utmost caution is needed in drawing from them any conclusions about the determination of prices, production or the rate of interest in the real world. Since, in the real world, land is limited in supply, the only possible quasi-stationary state is a strictly stationary state (or conceivably a contracting state[2]) : for an expanding quasi-stationary state would eventually be confronted with a shortage of land and its equilibrium would be destroyed. Hence v. Neumann's " quasi-stationary " state does not in fact bring his model any nearer to reality than would be the case with a strictly stationary state.

In spite of this v. Neumann's results are highly suggestive ; and it is interesting to explore in what respects the operation of his model may be relevant to the real world.

* Prof. v. Neumann does not use this particular rule in his article: He does, however, use the property that given the equilibrium intensities of the processes of production, the ratio of the value of the system's output to that of its input will be a minimum with respect to prices.

[1] This follows almost immediately from the definition of the expansion rate of a production system.

[2] Allowing for the existence of exhaustible resources, *e.g.* minerals, or for a system unable to provide the subsistence wages of the workers except by using up its stocks.

(1) As a first example, we may take the property that competition will ensure that equilibrium can only be reached if the maximum technically possible rate of expansion is achieved. This may immediately suggest an argument in favour of free enterprise in the real world. But quite apart from the point already mentioned that in a world with non-augmentable resources like land the maximum rate of expansion that is ultimately possible is zero (and hence competition would merely lead to an equilibrium position with no growth or contraction and with a zero rate of interest) the claim is strictly valid only if, as in v. Neumann's model, there is a slave-system and the object of production is mere enlargement without any advance in the standard of living. v. Neumann's model certainly does not suggest that competition secures the highest possible standard of living or the greatest possible rate of advance for living standards : for, on the assumptions of his model, the living standard is simply the minimum needed to persuade people to work.

(2) This point brings us to a second interesting implication of v. Neumann's results. He has successfully constructed an economic model in which the equilibrium level for real wages is simply whatever is needed to persuade people to work : it does not apparently depend on what industry can " afford to pay ". Suppose that the working-class effectively insists on a higher real wage, then this has the effect of increasing the input needed in any process (to secure a given output) by the amount of the extra fodder which the workers demand. Hence, there will be a change in the equilibrium conditions, and the position of quasi-stationary equilibrium will change to one with a lower rate of interest and a lower rate of expansion. This might suggest an argument for vigorous trade union activity : for in the model the result of standing out for higher real wages is to secure higher living standards at the expense of the owners of property : it is true that it is also at the expense of the rate of expansion of the system, but that is because in the model it is assumed that the propertied class save the whole of their income ; in the real world, where the propertied class also consume, it may be obtained at the expense of the consumption of the propertied class. Such an argument is suggested, but it is not certain whether it could be developed by means of any simple extension of the model.

(3) The question of consumption by the propertied class is also relevant to the theory of the rate of interest. The rate of interest will be determined as the greatest rate of expansion possible if all income from property is saved. A *rigorous* proof of this proposition is only possible if we assume that all income from property is in fact saved : this could happen, for example, if all property was owned by the State. On the other hand, even if part of the income from property were spent on consumption, and not saved, the rate of interest would not necessarily be much affected : it might still be *approximately* equal to the greatest expansion rate that *would* have been possible *if* all income from property had been saved. At the same time, the spending of part of the income from property would, of course, reduce the actual rate of expansion of the system ; this would now be well below the rate of interest and the maximum possible expansion rate.[1]

(4) An interesting feature of the model is that both prices and the outputs of the individual commodities are determined solely by the technical conditions of production. As was explained above, v. Neumann has proved (a) that competition will allow the system to be in equilibrium only if the five rules given above on pp. 13–15 are satisfied: these five rules of competitive equilibrium determine both the intensities of production of the individual commodities and their relative prices where all production processes

[1] The equality of the rate of interest and the rate of expansion in the model is, in fact, (once the existence of an equilibrium is proved) fairly obvious on the assumption that workers spend all their income and capitalists save all theirs.

are given. The model, it is true, ignores the possibility of increasing returns in the production of individual commodities, and does not allow for consumers' choice as an independent factor in the direction of productive activity. There is no room in the theory for an increase in population to make books cheaper and for a shift in demand from cotton to wool and from mutton to beef to send wool prices up and mutton prices down. But the important point is that these may conveniently be considered as the " special cases " of price-theory, to be introduced in the *second approximation* ; and not, as is common in traditional economics, at the centre of the theory. For the basic influences determining equilibrium prices v. Neumann's model provides a novel approach ; here, perhaps for the first time, is a self-contained theory of the determination of prices, ignoring the second approximation.

The role played by consumers' tastes in the determination of prices is suggested by considering how consumers' choice may be introduced into v. Neumann's model. The method is to allow several alternative production processes for obtaining " labour ", each process requiring a different bundle of goods as " real wages ", between which the labourer may be supposed indifferent. A change in the labourers' tastes will then be reflected in a change in the input required in the various processes producing " labour " : this in turn will react on the equilibrium position of the system and hence on relative prices. But the latter effect may be trivial, even if the change in tastes is significant ; and one is left with the impression that consumers' tastes play, in fact, a comparatively minor role in the determination of equilibrium prices.

It may be objected that the assumption that the propertied class save the whole of their income further restricts the scope which " marginal utility " can play in the determination of prices. This may be granted ; but this restriction is not so serious as it may appear to be : indeed the novelty of the distribution of emphasis which it implies is, from some points of view, an advantage. For even in the actual world the great bulk of productive activity (as measured, for example, by the distribution of labour between industries) is devoted to the production of intermediary products of one sort or another, which are mainly used as inputs in a series of other products. The prices (and relative outputs) of these intermediary goods can best be explained in terms of the considerations covered in v. Neumann's model.[1]

(5) Land is assumed by v. Neumann to be available in unlimited quantities. It is, however, possible to introduce land into his model by including the land used both in the input and the output of each process using it. In this case, since the quantity of " land " cannot be increased (or decreased), equilibrium is only possible in a stationary state. In such a state, the rate of interest will be zero and the workers will get the whole income. This suggests that if the assumption that all property income is saved is abandoned, the equilibrium in a system containing land may be a stationary state with a positive rate of interest and all income consumed. During the approach to this equilibrium the rate of interest will presumably fall as the increasing scarcity of land lowers the *potential* rate of expansion, and the *actual* rate of expansion may fall even faster owing to monetary complications. These considerations take us however, outside the assumptions made by v. Neumann, and away from the possibility of rigorous proof.

(6) In a world where the scarcity of non-augmentable resources exerts a major influence on the productive system, v. Neumann's model ceases to be so interesting. But even ignoring the complications due to " land ", there is still danger of another kind of complication. The rate of expansion of the system is determined, as we have

[1] And even in the case of final-consumers' goods, the prices (though not of course the relative intensities of production) are *largely* to be explained by the technical conditions of production, rather than " marginal utility ". (The exceptions being joint products, or commodities with largely increasing or decreasing cost.)

seen, by the goods whose supply can be expanded least rapidly. These may well be those goods which are created largely out of themselves, (*i.e.* in whose production processes input and output mainly consist of the same commodities), as, for example, whales or mathematical wranglers. The point of these examples is that the commodities with the lowest rate of expansion may be trivial goods. Yet, if it is impossible for the expansion of these goods to keep pace with the rest of commodities, it is they who, on v. Neumann's model, will rule the roost and determine the rate of expansion of the whole system !

The reason for this unnatural result is that there is no room in the model for processes which do *not* involve whales and wranglers ! It is expressly assumed that every good is involved (either as input or as output) in every process. Hence it is not possible in the model to reduce below a certain proportion the part played in the economy by such goods as whales and wranglers, and eventually the expansion of the system must be slowed down to their own pace. v. Neumann states that his assumption that every good enters every process does not really matter because they may be supposed to do so in very small quantities ; nevertheless the implications of this assumption need bearing in mind.

(7) It should be noted that although in the model the equilibrium rate of interest is uniquely determined, the system of prices and outputs are not *uniquely* determined : there may be any number of possible equilibrium positions. But each must satisfy the rules set out in section 2 above.

The ease with which these rules could be established once the existence of an equilibrium position was known, was due to the choice of assumptions which enabled constant prices and stable relative outputs to exist together under competition. The whole process of mathematics would become greatly complicated if increasing returns or monopoly were introduced.

It will be noted, of course, that the " equilibrium " of v. Neumann's model is a very long run equilibrium ; it may take many decades or even centuries for the system to settle down to the rate of expansion of the least expandable goods ; and over this period, the basic assumption of known technical possibilities remaining unchanged loses all reality. An important question, therefore, is how far v. Neumann's results are applicable to systems which are only in an approach to equilibrium ; and any rigorous examination of the properties of such a system would be bound to be most complicated.

Yet it is in the problems of the approach to equilibrium that economists are most interested. How can a country acquire the equipment needed to achieve the best system of production ? What prices should be used in its accounting system by a planning authority seeking to make the best use of its resources ? Here is a fruitful field for extending the powerful methods developed in Prof. v. Neumann's paper.

Oxford. D. G. Champernowne.

12

ECONOMIC GROWTH AT A MAXIMAL RATE *

TJALLING C. KOOPMANS

I. INTRODUCTION

In 1936 John von Neumann presented orally, for subsequent publication in an Austrian mathematical periodical little known to economists, a paper that has greatly influenced economic theory up to the present time, and of which all the ramifications have perhaps not yet become fully apparent.[1]

One can find in von Neumann's difficult short paper starting points for three distinct and extensive subsequent developments in

* The ideas for this paper were developed when visiting at Harvard University as Frank W. Taussig Professor of Economics in 1960–61. The paper was written after returning to Yale, mainly as part of research undertaken by the Cowles Foundation for Research in Economics under Task NR 047-006 with the Office of Naval Research. The manuscript was completed under a grant from the National Science Foundation.

I am indebted to Emmanuel Drandakis, Harold W. Kuhn and Lionel McKenzie for many valuable comments and suggestions.

1. von Neumann, J., "Über ein Ökonomisches Gleichungs-System und eine Verallgemeinerung des Brouwerschen Fixpunktsatzes," in Karl Menger, (ed.), *Ergebnisse eines Mathematischen Kolloquiums*, No. 8, 1935–36, published 1937. Translated as "A Model of General Economic Equilibrium," *Review of Economic Studies*, XIII (1945–46), 1–9.

economic theory. Two of these are not specifically connected with capital or growth theory. The paper contains the first explicit statement, known to this author, of what has subsequently been called the activity analysis model of production. This is a model in which there is a finite number of production processes, each of which is characterized by constant ratios of inputs to outputs, hence by constant returns to scale. The inputs and outputs involved in the various processes together make up a finite list of commodities (goods and services). The paper contains an explicit statement of the relations between commodity prices and the production coefficients (input-output ratios) that distinguish processes that are or may be used from other available processes that are not to be used. These relations are found to characterize both efficient use of resources (in a sense discussed below) and competitive equilibrium.

In fact, to exhibit a model of competitive equilibrium was the main purpose of the paper emphasized by von Neumann. In this regard, together with a preceding and a subsequent paper by Wald,[2] von Neumann's paper became again the starting point for a systematic development of abstract models of competitive equilibrium that has continued up to the present time.

Finally, and most importantly for our present purpose, the paper contains the first rigorous, formal, and fully explicit model in non-aggregative capital theory known to this author.

Paradoxically, von Neumann's paper shows that for a piece of work to spark several new developments in economic theory, it is not necessary that it have any particular claim to realism in its portrayal of economic life. Actually, the paper is rather poor economics. I am not speaking merely of the assumption of an unchanging technology, a highly unrealistic postulate often justified by the useful start it provides. A more unusual defect is that consumption is not treated as in any way an end in itself. Consumption goods occur only as inputs to processes that have labor, or various kinds of labor, as outputs, with ratios of inputs to outputs constant within each such process. In conjunction with the requirement of maximal growth to be introduced below, this implies that the only labor-producing processes that will be utilized are such as to absorb in some sense the minimum consumption input needed to produce

2. A. Wald, Über die Eindeutige Positive Lösbarkeit der neuen Produktionsgleichungen," *Ergebnisse eines Mathematischen Kolloquiums*, Vol. 6 (1935), pp. 12–20 and Vol. 7 (1936), pp. 1–6; Über einige Gleichungssysteme der mathematischen Ökonomie," *Zeitschrift für Nationalökonomie*, Vol. 7 (1936), pp. 637–70, translated as "On Some Systems of Equations in Mathematical Economics," *Econometrica*, Vol. 19 (Oct. 1951), pp. 368–403.

the required labor output. Thus the notion of consumption is one of enabling efficient subsistence, with possibly some scope for incentive goods. The purpose of economic activity is by implication assumed to be fastest growth rather than the enjoyment of life by all generations.

It seems equally arbitrary, and contrary to all experience about economic growth, to assume that all production and consumption activities grow in time at the same proportional rate. Worse than that, it seems quixotic to ignore completely the historically given capital stock available at the beginning of the time period under consideration, and to assume instead that out of some fourth dimension one can at time $t = 1$ pull forth a capital stock of precisely that composition that enables proportional growth to take place at a maximal rate and through a continuing competitive equilibrium.

Subsequent developments have fully vindicated the intuitions that led von Neumann to make these drastic and arbitrary-looking simplifications. More than twenty years later, Dorfman, Samuelson and Solow perceived an implication of von Neumann's model that removes two of the four objections just stated.[3] Holding on to the assumption of an unchanging technology of production and consumption, they accepted a historically given capital stock. Instead of von Neumann's objective of a maximal rate of *proportional* growth, they adopted as objective the attainment of a maximal capital stock of some specified composition at a given time point in a distant future. They then asked what growth path will best serve that objective, and suggested that if the target date is distant enough, the maximal growth path (in the sense indicated) will run along (or close to) the turnpike of the von Neumann path of fastest proportional growth for most of the period under consideration. By this happy conjecture the von Neumann model, thus far mainly a highly inspiring source of theoretical developments, was also given a bearing on certain real-world phenomena, to wit, the forced development of an economy in which the aim is to construct a definite productive capacity for some future date without independent regard for the raising of consumption levels in the meantime.

While the turnpike conjecture is valid in several important cases, the sketches of proofs presented by its originators were not rigorous. Kuhn was the first to point to a class of overlooked excep-

3. R. Dorfman, P. A. Samuelson, and R. M. Solow, *Linear Programming and Economic Analysis* (New York: McGraw Hill, 1958), Chap. 12.

tions.[4] Radner [5] defined one important class of cases for which he proved the conjecture, and Furuya and Inada,[6] Hicks,[7] Inada,[8] McKenzie,[9] Morishima,[1] Nikaido [2] and others obtained valuable additional results.

The main purpose of the present article is expository. Drawing where needed on the studies cited, we shall utilize a diagrammatic device that makes it possible to exhibit, in terms of a two-commodity world, the essentials of the von Neumann model and its maximal growth properties. Those who wish to examine an explicit mathematical discussion of the von Neumann model written without reference to the turnpike property are referred to a paper by Gale [3] or one by Koopmans and Bausch.[4] The diagrams in the present article have been developed from those in the latter paper by the addition, in projection, of a third dimension, in order to permit separate coordinate axes to be used for inputs and for outputs.

Von Neumann's original proof of the existence of a continuing competitive equilibrium exhibiting proportional growth at a maximal rate made use of Brouwer's fixed point theorem. More elementary proofs have since been given by Loomis,[5] by Georgescu-Roegen,[6]

4. H. W. Kuhn, "Comments on the Turnpike Theorems," mimeo., Dec. 1959.

5. R. Radner, "Paths of Economic Growth that are Optimal with Regard only to Final States: A Turnpike Theorem," *Review of Economic Studies*, XXVIII (Feb. 1961), 98–104.

6. H. Furuya and K. Inada, "Balanced Growth and Intertemporal Efficiency in Capital Accumulation," *International Economic Review*, Vol. 3 (Jan. 1962), pp. 94–101.

7. J. R. Hicks, "Prices and the Turnpike, I, The Story of a Mare's Nest," *Review of Economic Studies*, XXVIII (Feb. 1961), 77–88.

8. K. Inada, "Some Structural Characteristics of Turnpike Theorems," mimeo., undated.

9. Lionel W. McKenzie, "The Dorfman-Samuelson-Solow Turnpike Theorem," *International Economic Review*, Vol. 4 (Jan. 1963), pp. 29–43; "Turnpike Theorems for a Generalized Leontief Model," *Econometrica*, Vol. 31 (Jan.–April 1963), pp. 165–80; "The Turnpike Theorem of Morishima," *Review of Economic Studies*, XXX (Oct. 1963), 169–76; "Maximal Paths in the von Neumann Model," mimeo., Sept. 1963.

1. M. Morishima, "Prices and the Turnpike, II, Proof of a Turnpike Theorem: The 'No Joint Production Case,'" *Review of Economic Studies*, XXVIII (Feb. 1961), 89–97.

2. H. Nikaido, "Persistence of Continual Growth near the von-Neumann Ray: A Strong Version of the Radner Turnpike Theorem," *Econometrica*, Vol. 32 (Jan.–April 1964).

3. D. Gale, "The Closed Linear Model of Production," *Linear Inequalities and Related Systems*, eds. H. W. Kuhn and A. W. Tucker (Princeton University Press, 1956), pp. 285–303.

4. T. C. Koopmans and A. F. Bausch, "Selected Topics in Economics Involving Mathematical Reasoning," *SIAM Review*, Vol. I (July 1959), pp. 79–148, Topic 5.

5. L. H. Loomis, "On a Theorem of von Neumann," *Proceedings of the National Academy of Sciences*, Vol. 32 (Aug. 1946), pp. 213–15.

6. N. Georgescu-Roegen, "The Aggregate Linear Production Function and

and by Gale.[7] We shall follow the latter two in proving the existence of a path of maximal proportional growth from the closedness and boundedness of the relevant set of production possibilities, and in deducing the existence and the properties of prices associated with such a path from a separation theorem for convex sets.

II. A Model With Two Commodities

We shall consider a *technology* defined as a set of *feasible activities.* An activity in turn is defined as a procedure whereby a pair $x = (x_1, x_2)$ of inputs (one for each commodity), available at the beginning of any period, is converted into a pair $y = (y_1, y_2)$ of outputs, available at the end of that period. The amount of each input and of each output to an activity (x, y) is positive or zero. The technology remains the same for all future periods. The activities it contains are called feasible in the sense of technical feasibility of the required production processes. Availability of inputs for each period is to be ascertained as a separate matter, hence does not enter into the definition of the technology.

We shall now list the assumptions to be made about the technology.

Proportionality. We first of all make an assumption of constant returns to scale: If an activity $(x, y) = ((x_1, x_2), (y_1, y_2))$ is feasible, then all the activities $\lambda \cdot (x, y) = (\lambda x, \lambda y) = ((\lambda x_1, \lambda x_2), (\lambda y_1, \lambda y_2))$ obtained by multiplying all inputs and outputs by the same nonnegative number λ are likewise feasible. Since $\lambda = 0$ is permitted, this implies that the *null activity* $((0,0), (0,0))$ with no inputs and outputs is feasible if any activity is. The set of all activities proportional to some given nonnull activity will be called a *process.* Any nonnull activity of a process can, of course, be used to define the process. If a specific activity is used for this purpose, it will be called a *defining activity.*

Additivity. We further assume that different activities neither reinforce nor interfere with each other: If two activities (x, y) and (x', y') are both feasible, then their sum $(x+x', y+y') = ((x_1+x_1', x_2 + x_2'), (y_1 + y_1', y_2 + y_2'))$, a new activity whose inputs and outputs are the sums of those of the two given activities, is also feasible. In a context in which different activities are pursued by different firms this assumption is often called "absence of external

its Applications to von Neumann's Economic Model," Chap. IV of T. C. Koopmans (ed.), *Activity Analysis of Production and Allocation* (New York: Wiley, 1951), pp. 98–115.

7. Gale, *op. cit.*

economies or diseconomies." Where we do not necessarily presuppose organization through firms, the term "additivity" appears more appropriate.

Fact of life. We assume further that with limited inputs one cannot obtain unlimited outputs. That is, corresponding to any pair of positive bounds ξ_1, ξ_2 on the inputs, there is a pair of positive bounds η_1, η_2 on the outputs, such that for all feasible activities for which $x_1 \leqq \xi_1$, $x_2 \leqq \xi_2$, one must have[8] $y_1 \leqq \eta_1$, $y_2 \leqq \eta_2$.

Closedness. For mathematical convenience, we also assume that the set of feasible activities (x, y) in the space with four coordinates x_1, x_2, y_1, y_2 is *closed*, that is, contains all points of its boundary.[9]

Free Disposal. We assume next that if an activity (x, y) is feasible, and if (x', y') is an activity with no smaller inputs ($x_1' \geqq x_1$ and $x_2' \geqq x_2$) and no larger outputs ($0 \leqq y_1' \leqq y_1$ and $0 \leqq y_2' \leqq y_2$), then (x', y') is likewise feasible. The consideration thus expressed is that one can, either at the beginning or at the end of a period during which the activity (x, y) takes place, dispose without cost of any excess inputs $(x_1' - x_1,\ x_2' - x_2)$ or excess outputs $(y_1 - y_1', y_2 - y_2')$ that arise if (x', y') is the activity that is wanted.

Output Positivity. Finally, it is assumed that there is a feasible activity (x, y) of which *both* outputs are positive, $y_1 > 0$, $y_2 > 0$.

The reason for this assumption is that we will deal only with cases where no flows of commodities enter the system from the outside — except for what is available at the beginning of the first period. Hence the inputs for the second period have to be found from the outputs of the first, and so on. If the output of a commodity were zero in all feasible activities, then that commodity if initially present would disappear from the system after one round of production. If, on the other hand, for either commodity there is an activity producing some of it, then the addition of these two

8. Note that this implies a corresponding assumption by Gale to the effect that one cannot produce something from nothing. That is, if (x, y) is feasible, and $x_1 = x_2 = 0$, then $y_1 = y_2 = 0$. For, if we had $x_1 = x_2 = 0$ and $y_1 > 0$, say, we could by the proportionality assumption choose a λ such that $\lambda x_1 = \lambda x_2 = 0 \leqq \xi_1$, ξ_2 but $\lambda y_1 > \eta_1$.

9. A point w is said to be in the boundary of a set W if, within any positive distance from w (no matter how small) one can find both points of W and points not of W.

The closedness assumption, devoid of empirical content because of the approximate nature of all measurement, enables us to attain logical sharpness with simpler formulations than would be required without it. It permits us to speak below of a feasible maximal growth path, rather than a possibly unfeasible "maximal" growth path that can be approximated arbitrarily closely by feasible growth paths.

Gale shows that closedness of the production set together with his assumption cited in the preceding footnote imply our fact-of-life assumption.

activities yields an activity that produces some of both commodities, and our last assumption is satisfied.

All the assumptions stated above will be maintained in what follows. In the von Neumann model as originally presented some further assumptions were made, of which we mention one. This is that there is given a *finite* number of *basic feasible activities*, from which all other feasible activities can be derived by proportional variation, addition, disposal, or combinations of these. In some of our examples below this assumption is satisfied.

Since we are interested in properties of the two-commodity model that carry over into models with n commodities, there is no need to associate particular named commodities with the inputs and outputs. However, we shall in some cases below use a simple example where the two commodities are food and tools, and where the technology has a finite basis.

III. Growth Paths and Proportional Growth Paths

Any sequence of feasible activities $(x^t, y^t) = ((x_1^t, x_2^t), (y_1^t, y_2^t))$, carried out in successive periods labeled $t = 1, 2, \ldots, T$ will be called a *growth path* if the output pair from each period's activity equals[1] the input pair for that of the next period,

$$y^t = (y_1^t, y_2^t) = (x_1^{t+1}, x_2^{t+1}) = x^{t+1}.$$

In the commodity space with coordinates x_1, x_2, a growth path can be represented, as in Figure I, by the sequence of points or *states*

$$x^1,\ y^1 = x^2,\ y^2 = x^3\ , \ldots ,\ y^{T-1} = x^T,\ y^T,$$

labeled by superscripts to indicate the order in which they occur.

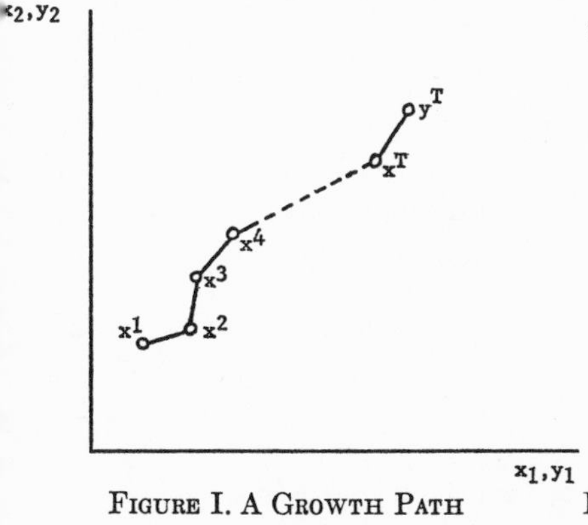

Figure I. A Growth Path

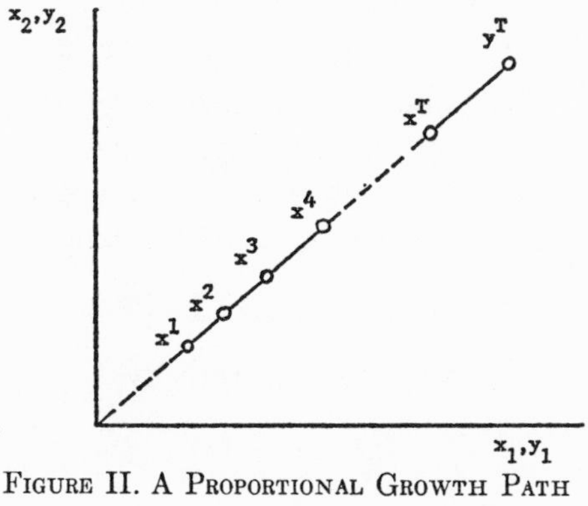

Figure II. A Proportional Growth Path

1. Since the disposal possibility has already been recognized in defining the set of feasible activities, we do not need to admit inequality here.

It is called a path even though actually it is a sequence of states rather than a continuous path. An activity made up of two successive states of a path will also be called a *step* of that path.

Von Neumann limited his discussion to *proportional growth paths,* in which each step is a *proportional growth activity.* The latter is defined as a nonnull activity $(x, y) = ((x_1, x_2), (y_1, y_2))$ in which the outputs are multiples

$$y_1 = \mu x_1, \qquad y_2 = \mu x_2, \qquad \mu > 0,$$

of the inputs, by a positive factor μ called the *growth factor.* The same growth factor μ applies to all steps in the path. There is actual growth if $\mu > 1$, stationarity if $\mu = 1$, contraction if $\mu < 1$. The terminal outputs $y_1{}^T$, $y_2{}^T$ of a proportional growth path with initial inputs $x_1{}^1$, $x_2{}^1$ and a growth factor μ are, of course,

$$y_1{}^T = (\mu)^{T+1} \cdot x_1{}^1, \qquad y^T{}_2 = (\mu)^{T+1} \cdot x_2{}^1,$$

where $(\mu)^t$ denotes "μ raised to the power t" (as distinct from the use of a time superscript in x^t, y^t). Figure II illustrates such a path.

Instead of the growth factor μ we will sometimes use the *growth rate* $\mu - 1$.

IV. Geometrical Representation of the Technology

While the two-dimensional diagram of Figures I and II gives a clear image of a growth path, the same diagram is poorly suited to represent feasibility considerations. Actually, each activity has four coordinates, x_1, x_2; y_1, y_2. To represent the set of feasible activities explicitly by a geometrical figure would therefore require a four-dimensional space. However, the proportionality assumption makes it possible to cut this requirement down to three dimensions. There are many ways of doing this, out of which we shall choose a particular *normalization* of the inputs. If (x', y') is a nonnull activity, at least one of the inputs x_1', x_2' must be positive, because if both inputs were zero the outputs would vanish also, by one of our assumptions. Hence the sum of the inputs $x_1' + x_2'$ is positive. By applying a positive factor $\lambda = \dfrac{1}{x_1' + x_2'}$ to the given activity (x', y'), we obtain an activity

$$(x, y) = (\lambda x', \lambda y') = \left(\frac{x'}{x_1' + x_2'}, \frac{y'}{x_1' + x_2'}\right) =$$

$$\left(\left(\frac{x_1'}{x_1' + x_2'}, \frac{x_2'}{x_1' + x_2'}\right), \left(\frac{y_1'}{x_1' + x_2'}, \frac{y_2'}{x_1' + x_2'}\right)\right)$$

with the property that the sum of the inputs is unity:

$$x_1 + x_2 = \frac{x_1'}{x_1' + x_2'} + \frac{x_2'}{x_1' + x_2'} = 1.$$

The fact that we are adding bushels of wheat to plows does not need to detain us here. The procedure is an arbitrary normalization device, which will yield us the same logical propositions if we choose to add pounds of wheat to dozens of plows.

Each nonnull process is now represented by just one normalized activity. Conversely, the coordinates of each normalized activity can again be increased or decreased proportionally to reproduce any other activity of the process it represents. We shall therefore have obtained a useful geometrical representation of the technology if we can exhibit the set of normalized activities. Since the two inputs add up to unity, they can be represented together by a single point on a line segment of unit length. As indicated in Figure III, the

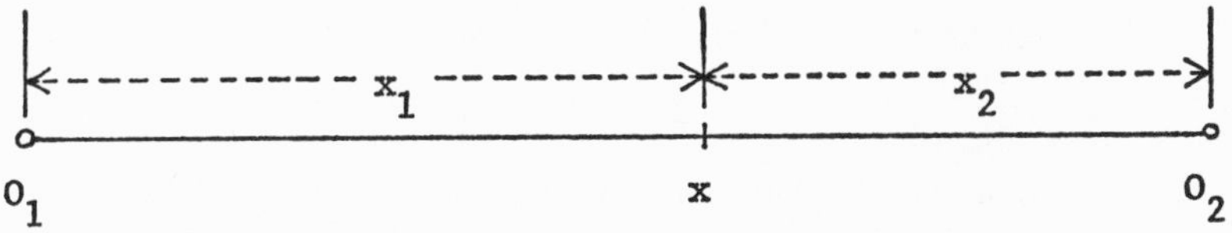

FIGURE III. REPRESENTATION OF NORMALIZED INPUTS x_1, x_2

position of the point labeled x on that segment, relative to an origin in the left endpoint O_1, fixes the first input x_1, measured toward the right. The position of that same point x relative to an "alternate origin" O_2 in the right endpoint fixes the second input x_2, measured toward the left.

We shall call this segment the x-segment. The line containing it serves simultaneously as x_1-axis, with O_1 as origin, and as x_2-axis, with O_2 as origin. At right angles to the x_1-axis, we choose additional coordinate axes for y_1 and y_2, respectively, indicated in Figure IV in projection. The technology is now represented by a set Z of points $z = (x_1, y_1, y_2)$, each point z representing a normalized feasible activity $((x_1, 1 - x_1), (y_1, y_2))$ in which the input $x_2 = 1 - x_1$ of the second commodity is implied in that of the first. We shall therefore hereafter freely use the expression "activity z," even though z has only three coordinates. The points of Z are all "above" or in the (horizontal) x_1-y_1-plane, "in front of" or in the (vertical) x_1-y_2-plane, and between, or in one of, two other (vertical) planes, one being the y_1-y_2-plane through the origin $O_1 = (0, 0, 0)$, the other parallel to it through the alternate origin $O_2 = (1, 0, 0)$. The

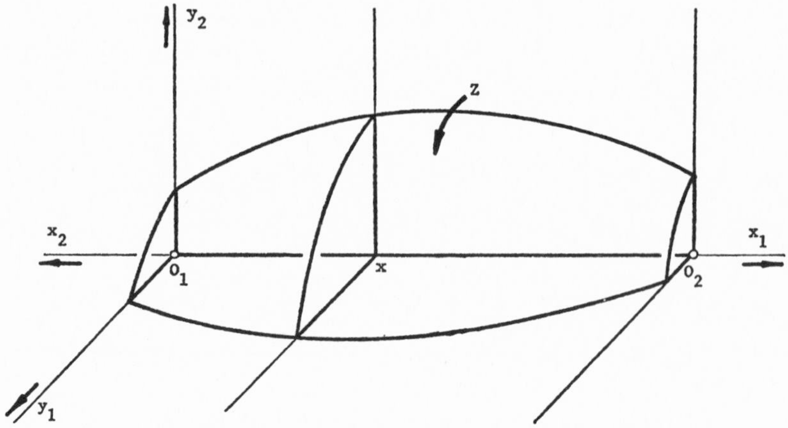

FIGURE IV. A FEASIBLE SET IN THE NORMALIZED COMMODITY SPACE

set Z will be variously called the (normalized) feasible set, or technology set.

It will be useful to introduce a special term for all those points (or activities) $z = (x_1, y_1, y_2)$ of Z with the property that Z contains no points of the form $z' = (x_1, \lambda y_1, \lambda y_2)$ with $\lambda > 1$. These points represent activities such that a proportional increase in both outputs is not feasible from the same inputs. We shall call such points, and all activities proportional to such points, *maximal.* Normalized maximal activities are, of course, found only in the boundary of Z. Since each of our normalized inputs is at most unity, the fact-of-life assumption entails that both outputs are also subject to upper bounds, $y_1 \leqq \bar{\eta}_1$, $y_2 \leqq \bar{\eta}_2$, hence that the entire set Z is *bounded* (contained in a finite box). Furthermore, the set Z is *convex*: if two points $z = (x_1, y_1, y_2)$, $z' = (x_1', y_1', y_2')$ belong to Z, then all points of the line segment $\overline{zz'}$ joining z with z' belong to Z. To argue this for the midpoint z'' of $\overline{zz'}$ one scales down each of the activities (x, y) and (x', y') — where, of course $x_2 = 1 - x_1$, $x_2' = 1 - x_1'$ – by applying a factor $\lambda = 1/2$, and adds the resulting inputs and outputs. The proportionality and additivity assumptions assure us that the resulting activity (x'', y'') is again feasible. Arithmetic shows that it is again normalized,[2] and therefore represented in Z by the midpoint z'' in question. Similar reasoning[3] applies to any other point of $\overline{zz'}$. Finally, Z is again closed.[4]

2. $x_1'' + x_2'' = \dfrac{x_1 + x_1'}{2} + \dfrac{x_2 + x_2'}{2} = \dfrac{x_1 + x_2}{2} + \dfrac{x_1' + x_2'}{2} = \dfrac{1}{2} + \dfrac{1}{2} = 1\,.$

3. Substituting λ and $1 - \lambda$ for $1/2$ and $1/2$, where $0 < \lambda < 1$.

4. As the intersection of the (closed) production set with the (closed) normalization set $x_1 + x_2 = 1$.

Figure IV indicates one possible shape of Z. For any particular normalized input, such as that indicated by x in the figure, the set of feasible outputs is found by intersecting Z with a vertical plane through $x = (x_1, 0, 0)$ parallel to the y_1-y_2-plane.

Figure V shows the implications of free disposal for the shape

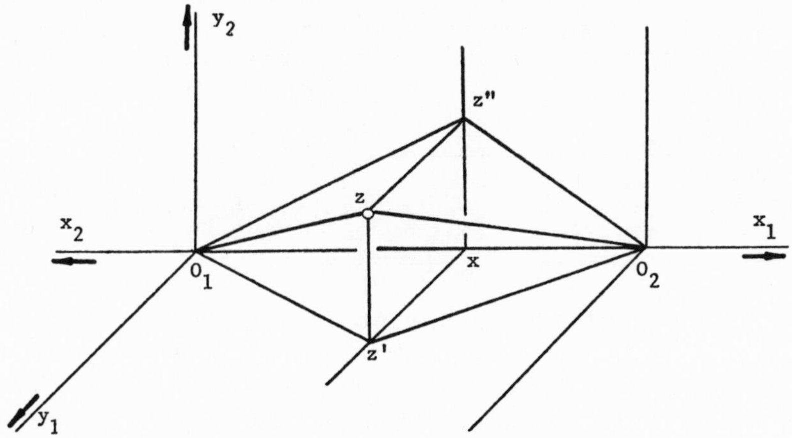

FIGURE V. IMPLICATIONS OF FREE DISPOSAL

of Z. If a point $z = (x_1, y_1, y_2)$ belongs to Z, then by disposal of part or all of one or both outputs one can get to any point of the rectangle $xz'zz''$ shown. Therefore all of these points belong to Z. On the other hand, the two origins O_1, O_2 belong to *any* normalized production set, hence to Z, because the activities $((0, 1), (0, 0))$ and $((1, 0), (0, 0))$ they represent, respectively, are obtained by disposal of one unit of one or the other input followed by the null activity. By the convexity of Z, therefore, the entire polyhedron $O_1z'zz''O_2$ must be contained in Z, any point of it being "producible" by disposal of none, some, or all of one of the inputs, production proportional to $((x_1, 1 - x_1), (y_1, y_2))$, and disposal of none, some or all of one or both outputs. We note that, because of the assumption of output positivity, there is always a point $z = (x_1, y_1, y_2)$ in Z with both outputs y_1, y_2 positive. It follows that Z cannot be contained in a line or plane, but is always a three-dimensional body, containing *interior points*.

If the polyhedron $O_1z'zz''O_2$ in Figure V is itself the technology set Z, it constitutes the simplest example of a normalized technology set satisfying von Neumann's assumption of a finite basis. Apart from disposal, there is just one basic activity, represented by z. Data for a somewhat more complicated example are given in Table

I. There are two commodities, tools and food, where food as an input is identified with the labor it makes possible.

TABLE I

Basic Activities at Normalized Unit Levels

	Producing Food				Producing Tools	
	(1)	(2)	(3)	(4)	(5)	(6)
Outputs						
1. Tools		.1	.3	.5	.5	.6
2. Food	1	1.3	1.5	1.55		
Inputs						
1. Tools		.2	.5	.8		.1
2. Food = labor	1	.8	.5	.2	1	.9

The basic activities fall into two categories, those for producing food and those for producing tools. In each category, activities are labeled in an order of increasing tool intensiveness. Tool-using activities yield an output of remaining serviceable tools smaller than the tool input, to allow for scrapping of worn-out tools in a ratio that decreases as tool intensity increases. The normalized technology set for this example is shown in Figure VIII below. It will be clear that a technology with a finite basis always gives rise to a normalized set Z that is polyhedral in shape.

V. Representation of Proportional Growth

Given the technology, the highest proportional growth rate that can be achieved from given initial inputs will in general depend on these inputs, more precisely, on their ratio. We shall now look for the highest rate achievable with any inputs, and for the ratio of inputs that makes that rate possible. It has already been pointed out that in this formulation historically given initial inputs are ignored. It is assumed for the time being that whatever initial inputs may be needed for a maximal proportional growth path can be procured.

To facilitate our search, let us first consider how proportional growth can be represented in our diagram without regard to its feasibility. Since proportional growth is defined only for nonnull activities, it suffices to consider only normalized activities. Figure VI represents all such activities showing proportional growth by a factor μ. The input pair $x^{(1)} = (0, 1)$ represented by O_1 gives rise

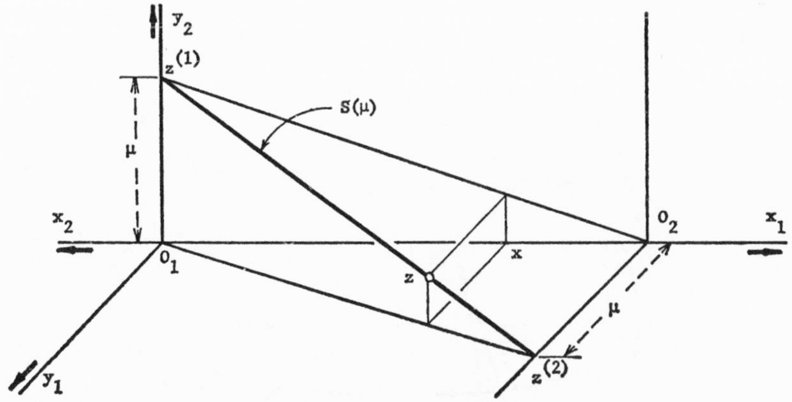

FIGURE VI. REPRESENTATION OF PROPORTIONAL GROWTH

to an activity point $z^{(1)} = (0, 0, \mu)$ found on the positive y_2-axis at a distance μ from O_1. The input pair $x^{(2)} = (1, 0)$ represented by O_2 similarly leads to $z^{(2)} = (1, \mu, 0)$ found on the "alternate" positive y_1-axis at a distance μ from O_2. For all other normalized input pairs $x = (x_1, x_2)$, proportional outputs $y_1 = \mu x_1$, $y_2 = \mu x_2$ are represented, separately, by points of the line segments $\overline{z^{(1)}O_2}$ and $\overline{O_1 z^{(2)}}$, respectively, and hence jointly by points z of the segment $\overline{z^{(1)}z^{(2)}}$.

A higher growth factor μ' gives rise to a similar segment with the distances from O_1 to $z^{(1)}$ and from O_2 to $z^{(2)}$ increased to μ'. To indicate its dependence on μ, we shall hereafter denote the segment $\overline{z^{(1)}z^{(2)}}$ by $S(\mu)$.

VI. DETERMINATION OF A MAXIMAL PROPORTIONAL GROWTH PATH

By putting together the diagrams of Figures IV and VI in Figure VII we can now find a normalized activity that represents proportional growth at a maximal rate. We observe that feasible proportional growth by a factor μ is represented by a point of Z which is at the same time a point of $S(\mu)$. We are therefore looking for the largest value μ^* of μ for which Z and $S(\mu)$ have at least one point in common.

Now first of all the segment $S(0) = O_1O_2$, representing a zero growth factor (i.e., complete collapse of the economy in one period), is entirely contained in Z. Better than that, a comparison with Figure V shows that, if μ does not exceed some small enough positive value $\underline{\mu}$, then the segment $S(\underline{\mu})$ still has points in common with Z. At the other extreme, if we choose $\bar{\mu}$ slightly above the larger of the

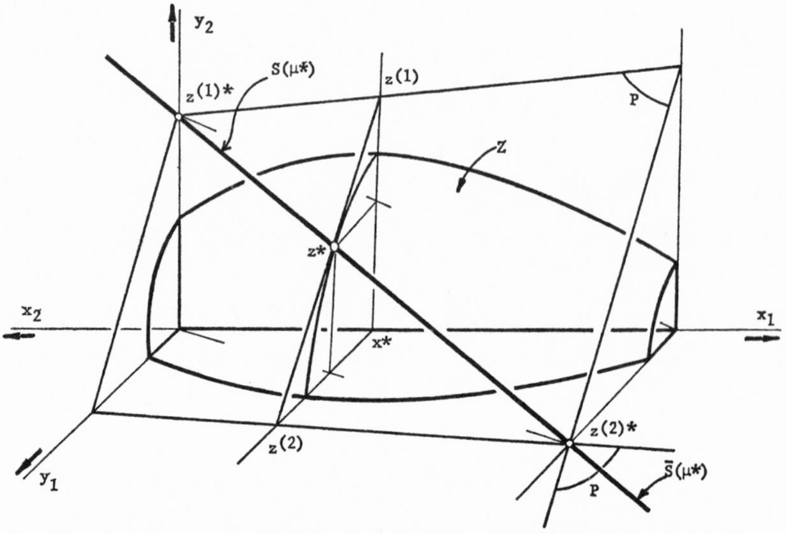

FIGURE VII. CONSTRUCTION OF A MAXIMAL PROPORTIONAL GROWTH (VON NEUMANN) ACTIVITY

two numbers $\bar{\eta}_1$, $\bar{\eta}_2$, then $S(\bar{\mu})$ lies entirely outside the box of dimensions 1 by $\bar{\eta}_1$ by $\bar{\eta}_2$ that contains Z. Hence $S(\mu)$ and Z do not intersect whenever $\mu \geqq \bar{\mu}$.

There is therefore a unique largest value μ^* of μ for which Z and $S(\mu)$ have a point in common,[5] and μ^* is positive but finite because

$$0 < \underline{\mu} \leqq \mu^* < \bar{\mu}.$$

Any common point z^* of Z and $S(\mu^*)$ will be called a von Neumann point, and the corresponding activity a (normalized) von Neumann activity. Any von Neumann activity achieves proportional growth by a maximal factor μ^*. The collection of all (von Neumann) activities proportional to a given one will be called a *von Neumann process.*

Figure VII is so drawn that there exists just one normalized von Neumann activity. This is due to the rounded shape of the boundary of Z (outside the coordinate planes). To be more precise, we shall call the technology in general, and the set Z in particular, *strictly convex* if any weighted average of the inputs of any two

5. Let $d(\mu)$ be the shortest distance between a point of Z and a point of $S(\mu)$. Since both sets are closed and bounded, $d(\mu)$ exists, and $d(\mu) = 0$ if and only if Z and $S(\mu)$ intersect. It is easily seen that $d(\mu)$ is a continuous function of μ. Furthermore, if $d(\mu) = 0$ and $\mu > \mu'$, then $d(\mu') = 0$, because of free disposal. Hence the set of μ for which Z and $S(\mu)$ intersect is an interval $[0, \mu^*]$, which contains its positive endpoint μ^* because $d(\mu)$ is continuous.

different nonnull feasible activities allows production of the same weighted average of the outputs multiplied by some factor in excess of unity.[6] Then strict convexity of the technology entails uniqueness of the von Neumann process.[7]

In addition, Figure VII represents a case where the von Neumann activity involves positive inputs and outputs of both commodities, because z^* is different from either endpoint $z^{(1)*}$, $z^{(2)*}$ of $S(\mu^*)$.

Other cases than those exhibited in Figure VII will be considered below.

A proportional growth path consisting of activities drawn from the same von Neumann process will be called a *von Neumann path.* There is no alternative proportional growth path with a higher rate of growth, regardless of the initial input x^1 of the alternative path.

We summarize our results in

PROPOSITION 1. *Under the assumptions of Section 2, there exists a positive highest proportional growth rate* μ^* *inherent in the technology, attainable by at least one von Neumann process. This process is unique whenever the technology is strictly convex.*

We shall end this section with an example that shows up the possible artificiality of the search for a maximal proportional growth activity. In the economy of Table II based on just two processes,

TABLE II

BASIC ACTIVITIES AT DEFINING UNIT LEVELS[1]

	Reproduction of[2]	
	(1) Rabbit Population	(2) Human Population
Outputs		
(1) rabbits	100	
(2) people		2
Inputs		
(1) rabbits	1	500
(2) people		1

1. The defining activity of process 2 is not normalized.
2. One time unit is 25 years.

6. In terms of normalized activities the definition of strict convexity is that, if $z = (x_1, y_1, y_2)$, $z' = (x_1', y_1', y_2')$ are different points of Z, and if $0 < \lambda < 1$, then there exists a number $\nu > 1$ such that $(\lambda x_1 + (1 - \lambda)x_1',$ $\nu(\lambda y_1 + (1 - \lambda)y_1'),$ $\nu(\lambda y_2 + (1 - \lambda)y_2'))$ is also in Z.

7. Suppose there are two different von Neumann activities z^* and $z^{*\prime}$ with the maximal growth rate μ^*. Then, taking $\lambda = 1/2$, the input vector x of the activity $z = 1/2, (z^* + z^{*\prime})$ would permit an output vector $\nu y = \nu\mu^* x$ with $\nu > 1$, contradicting the maximality of μ^*.

the highest proportional growth rate $\mu^* = 100$ can be attained only in the point $z^* = z^{(2)*} = (1, 100, 0)$, by having no human population at all, turning the world over to the rabbits. The highest proportional growth rate subject to the condition that there be a human population is clearly $\mu^{**} = 2$.

This example suggests that, if there are n commodities, there may in special cases be a hierarchy of maximal growth rates, each associated with a proportional growth path in a subspace of the commodity space defined by the absence of one or more suitably chosen commodities from the economy. Such a hierarchy has been studied by Kemeny, Morgenstern and Thompson [8] and by McKenzie.[9]

VII. A Price System Sustaining a Given von Neumann Path

In von Neumann's discussion, the maximality of the growth rate was established as an implication of the existence of a price system that sustains a von Neumann path. Our reversal of the order in which these two properties are established is favored by the simpler mathematical tool we use. We shall use the following:

Separation theorem for convex sets: [1] *If* A *and* B *are convex sets in three-dimensional space which have no point in common, then there exists a plane P which separates A and B, in the sense that every point of A is either in P or on one side of P, whereas every point of B is either in P or on the other side of P.*

The application we shall make of this theorem will at the same time serve as an illustration of its meaning and use. We start from a von Neumann point z^*, which may but need not be unique. If, as in Figure VII, z^* is not an endpoint of the segment $S(\mu^*)$, it will suffice to take $S(\mu^*)$ itself as the set A in the theorem. However, in order to include also cases where z^* is an endpoint it will help to choose for A the line $\bar{S}(\mu^*)$ obtained by extending $S(\mu^*)$ indefinitely beyond both endpoints.

8. J. G. Kemeny, O. Morgenstern and G. L. Thompson, "A Generalization of the von Neumann Model of an Expanding Economy," *Econometrica*, Vol. 24 (April 1956), pp. 115–35.

9. Lionel W. McKenzie, "Maximal Paths in the von Neumann Model," mimeo., Sept. 1963.

1. For a proof of this theorem in n dimensions, see Corollary 3 in G. Debreu, "Separation Theorems for Convex Sets," Appendix to Topic 2 of Koopmans and Bausch, *op. cit.* For a discussion of the importance of this theorem in the theory of allocation of resources, see Koopmans, "Allocation of Resources and the Price System," the first of *Three Essays on the State of Economic Science* (New York: McGraw Hill, 1957).

For B we choose the *interior* $\mathring{Z}$ of the normalized production set Z, that is, all points of Z not in its boundary. We have already concluded from the free disposal and output positivity assumptions that Z does have interior points. It is intuitively clear that $\mathring{Z}$ and $\bar{S}(\mu^*)$ have no point in common.[2] By the separation theorem, therefore, there is a plane P separating $\bar{S}(\mu^*)$ and $\mathring{Z}$. Since $\mathring{Z}$ is three-dimensional, not all points of $\mathring{Z}$ can be in P, and hence some of them will be "behind" P. Moreover, since the boundary of Z is only a skin without thickness, all points of Z are in or behind P, hence P "separates" $\bar{S}(\mu^*)$ and Z as well.[3] In particular the point z^* common to $\bar{S}(\mu^*)$ and Z must lie in P. But if all points of the straight line $\bar{S}(\mu^*)$ are in or in front of P, and one of them, z^*, is in P, all points of $\bar{S}(\mu^*)$ must be in P, and a fortiori all points of $S(\mu^*)$ are in P. This includes all other von Neumann points $z^{*\prime}$ in case z^* should not be unique.

Figure VII shows the construction of the separating plane P. As already explained, the diagram uses a strictly convex production set Z, in which case P and Z have only one point z^* in common. However, we shall in what follows use the strict convexity assumption only where that is explicitly mentioned.

Let us write the equation of P as

$$q\ x_1 + p_1\ y_1 + p_2\ y_2 = q_2.$$

Since $z^{(1)*} = (0, 0, \mu^*)$ and $z^{(2)*} = (1, \mu^*, 0)$ are in P, substitution of these coordinates for (x_1, y_1, y_2) in the equation gives

$$\mu^*\ p_2 = q_2, \qquad \mu^*\ p_1 = q_2 - q = q_1, \quad \text{say.}$$

Reintroducing the input $x_2 = 1 - x_1$ of the second commodity, we can therefore write the equation of P in the symmetrical form

$$(P) \qquad \pi(x, y) = p_1\ y_1 + p_2\ y_2 - \mu^*\ (p_1\ x_1 + p_2\ x_2) = 0,$$

2. For a proof, refer to the definition of an interior point z of Z. Supplementing the definition of boundary points in the footnote above, a point z is interior to Z if there exists a positive number δ such that all points at a distance from z no larger than δ belong to Z. Suppose $z = (x_1, y_1, y_2)$ is both in $\mathring{Z}$ and in $\bar{S}(\mu^*)$. Since z is in Z, $0 \leqq x_1 \leqq 1$, and hence z is not in the extensions of $S(\mu^*)$, for which either $x_1 < 0$ or $1 < x_1$. Hence z is in $S(\mu^*)$. But then, for any $\epsilon > 0$, $S((1+\epsilon)\mu^*)$ contains a point $z_\epsilon = (x_1, (1+\epsilon)y_1, (1+\epsilon)y_2)$ of which the distance from z is $\epsilon\sqrt{y_1^2 + y_2^2}$. Since by suitable choice of ϵ this distance can be made less than δ, z_ϵ can be made to fall in Z. But then μ^* is not the maximum feasible rate of proportional growth, contrary to the definition of μ^*.

3. Suppose z of Z is "in front of" P, and D is a small sphere, constructed on a center in $\mathring{Z}$ behind P, so as to be both behind P and in Z. Then, by the convexity of Z, the convex hull E of D and z is contained in Z. But then E contains points of $\mathring{Z}$ in front of P, a contradiction.

it being understood that x_2 needs to be replaced by $1 - x_1$ to make this the equation of a plane in our three-dimensional space of normalized activities (x_1, y_1, y_2). We have introduced the notation $\pi(x, y)$ as a short symbol for the linear function[4] in the middle member of (P).

The function $\pi(x, y)$ is positive on one side of P, negative on the other. Since we are still free to change the signs of both p_1 and p_2 in (p), we shall choose the signs in such a way that

$$(\bar{P}) \qquad \pi(x, y) = p_1\, y_1 + p_2\, y_2 - \mu^* (p_1\, x_1 + p_2\, x_2) \leqq 0$$

for all points in or behind P. This includes all points of Z. In particular, the $<$ sign in $(\bar{P})$ must apply to all points of Z other than z^* whenever z^* is the only point Z and P have in common.

We know that Z contains the two origins (0, 0, 0) and (1, 0, 0). Inserting of their coordinates in $(\bar{P})$ yields

$$p_1 \geqq 0, \quad p_2 \geqq 0, \quad \text{but not} \quad p_1 = p_2 = 0,$$

because in the latter case (P) would not be the equation of a plane. If, as in Figure VII, both origins are "behind" P, we have

$$p_1 > 0, \quad p_2 > 0.$$

We will now interpret p_1 and p_2 as *prices* of commodities "1" and "2," respectively, which we think of as constant through time. Likewise we interpret $\mu^* - 1 = r$ as an *interest rate* for a time span of one period, hence $\mu^* = 1 + r$ as an *interest factor*. The left-hand member $\pi(x, y)$ in (P) then represents the value of the outputs y_1, y_2 at the end of the period, minus the value of the inputs x_1, x_2 at the beginning of the period multiplied by an interest factor to account for the time lead of one period by which inputs must precede outputs. This is precisely the *profit* that arises from engaging in the activity (x, y) during one period, evaluated in the *price system* p_1, p_2, r for a time of reference at the end of that period. Since z^* is in P, the profit $\pi(x^*, y^*)$ from the maximal proportional growth activity is precisely zero. Moreover, by $(\bar{P})$, the profit $\pi(x, y)$ from any feasible activity (x, y) is nonpositive.[5] In this sense, it can be said that the price system p_1, p_2, r, if remaining constant through time, *sustains* the (or all) von Neumann growth path(s). It is immaterial for this statement whether the price system in

4. Since x_2 was reintroduced, this function is so defined whether (x, y) is normalized or not.

5. Strictly, Figure VII shows this only for the normalized activities of Z. However, since any feasible activity is obtainable from a normalized activity by multiplying all coordinates with a nonnegative factor λ, the profit is likewise multiplied by λ, leaving the above statement true.

question is thought of as determined in competitive markets in a growing economy, or whether it is regarded as a set of centrally determined steering prices guiding allocations in a planned economy. If the maximal growth activity is itself a basic activity that can be arranged for in a single productive process or establishment, the price system will permit continual growth of that activity if the interest charge is the only obstacle to investment, because no loss is incurred by meeting it. Neither does there exist any other feasible activity which, by yielding a positive profit, would lure resources away from the maximal growth path.

It is, of course, also possible that the (or a) maximal growth activity is a composite

$$(x^*, y^*) = \lambda_1 \cdot (x^1, y^1) + \lambda_2 \cdot (x^2, y^2) + \ldots + \lambda_k \cdot (x^k, y^k)$$

of k basic activities (x^h, y^h), $h = 1, \ldots, k$ with *positive* weights λ_h. In that case *each* of these basic activities must also break even.[6] Continued use of each of these activities is again sustained by the fact that there is no competing feasible activity promising a positive profit. Moreover, once the levels of these activities have the proportions $\lambda_1, \lambda_2, \ldots, \lambda_k$ occurring in the above representation of (x^*, y^*), the outputs from each round of production will just suffice as inputs for the next round at levels stepped up by the factor μ^*. We summarize our results in

PROPOSITION 2. *With each maximal proportional growth (von Neumann) process one can associate a pair of nonnegative prices (not both zero) and an interest rate exceeding −1, that together sustain maximal proportional growth, in the sense that any von Neumann activity breaks even in that price system, and no feasible activity yields a profit. If the technology is strictly convex, only von Neumann activities (unique but for normalization) break even. If a von Neumann activity is a weighted sum of other feasible activities, then the latter activities all break even regardless of whether or not taken separately they are von Neumann activities.*

The price ratio $p_1 \div p_2$ can be read off from Figure VII as follows: The equations of the line $\overline{z^{(1)}z^{(2)}}$ in which P intersects the plane through z^* parallel to the y_1-y_2-plane are found from (P) to be

$$\begin{cases} p_1y_1 + p_2y_2 = \mu^*(p_1x_1^* + p_2x_2^*) = c^*, \quad \text{say} \\ x_1 = x_1^*. \end{cases}$$

Hence $-p_1/p_2$ is the slope of y_2 on y_1 read off from that line. In

6. This follows because, since $\pi(x, y)$ is linear in (x, y), $0 = \pi(x^*, y^*) = \lambda_1 \pi(x^1, y^1) + \ldots + \lambda_k \pi(x^k, y^k)$. But $\lambda_h > 0$, $\pi(x^h, y^h) \leqq 0$, for $h = 1, \ldots, k$. It follows that $\pi(x^h, y^h) = 0$ for $h = 1, \ldots, k$.

Figure VII this slope is uniquely determined by the smooth shape of Z. A limited indeterminacy in p_1/p_2 can arise, for instance, if z^* should just happen to be a vertex of a polyhedral Z.

It will be useful later if we also determine the slope of the line $\overline{z^{(1)*}z^{(1)}}$ in which P intersects the x_1-y_2-plane. (If $p_2 = 0$ we must use the x_1-y_1-plane instead.) From (P) we have, if $y_1 = 0$,

$$p_2y_2 = \mu^*(p_1x_1 + p_2(1 - x_1)) = \mu^*(p_1 - p_2)x_1 + \mu^*p_2.$$

Hence the slope of y_2 on x_1 is $\mu^* \cdot \dfrac{p_1 - p_2}{p_2}$. It depends on the price ratio p_1/p_2, and also on μ^* whenever $p_1 \neq p_2$.

VIII. Is Any Proportional Growth Path Sustained By A Price System Maximal?

We have found that with any proportional growth activity with the maximal growth factor μ^* one can associate a price system p_1, p_2, $r = \mu^* - 1$ which sustains that activity. It is worth looking at the reverse question: Suppose one has obtained a proportional growth activity $(x', y') = (x', \mu'x')$ with $\mu' > 0$ and a price system $p_1' \geqq 0$, $p_2' \geqq 0$ (not both $= 0$), $r' = \mu' - 1$ which sustains it, in the sense that $\pi'(x, y) = p_1'y_1 + p_2'y_2 - \mu'(p_1'x_1 + p_2'x_2) \leqq 0$ for all feasible activities (x, y). (Inserting (x', y') in this inequality obviously gives the $=$ sign, because $y' = \mu'x'$.) Does it follow that $\mu' = \mu^*$ and hence that the given activity is a von Neumann activity?

The answer is affirmative whenever the given prices p_1', p_2' are both positive. To see this, we evaluate a von Neumann activity $(x^*, y^*) = (x^*, \mu^*x^*)$ — we already know from Proposition 1 that there exists one — in the given price system. Since (x^*, y^*) is feasible

$$\pi'(x^*, y^*) = p_1'y_1^* + p_2'y_2^* - \mu'(p_1'x_1^* + p_2'x_2^*) \leqq 0.$$

On the other hand, since $y^* = \mu^*x^*$,

$$p_1'y_1^* + p_2'y_2^* - \mu^*(p_1'x_1^* + p_2'x_2^*) = 0.$$

Subtracting we have, after cancellations,

$$(\mu^* - \mu')\ (p_1'x_1^* + p_2'x_2^*) \leqq 0.$$

Now x_1^*, x_2^* are nonnegative and not both zero, and p_1', p_2' are both positive by assumption. Hence $p_1'x_1^* + p_2'x_2^* > 0$, and therefore $\mu^* - \mu' \leqq 0$. On the other hand, since μ^* is the maximal proportional growth rate that is feasible, $\mu^* - \mu' \geqq 0$. It follows that $\mu' = \mu^*$, and hence that the given activity (x', y') is a von Neumann activity, the given price system p_1', p_2', is an associated sustaining price system.

The foregoing reverse reasoning, from a given sustaining price system to the maximality of a proportional growth activity, is important in verifying, for a numerically defined production set Z, that a proposed proportional growth activity is indeed a maximal one. Proof is rendered by exhibiting positive sustaining prices p_1', p_2'. This reasoning does not hold if, say, $p_1' = 0$, while $x_2^* = 0$ for the von Neumann activity, a possible case in the example of Table II above. In that example, growth of the human population at the rate $\mu' = 2$ can be "sustained" by the "price system" $p_1' = 0$, $p_2' = 1$, $r' = 1$.

PROPOSITION 3. *A proportional growth activity sustained, in the sense of Proposition 2, by a pair of positive prices and an interest rate exceeding* -1 *is a von Neumann activity.*

IX. A Numerical Example

We shall illustrate the determination of the maximal proportional growth activity and the associated price system in terms of the technology with six basic activities shown in Table I above. A glance at Figure VIII (before $S(\mu^*)$ is drawn in) suggests that the

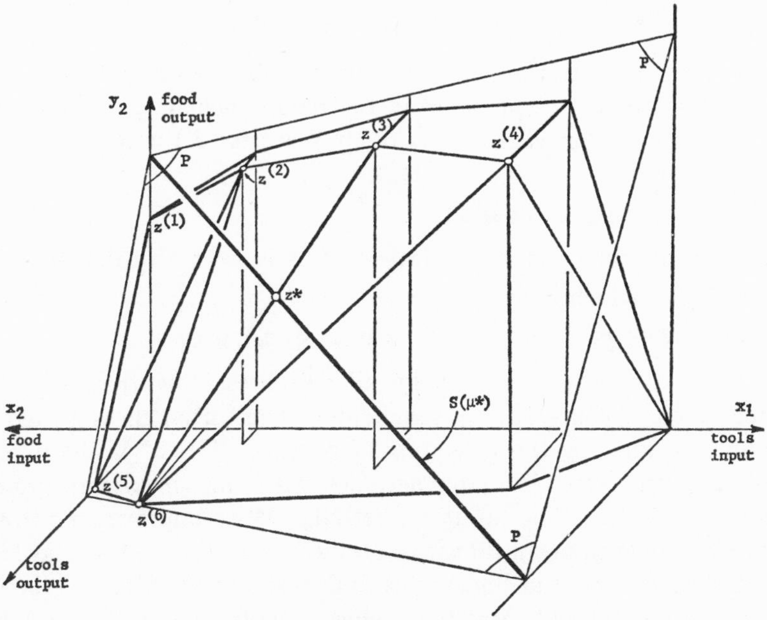

FIGURE VIII. VON NEUMANN ACTIVITY AND SEPARATING PLANE FOR THE TECHNOLOGY OF TABLE I

segment $S(\mu^*)$ will cut one, or just possibly two, of the edges leading from activity $z^{(6)}$ to activities $z^{(2)}$, $z^{(3)}$ or $z^{(4)}$. Without looking for a systematic method for determining $S(\mu^*)$ and its intersection with a polyhedral Z in more complicated cases, let us guess that $S(\mu^*)$ cuts only the edge $\overline{z^{(3)}z^{(6)}}$. Then μ^* can be determined from the condition that the point

$$(x_1^*, y_1^*, y_2^*) = z^* = \lambda\, z^3 + (1 - \lambda)\, z^6$$

on the edge $\overline{z^{(3)}z^{(6)}}$ have outputs proportional to inputs, the factor of proportionality being μ^*. Using the coordinates of $z^{(3)}$, $z^{(6)}$ given in Table I, this requires

$$\begin{aligned} .3\lambda + .6(1 - \lambda) &= \mu^*(.5\lambda + .1(1 - \lambda)) \quad \text{for tools,} \\ 1.5\lambda \qquad\qquad &= \mu^*(.5\lambda + .9(1 - \lambda)) \quad \text{for food,} \end{aligned}$$

each of which can be solved for λ to give

$$\lambda = \frac{9\mu^*}{4\mu^* + 15} = \frac{6 - \mu^*}{4\mu^* + 3}.$$

The requirement that the two values are equal yields a quadratic equation in μ^* with

$$\mu^* = 1.292\ldots$$

as the only positive, hence meaningful, root. The corresponding von Neumann activity is found to be, within errors of rounding,

$$(x^*, y^*) = ((.331, .669), (.427, .865)),$$

provided our initial guess was correct. To verify that point, we determine the prices p_1, p_2 from the requirement that the coordinates of $z^{(6)}$ and hence also those of $z^{(3)}$) satisfy (P) with $\mu^* = 1.292$. The result is

$$(p_1, p_2) = (2.48, 1),$$

if we choose food as the numéraire. Finally we verify that the condition $(\overline{P})$, which now runs

$$2.48\, y_1 + y_2 - 1.292\,(2.48\, x_1 + x_2) \leqq 0,$$

is satisfied with the $<$ sign by all activities other than $z^{(3)}$, $z^{(6)}$ (for which, of course, the $=$ sign holds). Our initial guess is thereby confirmed and, by the reasoning of Section VIII, z^* is the unique (normalized) von Neumann activity, with the (maximal) growth rate $\mu^* = 1.292$. The failure of activity $z^{(4)}$ to improve on $z^{(3)}$ can be interpreted to mean that with an interest rate $r = \mu^* - 1$ as high as 29.2 per cent, the higher "capital cost" of activity (4) is not fully compensated for by the higher outputs and the lower labor input.

Figure VIII shows the maximal growth activity z^*, the segment $S(\mu^*)$ and the plane P for the present example.

X. The Turnpike Conjecture

There is nothing in the assumptions we have made about the technology that should limit the discussion to a comparison of alternative paths of *proportional* growth. Dorfman, Samuelson and Solow therefore considered growth paths that are maximal in some wider sense. They accepted as given the initial inputs $x^1 = (x_1{}^1, x_2{}^1)$, and required that the terminal outputs $y_1{}^T$, $y_2{}^T$ for a planning horizon of T periods be proportional to two prescribed nonnegative numbers, h_1, h_2, not both zero, which we have normalized to have a unit sum,

$$y_1{}^T = \kappa h_1, \quad y_2{}^T = \kappa h_2, \quad h_1 \geqq 0, \quad h_2 \geqq 0, \quad h_1 + h_2 = 1,$$

They maintained the requirement that each period's outputs are all that is available, subject to free disposal, for use as inputs for the next period. We shall call a growth path subject to these specifications *maximal* (they called it *optimal*) if it achieves the highest value κ^* of the factor of proportionality κ attainable by any growth path meeting these specifications. They then formulated the following conjecture as to the nature of the maximal growth path:

. . . if the programming period is very long, the corresponding optimal capital program will be describable as follows: The system first invests so as to alter its capital structure *toward the special von Neumann proportions.* When it has come close to these proportions, it spends most of the programming period performing steady growth at the maximal rate (more precisely, something close to maximal steady growth). The system *expands along or close to the von Neumann ray Ox** until the end of the programming period approaches. Then it bends away from *Ox** and invests in such a way as to *alter the capital*

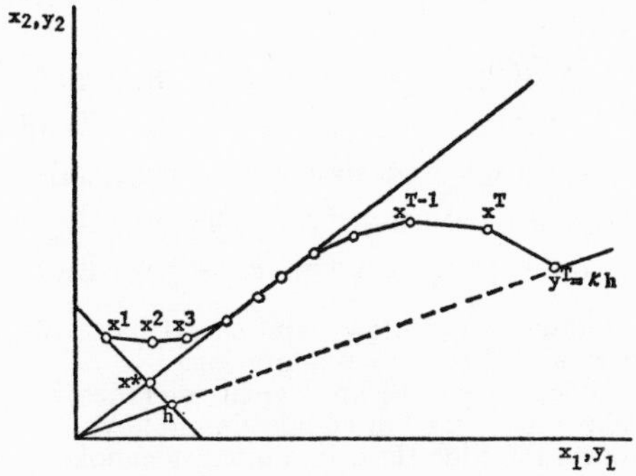

Figure IX. Illustration of the Turnpike Conjecture

structure to the desired terminal proportions, arriving at y^T as the period ends.[7]

Thus, in an economy oriented toward accumulation rather than consumption, the von Neumann path acts like a turnpike that attracts all discerning long-distance traffic by the shorter travel time it makes possible, even though the road mileage may be lengthened thereby. Figure IX illustrates this idea. The path that starting with the normalized initial input x^1 reaches the farthest point κh on the ray Oh reachable in T periods runs close to the von Neumann path Ox^* for most of its course, if T is sufficiently large.[8]

We shall consider a sequence of possible cases in order to bring out under what conditions this remarkable conjecture is valid, and to indicate how the counterexamples noted by Kuhn and Morishima arise.

XI. Access To or From The von Neumann Path

We must stop for a moment to consider the question whether one can, from any given normalized point $x = (x_1, x_2)$, $x_1 + x_2 = 1$, in the commodity space reach a *positive* multiple κy of any given other point $y = (y_1, y_2)$ at some time. If both x_1 and x_2 are positive, this can be done instantaneously for any y by disposal of part of x_1, or of x_2, or of neither. If $x_2 = 0$, say, it can be done in one step for any y if the technology contains an activity $((1, 0), (\bar{y}_1, \bar{y}_2))$ producing positive amounts $\bar{y}_1$, $\bar{y}_2$ of both commodities from an input of the first one alone. If the only activities with a zero input of the second commodity were to be of the type $((1, 0), (0, \bar{y}_2))$, where $\bar{y}_2 > 0$, it could still be done for any y in two steps if there also is a feasible activity $((0, 1), (\bar{y}_1, \bar{y}_2))$ with $\bar{y}_1 > 0, \bar{y}_2 > 0$. If no such activity exists either, then a positive multiple of a point $y = (y_1, y_2)$ with both $y_1 > 0$ and $y_2 > 0$ cannot be reached in any number of steps.

Two questions of accessibility arise in what follows. In the first place, if the initial endowment lacks a commodity which in consequence of that fact can never be produced, then there is no point in including that commodity in the model.

Second, we must preclude the case in which the unique von

7. Dorfman, Samuelson, Solow, *op. cit.*, Chap. 12, p. 331, quotation changed only to correspond to present notation.

8. One is reminded of the technological reference in Lenin's well-known dictum: "Soviets plus electrification equals communism." The turnpike proposition at least supports the idea that, in a given technology, a particular choice and mixture of methods of production may be most conducive to long-run growth regardless of the more distant objectives of the full-grown economy.

Neumann activity[9] lacks a commodity present in the terminal bundle (h_1, h_2), while the technology is unable to perform the needed transformation. This case occurs in Table II of Section VI if humans are to occur in the terminal bundle. In such a case the turnpike proposition is not valid in any of the forms discussed here.[1]

To avoid such complications, we specify

ASSUMPTION A (Accessibility). *The points x^1, x^*, h in the commodity space representing, respectively, the initial stock, a von Neumann point, and a point defining the final stock ratio, can be supplemented by points x^2, x' such that, for suitable positive numbers ν, ξ, the activities (x^1, x^2), $(x^2, \nu x^*)$, (x^*, x'), $(x', \xi h)$ are all feasible.*

XII. Rates of Growth in von Neumann Value

To associate a numerical growth rate or factor with a step or a sequence of steps in a commodity space of at least two dimensions, one has to reduce a comparison of two vectors to a scalar measure of "growth." In von Neumann's discussion this is done by considering only proportional growth, the factor of proportionality providing the wanted scalar. We now observe that the prices $p = (p_1, p_2)$ found as a by-product of the study of maximal proportional growth can be used to extend this scalar to nonproportional growth.

We shall use the abbreviated notation

$$px = p_1 x_1 + p_2 x_2$$

for the value of a commodity pair $x = (x_1, x_2)$ at a given pair of prices $p = (p_1, p_2)$. If these are *von Neumann prices* associated with maximal proportional growth, we shall call px the (*von Neumann*) *value* of the pair x. Since no normalization has been imposed on p, von Neumann value is determined up to a positive constant factor, except if at least two (and hence infinitely many) nonproportional von Neumann price pairs exist. In the latter case, we arbitrarily choose one price pair (with both prices positive), keeping it constant in all that follows.

Given any activity (x, y) for which the von Neumann input value px is positive, we can now use

$$\mu(x, y) = \frac{py}{px}$$

9. For $n > 2$, substitute "all von Neumann activities."

1. See, however, McKenzie, "Maximal Paths in the von Neumann Model," *op. cit.*, for a modified analysis of such cases.

as a scalar measure of growth, to be called simply the *value growth factor* [2] for the activity. Clearly, for proportional growth the value growth factor equals the factor of proportionality.

Radner's analysis is based on a study of inequalities that constrain the value growth factors for feasible activities in general, and for the activities of a maximal growth path in particular.

First of all, the no profit condition $(\bar{P})$ for feasible activities now runs

$$(\bar{P}') \qquad py \leqq \mu^* \cdot px$$

which implies in turn that

$$(\bar{P}'') \qquad \mu(x, y) \leqq \mu^*$$

for all activities with a positive input value. Thus the maximal proportional growth factor is at the same time an upper bound for the value growth factors of all feasible activities.

Now let (x^t, y^t), $t = 1, \ldots, T$, be a maximal growth path as defined in Section X and illustrated in Figure IX. Thus x^1 is the given initial stock, which for simplicity we normalize by $x_1{}^1 + x_2{}^1 = 1$. Furthermore, $y^t = x^{t+1}$ for all t, and $y^T = \kappa^* h$ is the maximal terminal stock having proportions given by $h = (h_1, h_2)$. In order to be sure that the various value growth factors occurring in the analysis are defined, we must make

ASSUMPTION B (Value positivity). *The normalized terminal bundle h possesses positive von Neumann value ph.*

This assumption is clearly satisfied if both prices are positive.

We denote the value growth factor for the *t-th* step of the given maximal growth path by

$$\mu_t = \mu(x^t, y^t) = \frac{py^t}{px^t}.$$

Then the growth factor for the entire path is [3]

$$\frac{py^T}{px^1} = \frac{py^1}{px^1} \cdot \frac{py^2}{px^2} \cdot \ldots \cdot \frac{py^T}{px^T} = \mu_1 \, \mu_2 \ldots \mu_T.$$

We shall now follow Radner in a calculation showing that only a limited number of the factors μ_t can fall substantially below the upper bound μ^*. To this end we consider a *comparison path* $(\bar{x}^t, \bar{y}^t)$,

2. Gale, *op. cit.*, calls $\mu(x, y)$ the economic expansion rate of the activity (x, y).

3. $ph > 0$ by assumption B, so $py^T > 0$ provided $\kappa^* > 0$, which is confirmed below. If we had $px^t = 0$ for any $t \leqq T$, this would imply $py^s = 0$ for $s = t, \ldots, T$ because of $(\bar{P}')$, contradicting that $py^T > 0$.

$t = 1, \ldots, T$, constructed as follows. The initial stock $\bar{x}^1 = x^1$ is the same as before. The first two steps are used to arrive at the highest multiple

$$\bar{y}^2 = \nu x^*, \qquad \nu > 0,$$

of the von Neumann point x^* of Assumption A that can be attained in two steps. The next $T - 4$ steps proceed along the von Neumann path at maximum growth

$$\bar{y}^t = \mu^* \bar{x}^t, \qquad t = 3, \ldots, T - 2.$$

The last two steps are used to attain the highest attainable multiple

$$\bar{y}^T = \bar{\kappa} h, \qquad \bar{\kappa} > 0,$$

of the prescribed bundle $h = (h_1, h_2)$, attainable from $\bar{y}^{T-2}$ in two steps. Obviously the latter multiple $\bar{\kappa}$ cannot exceed the highest multiple κ^* attainable from x^1 in T unrestricted steps, which is attained along the given maximal path. Therefore $\kappa^* \geqq \bar{\kappa} > 0$, and, since $ph > 0$ by Assumption B,

$$py^T = \kappa^* \cdot ph \geqq \bar{\kappa} \cdot ph = p\bar{y}^T.$$

If we now factorize the value growth factor for the entire comparison path in a similar manner, we find that [4]

$$\frac{p\bar{y}^T}{px^1} = \frac{p\bar{y}^T}{p\bar{x}^1} = \bar{\mu}_1 \bar{\mu}_2 \cdot (\mu^*)^{T-4} \cdot \bar{\mu}_{T-1} \bar{\mu}_T ,$$

where the $\bar{\mu}_t = \mu(\bar{x}^t, \bar{y}^t)$ are value growth factors for the steps of the comparison path. Bringing all these results together, we find that

$$\mu_1 \mu_2 \ldots \mu_T \geqq \bar{\mu}_1 \bar{\mu}_2 (\mu^*)^{T-4} \bar{\mu}_{T-1} \bar{\mu}_T.$$

Now let us choose any small positive number δ, and, remembering that $\mu_t \leqq \mu^*$ for all t, let us denote by T' the number of value growth factors μ_t in the given maximal growth path that fall short of μ^* by more than δ,

$$\mu_t < \mu^* - \delta \text{ in } T' \text{ out of } T \text{ cases.}$$

Then clearly

$$(\mu^*)^{T-T'} (\mu^* - \delta)^{T'} \geqq \mu_1 \mu_2 \ldots \mu_T \geqq \bar{\mu}_1 \bar{\mu}_2 \bar{\mu}_{T-1} \bar{\mu}_T (\mu^*)^{T-4},$$

or, dividing through by $(\mu^*)^T$,

$$\left(\frac{\mu^* - \delta}{\mu^*}\right)^{T'} \geqq \frac{\bar{\mu}_1 \bar{\mu}_2 \bar{\mu}_{T-1} \bar{\mu}_T}{(\mu^*)^4} = M, \text{ say.}$$

4. Again all denominators and numerators are positive by Assumption B.

Since δ and μ^* are positive,

$$0 < \frac{\mu^* - \delta}{\mu^*} = 1 - \frac{\delta}{\mu^*} < 1 \text{ as long as } \delta < \mu^* .$$

It follows that $(1 - \delta/\mu^*)^n$ decreases as the integer n increases, and approaches zero as n increases beyond bound. Since $0 < M \leqq 1$ there must therefore be a largest value of n for which $(1 - \delta/\mu^*)^n \geqq M$. Denoting this value by T_δ we then have

$$T' \leqq T_\delta, \qquad \text{where } T_\delta \geqq 0.$$

Thus the calculation has shown that there is an upper bound T_δ on the number of steps in a maximal growth path for which $\mu_t < \mu^* - \delta$. It is true that, whenever $M < 1$, this bound will increase again and again if δ is chosen smaller and smaller. T_δ also depends, through M, on the initial and final stock ratios given by x^1, h, and, of course, on the shape of the production set Z. The important point is however that, once δ and these other data are given, T_δ does *not* depend on the length T of the path. For $\bar{\mu}_{T-1} \cdot \bar{\mu}_T$ depends only on the normalized points x^*, h rather than on the scalar factors defining their respective multiples $\bar{y}^{T-2}$, $\bar{y}^T$.

The simple reason for this beautiful result is clear. As the path length T increases, the value growth factor for the entire comparison path keeps piling up factors μ^*. Since value growth factors in excess of μ^* are impossible in any path, too many factors less than $\mu^* - \delta$ in the maximal growth path would cause its terminal value py^T to fall below that of the comparison path. More precisely, for any given δ the upper bound T_δ to the number of such factors is determined by the "relative" growth factors $\bar{\mu}_1/\mu^*$, $\bar{\mu}_2/\mu^*$, $\bar{\mu}_{T-1}/\mu^*$, $\bar{\mu}_T/\mu^*$, associated with the "weak links" in the comparison path. If more nearly maximal paths of comparison can be found, these will lead to sharper bounds.

XIII. "Profit" Effects of An Interest Rate Reduction

There is a natural economic interpretation for those $T - T'$ steps in the maximal growth path whose value growth factors μ_t stay within δ from the maximum μ^*,

$$\mu_t \geqq \mu^* - \delta.$$

Consider a price system having the same commodity prices, but an interest rate r' reduced by δ,

$$r' = r - \delta.$$

In this modified price system, the profit function is

$$\pi'(x, y) = py - (\mu^* - \delta) \cdot px.$$

By dividing both sides by px we see that the steps in question are precisely those that yield a positive or zero profit in the modified price system. Hence our result can also be formulated thus: For any reduction in the interest rate, no matter how small, the number of steps in a maximal growth path with given initial and terminal stock composition that remain unprofitable is limited regardless of the length of the path.

XIV. A Variant of Radner's Turnpike Theorem

The implications of this result for the course of a maximal growth path depend on the precise shape of the production set Z. The simplest case is defined by

ASSUMPTION C (Unique break-even point). *The separating plane P can be so chosen that P and the production set Z have only the point z^* in common.*[5]

This assumption implies that both prices p_1, p_2 are positive, since otherwise one or the other of the two origins would be both in Z and in P, and z^* would not be the only such point. Hence Assumption C implies Assumption B. The converse is not true.

Assumption C is necessarily satisfied if Z is strictly convex. It can also be valid, for instance, if z^* just happens to be a vertex of a polyhedral Z.

By applying Assumption C to the results of Section VII, we find that the profit $\pi(x, y)$ in the original price system (p_1, p_2, r) is negative in any point x of Z other than z^*. On the other hand, the condition

$$(\underline{P'}) \qquad \pi'(x, y) = py - (\mu^* - \delta) \cdot px \geqq 0$$

of *nonnegative* profit in the modified price system (p_1, p_2, r') cuts a slice, Z_δ say, off the production set. In Figure X this slice, and the plane

$$(P') \qquad \pi'(x, y) = py - (\mu^* - \delta) \cdot px = 0$$

that cuts it off,[6] are shown for a production set similar to that of Figure VII.

5. It follows directly that z^* is the only (normalized) von Neumann activity, since every such activity is in $S(\mu^*)$ and $S(\mu^*)$ is in P.

6. The planes P and P' in Figure X are parallel only if $p_1 = p_2$. If $p_1 \neq p_2$, the two planes intersect the x-axis in the same point. This point is outside the segment $0 \leqq x_1 \leqq 1$ except if either p_1 or p_2 vanishes, in which case the point is O_2 or O_1, respectively.

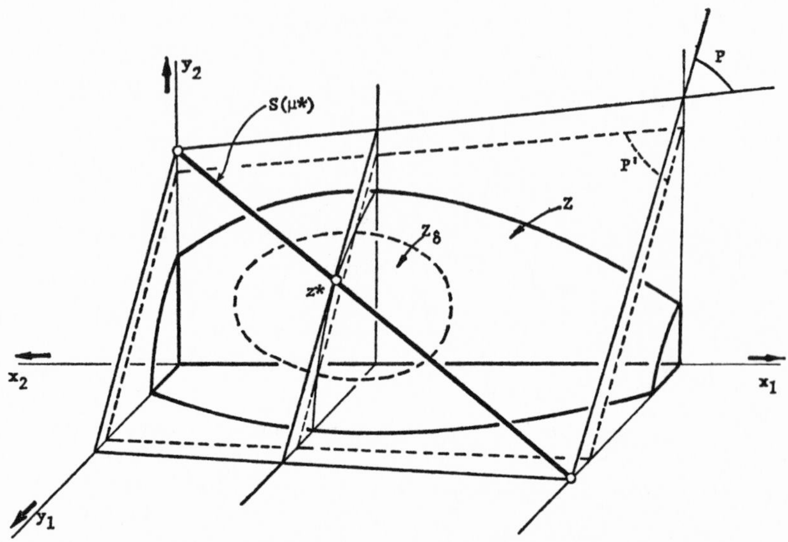

FIGURE X. EFFECT OF AN INTEREST RATE REDUCTION

Clearly, in the limiting case $\delta = 0$, the slice Z_δ consists of the single point z^*. Moreover, z^* is contained in Z_δ for every positive δ. The significance of Assumption C is that it makes z^* the only point with the latter property. For any other point z of Z, since the original profit is negative in z, there exists an interest rate reduction δ small enough to leave the modified profit negative in z. It follows that the slices Z_δ, nested one inside the other as δ becomes smaller, shrink down to the point z^* as δ tends to zero.

This mathematical fact is responsible for the turnpike theorem in its present, simplest, version. It also suggests that it will be convenient to use δ as a measure of the distance, in the three-dimensional space of normalized activities, between z^* and any other maximal[7] point z of Z, instead of Radner's measure of angular distance between points of the (two-dimensional) commodity space. Specifically, given any maximal point z, we will define "interest rate distance" $\delta(z)$ as the smallest value of δ for which z is still in Z_δ. In economic terms, $\delta(z)$ is the smallest interest rate concession that prevents z from yielding a loss. From continuity considerations, that concession will then just make z break even.

We can now summarize the results of our reasoning in

PROPOSITION 4. *If Assumptions* A *and* C *are satisfied, then*

7. Since clearly all steps in a maximal path are themselves maximal activities (as defined in Section IV), a distance concept applicable only to maximal points is sufficient for our purpose.

there exists for each (small) positive number δ an integer T_δ such that, in a maximal path of any length, $\delta(z^t) \geqq \delta$ for at most T_δ steps of the path. Here $\delta(z)$ is a measure of the proximity of a normalized maximal activity z to the von Neumann activity z^* of Assumptions A *and* C. *This measure of proximity is that reduction in the interest rate that will make the activity z break even. It reflects the shape of the production set in a neighborhood of z^*. The upper bound T_δ to the number of steps which upon normalization are more than δ "away from" z^* increases as δ decreases, and depends also on the initial and final stock proportions x^1, h, but not on the length of the path.*

XV. A Catenary Property of Maximal Growth Paths

Proposition 4 is silent on the question where in a maximal growth path the exceptional activities more than δ removed from a unique von Neumann activity z^* may occur. The considerations that led Dorfman, Samuelson and Solow to formulate the turnpike conjecture, however, suggested from the beginning that the exceptional steps can occur only near the beginning or near the end. Speaking very roughly, the notion is that any sufficiently long maximal growth path has somewhat the shape of a chain suspended from the points x^1, y^T in a field of gravitational attraction toward the ray of the von Neumann path. This was confirmed and made more precise, under various assumptions, in studies by Samuelson [8] (using a continuous time variable), McKenzie,[9] Nikaido.[1] While Nikaido's result is perhaps not the strongest that can be obtained by more detailed analysis, it has a merit of simplicity of proof. We shall sketch here a reasoning suggested by his study, with appropriate modifications to fit the definitions and assumptions used here. The reasoning is based on a repeated application of the ideas of Radner's proof. It uses one additional assumption not used above, which explains itself.

ASSUMPTION D. *Both inputs x_1^*, x_2^* to the unique von Neumann activity (x^*, y^*) are positive.*

We already know from Proposition 4 that, given x^1, h, and some positive number ϵ, there are at most T_ϵ activities in a maximal

8. P. A. Samuelson, "Efficient Paths of Capital Accumulation in Terms of the Calculus of Variations," Paper 6 in *Mathematical Methods in the Social Sciences*, Stanford Symposium (Stanford; Stanford University Press, 1960).

9. McKenzie, "The Dorfman-Samuelson-Solow Turnpike Theorem," *op. cit.*

1. Nikaido, *op. cit.*

growth path of any length T that are, after normalization, more than ϵ removed from z^*. It follows that the time indices r, s, of the *first* and *last* steps within ϵ from z^* must be such that

$$1 \leqq r \leqq T_\epsilon + 1, \qquad T - T_\epsilon \leqq s \leqq T.$$

We now assign to the input pair x^r and the output pair y^s of steps r and s, respectively, the roles played by x^1 and h in Section XII. Then, clearly, the "subpath" (x^t, y^t), $t = r, \ldots, s$, of the original maximal path is again maximal with reference to initial and terminal constraints given by x^r, y^s. The only difference from the previous discussion is that (x^r, y^r) and (x^s, y^s) are themselves already (after normalization) within[2] ϵ from z^*. For small enough ϵ, therefore, both x^r and y^s have only positive components $x_1{}^r$, $x_2{}^r$, $y_1{}^s$, $y_2{}^s$. This makes available a comparison path $(\bar{x}^t, \bar{y}^t)$, $t = r, \ldots, s$, leading from $\bar{x}^r = x^r$ in *one* step to a point $\bar{y}^r = \nu \cdot x^*$ of the von Neumann path by minimal required disposal, continuing by maximal steps along the von Neumann path, and making one final step from $\bar{y}^{s-1} = (\mu^*)^{s-1-r} \cdot \nu x^*$ to $\bar{y}^s = \bar{\kappa} y^s$ again by minimal required disposal. But then, in the analysis of Section XIV applied to the subpath (x^t, y^t), $t = r, \ldots, s$, given a positive δ we arrive at an inequality

$$\left(1 - \frac{\delta}{\mu^*}\right)^{T'} \geqq \frac{\bar{\mu}_r \bar{\mu}_s}{(\mu^*)^2} = M, \text{ say,}$$

governing the number of steps in the subpath more than δ removed from z^*. But now M is a number that can be brought arbitrarily close to 1 by taking ϵ small enough to make the "minimal required disposals" as small as needed. Therefore, if we choose ϵ so small as to make

$$M > 1 - \delta/\mu^*,$$

the only possibility is $T' = 0$, and no steps more than δ removed from z^* are found in the given maximal path with time indices between r and s, or a fortiori[3] between $T_\epsilon + 1$ and $T - T_\epsilon$.

Thus, in a general sense, under Assumptions A, C, D, the steps in a long maximal growth path not close to the von Neumann path must if anywhere be near the beginning or end of the path.

2. Since all steps of a maximal path are obviously also maximal when taken as individual activities, the distance concept applies to the (normalized) steps r and s.

3. Of course, the ϵ that does the trick is a function of δ, and may well be smaller than δ.

XVI. The Turnpike Conjecture in Other Cases

What can be said if, contrary to Assumption C, the separating plane P and the feasible set Z have more than one point in common? Matters remain relatively simple if by some miraculous coincidence the common points of P and Z were to make up a line segment S^* *contained in* $S(\mu^*)$. This case is illustrated by a polyhedral example in Figure XI. All points of S^* are now points of

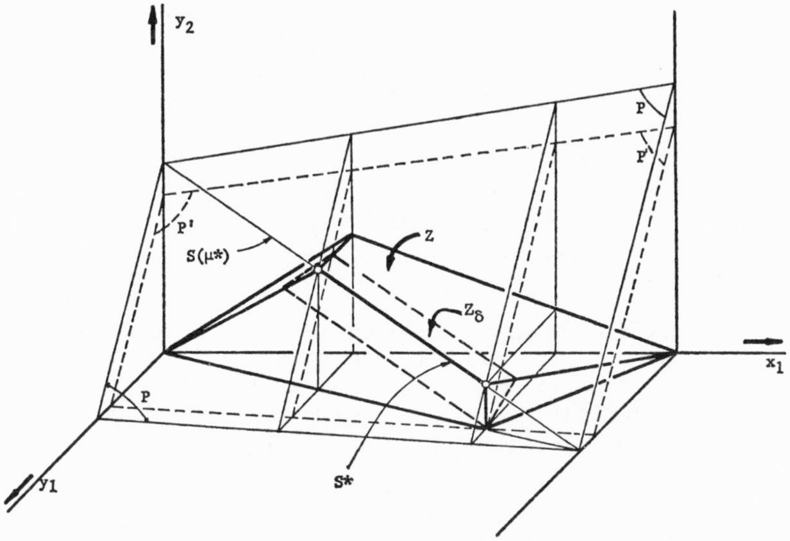

Figure XI. Case of Many von Neumann Activities

maximal proportional growth, and define as many von Neumann paths, all sustainable by the same price system (p_1, p_2, r) (which need not be unique). The slices Z_δ all contain S^*, and shrink down to S^* as δ tends to zero. Hence, in any maximal growth path now the number of steps outside a Z_δ which closely hugs S^* is limited.

Further complications arise if P and Z intersect in a line segment S *not* contained in $S(\mu^*)$. In that case, S and $S(\mu^*)$ have only the unique von Neumann activity z^* in common. A case of this kind is not in any way a result of coincidence. In fact it is likely to arise *except for coincidences* in any technology with a finite basis. In McKenzie's work [4] cases of this kind are analyzed in detail for

4. "Turnpike Theorems for a Generalized Leontief Model," *op. cit.*, "The Turnpike Theorems of Morishima," *op. cit.*, "Maximal Paths in the von Neumann Model," *op. cit.*

n-commodity models. The present section is intended only as an intuitive exploration of the possibilities.

To avoid still further complications, let us assume that positive prices p_1, p_2 can be associated with z^*. The situation is then as illustrated in Figure XII. It remains true that the slices Z_δ shrink

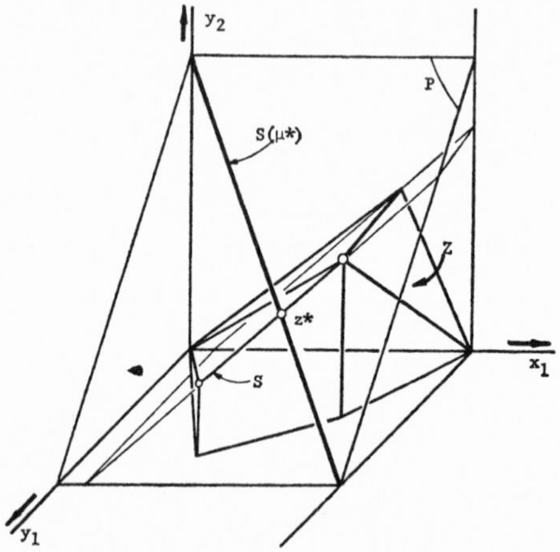

FIGURE XII. SINGLE VON NEUMANN ACTIVITY IN A TECHNOLOGY WITH A FINITE BASIS

down to S, and that the number of steps in a maximal growth path outside a given slice is limited. It no longer follows without further analysis that therefore a maximal growth path has to be close to the von Neumann ray except for a limited number of steps. The new complication is that S may contain points far removed from z^* in terms of angular distance.[5] In other words, a small "interest rate distance" no longer implies a small angular distance. The turnpike conjecture will therefore be true in the present case only if we can show that, in order to be close to points of S most of the time, a growth path actually has to be close to z^* most of the time in which it is close to S. This may indeed be the case. To examine this question, we must remember that we have not yet made use of the equality $y^t = x^{t+1}$ between a period's outputs and the next period's inputs. (So far we have only needed to use the value equality $py^t = px^{t+1}$.)

It seems intuitively plausible that this question can be clarified by first studying *(von-Neumann-) value-preserving* growth paths. These are defined as paths that consist of zero-profit activities only, hence are entirely constructed from activities represented by points

5. Measured, for instance, by $|x_1 - x_1^*| + |y_1 - y_1^*| + |y_2 - y_2^*|$ for a normalized activity $z = (x_1, y_1, y_2)$.

of S. By the analysis of Section XIV these are themselves maximal growth paths. It seems plausible, moreover, that any maximal growth path of sufficient length will, for most of its course, run close to a value-preserving growth path. This is confirmed by McKenzie's findings.[6]

In order to visualize the possible value-preserving paths, it will help us to change the units of the two commodities in such a way that their prices become equal,

$$p_1 = p_2 = 1, \qquad \text{so } px = x_1 + x_2.$$

A normalized input then becomes identical with an input of unit value. Thereafter we make the units of both commodities dependent on the time period t by multiplying each unit by $(\mu^*)^t$. This makes the new maximal "growth" factor equal to unity, the new "interest rate" equal to zero. The service rendered by this somewhat artificial redefinition of the units is that a zero-profit activity (x, y) now satisfies

$$px - py = 0,$$

and hence converts a normalized input x into a normalized output y. Figure XII has already been drawn on this basis.

The analysis can now be completed within the zero-profit plane P, which we can project, out of its position in Figure XII, onto the vertical plane, identified with the plane of the paper in Figure XIII. In this diagram the measurement of y_1 and y_2 along the vertical axis

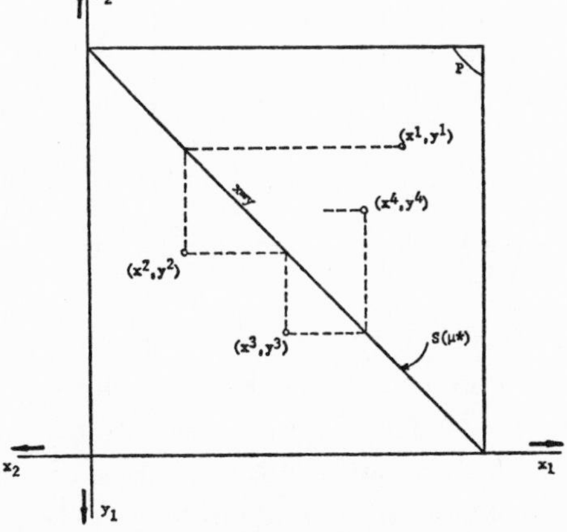

FIGURE XIII. VALUE-PRESERVING PATH

6. "Turnpike Theorems for a Generalized Leontief Model," *op. cit.*

has become completely symmetrical to that of x_1 and x_2 along the horizontal axis, described in Section IV.

Disregarding technological feasibility, any growth path consisting of zero-profit activities only is now representable by a sequence of points (x^t, y^t), $t = 1, 2, \ldots$, connected by the identity $y^t = x^{t+1}$ in the manner indicated in Figure XIII. Feasibility considerations are introduced by insisting in addition that all points (x^t, y^t) belong to the segment S.

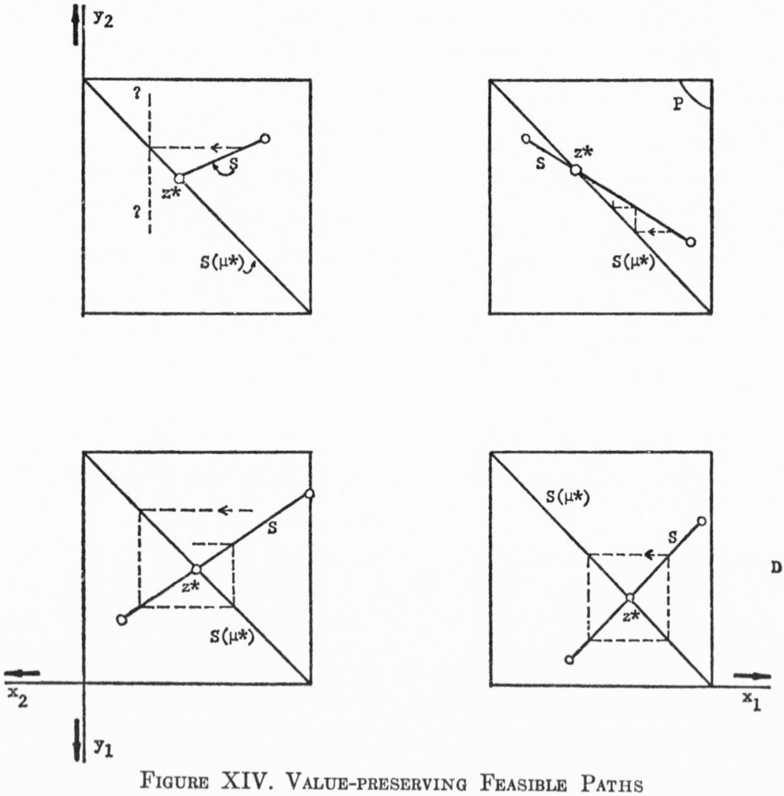

FIGURE XIV. VALUE-PRESERVING FEASIBLE PATHS

If, as in Figure XIVA, the von Neumann point z^* is an endpoint of S, and if at the same time the slope of S (in the present diagram) is opposite in sign to that of $S(\mu^*)$, then the only feasible sequence of zero-profit activities consists of a repetition of the von Neumann activity z^*. If as suggested any maximal growth path of sufficient length is close to a value-preserving path for most of its length, then the turnpike conjecture is valid in this case as well. If as in Figure XIVB the slope of S is of the same sign as that of $S(\mu^*)$, then there exist infinitely many feasible sequences of zero-profit activities, that either converge toward, or move away from, z^*, depending on whether the slope of S is absolutely smaller (as in Figure XIVB) or larger than that of $S(\mu^*)$. This holds regardless of whether z^* is an endpoint of S or not.

If z^* is not an endpoint, and if the slope of S is opposite in sign but not equal in absolute value to that of $S(\mu^*)$, there are again infinitely many value-preserving paths, oscillating on S toward or away from z^*, depending on whether the slope of S is absolutely smaller (as in Figure XIVC) or larger than that of $S(\mu^*)$. Since in both cases the value-preserving paths converge to z^* if time is taken forward or backward as may be needed, the turnpike conjecture is still valid. However, for a given angular distance δ, a proportionately larger bound T_δ on the number of steps more than δ away from z^* must now be allowed than would apply in terms of "interest rate distance." The reason is that the value-preserving path to which some given maximal growth path is "close" most of the time may itself take considerable time getting close to, or moving away from, z^*. Thus the turnpike assertion for these cases is the more academic, the nearer one comes to the following last case.

In this case, which includes Kuhn's counterexample, the slopes of S and $S(\mu^*)$ are opposite in sign and absolutely equal (Figure XIVD). There now exist infinitely many oscillating maximal growth paths consisting of zero-profit activities, that never come near the von Neumann point z^*, as well as many other maximal growth paths each close to one of these, for which the same is true. Hence the turnpike conjecture is false in this case.[7]

XVII. Concluding Remarks

Which analysis is more relevant to the real world, the Radner-Nikaido case of Sections XIV, XV, or the McKenzie cases of Section XVI? Mathematically, the distinction between the two analyses turns on whether or not Assumption C is satisfied. For purposes of these final evaluative remarks, we shall identify the Radner-Nikaido analysis with the case of a strictly convex technology, which implies Assumption C, even though that assumption could by accident hold in a nonstrictly convex technology. That is, we ignore that accident because it is both unlikely and unforeseeable.

7. Further counterexamples arise in the case where P and Z have a two-dimensional convex set in common. A more general analysis has been given by McKenzie, "Turnpike Theorems for a Generalized Leontief Model," *op. cit.*, and "Maximal Paths in the von Neumann Model," *op. cit.*

In contrast, the more complicated McKenzie type of analysis, of which we have sketched only the barest outline, will apply, again barring accidents, if every point in the boundary of Z is on a straight line segment contained in the boundary of Z. We have already recognized that any technology with a finite basis is in this category. A partly overlapping case in the same category, analyzed by Hicks,[8] Morishima,[9] McKenzie,[1] and Drandakis,[2] is equally interesting from the point of view of its interpretation. In this case there may well be a (discrete or continuous) infinite collection of basic processes for the production of each good. However, there are no processes jointly producing more than one good other than combinations of the basic processes already mentioned. For reasons similar to those underlying Samuelson's [3] well-known theorem on substitutability in open Leontief models, the boundary of Z now is, in the two-goods case, a ruled surface. As illustrated in Figure XV, it is generated by rolling a common tangent plane along two curves, one in the x_1-y_1-plane, one in the x_1-y_2-plane, that separately represent the

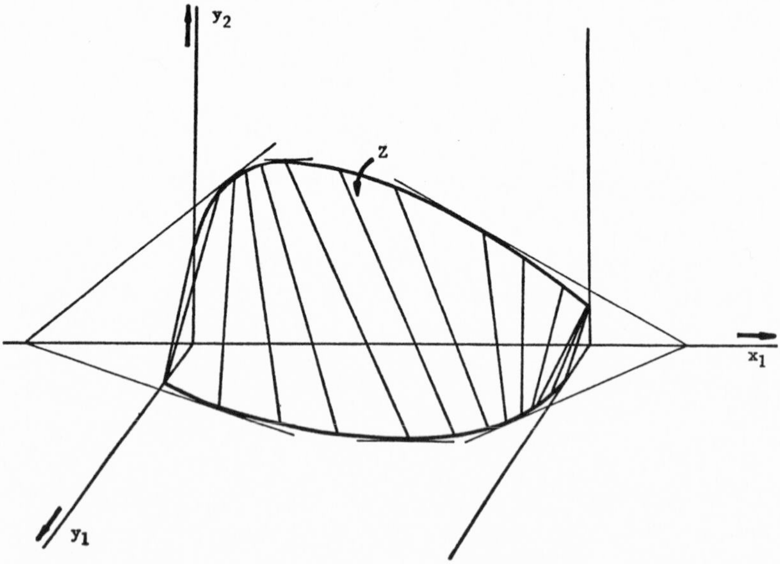

FIGURE XV. FEASIBLE SET IF THERE ARE NO ECONOMIES OF JOINT PRODUCTION

8. *Op. cit.*
9. *Op. cit.*
1. "The Turnpike Theorem of Morishima," *op. cit.*
2. E. M. Drandakis, "On an Asymptotic Nonsubstitution Theorem in the Two-Sector Closed Production Model," Cowles Foundation Discussion Paper No. 165, Dec. 1963.
3. P. A. Samuelson, "Abstract of a Theorem Concerning Substitutability in Open Leontief Models," Chap. 8 of *Activity Analysis of Production and Allocation*, ed. T. C. Koopmans (New York: Wiley, 1951), pp. 142–46.

technologies for each "industry" as defined in terms of its output commodity. Similarly, in the n-goods case, each boundary point of Z belongs to an $(n - 1)$-dimensional flat section contained in that boundary.

This example suggests that the comparative relevance of the Radner-Nikaido versus the Morishima-McKenzie-Drandakis analysis hinges on the following empirical question: Does the coexistence of several processes make some of these processes more productive than each of them would be if it existed by itself alone? We shall not try to find an answer here. One can indeed think of several factors that give rise to economies external to the processes. Most of these factors however, lie outside the present model. Presumably the economic reasons for producing many different steel products by joint use of important components of capital equipment reside in the greater scale of the plant, equipment and organization thus made possible — a consideration excluded by the present assumption of constant returns to scale. It is also plausible that the joint "production" process of general education is furthered by a mixture of talents and individual objectives. While this could to some extent be expressed in the present model, similar factors such as the relatedness and transferability of industrial skills and the restlessness and desire for variety of activity in many individuals give an advantage to jointness mainly through the generation of technological improvement here assumed away.

A similar remark should be made about the counterexamples to the turnpike conjecture. All the counterexamples involve an oscillation, or a more complicated continual change, in the levels at which some processes are used. We have also had to consider similar oscillations, although damped or expanding, in the value-preserving paths that need to be studied in some of the cases of Figure XIV if strict convexity is not assumed. The assumptions of our model ignore a consideration that weakens the claim of such oscillating paths to a long-run growth capacity equalling that of maximal proportional growth. It is a well-documented fact of experience that the mere repetition of a production process facilitates its gradual improvement through learning of the operations, even without the introduction of new technological principles here assumed away. Much of this advantage is lost in a path in which a substantial part of the labor force oscillates regularly between different methods of production. While again this consideration lies outside the model that we have studied, it may influence the degree of detail in which one wishes to pursue its study.

A final observation on the entire problem area that has given rise to theorems of the turnpike type. It was stated in Section I that the von Neumann model, in its original version quite remote from any real world problem, was given some bearing on the problem of forced economic growth by the discovery of the turnpike proposition. It should now be admitted that the problem of growth at a maximal rate is still a somewhat narrow and perhaps unnatural one. One would want to go on to the further study of optimal growth where the criterion of optimality expresses a concern with the desire for consumption levels that, if possible, are at all times above the minimum needed for self-reproduction of an efficient labor force, at the no longer maximal but now "optimal" growth rate envisaged. One may want further to leave scope for an uncertain degree and kind of technological progress, and for a desire for flexibility in future consumer's preference.[4] Granted the need for these further steps of generalization, however, the study of economic growth at a maximal rate in a constant technology seems nevertheless to have some justification beyond its immediate results. The solutions of problems obtained by generalizing or complicating another simpler problem often continue to bear some of the traits of the solution of the simple problem. Thus we may find as time goes on that the study of growth at a maximal rate is yielding returns that go beyond the confines of the original formulations.

YALE UNIVERSITY

4. See T. C. Koopmans, "On Flexibility of Future Preference," to appear in G. L. Bryan and M. W. Shelly, *Human Judgments and Optimality* (New York: Wiley, 1964).

13

PATHS OF ECONOMIC GROWTH THAT ARE OPTIMAL WITH REGARD ONLY TO FINAL STATES: A TURNPIKE THEOREM[1]

By R. Radner

1. *Introduction*[2]

In this paper I consider the problem of determining best paths of economic growth, when the citerion of preference among paths focuses entirely upon the final state. This problem is considered within the framework of a model of a closed economy with constant returns to scale, of the type proposed by von Neumann in his paper on balanced growth equilibrium [5]. The main result (section 5) is that under certain conditions all best growth paths must be " close " to the von Neumann path of balanced growth, except possibly for a finite number of periods, which number is independent of the length of the path. Within the framework of this model of the closed economy, the two most restrictive conditions are (1) that the preference function on the final states be homogeneous, and (2) that the von Neumann balanced growth path be the unique profit maximizing direction of growth under the von Neumann equilibrium prices.

One source of interest in such results may be the general problem of planning economic growth. In particular, they point to the possibility of planning the direction of growth over a fairly long period without precise specification of a social preference ordering of final states.

Although in the optimization problems discussed here the criterion of preference is focused upon the final states, this does not imply that social wants during intermediate states are necessarily ignored. Human services constitute an important group of " commodities," and consumption needs can be expressed in a limited way in terms of the technology of the production of services.

The problem and results considered in this paper were suggested by certain problems of efficient capital accumulation discussed by Dorfman, Samuelson and Solow in [1]. The problem I pose is, however, somewhat more general than theirs in certain directions, and the methods of proof are different.

I believe that this problem area has come to be known under the general heading of " The Turnpike Theorem," the " turnpike " in this case being the von Neumann path.[3]

[1] This research was supported by the Office of Naval Research under contract Nonr-222(77), project NR 049 029 with the University of California. Reproduction in whole or in part is permitted for any purpose of the United States government.

[2] I wish to thank G. Debreu, F. Hahn, and R. Solow for helpful comments and criticisms.

[3] I am indebted to a recent talk by Professor J. R. Hicks for my own introduction to this topic.

98

No attempt will be made here, however, to trace the history of this topic, nor of the general topic of balanced growth. The model of production and balanced growth used here is essentially due to Gale [2]. I have followed the excellent treatment of Karlin in chapter 9 of [3], to which the reader is also referred for references to other work. A recent paper by Malinvaud [4] should also be mentioned.

Section 2 below sets out the model of production used here, section 3 the class of preference functions for final states, and section 4 the concepts of prices, interest, profit, and balanced growth equilibrium. The " turnpike theorem " is presented and proved in the final section.

2. *Production*

I will deal with the so-called " closed model of production," which is somewhat of a generalization of the model used by von Neumann in his well-known paper [5] on balanced growth (for a discussion of the general closed model, with references, see, for example, Karlin [3], section 9.10).

There is a fixed list of commodities, numbered from 1 to M. Production takes place during each of a sequence of periods. At the beginning of each period, some vector x of nonnegative quantities of the various commodities is used up as an *input*, and at the end of the period a vector y is produced as an *output*, this output being available for use as input for production in the next period. The vectors x and y are of course each in M-dimensional Euclidean space, the nonnegative part of which will be called the commodity space. The set of technologically possible pairs (x, y) is assumed to be the same for every period, and is denoted by T.

I will assume throughout this paper:

*A*1. *T is a closed cone in the nonnegative orthant of* $2M$*-dimensional Euclidean space.*

*A*2. *If* $(0, y)$ *is in* T, *then* $y = 0$.

The interpretation of $A1$ is that the technology exhibits continuity and constant returns to scale. The interpretation of $A2$ is that it is impossible to produce something from nothing.

The following definitions will be useful:

*D*1. x is balanced if there is a real number $\rho > 0$ such that $(x, \rho x)$ is in T. The number ρ is called an associated *growth factor*. (The associated growth rate is $(\rho - 1)$.)

*D*2. The *coefficient of expansion* of any pair (x, y) is[1]

$$\lambda(x, y) = \max \{c \mid y \geqq cx\}.$$

*D*3. A sequence $\{x_n\}_{n=0}^{N}$ of commodity vectors is called *feasible*, given x_0, if (x_n, x_{n+1}) is in T for $n = 0, 1, \ldots, N-1$.

[1] For vectors y and z, $y \geqq z$ denotes $y_i \geqq z_i$, $i = 1, \ldots, M$; $y \geq z$ denotes $y \geqq z$ and $y \neq z$; and $y > z$ denotes $y_i > z_i$, $i = 1, \ldots, M$.

Example 2.1. $M = 2$, and T is the set of all (x, y) such that

$$y_1^2 + y_2^2 \leqq k\, x_1 x_2,$$

$$x_1,\ x_2,\ y_1,\ y_2 \text{ all } \geqq 0,$$

where k is some positive number.

Example 2.2 (von Neumann).

$$T = \{(x,y) \mid y = Ba,\ x = Aa,\ a \geqq 0\}$$

where A and B are matrices with nonnegative elements. The co-ordinates of the vector a are to be interpreted as the " levels " or " intensities " of a certain finite number of productive processes. In this case T is a polyhedral cone.

3. *Terminal Objectives*

This paper is concerned with feasible sequences that, given N and x_0, maximize $u(x_N)$ in the set of all feasible sequences $\{x_n\}_{n=0}^{N}$, where u is some given function on the commodity space. Such a sequence will be called *u-optimal.*

The interpretation of the above is that the planner's (or " society's ") preferences among feasible sequences depend only upon comparisons among the *terminal* states of such sequences, the function u representing those preferences.

The following assumptions are made about the preference function u.

*A*3. *u is nonnegative and continuous on the commodity space, and there exists x such that* $u(x) > 0$.

*A*4. *u is " quasi-homogeneous," i.e., for all nonnegative M-dimensional vectors* x' *and* x'', *and all numbers* $k > 0$, $u(x') \geqq u(x'')$ *if and only if* $u(kx') \geqq u(kx'')$. Without loss of generality one may *take u to be homogeneous of degree* 1.

Example 3.1. $u(x) = \Pi_{i=1}^{M} x_i^{\alpha_i}$, where the α_i are fixed nonnegative numbers.

Example 3.2. $u(x) = \max\{c \mid x_i \geqq c\alpha_i,\ i = 1, \ldots, M\}$, where the α_i are fixed nonnegative numbers with $\Sigma\alpha_i = 1$. In this case the numbers $\alpha_i, \ldots, \alpha_M$ represent the " desired proportions " of the several commodities.

Example 3.3. $u(x) = \Sigma_{i=1}^{M} w_i x_i$, where $w \geqq 0$. In this example, w_i could be the price of commodity i, so that $u(x)$ would be the value of x under the set of prices $w_1, \ldots, w_M$.

4. *Prices, Interest, Profit, and Balanced Growth Equilibrium*

The proof of the turnpike theorem of this paper makes use of certain " shadow prices," by comparing the growth of a corresponding " shadow profit " along alternative paths of growth. Thus, for any nonegative M-dimensional vector p, any positive real number μ, and any pair (x,y) of commodity vectors, the quantity

$$p{\cdot}(y - \mu x)$$

may be interpreted as *profit*, if p is thought of as a *price vector* and μ an *interest factor* (where $p{\cdot}z$ denotes the scalar product $\Sigma_{i=1}^{M} p_i z_i$), although these terms are only suggestive.

D4. (p, μ) is called an *equilibrium price-interest* pair if

(*a*) $p \cdot (y - \mu x) \leqq 0$ for all (x,y) in T;

(*b*) $p \geqslant 0$, $\mu > 0$.

Von Neumann, and others following him, showed that under certain conditions on the production possibility set T, there exist $\hat{x}$, p and ρ such that

(1) $\hat{x}$ is balanced, with growth factor ρ,

(2) (p,ρ) is an equilibrium price-interest pair.

A triple $(\hat{x},p,\rho)$ satisfying (1) and (2) will here be called a ***von Neumann balanced growth equilibrium.***

For example, it can be shown that conditions (1) and (2) follow from assumption *A*2, and the following assumptions (see Karlin [3], vol. 1, sec. 9.10, and the references given there):

*A*1′. *T is a closed convex cone in the nonnegative orthant of 2M-dimensional Euclidean space.*

*A*5. *If (x,y) is in T, and $x' \geqq x$, $y' \leqq y$, then (x', y') is in T.*

*A*6. *For every $i = 1, \ldots, M$, there is an (x,y) in T for which the ith co-ordinate of y is strictly positive.*

The interpretation of *A*1′ is that, in addition to *A*1, when some variables are fixed, one has nonincreasing marginal productivity in all other variables. *A*5 can be interpreted as stating that disposal activity is costless; *A*6, that every commodity can be produced.

The ray through $\hat{x}$ will be called the von Neumann ray.

An additional consequence of the above assumptions is

$$\rho = \max_{(x,\, y) \in T} \lambda(x,y), \tag{3}$$

i.e., that x, when used as an input, yields the greatest possible coefficient of expansion. Indeed, it is this last fact that leads one to suspect that there is some intimate connection between optimal growth and von Neumann equilibrium.

5. *A "Turnpike Theorem": The Relation between u-Optimal Sequences and von Neumann Balanced Growth Equilibrium*

In this section I show that under certain conditions, including a uniqueness property of the von Neumann ray, all u-optimal sequences must be "close" to the von Neumann ray except possibly for a finite number of periods, which number is independent of the length of the sequence.

First, I define a "distance" between two vectors that is essentially equivalent to the angle between them.

*D*5. $d(x,z) \equiv \left| \dfrac{x}{\|x\|} - \dfrac{z}{\|z\|} \right|$,

(where, as usual, $\|x\| = (x \cdot x)^{1/2}$).

THEOREM. *Under assumptions A*1 *to A*4, *if*

(i) $(\hat{x}, p, \rho)$ *is a von Neumann equilibrium,*

(ii) $p{\cdot}(y - \rho x) < 0$ for all (x, y) in T that are not proportional to $(\hat{x}, \rho\hat{x})$,

(iii) there is a number $K > 0$ such that for all commodity vectors x, $u(x) \leqq Kp{\cdot}x$,

(iv) an initial commodity vector x_0 is given such that for some number $L > 0$, $(x_0, L\hat{x})$ is in T,

(v) $u(\hat{x}) > 0$;

then, for any $\varepsilon > 0$ there is a number S such that for any N and any u-optimal sequence $\{x_n\}_{n=0}^{N}$, the number of periods in which $d(x_n, \hat{x}) \geqq \varepsilon$ cannot exceed S.

It should be noted that the number S is independent of the length N of the sequence considered.

A number of remarks on conditions (i) to (v) follow the proof of the theorem.

LEMMA. *Under assumptions* $A1$ *and* $A2$, *and conditions* (i) *and* (ii) *of the theorem, for any* $\varepsilon > 0$ *there exists a* $\delta > 0$ *such that for any* (x, y) *in* T *for which* $d(x,\hat{x}) \geqq \varepsilon$, *it follows that*

$$p{\cdot}y \leqq (\rho - \delta)\, p{\cdot}x.$$

Proof of Lemma. It follows from $A1$ and $A2$ that the set

$$T_1 \equiv \{y \mid (x,y) \text{ in } T.\ \ \|x\| = 1\}$$

is bounded. For if not, there is a sequence (x_k, y_k) such that $\|x_k\| = 1$, and $\|y_k\| \longrightarrow \infty$; but then the sequence

$$\left(\frac{x_k}{\|y_k\|}, \frac{y_k}{\|y_k\|}\right), \qquad k = 1, 2, \text{etc.},$$

being bounded and in T, has a limit point $(0,\bar{y})$ in T, with $\|\bar{y}\| = 1$, which contradicts $A2$.

I now proceed to prove the lemma.

Suppose to the contrary that there is an $\varepsilon > 0$ and a sequence (x_k, y_k) in T such that $p{\cdot}x_k > 0$, $d(x_k, \hat{x}) \geqq \varepsilon$ and

(4) $$\frac{p \cdot y_k}{p \cdot x_k} \longrightarrow \rho.$$

By normalization, one may take

$$\|x_k\| = 1, \qquad k = 1, 2, \text{etc.}$$

Hence the sequence (x_k, y_k) is bounded, and so has a limit point $(\bar{x}, \bar{y})$. Since the sequence $p \cdot x_k$ is also bounded, it follows from (4) that $p \cdot (\bar{y} - \rho\bar{x}) = 0$; but this last, together with the fact that $(\bar{x}, \bar{y})$ cannot be proportional to $(\hat{x}, \rho\hat{x})$, contradicts condition (ii). Thus the lemma is proved.

Proof of Theorem. First define a feasible sequence $(\tilde{x}_n)_{n=0}^{N}$ by

(5) $$\begin{cases} \tilde{x}_0 = x_0 \\ \tilde{x}_1 = L\hat{x} \\ \tilde{x}_n = L\rho_{n-1}\hat{x}, \qquad n = 1, \ldots, N. \end{cases}$$

The idea of the proof is to show that the sequence $\{\tilde{x}_n\}$ is better than any sequence that departs too far for too long from the von Neumann ray (even though $\{\tilde{x}_n\}$ may not itself be u-optimal). Consider any $\varepsilon > 0$ and any sequence $\{x_n\}_0^N$ that is feasible given x_0. For any period n for which $d(x_n,\hat{x}) \geqq \varepsilon$, it follows from the lemma that

(6) $$p \cdot x_{n+1} \leqq (\rho - \delta)p \cdot x_n,$$

where $\delta > 0$ is as in the lemma. On the other hand, it follows from the definition of a von Neumann equilibrium that for all n one has at least

(7) $$p \cdot x_{n+1} \leqq \rho p \cdot x_n.$$

Suppose that $d(x_n, \hat{x}) \geqq \varepsilon$ for P periods. Then from (6) and (7) one has

(8) $$p \cdot x_N \leqq (\rho - \delta)^P \rho^{N-P} p \cdot x_0.$$

Hence, by condition (iii),

(9) $$u(x_N) \geqq K(\rho-\delta)^P \rho^{N-P} p \cdot x_0.$$

On the other hand, by (5) and the homogeneity of u,

(10) $$u(\tilde{x}_N) = L\rho^{N-1} u(\hat{x}) > 0.$$

Combining (9) and (10) gives

$$\frac{u(x_N)}{u(\tilde{x}_N)} \leqq C\left(\frac{\rho - \delta}{\rho}\right)^P$$

where

$$C \equiv \frac{K\rho p \cdot x_0}{Lu(\hat{x})}$$

Hence, for $\{x_n\}_0^N$ to be optimal, surely

$$C\left(\frac{\rho - \delta}{\rho}\right)^P \geqq 1,$$

or

$$P \leqq \frac{\log C}{\log \dfrac{\rho}{\rho - \delta}}.$$

Hence the proof is completed by taking

(11) $$S = \max \left[1, \frac{\log C}{\log (\rho/\rho - \delta)}\right].$$

Remark 1. Condition (ii) of Theorem 1 is fulfilled if, in particular, T is a " strictly-convex cone " with nonempty interior.[1] To see this, suppose to the contrary that (x', y') in T is not proportional to $(\hat{x}, \hat{y})$ (where $\hat{y} = \rho\hat{x}$), and that $p \cdot (y' - \rho x') = 0$. Let $(x,y) = \frac{1}{2}(\hat{x},\hat{y}) + \frac{1}{2}(x',y')$; then it follows that $p \cdot (y - \rho x) = 0$. But (x,y) is in the interior of T; hence there exist sufficiently small commodity vectors a and b such that $(x + a, y + b)$ is in T, and such that $p \cdot (b - \rho a) > 0$. This last implies, however, that $p \cdot [(y + b) - \rho(x + a)] > 0$, which contradicts the assumption that $(\hat{x}, p, \rho)$ is a von Neumann equilibrium.

[1] A convex cone C will be said to be a " strictly-convex cone " if for any and b in C that are not proportional, and any α for which $0 < \alpha < 1$, the point $\alpha a + (1 - \alpha)b$ is in the interior of C. Note that a " strictly-convex cone " is not a strictly convex set!

It should be added that the converse of this remark is not true. It would be interesting to have a simple characterization of those cones T that do satisfy (ii). It should also be added that (ii) is typically not satisfied when T is polyhedral (the case treated by von Neumann).

Remark 2. Condition (iii) is fulfilled if, for example, all the co-ordinates of p are positive.

Remark 3. Condition (iv) is fulfilled if, for example, there is free disposal ($A5$) and x_0 provides positive amounts of all those commodities for which $\hat{x}$ is positive. On the other hand, Condition (iv) can be weakened to the following: an initial vector x_0 is given such that for some number $L > 0$ and some integer $N_0 \geqq 1$, there is a feasible sequence from x_0 to $L\hat{x}$ in N_0 periods.

Remark 4. Condition (v) can be weakened to the following: for some integer $N_1 \geqq 0$ and some commodity vector y for which $u(y) > 0$, there is a feasible sequence from $\hat{x}$ to y in N_1 periods.

With Conditions (iv) and (v) modified as indicated in Remarks 3 and 4, equation (11) would have to be modified to read

$$(11') \qquad S = \max\left[N_0 + N_1, \frac{\log C}{\log(\rho/\rho - \delta)}\right].$$

Remark 5. Consider the special case of Example 3.3 in which $u(x) = w \cdot x$, where w is some fixed vector $\geqslant 0$. A necessary and sufficient condition that (iii) be satisfied in this case is that $w_i = 0$ for all i for which $p_i = 0$. (In other words, the preference function must give no weight to goods that are " free " under the von Neumann equilibrium prices.) Under these circumstances the smallest value of K that can be used in (iii) is

$$K = \max_{p_i > 0} \frac{w_i}{p_i},$$

and, correspondingly, this gives a value of C in the theorem of

$$C = \frac{\rho p \cdot x_0}{Lw \cdot \hat{x}} \max_{p_i > 0} \frac{w_i}{p_i}.$$

Note that this last value for C is not affected by multiplying either p, w, or $\hat{x}$ by a positive constant, as is to be expected.

Berkeley, California. ROY RADNER.

REFERENCES

[1] Dorfman, R., P. A. Samuelson, and R. M. Solow, *Linear Programming and Economic Analysis*, New York: McGraw-Hill, 1958.

[2] Gale, D., " The closed linear model of production," in Kuhn and Tucker (eds.), *Linear Inequalities and Related Systems*, Annals of Math. Study No. 38, Princeton, N. J.: Princeton University Press, 1956, pp. 285-303.

[3] Karlin, S., *Mathematical Methods and Theory in Games, Programming and Economics* Vol. 1, Reading, Mass.: Addison-Wesley, 1959.

[4] Malinvaud, E., " Programmes d'expansion et taux d'interet," *Econometrica*, Vol. 27, No. 2 (April, 1959), pp. 1-9.

[5] von Neumann, J., "A model of general economic equilibrium," *Review of Economic Studies*, Vol. 13 (1945-6), pp. 1-9.

14

OPTIMAL GROWTH IN A TWO-SECTOR MODEL OF CAPITAL ACCUMULATION[1]

BY H. UZAWA

I INTRODUCTION

One of the basic problems in economic planning, in particular in underdeveloped countries, is concerned with the rate at which society should save out of current income to achieve a maximum growth. It is closely related to the problem of how scarce resources at each moment of time should be divided between consumers' goods industries and capital goods industries. In the present paper, we shall analyze the problem in the framework of the two-sector growth model as introduced by Meade [3], Srinivasan [6], and Uzawa [8]. We shall abstract from the complications which would arise by taking into account those factors such as changing technology and structure of demand, the role of foreign trade (in particular, of capital imports), and tax policy that are generally regarded as decisive in the determination of the course of economic development. Instead, we shall focus our attention on evaluating the impact of roundabout methods of production upon the welfare of society, as expressed by a discounted sum of per capita consumption. However, since our primary concern is with economic planning in underdeveloped countries, we shall depart with respect to one important point from the two-sector growth model as formulated in [3, 6, 8] which is, in general, concerned with an economy with fairly advanced technology and relatively abundant capital; namely, we shall postulate that a certain quantity of consumers' goods (per capita) is required to sustain a given rate of population growth. This restraint becomes ineffective for an economy with relatively abundant capital; however, for an economy with a low capital-labor ratio and high rate of population growth, it results in the phenomenon frequently referred to as "the vicious circle of poverty".[2] In the course of the discussion below on optimal growth, we shall briefly investigate the existence of such a vicious circle and its implications upon patterns of optimal growth.

Mathematically, our problem is that of finding a growth path over which the criterion function (i.e., the discounted sum of per capita consumption over the whole period) is maximized among all feasible growth paths. It is a problem in concave programming in linear spaces, to use the term of Hurwicz [2], and the techniques developed by him and others, particularly the extensions of the Kuhn-Tucker theorem, may be applicable. In the present case, however, it is possible to solve our problem without recourse to those advanced methods, and the optimal growth paths are instead characterized by a simple extension of the Euler equations in the classical calculus of variations. The mathematical structure of the auxiliary differential equations arising from the Euler equations differs markedly, according to whether consumers' goods are more or less capital-intensive than capital goods, and the detailed structure of the optimal growth path differs in these two cases. Therefore, for the convenience of analysis, we shall first present the discussions

[1] This work was supported by the National Science Foundation under Grant GS-51 and by the Office of Naval Research under Task NR-047-004, both at Stanford University. Reproduction in whole or in part is permitted for any purpose of the United States Government. The author is greatly indebted to Professors Kenneth J. Arrow and Samuel Karlin for their valuable comments and suggestions.

[2] See, e.g., Nurkse [5, p. 4 f.] and Myrdal [4, p. 11 f.].

for these two cases separately, and then the general case in which no restrictions are imposed on relative capital intensities will be briefly discussed. It will be generally shown that for any economy with relatively a low capital-labor ratio, consumers' goods are produced in the amounts just necessary to satisfy the minimum requirements until a certain critical level is reached, and from then on the rate of production of consumers' goods is gradually increased toward a certain balanced rate. Our results are thus extensions of those obtained by Srinivasan [6] for the case in which the minimum wage rate is zero and for which consumers' goods are always more capital-intensive than capital goods.

II A TWO-SECTOR MODEL OF CAPITAL ACCUMULATION

To begin with, let us describe the basic premises of our two-sector model in terms of a mathematical model.[1] We are concerned with an economy in which consumption goods and capital goods are composed of homogeneous quantities. Both goods are produced by combinations of two factors of production, labor and capital, but the possibility of joint products is excluded. The sole aim of the economy is to consume consumption goods, while capital goods are produced only to increase future production of consumption goods. Consumption goods may be assumed instantaneously consumed and capital goods to depreciate at a certain rate, say μ, which is technologically given. It will be assumed that technological knowledge remains constant in the whole period in question, constant returns to scale and diminishing marginal rates of substitution between capital and labor prevail in each sector, and there exist no external (dis-) economies. The sector producing consumption goods will be referred to as the C-sector, while that producing capital goods as the I-sector.

To make the analysis simpler, it is assumed that the size of the working population and the rate at which it grows are exogeneously given, and that labor is inelastically offered for employment at any moment of time. Let $L(t)$ denote the size of the working population at time t, then

$$\dot{L}(t)/L(t) = n, \tag{1}$$

where n stands for the rate of increase in labor forces.

It is furthermore assumed that the working population is a stationary proportion of the total population and that no external (dis-) economies exist for consumption, so that the minimum amount of consumption goods per capita required to sustain the given labor growth n may be assumed determinate. Let w_{min} denote the minimum wage rate in terms of consumption goods corresponding to the labor growth n.[2] In general, the minimum wage rate w_{min} is assumed positive.[3]

The aggregate quantity of capital $K(t)$ existing at any moment of time is determined by the accumulation of capital goods which have been produced in the past; namely, the rate of change in the aggregate stock of capital at time t, $\dot{K}(t)$, is given by

$$\dot{K}(t) = Y_I(t) - \mu K(t), \tag{2}$$

where $Y_I(t)$ stands for the rate at which new capital goods are produced at time t.

[1] Such a model of the two-sector economy was first introduced in Meade [3]. The present formulation modifies slightly that introduced in Uzawa [8].

[2] Several authors, in particular Buttrick [1] and Tsiang [7], have postulated certain relationships between the rate of labor growth and minimum wages, and have effectively analyzed the characteristics of various stages of economic growth.

[3] The case discussed by Srinivasan [6] and Uzawa [8] may be considered as a limiting case when the minimum wage rate tends to zero, which in the present paper will be discussed only to illustrate the techniques to be used for the general case.

The rate $Y_I(t)$ at which new capital goods are produced, on the other hand, is determined by the quantities of capital and labor allocated to the I-sector, $K_I(t)$ and $L_I(t)$; namely

$$Y_I(t) = F_I(K_I(t),\ L_I(t)), \tag{3}$$

where F_I is the production function which summarizes the production processes in the I-sector.

The rate of production of consumption goods at time t, $Y_C(t)$, is similarly determined by

$$Y_C(t) = F_C(K_C(t),\ L_C(t)), \tag{4}$$

where $K_C(t)$ and $L_C(t)$, respectively, are the quantities of capital and labor employed in the C-sector at time t.

The quantities of capital and labor allocated to the two sectors should remain within the available quantities existing in the economy as a whole; i.e.,[1]

$$K_I(t) + K_C(t) = K(t), \tag{5}$$

$$L_I(t) + L_C(t) = L(t). \tag{6}$$

The conditions (5) and (6) in particular imply that both capital and labor may be transferred from one sector to another without any cost; our capital thus is malleable in Meade's terminology ([3], p. 45).

The quantity of consumption goods, on the other hand, must be sufficient to afford the minimum wage rate w_{min}; hence, we have inequality:

$$Y_C(t) \geqq w_{min} L(t). \tag{7}$$

The quantity of capital available to the economy at the beginning ($t = 0$), $K(0)$, is given as one of the data, together with technological conditions and population growth. A continuous path of consumption $\{Y_C(t);\ t \geqq 0\}$ is termed *feasible* if it is possible to find allocations of capital and labor at each moment of time such that all the conditions (2-7) are satisfied.

In what follows, it will be assumed that production in each sector is subject to constant returns to scale, the marginal rate of substitution between capital and labor is smooth and diminishing, the marginal physical products of both factors are always positive, and both factors are indispensable. Let $k_j = K_j/L_j$ be the capital stock per unit of employment in the jth sector ($j = C, I$), and the function $f_j(k_j)$ be defined by:

$$f_j(k_j) = F_j(k_j, 1),\ j = C, I.$$

Then $f_j(k_j)$ is continuously twice differentiable and

$$f_j(k_j) > 0,\ f_j'(k_j) > 0,\ f_j''(k_j) < 0, \text{ for all } k_j > 0, \tag{8}$$

$$f_j(0) = 0,\ f_j(\infty) = \infty, \tag{9}$$

$$f_j'(0) = \infty,\ f_j'(\infty) = 0. \tag{10}$$

III OPTIMAL GROWTH IN THE TWO-SECTOR MODEL

Since there is only one consumption good in our two-sector economy, the social welfare may be determined, once we specify the rate of discount by which future consumption is weighed against present consumption. It will be assumed that the rate of discount is held at a fixed positive level δ. A feasible path will be termed *optimal* (relative to the rate of discount δ) if it maximizes the discounted sum of per capital consumption

[1] In view of the assumptions made below, (8-10), both capital and labor are fully employed at any optimal growth path, and we may without loss of generality postulate the full employment of both capital and labor at any moment of time.

(11) $$\int_0^\infty \frac{Y_C(t)}{L(t)} e^{-\delta t} dt$$

among all feasible paths of consumption arising from the given capital stock $K(0)$ initially held in the economy.

In view of the assumptions (8-10), it is easily seen that the quantity (11) is finite for any feasible path, provided that

(12) $$\lambda = n + \mu > 0.$$

It may be noted first that *an optimal path, if it exists, is uniquely determined.* Indeed, suppose two growth paths, $(K^0(t), Y_I^0(t), Y_C^0(t))$ and $(K^1(t), Y_I^1(t), Y_C^1(t))$ are both optimal with respect to the initial stock of capital $K(0)$ and labor growth $L(t)$. Let capital and labor allocations at time t be $K_I^j(t), K_C^j(t), L_I^j(t), K_C^j(t)$ for the optimal growth j ($j = 0, 1$). Then we have, for $j = 0, 1$,

(13) $$\int_0^\infty \frac{Y^0(t)}{L(t)} e^{-\delta t} dt = \int_0^\infty \frac{Y^1(t)}{L(t)} e^{-\delta t} dt,$$

(14) $$\dot{K}^j(t) = Y_I^j(t) + \mu K^j(t),$$

(15) $$Y_I^j(t) = F_I[K_I^j(t), L_I^j(t)],$$

(16) $$Y_C^j(t) = F_C[K_C^j(t), L_C^j(t)],$$

(17) $$K_I^j(t) + K_C^j(t) = K^j(t),$$

(18) $$L_I^j(t) + L_C^j(t) = L(t),$$

where

$$K^j(0) = K(0),\ j = 0, 1.$$

Let us define, for $0 \leqq \theta \leqq 1$,

$$K^\theta(t) = (1-\theta)K^0(t) + \theta K^1(t),$$
$$K_I^\theta(t) = (1-\theta)K_{_0}(t) + \theta K_I^1(t),$$
$$K_C^\theta(t) = (1-\theta)K_C^0(t) + \theta K_C^1(t),$$
$$Y_I^\theta(t) = (1-\theta)\,Y_I^0(t) + \theta\,Y_I^1(t),$$
$$Y_C^\theta(t) = (1-\theta)\,Y_C^0(t) + \theta\,Y_C^1(t).$$

Then we have

(19) $$\int_0^\infty \frac{Y^\theta(t)}{L(t)} e^{-\delta t} dt = \int_0^\infty \frac{Y^0(t)}{L(t)} e^{-\delta t} dt,$$

(20) $$\dot{K}^\theta(t) = Y_I^\theta(t) - \mu K^\theta(t),$$

(21) $$Y_I^\theta(t) \leqq F_I[K_I^\theta(t), L_I^\theta(t)],$$

with strict inequality if $K_I^0(t)/L_I^0(t) \neq K_I^1(t)/L_I^1(t)$,

(22) $$Y_C^\theta(t) \leqq F_C[K_C^\theta(t), L_C^\theta(t)],$$

with strict inequality if$K_C^0(t)/L_C^0(t) \neq K_C^1(t)/L_C^1(t)$,

(23) $$K_I^\theta(t) + K_C^\theta(t) = K^\theta(t),$$

(24) $$L_I^\theta(t) + L_C^\theta(t) = L(t),$$

with $K^\theta(0) = K(0)$.

If $K_C^0(\bar{t})/L_C^0(\bar{t}) \neq K_C^1(\bar{t})/L_C^1(\bar{t})$ at some time $\bar{t}$, then, because of (22), $Y_C^0(t)$ may be increased in some period around $\bar{t}$ without violating the feasibility conditions. Hence, there exists a feasible path on which the value of the criterion function (11) is greater than

$$\int_0^\infty \frac{Y_C^0(t)}{L(t)} e^{-\delta t} dt,$$

thus contradicting the optimality of the path $(K^0(t), Y_I^0(t), Y_C^0(t))$. On the other hand, if $K^0(\bar{t})/L_I^0(\bar{t}) \neq K_I^1(\bar{t})/L_I^1(\bar{t})$ at some time $\bar{t}$, then, because of (21) and (23), it is possible to increase the value of $Y_C^0(t)$ in some period around $\bar{t}$ by reducing $K_I^0(t)$ and increasing $K_C^0(t)$ in small quantities. It is again possible to find a feasible path on which (11) is greater than $\int_0^\infty \frac{Y_C^0(t)}{L(t)} e^{-\delta t} dt$, thus contradicting the optimality of the path $(K^0(t), Y_I^0(t), Y_C^0(t))$. Therefore, we must have

$$\frac{K_I^0(t)}{L_I^0(t)} = \frac{K_I^1(t)}{L_I^1(t)}, \tag{25}$$

$$\frac{K_C^0(t)}{L_C^0(t)} = \frac{K_C^1(t)}{L_C^1(t)}, \text{ for all } t. \tag{26}$$

Let

$$k_i(t) = \frac{K_i^j(t)}{L_i^j(t)}, \; j = 0, 1, \; i = I, C, \tag{27}$$

then we have

$$\frac{K_i^\theta(t)}{L_i^\theta(t)} = k_i(t), \text{ for all } i = I, C, \; 0 \leqq \theta \leqq 1, \; t \geqslant 0. \tag{28}$$

The relations (23), (24), and (28) together imply that

$$L_I^\theta(t) = \frac{k_C(t)\, L(t) - K^\theta(t)}{k_C(t) - k_I(t)}, \quad L_C^\theta(t) = \frac{L(t) - k_I(t) K^\theta(t)}{k_C(t) - k_I(t)}; \tag{29}$$

since (21) holds with equality and $F_I(K_I, L_I)$ is homogeneous of order one, we have

$$Y_I^\theta(t) = f_I(k_I(t)) \frac{k_C(t) L(t) - K^\theta(t)}{k_C(t) - k_I(t)}. \tag{30}$$

Hence,

$$\dot{K}^\theta(t) = \frac{k_C(t) f_I(k_I(t))}{k_C(t) - k_I(t)} L(t) - \left(\frac{f_I(k_I(t))}{k_C(t) - k_I(t)} + \mu\right) K^\theta(t), \tag{31}$$

with $K^\theta(0) = K(0)$, $0 \leqq \theta \leqq 1$. Therefore, $K^0(t)$ and $K^1(t)$ both satisfy the identical differential equation (31) with initial condition $K(0)$; hence, by the uniqueness of the solution to (31), we have

$$K^0(t) = K^1(t), \text{ for all } t. \tag{32}$$

From (28), (29), and (32), the two optimal growth paths $(K^0(t), Y_I^0(t), Y_C^0(t))$ and $(K^1(t), Y_I^1(t), Y_C^1(t))$ are necessarily identical.

Let us now introduce auxiliary variable (Lagrange multipliers) $q(t)$, $p_I(t)$, $p_C(t)$, $r(t)$, $w(t)$, and $v(t)$, respectively, corresponding to the restraints (2), (3), (4), (5), (6) and (7), and consider the following quantity:

$$(33)\quad \int_0^\infty \{Y_C(t) + p_C(t)\Big(F_C(K_C(t), L_C(t)) - Y_C(t)\Big) + p_I(t)\Big(F_I(K_I(t), L_I(t)) - Y_I(t)\Big)$$

$$+ r(t)(K(t) - K_C(t) - K_I(t)) + w(t)(L(t) - L_C(t) - L_I(t))$$

$$+ q(t)(Y_I(t) - \mu K(t) - \dot{K}(t)) + v(t)(Y_C(t) - w_{min}L(t))\}e^{-(n+\delta)t}\,dt,$$

where all variables are non-negative and $K(0)$ is a given quantity.

The expression (33) is concave in $Y_C(t)$, $Y_I(t)$, $K_C(t)$, $K_I(t)$, $K(t)$, $L_C(t)$ and $L_I(t)$. Suppose we have found a set of auxiliary variables $p_C(t), p_I(t), q(t), v(t)$ for which the variables $Y_C(t)$, $Y_I(t)$, $K_C(t)$, $K_I(t)$, $K(t)$, $L_C(t)$, $L_I(t)$, maximizing the quantity (33) without any restraint, satisfy the feasibility conditions (2-7). Then the path of the corresponding $Y_C(t)$ is an optimal path. Our optimum problem thus is reduced to that of maximizing the quantity (33) for a given set of auxiliary variables. The latter is a concave problem in the calculus of variations and its solution may be obtained by solving the following Euler equations:

$$(34)\qquad v(t) \geqq 0,$$

with equality if $Y_C(t) > w_{min}L(t)$;

$$(35)\qquad 1 + v(t) - p_C(t) = 0;$$

$$(36)\qquad q(t) - p_I(t) \leqq 0,$$

with equality if $Y_I(t) > 0$;

$$(37)\qquad p_C(t)\frac{\partial F_C(t)}{\partial K_C(t)} - r(t) \leqq 0,$$

with equality if $K_C(t) > 0$;

$$(38)\qquad p_I(t)\frac{\partial F_I(t)}{\partial K_I(t)} - r(t) \leqq 0,$$

with equality if $K_I(t) > 0$;

$$(39)\qquad p_C(t)\frac{\partial F_C(t)}{\partial L_C(t)} - w(t) \leqq 0,$$

with equality if $L_C(t) > 0$;

$$(40)\qquad p_I(t)\frac{\partial F_I(t)}{\partial L_I(t)} - w(t) \leqq 0,$$

with equality if $L_I(t) > 0$;

$$(41)\qquad r(t) - \mu q(t) = (n + \delta)q(t) - \dot{q}(t),$$

where $K(0)$ is a given quantity and all variables are non-negative and bounded.

IV REDUCTION OF OPTIMALITY CONDITIONS

In view of the constant-returns-to-scale assumption, it is possible to reduce the system of Euler equations (34-41) and the feasibility conditions (2-7) to those involving only per capita quantities.

Let ω be an arbitrarily given wage-rentals ratio and define the optimum capital-labor ratio k_j in each sector by solving

$$\omega = \frac{f_j(k_j)}{f_j'(k_j)} - k_j \quad (j = C, I), \tag{42}$$

in terms of k_j. By assumptions (8-10), such a capital-labor ratio k_j is uniquely determined for any wage-rentals ratio ω and it will be denoted by $k_j(\omega)$. From (42), we have

$$\frac{dk_j(\omega)}{d\omega} = \frac{[f_j'(k_j(\omega))]^2}{-f_j(k_j(\omega))f_j''(k_j(\omega))} > 0. \tag{43}$$

We next introduce the supply price of capital, $p(\omega)$, in terms of consumption goods:

$$p(\omega) = \frac{f_C'(k_C(\omega))}{f_I'(k_I'(\omega))}. \tag{44}$$

The supply price thus defined corresponds to the price of capital (in terms of consumers' goods) which would just induce each entrepreneur in a competitive economy to produce an additional unit of new capital goods under the prevailing wage-rentals ratio ω. Logarithmically differentiate (44) and substitute (43) to get

$$\frac{1}{p(\omega)}\frac{dp(\omega)}{d\omega} = \frac{1}{k_I(\omega) + \omega} - \frac{1}{k_C(\omega) + \omega}, \tag{45}$$

which is positive or negative, according to whether consumption goods are more or less capital-intensive than capital goods.

Let us finally introduce:

$$y_j(t) = \frac{Y_j(t)}{L(t)},$$
$$k_j(t) = \frac{K_j(t)}{L_j(t)},$$
$$l_j(t) = \frac{L_j(t)}{L(t)}, \quad j = I, C$$
$$k(t) = \frac{K(t)}{L(t)}.$$

A simple manipulation shows that the Euler equations (34-41) and the feasibility conditions (2-6) together are reduced to the following system:

$$y_C(t) = f_C(k_C(t))l_C(t), \; y_I(t) = f_I(k_I(t))l_I(t), \tag{46}$$
$$k_C(t)l_C(t) + k_I(t)l_I(t) = k(t), \tag{47}$$
$$l_C(t) + l_I(t) = 1, \tag{48}$$
$$y_C(t) \geqq w_{min}, \tag{49}$$
$$p(t) \leqq q(t), \text{ if } y_I(t) > 0, \tag{50}$$
$$p(t) \geqq q(t), \text{ if } y_C(t) > w_{min}, \tag{51}$$
$$k(t) = y_I(t) - \lambda k(t), \tag{52}$$
$$\dot{q}(t) = (\delta + \lambda)q(t) - r(t), \tag{53}$$

where all variables are non-negative and bounded,

$$k_C(t) = k_C(\omega(t)),\ k_I(t) = k_I(\omega(t)),$$

$$p(t) = p(\omega(t)),$$

$$r(t) = f'\,(k_C(t)),$$

$$\lambda = \mu + n > 0$$

and $$k(0) = K(0)/L(0) \text{ is given.}$$

The auxiliary variable, $q(t)$, may be interpreted as the *demand price of capital* (in terms of consumers' goods) at time t. The relations (50) and (51) then simply mean that no capital goods are produced when the supply price of capital $p(t)$ exceeds the demand price of capital $q(t)$, while consumers' goods are produced just enough to meet the minimum requirement when the demand price $q(t)$ exceeds the supply price $p(t)$.

Our optimum problem now is reduced to solving the system of the optimality conditions (46-53). We shall first discuss the case in which consumption goods are always more capital-intensive than capital goods, and proceed to discuss the case in which consumption goods are always less capital-intensive than capital goods. Finally, the general case will be briefly discussed by using the results obtained for these two special cases.

V THE CASE WHEN CONSUMPTION GOODS ARE ALWAYS MORE CAPITAL-INTENSIVE THAN CAPITAL GOODS

Let us first consider the case in which consumption goods are always more capital-intensive than capital goods; namely,

(54) $$k_C(\omega) > k_I(\omega), \text{ for all } \omega > 0.$$

To solve the system (46-53), it is found useful to investigate the structure of the differential equations which describe the behavior of the capital-labor ratio k and the wage-rentals ratio ω when capital goods are produced with positive quantities, and consumption goods exceed minimum requirements. In such a case, we have from (46), (47), (48), (50), and (51) that

(55) $$p(t) = q(t)$$

(56) $$y_C(t) = \frac{k(t) - k_I(t)}{k_C(t) - k_I(t)} f_C(k_C(t)),\ y_I(t) = \frac{k_C(t) - k(t)}{k_C(t) - k_I(t)} f_I(k_I(t)).$$

The differential equations (52) and (53) are accordingly reduced to:

(57) $$k = \frac{k_C(\omega) - k}{k_C(\omega) - k_I(\omega)} f_I(k_I\omega)) - \lambda k,$$

(58) $$\frac{\dot{p}(\omega)}{p(\omega)} = \lambda + \delta - f_I'(k_I(\omega)),$$

where for the sake of simplicity the variables are described without explicitly referring to the time variable t. The differential equations (57) and (58) will be referred to as the *auxiliary differential equations.*

In view of (45) and (54), the auxiliary differential equations (57) and (58) may be written as:

(59) $$k = \left\{\frac{f_I[k_I(\omega)]}{k_C(\omega) - k_I(\omega)} + \lambda\right\}(\hat{k}(\omega) - k),$$

(60) $$\dot{\omega} = \frac{\lambda + \delta - f_I'(k_I(\omega))}{\dfrac{1}{k_I(\omega) + \omega} - \dfrac{1}{k_C(\omega) + \omega}},$$

where

(61) $$\hat{k}(\omega) = \frac{f_I[k_I(\omega)]}{f_I[k_I(\omega)] + \lambda[k_C(\omega) - k_I(\omega)]}\, k_C(\omega).$$

The quantity $\hat{k}(\omega)$ is always smaller than $k_C(\omega)$ and it is larger than $k_I(\omega)$ if and only if

$$\frac{f_I[k_I(\omega)]}{k_I(\omega)} > \lambda.$$

Since the average productivity of capital, $\dfrac{f_I(k_I)}{k_I}$, is a decreasing function of k_I and $k_I(\omega)$ is an increasing function of ω, we have

$$k_I(\omega) < \hat{k}(\omega) < k_C(\omega) \text{ if and only if } \omega < \omega_\lambda,$$

where ω_λ is defined by

(62) $$\frac{f_I(k_I(\omega_\lambda))}{k_I(\omega_\lambda)} = \lambda.$$

Let us now define *the balanced wage-rentals ratio*, ω^*, by

(63) $$f_I'(k_I(\omega^*)) = \lambda + \delta.$$

Define $k^* = \hat{k}(\omega^*)$, $k_I^* = k_I(\omega^*)$, $k_C^* = k_C(\omega^*)$. The determination of ω_λ and ω^* may be illustrated by Figure 1. The ratio ω_λ is always greater than the balanced ratio ω^*; in particular,

$$k_I^* < k^* < k_C^*.$$

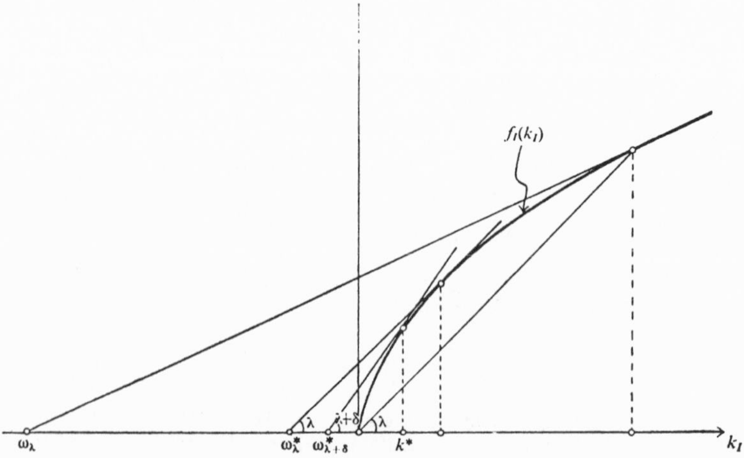

FIGURE 1

The relationships between $k_C(\omega)$, $k_I(\omega)$, and $\hat{k}(\omega)$ are illustrated by Figure 2.

For any initial condition, the solution to the auxiliary differential equations (57) and (58) will be assumed to exist and to change continuously as the initial condition changes. The rate of change in k is positive, zero, or negative according to whether k is smaller

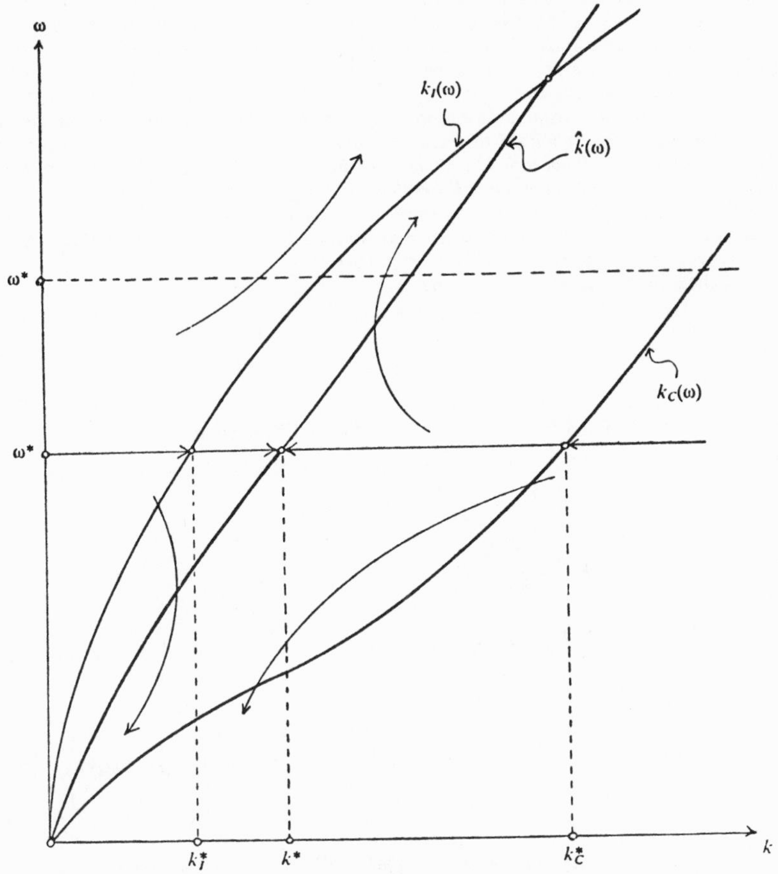

FIGURE 2

than, equal to, or larger than $\hat{k}(\omega)$, while the rate of change in ω is positive, zero, or negative according to whether ω is larger than, equal to, or smaller than the balanced ratio ω^*. Therefore, the structure of the solution paths to the auxiliary differential equations may be described by the arrow curves as illustrated in Figure 2.

The structure of the solution to the auxiliary differential equations described above will be used to solve the system (46-53) of the optimality conditions. To illustrate the method, let us first discuss the limiting case in which the minimum wage rate is zero:

$$w_{min} = 0$$

It is first noted that if the supply price of capital $p(t)$ is identical with the demand price $q(t)$ at any point on the $k_I(\omega)$ curve below the ω^*-line, and if the economy is specialized to the production of capital goods, then the demand price $q(t)$ satisfying the equation (53) falls while the supply price $p(t)$ rises; therefore, the economy continues the specialization in capital goods. This is easily seen from Figure 2, or it may be analytically shown by solving for the case in which the economy is specialized to capital goods.

It is similarly shown that if the supply price $p(t)$ is identical with the demand price $q(t)$ on the $k_C(\omega)$ curve above the ω^*-line, and if the economy is specialized in consumption goods, then the demand price rises while the supply price falls along the optimal path.

These considerations lead us to the following solutions to the optimality conditions (46-53): (a) *If the initial capital-labor ratio $k(0)$ is smaller than k_I^*, then, along the optimal path, the economy is specialized to the production of capital goods until the capital-labor ratio $k(t)$ reaches the critical ratio k_I^*. When the critical ratio k_I^* is reached, both consumption goods and capital goods are produced, keeping the wage-rentals ratio at the level ω^*. The optimal path then approaches asymptotically the balanced ratio k^* along the ω^*-line.* The precise analytical expressions may be given as follows, and it is easily shown that the path characterized by (64-76) satisfies all the optimality criteria (46-53).

Let the critical time t^* be defined by

(64) $$t^* = \int_{k(0)}^{k_I^*} \frac{dk}{f_I(k) - \lambda k}.$$

For $0 \leqq t \leqq t^*$*:* $k(t)$ and $\omega(t)$ are respectively obtained by solving

(65) $$\int_{k(0)}^{k(t)} \frac{dk}{f_I(k) - \lambda k} = t,$$

(66) $$k(t) = k_I(\omega(t)),$$

and

(67) $$y_I(t) = f_I(k(t)),$$

(68) $$y_C(t) = 0,$$

(69) $$p(t) = p[\omega(t)],$$

(70) $$q(t) = e^{-(\lambda+\delta)(t^*-t)}\left\{\int_t^{t^*} f_C'[k_C(\omega(\tau))]e^{(\lambda+\delta)(t^*-\tau)}d\tau - p(t^*)\right\}.$$

For $t \geqq t^*$*:*

(71) $$k(t) = k^* - (k^* - k_I^*)e^{-\theta(t-t^*)},$$

where

(72) $$\theta = \frac{f_I[k_I(\omega^*)]}{k_C(\omega^*) - k_I(\omega^*)} + \lambda,$$

(73) $$\omega(t) = \omega^*,$$

(74) $$y_I(t) = \frac{k_C^* - k(t)}{k_C^* - k_I^*} f_I(k_I^*),$$

(75) $$y_C(t) = \frac{k(t) - k_I^*}{k_C^* - k_I^*} f_C(k_C^*),$$

(76) $$p(t) = q(t) = p(\omega^*).$$

It is easily seen that $k(t)$ increasingly converges to k^*, $y_I(t)$ decreasingly converges to $y_I^* = \frac{k_C^* - k^*}{k_C^* - k_I^*} f_I(k_I^*)$, and $y_C(t)$ increasingly converges to $y_C^* = \frac{k^* - k_I^*}{k_C^* - k_I^*} f_C(k_C^*)$.

(b) *If the initial capital-labor ratio $k(0)$ is larger than k_C^*, then along the optimal path the economy is specialized to the production of consumption goods until the capital-labor ratio $k(t)$ is reduced to the ratio k_C^*. When the capital-labor ratio k_C^* is reached, both consumption goods and capital goods are produced, keeping the wage-rentals ratio at the level ω^*. The optimal path then asymptotically approaches the balanced ratio k^*.* The analytical expressions for this case may be given as follows:

The critical time t^* is defined by

(77) $$t^* = \frac{1}{\lambda} \log \frac{k(0)}{k_C^*}.$$

For $0 \leqq t \leqq t^*$:

(78) $$k(t) = k(0)e^{-\lambda t},$$

and $\omega(t)$ is obtained by solving

(79) $$k(t) = k_C(\omega(t)),$$

and

(80) $$y_I(t) = 0,$$

(81) $$y_C(t) = f_C(k(t)),$$

and $p(t)$, $q(t)$ are given by (69) and (70).

For $t \geqq t^*$:

(82) $$k(t) = k^* + (k_C^* - k^*)e^{-\theta(t-t^*)},$$

where the parameter θ is defined by (72), and $\omega(t)$, $y_I(t)$, $y_C(t)$, $p(t)$, and $q(t)$ are the same as those given by (73-76).

In this case, $k(t)$ decreasingly converges to k^*, $y_I(t)$ increasingly converges to y_I^* and $y_C(t)$ decreasingly converges to y_C^*.

The optimal growth paths are indicated by the heavy arrow curves in Figure 3.

Let us now extend our analysis to the case in which the minimum wage rate is positive:

$$w_{min} > 0.$$

Then the per capita consumption $y_C(t)$ given by (56) is greater than the minimum wage rate w_{min} if and only if

(83) $$k(t) > k_{min}(\omega(t)),$$

where the function $k_{min}(\omega)$ is defined by

(84) $$k_{min}(\omega) = k_I(\omega) + \frac{k_C(\omega) - k_I(\omega)}{f_C(k_C(\omega))} w_{min}.$$

By assumption (54), $k_{min}(\omega)$ is always larger than $k_I(\omega)$, while it is smaller than $k_C(\omega)$ if and only if $f_C[k_C(\omega)] > w_{min}$.

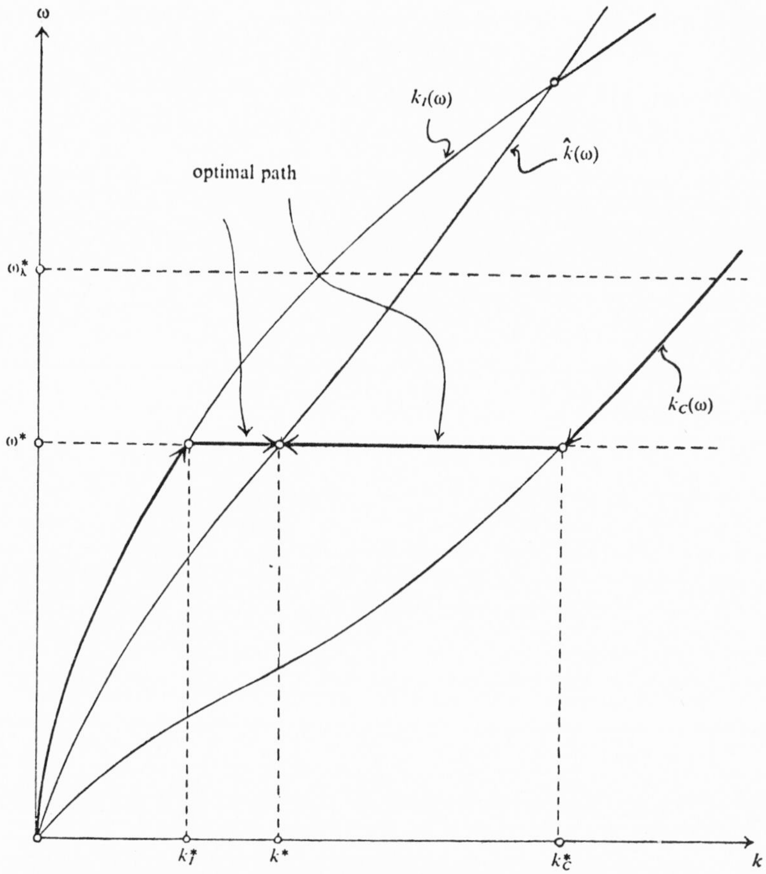

FIGURE 3

Let the wage-rentals ratio ω_{min} be defined as the one satisfying

(85) $$f_C[k_C(\omega_{min})] = w_{min}.$$

Then we have that

(86) $$k_I(\omega) < k_{min}(\omega) < k_C(\omega) \text{ if and only if } \omega > \omega_{min}.$$

On the other hand, $k_{min}(\omega) < \hat{k}(\omega)$ if and only if

(87) $$\frac{f_I(k_I(\omega)) - \lambda k_I(\omega)}{f_I(k_I(\omega)) - \lambda k_I(\omega) + \lambda k_C(\omega)} f_C(k_C(\omega)) > w_{min}.$$

The left-hand side of the inequality (87) is an increasing function of ω, provided $\omega < \omega_\lambda^*$, where ω_λ^* is the wage-rentals ratio for which the optimum marginal productivity in the I-sector is λ; i.e.,

(88) $$f_I'(k\,(\omega_\lambda^*)) = \lambda.$$

Hence, by defining the wage-rentals ratio $\hat{\omega}$ by

$$\frac{f_I(k_I(\hat{\omega})) - \lambda k_I(\hat{\omega})}{f_I(k_I(\hat{\omega})) - \lambda k_I(\hat{\omega}) + \lambda k_C(\hat{\omega})} f_C(k_C(\hat{\omega})) = w_{min}, \tag{89}$$

we have that, for $\omega < \omega_\lambda^*$,

$$k_{min}(\omega) < \hat{k}(\omega) \text{ if and only if } \omega > \hat{\omega}. \tag{90}$$

The relationships of the $k_{min}(\omega)$ curve to the $k_C(\omega)$, $k_I(\omega)$, and $\hat{k}(\omega)$ curves may be typically illustrated in Figure 4.

Let us now define the capital-labor ratios $\hat{k}$ and k_{min} corresponding to the wage-rentals ratios $\hat{\omega}$ and ω_{min}, respectively by

$$\hat{k} = \hat{k}(\hat{\omega}) = k_{min}(\hat{\omega}), \tag{91}$$

$$k_{min} = k_C(\omega_{min}) = k_{min}(\omega_{min}). \tag{92}$$

It is easily established that if the initial capital-labor ratio $k(0)$ is smaller than $\hat{k}$, then the capital-labor ratio $k(t)$ is decreasing over any feasible path and eventually reaches the capital-labor ratio k_{min}. However, if the capital-labor ratio is smaller than the ratio k_{min}, the economy is not able to produce consumption goods to afford the minimum requirement even though all capital and labor are allocated to the C-sector. Therefore, if the capital-labor ratio is smaller than k_{min}, our model is inconsistent in the sense that no feasible solution satisfying the minimum wage requirement may be found. To explain fully the phenomena would require the introduction of a certain Malthusian function explicitly relating the population growth to the minimum wage rate. In the present paper, however, we assume that the economy has somewhow attained a capital-labor ratio larger than the critical capital-labor ratio $\hat{k}$.

The structure of the optimal growth is then analyzed, and is analogous to the previous case; namely, we have that: (a) *If the initial capital-labor ratio* $k(0)$ *is smaller than* k_I^* *but larger than the critical ratio* $\hat{k}$, *then along the optimal path the economy produces just enough consumption goods to meet the minimum requirements, until the time when the capital-labor reaches the level* $k_{min}(\omega^*)$, *and from then on it proceeds to produce both capital goods and consumption goods for more than the minimum requirements. The optimal path increasingly approaches the balanced capital-labor ratio* k^*.

(*b*) *If the initial capital-labor ratio* $k(0)$ *is larger than* k_C^*, *then the optimal path proceeds exactly as in the case with zero minimum wage rate.*

The analytical expressions are similar to those for the previous case. In Figure 4, the structure of the optimal path is depicted with the heavy arrow curves.

VI THE CASE WHEN CAPITAL GOODS ARE ALWAYS MORE CAPITAL-INTENSIVE THAN CONSUMPTION GOODS

Let us next consider the case where *the capital good is always more capital-intensive than the consumption good;* namely

$$k_I(\omega) > k_C(\omega), \text{ for all } \omega > 0. \tag{93}$$

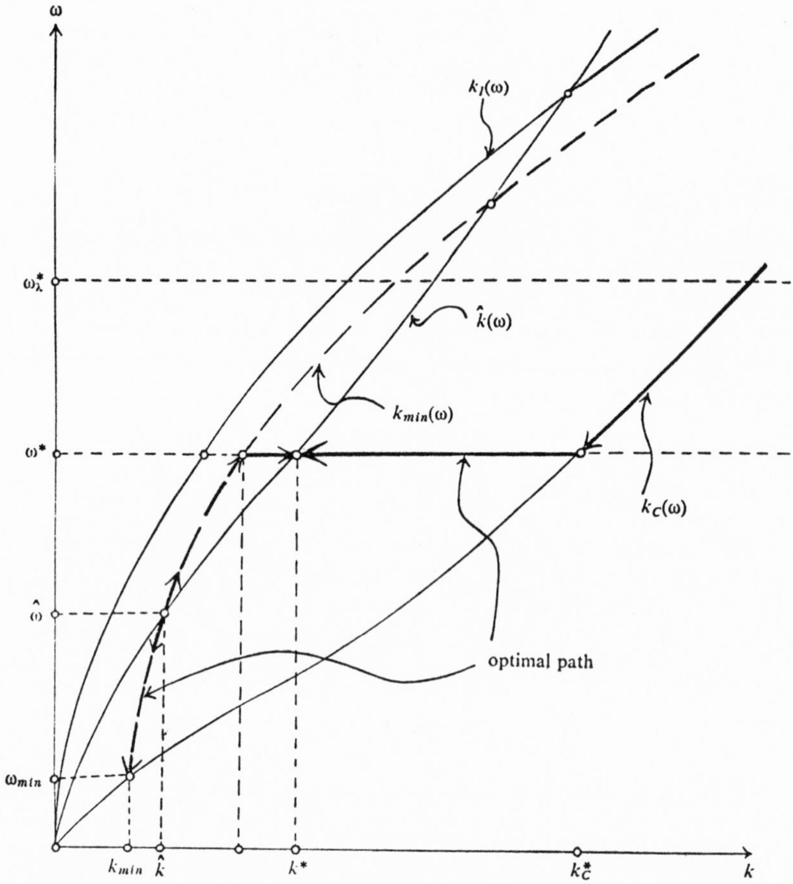

FIGURE 4

In this case, the auxiliary differential equations (57) and (58) may be rewritten as:

$$\dot{k} = \left\{\frac{f_I[k_I(\omega)]}{k_I(\omega) - k_C(\omega)} - \lambda\right\}(k - \hat{k}(\omega)), \tag{94}$$

$$\dot{\omega} = \frac{f_I'[k_I(\omega)] - \lambda - \delta}{\dfrac{1}{k_C(\omega) + \omega} - \dfrac{1}{k_I(\omega) + \omega}}, \tag{95}$$

where

$$\hat{k}(\omega) = \frac{f_I[k_I(\omega)]}{f_I[k_I(\omega)] - \lambda[k_I(\omega) - k_C(\omega)]}\, k_C(\omega). \tag{96}$$

The quantity $\hat{k}(\omega)$ is always larger than $k_C(\omega)$ and smaller than $k_I(\omega)$ if and only if $\omega < \omega_\lambda$, where ω_λ is defined by (62).

The relationships among $k_C(\omega)$, $k_I(\omega)$, and $\hat{k}(\omega)$, are then illustrated by Figure 4.

For a wage-rentals ratio ω satisfying

$$\lambda < \frac{f_I[k_I(\omega)]}{k_I(\omega) - k_C(\omega)},$$

the rate of change in k has the same sign as $k - \hat{k}(\omega)$; namely, k is increased or decreased according to whether k is larger or smaller than $\hat{k}(\omega)$. On the other hand, ω is increased or decreased according to whether ω is smaller or larger than ω^*.

The auxiliary differential equations are unstable in k. However, *for any given wage-rentals ratio* ω_0, *it is possible to find a corresponding* k_0 *such that the solution* $(k(t), \omega(t))$ *to the auxiliary differential equations* (94) *and* (95) *with initial condition* (k_0, ω_0) *converges to* (k^*, ω^*). The existence of such a k_0 may be established simply by taking the supremum of the initial values of k for which the k-component of the solution to the auxiliary differential equation approaches zero. It is explicitly given by the following formula:

(97)
$$k_0 = \int_{\omega_0}^{\omega^*} e^{-A(\omega,\omega_0)}\alpha(\omega)\hat{k}(\omega)d\omega,$$

where

(98)
$$\alpha(\omega) = \frac{\dfrac{f_I[k_I(\omega)]}{k_I(\omega) - k_C(\omega)} - \lambda}{f_I'[k_I(\omega)] - \lambda - \delta}\left(\frac{1}{k_C(\omega) + \omega} - \frac{1}{k_I(\omega) + \omega}\right),$$

(99)
$$A(\omega, \omega_0) = \int_{\omega_0}^{\omega} \alpha(\omega)d\omega.$$

In fact, the k-component of the solution $(k(t), \omega(t))$ to the auxiliary differential equations with initial condition (k_0, ω_0) is given by:

(100)
$$k(t) = e^{A[\omega(t),\omega_0]}\left\{k_0 - \int_{\omega_0}^{\omega(t)} e^{-A(\omega,\omega_0)}\alpha(\omega)\hat{k}(\omega)d\omega\right\}.$$

Now we have that

$$\lim_{t\to\infty} \omega(t) = \omega^*, \quad \lim_{\omega\to\omega^*} A(\omega, \omega_0) = \infty;$$

hence, if $k(t)$ converges to k^*, as t tends to infinity, then

$$k_0 = \lim_{t\to\infty} \int_{\omega_0}^{\omega(t)} e^{-A(\omega,\omega_0)}\alpha(\omega)\hat{k}(\omega)d\omega$$

$$= \int_{\omega_0}^{\omega^*} e^{-A(\omega,\omega_0)}\alpha(\omega)\hat{k}(\omega)d\omega.$$

On the other hand, let k_0 be given by (97). Then, by using L'Hospital's rule, we have

$$\lim_{t\to\infty} k(t) = \lim_{\omega\to\omega^*} \frac{k_0 - \int_{\omega_0}^{\omega} e^{-A(\omega',\omega_0)}\alpha(\omega')\hat{k}(\omega')\delta\omega'}{e^{-A(\omega,\omega_0)}}$$

$$= \lim_{\omega\to\omega^*} \frac{-e^{-A(\omega,\omega_0)}\alpha(\omega)\hat{k}(\omega)}{-e^{-A(\omega,\omega_0)}\dfrac{\partial A(\omega, \omega_0)}{\partial\omega}}$$

$$= \lim_{\omega\to\omega^*} \hat{k}(\omega) = \hat{k}(\omega^*).$$

It is easily seen that, for any positive ω_0, the integral in (97) exists and is positive; we may write

$$k_0 = k_0(\omega_0).$$

The relationship of $k_0(\omega_0)$ to $k_C(\omega)$, $k_I(\omega)$, $\hat{k}(\omega)$ may be described by Figure 5.

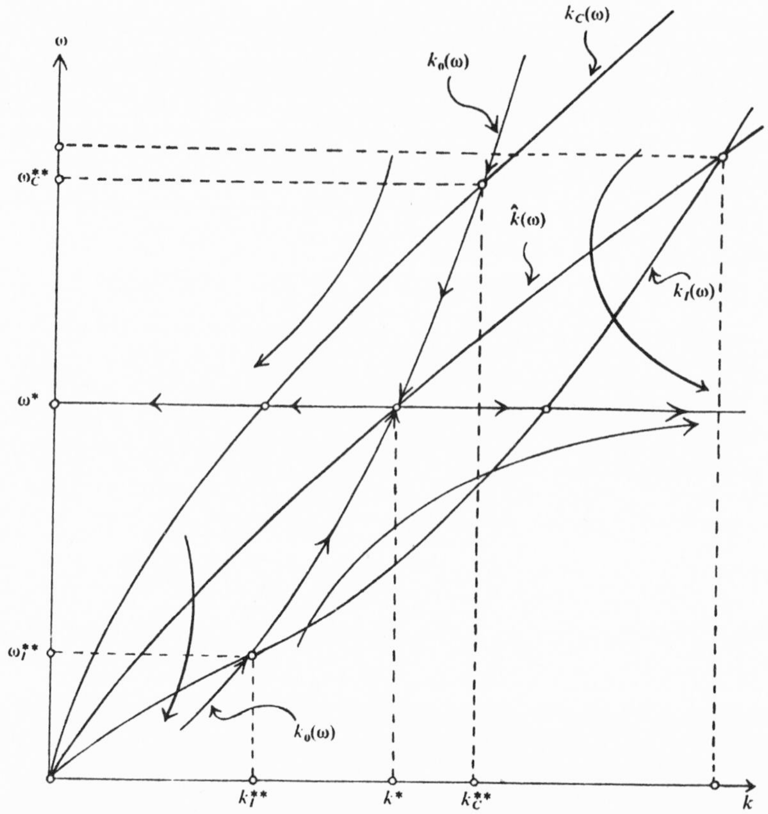

FIGURE 5

The structure of optimal growth is analyzed by a method similar to one we have used in the previous case. Let us first discuss the limiting case in which the minimum wage rate is zero. Let the two critical points $(k_I^{**}, \omega_I^{**})$ and $(k_C^{**}, \omega_C^{**})$ be defined as the intercepts of the $k_0(\omega)$ curve with the $k_I(\omega)$ curve and the $k_C(\omega)$ curve respectively:

$$k_I^{**} = k_0(\omega_I^{**}) = k_I(\omega_I^{**}),$$
$$k_C^{**} = k_0(\omega_C^{**}) = k_C(\omega_C^{**}).$$

We have

(101) $$k_I^{**} < k^* < k_C^{**}.$$

It is noted that if the supply price of capital $p(t)$ is equal to the demand price of capital $q(t)$ on the $k_I(\omega)$ curve below the critical point $(k_I^{**}, \omega_I^{**})$, and if the economy is specialized in capital goods, then the demand price of capital along the differential equation (33) falls while the supply price rises, and the economy continues the specialization in capital goods along the optimal path. Similarly, if the supply price of capital is equal to the demand price of capital on the $k_C(\omega)$ curve above the critical point $(k_C^{**}, \omega_C^{**})$, and if the economy specializes in consumption goods, then the supply price rises while the demand price falls; thus the economy continues the specialization in consumption goods along the optimal path.

Therefore, the optimal paths are characterized by the following two propositions:

(a) *If the initial capital-labor ratio $k(0)$ is smaller than the critical ratio k_I^{**}, then along the optimal path the economy is specialized to capital goods until the capital-labor ratio $k(t)$ reaches the critical ratio k_I^{**}. Once the critical level k_I^{**} is reached, the economy proceeds along the $k_0(\omega)$ curve toward the balanced state (k^*, ω^*).*

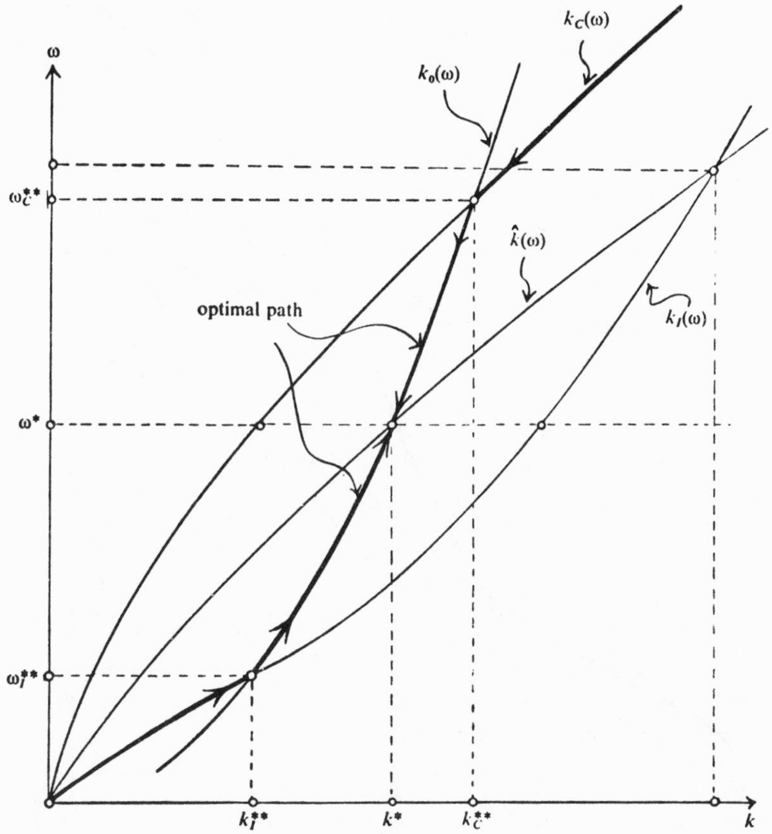

FIGURE 6

(b) *If the initial capital-labor ratio $k(0)$ is larger than the critical ratio k_C^{**}, then along the optimal path the economy is specialized to consumption goods until the capital-labor ratio $k(t)$ is reduced to the critical ratio k_C^{**}, and from then on it proceeds along the $k_0(\omega)$ curve toward the balanced state (k^*, ω^*).*

The analytical expressions for these two cases are similarly described in those given in (a) and (b) in the previous section.

In Figure 6, the optimal paths are indicated by the heavy arrow curves.

To discuss the general case in which the minimum wage rate is positive, let us introduce the function, $k_{max}(\omega)$, by:

$$k_{max}(\omega) = k_I(\omega) - \frac{k_I(\omega) - k_C(\omega)}{f_C(k_C(\omega))} w_{min}. \tag{102}$$

It is then shown that the per capita consumption $y_C(t)$ exceeds the minimum wage rate w_{min} if and only if

$$k(t) < k_{max}(\omega(t)). \tag{103}$$

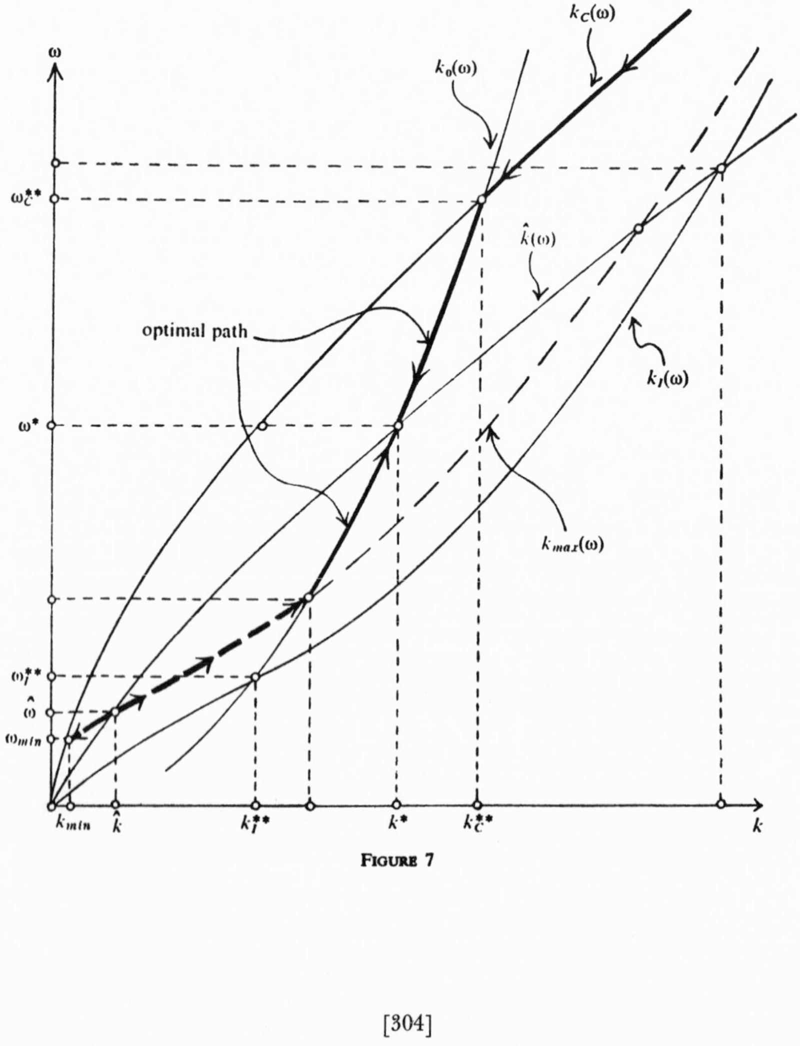

FIGURE 7

By assumption (93), $k_{max}(\omega)$ is always less than $k_I(\omega)$, while it is larger than $k_C(\omega)$ if and only if $f_C[k_C(\omega)] > w_{min}$; namely,

(104) $$k_{max}(\omega) > k_C(\omega), \text{ if and only if } \omega > \omega_{min}.$$

On the other hand, $k_{max}(\omega) > \hat{k}(\omega)$ if and only if the inequality (87) holds. Reasoning similar to that used in the previous section leads us again to the following conclusion that, for $\omega < \omega^*_\lambda$,

(105) $$k_{max}(\omega) > \hat{k}(\omega) \text{ if and only if } \omega > \hat{\omega},$$

where $\hat{\omega}$ is defined by (89).

The relationship of the $k_{max}(\omega)$ curve to the $k_C(\omega)$, $k_I(\omega)$, and $\hat{k}(\omega)$ curves is illustrated in Figure 7.

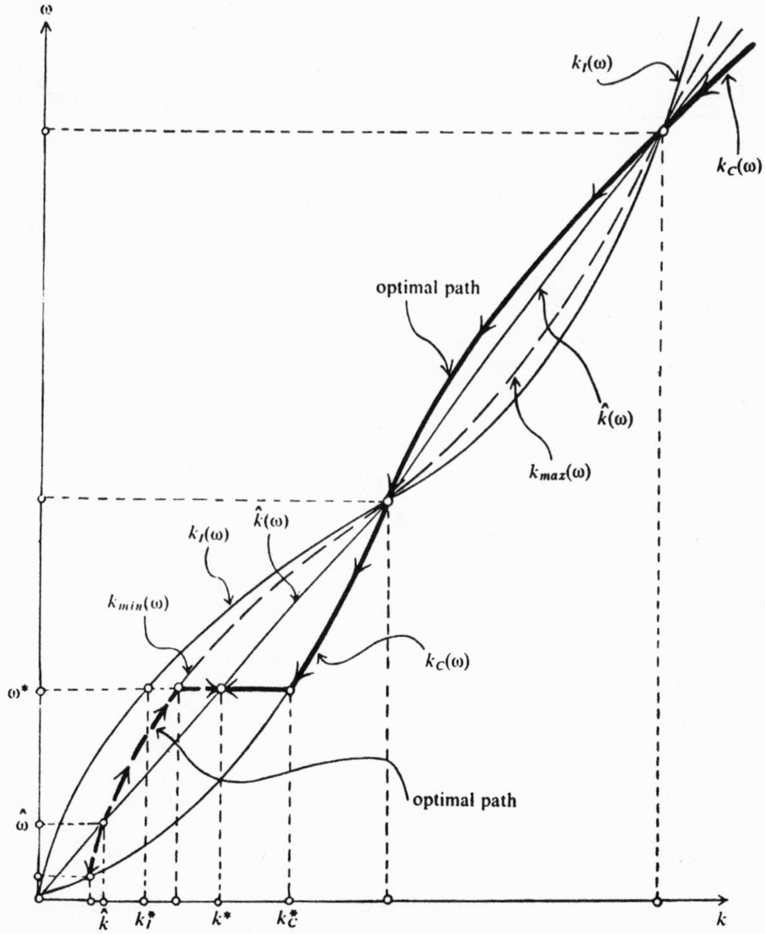

FIGURE 8

The critical capital-labour ratios $\hat{k}$ and k_{min} are defined by

(106) $$\hat{k} = \hat{k}(\hat{\omega}) = k_{max}(\hat{\omega}),$$

(107) $$k_{min} = k_C(\omega_{min}) = k_{max}(\omega_{min}).$$

The critical capital-labor ratio, $\hat{k}$, again represents the level of the capital-labor ratio below which the economy suffers from the steadily declining capital-labor ratio, whatever the allocation of the scarce resources may be, while below the minimum ratio, k_{min}, the economy cannot afford production of consumption goods with the minimum requirement even though capital goods are not produced. When the initial capital-labor ratio, $k(0)$, exceeds the critical ratio, $\hat{k}$, the structure of the optimal paths is characterized similarly to those described for the previous cases. In Figure 7, the optimal paths are depicted by the heavy arrow curves.

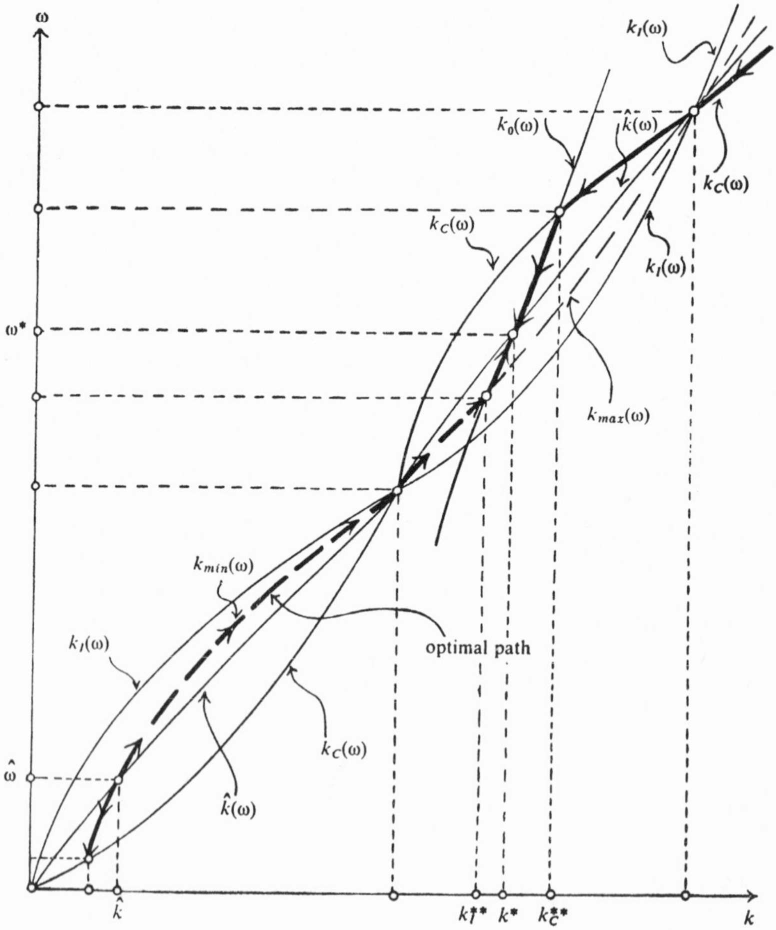

FIGURE 9

VII OPTIMAL GROWTH FOR THE GENERAL CASE

The foregoing analysis may be, without modification, applied to characterize the optimal paths for the general case in which the relative capital intensity may be reversed; namely, if consumption goods are more capital-intensive than capital goods for the balanced wage-rentals ratio ω^*, then the pattern described in Section 5 prevails for the optimal paths, while the pattern in Section 6 is applied for the optimal paths in the economy in which consumption goods are less capital-intensive than capital goods for the balanced wage-rentals ratio ω^*.

VIII SUMMARY

To analyze the patterns of optimum allocations of annual output between consumption and investment, we have employed the two-sector model of economic growth of the type introduced by Meade. Consumers' goods and capital goods are both composed of homogeneous quantities and are produced by labor and capital. All the neo-classical hypotheses are assumed for production processes in each sector, together with the malleability of capital. We have adapted the discounted sum of consumption per capita as the criterion by which various paths of capital accumulation are compared. The rate by which future consumption is discounted is assumed to be independent of the level of consumption.

At the beginning of time, we take as given the discount rate, the state of technological knowledge, the state of capital initially held in the economy, and the amount of labor available at each moment of time, to be assumed to grow at a constant rate. The problem is to find a path of capital accumulation over which the criterion function is maximized among all feasible paths. The optimum path always exists and is uniquely determined relative to the data stated above. Associated with a given rate of discount there exists a balanced capital-labour ratio, k^*, and two critical capital-labor ratios, k_I^{**} and k_C^{**}. If the initial capital-labor ratio, $k(0)$, is smaller than the critical ratio k_I^{**}, along the optimal path the economy is specialized to capital goods and consumption goods are produced for the minimum requirements, and when the economy reaches the critical ratio, k_I^{**}, it starts to produce both goods asymptotically to approach the balanced ratio k^*. Similarly, if the initial capital-labor ratio, $k(0)$, is larger than the critical ratio, k_C^{**}, along the optimal path the economy is specialized to consumption goods until the critical ratio, k_C^{**}; at k_C^{**} it starts to produce both goods asymptotically to approach the balanced ratio k^*. The structure of the optimal path is more precisely characterized by specifying the efficient wage-rentals ratio $\omega(t)$, and the efficient price of investment $q(t)$, at each moment of time t.

The optimum capital-labor ratio in each sector is uniquely determined by the wage-rentals ratio $\omega(t)$ so as to minimize the average cost; hence, the supply price $p(t)$ of capital goods in terms of consumption goods is also determined by the wage-rentals ratio $\omega(t)$ alone, as described by the equations (42) and (44). If the supply price $p(t)$ exceeds the efficient price $q(t)$, no investment goods are produced, while if the supply price $p(t)$ is less than the efficient price $q(t)$, the economy is specialized in investment goods. When the supply price $p(t)$ and the efficient price $q(t)$ are identical, both goods are produced, and the allocation of labor and capital between two sectors is simply determined by the conditions that labor and capital are both fully employed, as described by the equations (46) and (47). The rate of capital accumulation is determined by the gross investment and the depreciation, so that the rate of change in the capital-labor ratio $k(t)$ satisfies the equation (52). The change in the efficient price $q(t)$, as described by (53), is such that the net capital gain is equated to the interest charges; i.e., the capital market is competitive with perfect foresight.

The balanced capital-labor ratio k^* is determined at the level for which the aggregate capital-labor ratio and the efficient price of investment both remain stationary. The efficient price of investment q^* at such a balanced state must coincide with the supply price p^*, such that the marginal product of capital at the corresponding optimum capital-labor ratio k_I^* in the I-sector is equal to the sum of rates of population growth n, of depreciation μ, and of discount δ. The balanced capital-labor ratio k^* is then determined by the condition that the net rate of capital accumulation is zero; namely, it is given by:

$$k^* = \frac{f_I(k_I^*)}{f_I^*(k_I^*) + \lambda(k_C^* - k_I^*)} k_C^*,$$

where k_C^* is the corresponding optimum capital-labor ratio in the C-sector, and $f_I(k_I^*)$ is output per unit employment of capital goods.

The quantities per capita of consumption goods and capital goods at the balanced state are given by:

$$y_C^* = \frac{k^* - k_I^*}{k_C^* - k_I^*} f_C(k_C^*),$$

$$y_I = \frac{k_C^* - k^*}{k_C^* - k_I^*} f_I(k_I^*).$$

If, at the balanced state, the C-sector is more capital-intensive than the I-sector, i.e., if $k_C^* > k_I^*$, the critical capital-labor ratios k_I^{**} and k_C^{**} are respectively identical with the optimum capital-labor ratios k_I^* and k_C^*, for the case when the minimum wage rate w_{min} is zero. For the case of a positive w_{min}, k_C^{**} is adjusted so that consumption goods are produced for the minimum requirements.

On the other hand, if the C-sector is less capital-intensive than the I-sector at the balanced state ($k_C^* < k_I^*$), the critical capital-labor ratio k_I^{**} may differ from k_I^* but k_C^{**} is identical with k_C^*. The precise value of k_I^{**} is determined as the intersection of the $k_0(\omega)$ curve and the $k_I(\omega)$ curve, as described in Fig. 6, or as the intersection of the $k_0(\omega)$ curve and the $k_{max}(\omega)$, as described in Fig. 7, depending on whether w_{min} is zero or positive.

Along the optimal path, the capital-labor ratio $k(t)$, the wage-rentals ratio $\omega(t)$, the per capita consumption $y_C(t)$, and the per capita investment $y_I(t)$ all approach monotonically to the balanced capital-labor ratio k^*, wage-rentals ratio $\omega_{\lambda+\delta}^*$, per capita consumption y_C^*, and per capita investment y_I^*. The economy is specialized either in capital goods (consumption goods being produced only for minimum requirements) or in consumption goods until a certain critical level is reached for the capital-labor ratio.

The higher the discount rate δ, the lower the balanced capital-labor ratio k^* and the balanced wage-rentals ratio $\omega_{\lambda+\delta}^*$. As the discount rate δ tends to zero, the balanced wage-rentals ratio $\omega_{\lambda+\delta}^*$ approaches the level ω_λ^* defined by:

$$f_I'[k_I(\omega_\lambda^*)] = \lambda.$$

REFERENCES

[1] Buttrick, J. A. "A Note on Growth Theory", *Economic Development and Cultural Change*, Vol. 9 (1960), pp. 75-82.

[2] Hurwicz, L. "Programming in Linear Spaces", *Studies in Linear and Nonlinear Programming*, by K. J. Arrow, L. Hurwicz, and H. Uzawa. Stanford: Stanford University Press, 1958, pp. 38-102.

[3] Meade, J. A. *A Neo-classical Theory of Economic Growth.* New York: Oxford University Press, 1961.

[4] Myrdal, G. *Economic Theory and Under-Developed Regions.* London: Gerald Duckworth, 1957.

[5] Nurkse, R. *Problems of Capital Formation in Underdeveloped Countries.* New York: Oxford University Press, 1953.

[6] Srinivasan, T. N. " On a Two-Sector Model of Growth ", Cowles. Foundation Discussion Paper, 1962.

[7] Tsiang, S. C. " A Model of Economic Growth in Rostovian Stages ", 1962.

[8] Uzawa, H. " On a Two-Sector Model of Economic Growth, II ", *The Review of Economic Studies*, Vol. 30 (1963), pp. 105-118.

HIROFUMI UZAWA.

15

ON OPTIMAL DEVELOPMENT IN A MULTI-SECTOR ECONOMY[1]

By D. Gale

1. INTRODUCTION

The chief problem in the theory of dynamic economic planning is that of determining what amounts of resources should be allocated to the production of current consumption goods and what amounts should be allocated to the production of capital equipment to be used for producing consumption goods in the future. It appears that there is no completely rational way to attack this problem without considering development programmes over an infinite time horizon. It is true that one hears about five or ten year plans in which for the end of the plan period certain targets for capital accumulation have been set. The question then arises as to how these target levels of capital are decided on, and the rational answer would seem to be, by some sort of trade-off between the sacrifices required to accumulate the capital during the period of the plan and the benefits that will accrue from having it thereafter. But if this is so, then the planning decisions have actually been based on considerations about times well beyond the period of the plan, and this will be true whether the plan period is five years or five hundred.

There have been, as far as I am aware, two main approaches to the infinite time horizon problem. The first is to discount future consumptions by some arbitrary factor and then try to maximize the resulting infinite series or integral. The second is the approach pioneered by Ramsey in 1928 [1] and reworked quite recently by Samuelson and Solow [2], Koopmans [3] and von Weizsäcker [4] among others. The present paper continues along the latter lines and extends some of the Ramsey results to general technologies of the type that are usually considered in modern multi-sector analysis. The model will involve a very general constant returns to scale technology in which the only primary goods are various types of labour and these are all growing at the same exogenously given rate. The model includes neither technological change nor fixed exhaustible resources nor uncertainty.

The main result of the paper, given in section 10, proves the existence of optimal development programmes, in a sense to be described in the next section, for the class of models considered. To obtain this existence proof we have found it necessary to investigate first a number of subjects which have been central to much of the recent literature on dynamic production models including (1) optimal balanced growth programmes (" golden-rule " paths) (2) asymptotic properties of " good " programmes (" turn-pike " theorems) and (3) dynamic prices associated with optimal programmes (inter-temporal optimality), each of which is used in obtaining the final result. It may well be that there is a more direct way of obtaining our existence theorem, but even if this should turn out to be true, the present round-about approach would not be entirely a wasted effort since the facts we pick up along the way are of some economic interest in themselves describing properties of optimal paths particularly as they relate to long run stability and dynamic market structures.

As for applicability, the main interest of the present study would seem to be in the direction of national economic planning, not at the immediate practical level, of course,

[1] This research has been partially supported by the Office of Naval Research under Contract Nonr-222(83) with the University of California. Reproduction in whole or part is permitted for any purpose of the United States Government.

but rather as an attempt to lay some of the mathematical foundations for a planning theory. In this connection there is one objection which is frequently raised to considering an infinite time horizon. Even the most omniscient planner, it is argued, cannot know what the technological situation will be after ten years. What nonsense it is then to be planning hundreds and thousands of years into the future. The answer is, perhaps somewhat paradoxically, that infinite horizon plans do not, as one might think, involve making sensitive decisions about what to do hundreds of years hence. On the contrary, all reasonably good plans will look approximately the same for large values of time, approaching some fixed " balanced " path arbitrarily closely, as we shall see. On the other hand, the choice of infinite plan will affect very crucially what one does, say during the first five years, and even more sensitively what one does tomorrow. To describe the situation figuratively, one is guiding a ship on a long journey by keeping it lined up with a point on the horizon even though one knows that long before that point is reached the weather will change (but in an unpredictable way) and it will be necessary to pick a new course with a new reference point, again on the horizon rather than just a short distance ahead.

2. THE OPTIMALITY PROBLEM

We shall begin by describing the optimality problem in very general terms. For this purpose we assume there is given an abstract set S called the set of possible *economic states*. If s is a particular economic state, it will in general be possible in one time period to move on to some but not all other states of S. These possibilities are specified in the following manner:

Definition. A *technology* $\mathcal{T}$ is a subset of $S \times S$. A *programme* for $\mathcal{T}$ is a sequence (s_t), finite or infinite, such that (s_t, s_{t+1}) is in $\mathcal{T}$ for all t.

Interpretation. To say that (s, s') is in $\mathcal{T}$ means that it is possible to move from state s to state s' in one time period. The programmes (s_t) therefore describe all possible time paths of the economy.

In order to compare different programmes we introduce a *utility* or *social welfare* function u defined on the set S, where $u(s)$ is supposed to measure the aggregate satisfaction to the members of the economy from being in the state s. If (s_t) is a programme we define the corresponding *utility sequence* (u_t) by the rule $u_t = u(s_t)$.

Now, given an *initial set* $S_0 \subset S$, the *T-period optimality problem* is described as follows: Find a programme (s_t) such that

$$\sum_{t=1}^{T} u_t \text{ is a maximum} \qquad \text{...(2.1)}$$

subject to $s_1 \in S_0$.

This T-period problem is typical of dynamic problems occurring in many economic applications and has been extensively treated especially for the case in which $\mathcal{T}$ is a convex subset of a vector space and u is a concave function. In this case one is dealing with a decomposable concave programming problem for which a considerable theory has been developed.

For the infinite horizon problem one might be tempted to make the naive extension of (2.1) above and ask to maximize the infinite series $\sum_{t=1}^{\infty} u_t$. Of course, this maximization may be meaningless since in general this infinite series will diverge. The alternative Ramsey-Weizsäcker approach is based on the following fundamental:

Definition. A programme (s_t) is said to *overtake* a programme (s'_t) if there exists a T such that

$$\sum_{\tau=1}^{t} (u_\tau - u'_\tau) \geq 0 \text{ for all } t \geq T. \qquad \text{...(2.2)}$$

In words, one programme overtakes another if at some point of time it has provided more utility than the other and it continues to do so from that point on. Note that if the series $\sum_{t=1}^{\infty} u_t$ and $\sum_{t=1}^{\infty} u'_t$ do happen to converge then overtaking is equivalent to the usual ordering by sums. If further one wishes to introduce some discount rate δ one applies the overtaking definition to the series $\sum_{t=1}^{\infty} \delta^t u_t$ and obtains a partial ordering which agrees with the usual one if the discounted series happens to converge. Thus, the overtaking criterion generalizes the usual criteria that have been proposed for comparing infinite programmes.

A somewhat weaker form of the overtaking criterion is the following:

Definition. The programme (s_t) *catches up to* the programme (s'_t) if for any $\varepsilon>0$ there exist T_ε such that

$$\sum_{\tau=1}^{t} (u_\tau - u'_\tau) \geqq -\varepsilon \text{ for } t \geqq T_\varepsilon. \qquad \text{...(2.3)}$$

One easily sees that (2.3) is equivalent to

$$\liminf_{T\to\infty} \sum_{t=1}^{T} (u_t - u'_t) \geqq 0. \qquad \text{...(2.4)}$$

If we now consider only programmes starting from some initial set, S_0 we can give a precise description of the optimality problem.

Definition. A programme $(\bar{s}_t)$ starting from S_0 is called *optimal* (*strongly optimal*) if it catches up to (overtakes) all other programmes starting from S_0.

Even with " smoothness " and " boundedness " conditions on the set $\mathscr{T}$ and function u it is by no means necessary that there should exist optimal programmes as we shall show in the next section. It does turn out, however, that for a wide class of economically natural models there do exist optimal programmes. The rest of the paper will be concerned with establishing the existence of such programmes and analysing their properties.

3. SOME EXAMPLES

By way of contrast with the generality of the preceding section we now consider some concrete examples of programmes in order to crystallize ideas and indicate some of the difficulties involved in establishing the existence of optimal programmes.

Example 1. The model involves a single good which is capable of autonomous growth at a rate $\rho>1$. Given b units of the good one may consume an amount $c \leqq b$ and " invest " the balance $x = b-c$ which will then provide the amount ρx in the next time period. (A " state " in the sense of the preceding section is thus described by the pair (x, c)). If initially there is one unit of the good a programme is completely described by a sequence of investments (x_t) which must satisfy

$$x_1 \leqq 1,\ x_t \leqq \rho x_{t-1} \text{ for } t>1. \qquad \text{...(3.1)}$$

If we take the utility of consumption to be equal to the amount consumed then the utility sequence is given by

$$u_1 = 1 - x_1,\ u_t = \rho x_{t-1} - x_t \text{ for } t>1. \qquad \text{...(3.2)}$$

We will show that for this model there is no optimal programme by showing that any programme can be overtaken. Let (x_t) be any programme and suppose for $t = T$ we have $u_T = \rho x_{T-1} - x_T > 0$. We construct an overtaking programme (x'_t) by the rule

$$x'_t = x_t \text{ for } t \neq T,$$

and

$$x_T < x'_T \leqq \rho x_{T-1}.$$

Then clearly $u_t = u'_t$ for all t except T and $T+1$, for which we have

$$\begin{aligned} u_T + u_{T+1} &= \rho x_{T-1} - x_T + \rho x_T - x_{T+1} = \rho x_{T-1} - x_{T+1} + (\rho - 1)x_T \\ &< \rho x_{T-1} - x_{T+1} + (\rho - 1)x'_T = \rho x'_{T-1} - x'_T + \rho x'_T - x'_{T+1} \\ &= u'_T + u'_{T+1}. \end{aligned}$$

Thus (x_t) is not optimal. The only other case is that in which $u_t = 0$ for all t, but this is clearly the worst possible programme, being overtaken by all others.

Example 2. This is like Example 1 except the growth rate ρ is unity. This is the case of a society which has a piece of cake and may consume a certain amount each day until the cake is gone. Thus, the possible programmes correspond to sequences (c_t) where $\sum_{t=1}^{\infty} c_t \leqq 1$, c_t being the amount consumed in period t. If now the utility function u is a *strictly concave* function of consumption we can see again that there can be no optimal programme. If all c_t are zero, then as in Example 1 we have the worst possible programme. In any other programme there must be two successive values c_T and c_{T+1} which are not equal, but in this case we can construct a programme (c'_t) such that

$$c'_t = c_t \text{ for } t \neq T, T+1$$

$$c'_T = c'_{T+1} = (c_T + c_{T+1})/2.$$

By the strict concavity of u we have

$$u(c_T) + u(c_{T+1}) < 2u((c_T + c_{T+1})/2) = u(c'_T) + u(c'_{T+1})$$

so (c'_t) overtakes (c_t).

In this example although there do not exist optimal programmes, one can show the existence of ε-optimal programmes, meaning that for any $\varepsilon > 0$ there is a programme (c_t) such that no other programme can overtake (c_t) by more than ε. (To ensure this we must assume u satisfies a Lipschitz condition at $c = 0$.)

Example 3. Again there is a single good which can grow at the rate $\rho > 1$ as in Example 1. However, now there is the restriction that the amount x invested in each period cannot exceed unity. The condition is rather reasonable if one thinks of the production of this good requiring as input the good itself along with an equal amount (in suitable units) of labour which is assumed to be available in a fixed amount independent of the time.

A programme is again given by a non-negative sequence x_t where,

$$x_1 \leqq 1 \quad x_t \leqq \min\,[1, \rho x_{t-1}]. \qquad \text{...(3.3)}$$

In this case there is a strongly optimal programme given by $x_t = 1$ for all t. We denote this sequence by (I) and assume, as in Example 1, that $u_t = c_t = \rho x_{t-1} - x_t$, although the result also holds for u_t any concave function of c_t.

To show the optimality of the programme (I) let (x_t) be any other programme, where we may as well suppose $x_1 < 1$. The corresponding sequence (u_t) is then given by

$$u_1 = 1 - x_1,\ u_t = \rho x_{t-1} - x_t \text{ for } t > 1. \qquad \text{...(3.4)}$$

To say that the sequence (I) does not overtake (x_t) means there is an infinite sequence of times $t_0, t_1, \ldots$ such that

$$u_1 + \sum_{t=2}^{t_i} (u_t - (\rho - 1)) \geqq 0, \qquad \text{...(3.5)}$$

where we take $t_0 = 1$.

Substituting from (3.4) in (3.5) gives

$$0 \leqq 1-x_1+(\rho x_1-x_2-(\rho-1))+\ldots+(\rho x_{t_i-1}-x_{t_i}-(\rho-1))$$
$$= 1-x_1-\rho(1-x_1)+(1-x_2)-\rho(1-x_2)+\ldots-\rho(1-x_{t_i-1})+(1-x_{t_i}). \quad \ldots(3.6)$$

Letting $y_t = 1-x_t$ and $\delta = \rho-1$ (3.6) becomes

$$-\delta \sum_{t=1}^{t_i-1} y_t+y_{t_i} \geqq 0 \text{ or } y_{t_i} \geqq \delta \sum_{t=1}^{t_i-1} y_t. \quad \ldots(3.7)$$

We assert that $y_{t_n} \geqq (1+\delta)^{n-1}\delta y_1$. The proof for $n = 1$ follows at once from (3.7). Inductively suppose it is true up to n. Then from (3.7)

$$y_{t_{n+1}} \geqq \delta \sum_{i=0}^{n} y_{t_i} \geqq \delta(y_1+\delta y_1+\delta(1+\delta)y_1+\ldots+\delta(1+\delta)^{n-1}y_1)$$
$$= y_1\delta(1+\delta+\delta(1+\delta)+\ldots+\delta(1+\delta)^{n-1})$$
$$= \left(1+\delta\left(\frac{1-(1+\delta)^n}{-\delta}\right)\right)\delta y_1 = (1+\delta)^n\delta y_1$$

but as $(1+\delta)^n$ become infinite eventually $y_{t_n}>1$ which means $x_{t_n}<0$ which is not possible. It follows that the sequence (x_t) is overtaken by (I) as asserted.

In this example one could have started out with any initial amount of the good and there would be a unique strongly optimal programme, but the existence of such a programme especially if u is concave rather than linear is not such a simple matter. One way of trying to construct such a programme would be to construct optimal T-period programmes $(\bar{x}_t^T)$. As T approaches infinity there will always exist some limit programme $(\bar{x}_t)$ which is a natural candidate for the optimum. In Example 3 this limit programme will in fact be optimal but this is not the case with the other examples. In Example 1 it is easily seen that the T-period optimal programme is

$$x_t = \rho^t \quad \text{for } t<T$$
$$x_T = 0.$$

The limit programme $x_t = \rho^t$ for all t gives the utility sequence $u_t = 0$ for all t which is the worst rather than best programme.

Similarly for Example 2 the optimal T-period programme is

$$c_t = \frac{1}{T} \quad \text{for } t = 1, \ldots, T$$

and the limit is again the worst programme $c_t = 0$ for all t.

4. THE TECHNOLOGY: REDUCTION TO THE CASE OF CONSTANT LABOUR SUPPLY

We introduce the class of technologies we shall be dealing with by considering first the most important special case, the *von Neumann technology* with exogenous labour supply. The model will involve *n goods* and *m* types of *labour*. Goods are produced by *activities* which have a goods n-vector and labour m-vector as inputs and a goods n-vector as output. An activity can be operated at any non-negative *level* meaning that the input and output vectors may be multiplied by any non-negative number. If there are k such activities, the technology T is given in the familiar way by an $m \times k$ labour input matrix L, an $n \times k$ goods input matrix A and an $n \times k$ goods output matrix B, where L, A and B are all non-negative. For any non-negative k-vector v of activity levels the input vectors are Lv, Av and the output is Bv. The state of the economy in the sense of section 1 is thus determined by the vector v.

We next assume that the population and with it each type of labour is growing at a constant rate ρ, that the initial population is unity (by suitable choice of units), the initial vector of labour types is l_0, and the initial goods vector is y_0. A *programme* is then a sequence of non-negative k-vectors (v_t) such that

$$Lv_t \leqq \rho^{t-1} l_0 \text{ for } t \geqq 1 \qquad \text{...(4.1)}$$

$$Av_1 \leqq y_0, \quad Av_t \leqq Bv_{t-1} \text{ for } t>1. \qquad \text{...(4.2)}$$

The first condition states that labour inputs cannot exceed the available supply and the second states that the input in each period cannot exceed the output of the preceding period.

To complete the model we must introduce the utility function u, and here our approach is somewhat unorthodox. Instead of defining u on the goods vectors Av or Bv, we define it on the vector v of activity levels. Although this differs from the usual practice it is, we believe, the conceptually correct way to think about utility. As an illustration, it is in a sense bad grammar to speak of the utility of, say, a piece of cake. One really wishes to attach utility not to the cake but to the action of consuming the cake. Thus, if after one time period the cake has been depleted by one unit the associated utility will depend on how the unit was consumed, by how many people, how hungry they were, etc. These considerations can all be taken account of by including consumption activities in the technology and assigning utility to the corresponding activity levels. Observe also that by defining u on the vectors v we can include the utility (or disutility) associated with offering the labour input vector Lv, so that it is not necessary to include a separate function to measure the disutility of labour as Ramsey did.

Finally, for the programme (v_t) we define the corresponding utility sequence in *per capita* terms by the rule

$$u_t = u(v_t/\rho^{t-1}). \qquad \text{...(4.3)}$$

In effect, u_t measures the utility of some sort of average individual when society as a whole is indulging in the activities v_t.

It now turns out conveniently that the model just described can be reduced to an equivalent one in which $\rho = 1$, that is, in which the labour supply remains constant. Namely, we define a new technology $\mathcal{T}'$ with matrices L and B as before but A is replaced by $A' = \rho A$. A programme (v'_t) for $\mathcal{T}'$ is then given by

$$Lv'_t \leqq l_0 \qquad \text{...(4.1)}'$$

$$A'v'_1 \leqq y_0, \quad A'v'_t \leqq Bv'_{t-1} \qquad \text{...(4.2)}'$$

and

$$u'_t = u(v'_t). \qquad \text{...(4.3)}$$

Theorem 1. *The set of utility sequences u_t of $\mathcal{T}$ and u'_t of $\mathcal{T}'$ are identical.*

Proof. We simply observe that (v_t) is a programme for $\mathcal{T}$ if and only if (v_t/ρ^{t-1}) is a programme for $\mathcal{T}'$, for if v_t satisfies (4.1) and (4.2) then dividing (4.1) by ρ^{t-1} we have $L(v_t/\rho^{t-1}) \leqq l_0$ which is (4.1)′ and dividing (4.2) by ρ^{t-2} gives

$$B(v_{t-1}/\rho^{t-2}) \geqq A(v_t/\rho^{t-2}) = A'(v_t/\rho^{t-1})$$

which is (4.2)′. Conversely if v'_t is a programme for $\mathcal{T}'$ then $\rho^{t-1}v'_t$ is a programme for $\mathcal{T}$ as one sees by multiplying (4.1)′ by ρ^{t-1} and (4.2)′ by ρ^{t-2}. Finally, since

$$u'_t = u(v'_t) = u(v_t/\rho^{t-1}) = u_t,$$

the proof is complete.

Having reduced the problem to one with a constant labour force we can now reformulate it in a manner which can be generalized. If we assume that some kind of labour is required in every activity then the set of all possible vectors v is bounded. Define the convex polytope K by

$$K = \{v \mid v \geqq 0, Lv \leqq l_0\}.$$

We can now define the technology $\tilde{\mathcal{T}}$ to be a set of pairs (x, y) in $2n$-space defined by

$$\tilde{\mathcal{T}} = \{(x, y) \mid x = Av, y = Bv, v \in K\}.$$

Further, we may take a new utility function u defined on $\tilde{\mathcal{T}}$ by the rule

$$\tilde{u}(x, y) = \{\max u(v) \mid v \in K \text{ and } Av = x, Bv = y\}.$$

Thus $u(x, y)$ is the largest possible utility obtainable starting from stocks x and obtaining stocks y one period later.

The general technology which we shall work with for the rest of the paper will be like the von Neumann technology except that $\mathcal{T}$ need not be polyhedral. Specifically

Definition. A *technology* $\mathcal{T}$ is a compact convex subset of non-negative pairs (x, y) in $2n$-space.

A *programme* starting from the *initial vector* y_0 is a sequence (x_t, y_t) of points of $\mathcal{T}$, where $x_t \leqq y_{t-1}$ for all $t \geqq 1$.

To complete the description of the general model we need one more concept similar to that of a Lipschitz condition.

Definition. The *steepness* σ of a function f at a point x is defined by

$$\sigma = \sup_{x'} ((f(x') - f(x))/\| x - x' \|).$$

Note that the steepness of a function at a point may be positively infinite. Here $\| x - x' \|$ may be any convenient norm on R^n, but unless otherwise stated it will be the norm $\|(\xi_1, \ldots, \xi_n)\| = \operatorname{Max}_i |\xi_i|$.

Definition. A utility function is a concave function u defined on $\mathcal{T}$ such that u has finite steepness at all points (x, y) of $\mathcal{T}$.

This completes the description of the general model with which we shall be concerned.

5. REGULAR TECHNOLOGIES AND THE KUHN-TUCKER THEOREM

Given a technology $\mathcal{T}$, an initial goods vector y_0 and a utility function u we will be interested in the typical constrained maximum problem: Find $(\bar{x}, \bar{y})$ in $\mathcal{T}$ such that

$$u(\bar{x}, \bar{y}) = \max_{x \leqq y_0} u(x, y) \text{ for } (x, y) \text{ in } \mathcal{T}. \qquad \ldots(5.1)$$

Since $\mathcal{T}$ is compact and u is continuous, this maximum will always exist and we would like to make use of the *Kuhn-Tucker Theorem* which asserts:

There exists a non-negative n-vector $\bar{p}$ such that

$$u(x, y) + \bar{p} \,.\, (y_0 - x) \leqq u(x, y) \text{ for all } (x, y) \text{ in } \mathcal{T}. \qquad \ldots(5.2)$$

In [5] we have given a simple necessary and sufficient condition for the validity of the Kuhn-Tucker Theorem. In order to state the result we define a new function associated with $\mathcal{T}$ and u.

For any n-vector $z \geqq 0$ define the function $\mu_1(z)$ by the rule

$$\mu_1(z) = \max_{x \leqq z} u(x, y).$$

Thus, $\mu_1(z)$ gives the value of the one-period optimal programme as a function of the initial vector z. We now state without proof:

Theorem 2. *The Kuhn-Tucker Theorem holds for problem* (5.1) *if and only if the function* μ_1 *has bounded steepness* σ *at* $z = y_0$. *In this case the vector* $\bar{p} = (\bar{\pi}_1, \ldots, \bar{\pi})$ *can be chosen so that* $\sum_{i=1}^{n} \pi_i = \sigma$.

For a proof the reader is referred to [5].

We wish to be able to apply the Kuhn-Tucker Theorem freely and this will be legitimate for a wide class of technologies. To define them we introduce the set valued function T defined on non-negative n-vectors z by the rule,

$$T(z) = \{(x, y) | (x, y) \in \mathscr{T} \text{ and } x \leqq z\}.$$

The set $T(z)$ thus gives all pairs in $\mathscr{T}$ which are attainable from the initial vector z.

We now use the Hausdorf metric to define the distance $\| X - Y \|$ between sets X and Y, defined by

$$\| X - Y \| = \delta(X, Y) + \delta(Y, X)$$

where

$$\delta(X, Y) = \max_x \min_y \| x - y \|, \ \delta(Y, X) = \max_y \min_x \| x - y \|.$$

Definition. The technology $\mathscr{T}$ is *regular* if the function T satisfies a Lipschitz condition, that is, if there is a constant k such that

$$\| T(z) - T(z') \| \leqq k \| z - z' \|.$$

We can best illustrate the meaning of regularity by exhibiting a technology which is not regular. Let $\mathscr{T}$ be all pairs of numbers $(x, y) \geqq 0$ such that $y^2 \leqq x$ and $x \leqq 1$. Then $T(0) = \{0\}$ and $T(z) = \{(x, y) | \ x \leqq z, \ y^2 \leqq x\}$, hence $\| T(0) - T(z) \| = \sqrt{z}$ which does not satisfy a Lipschitz condition at 0.

The regularity condition seems an economically reasonable one. It says roughly that small changes in initial stocks cannot produce arbitrarily large proportional changes in final stocks. If $\mathscr{T}$ is a convex polytope then it is automatically regular, hence von Neumann technologies are always regular. From now on all technologies will be assumed to be regular. The importance of the concept for our purposes is expressed in the following,

Lemma 1. *If* $\mathscr{T}$ *is regular and* u *is any utility function then the function* μ_1 *has finite steepness for all* $z \geqq 0$.

Proof. Given $z, z' \geqq 0$, suppose $\mu_1(z') > \mu_1(z)$. Now $\mu_1(z') = u(x', y')$ and $\mu_1(z) = u(x, y)$ for some (x', y'), (x, y) in $\mathscr{T}$. Further if $(x', y') \in T(z)$ this would contradict $\mu_1(z') > \mu_1(z)$. Let (x_1, y_1) be the closest point to (x', y') in $T(z)$. Then by regularity

$$\|(x', y') - (x_1, y_1)\| \leqq k \| z' - z \|.$$

But if σ is the steepness of u then

$$u(x', y') - u(x, y) \leqq u(x', y') - u(x_1, y_1) \leqq \sigma \| (x', y') - (x_1, y_1) \| \leqq \sigma k \| z' - z \|$$

so

$$\mu_1(z') - \mu_1(z) \leqq \sigma k \| z' - z \|,$$

so μ_1 has steepness at most σk.

The main purpose of this section is to show that for regular technologies the Kuhn-Tucker Theorem also holds for T-period programmes.

Theorem 3. *If* $\mathscr{T}$ *is regular and* $(\bar{x}_t, \bar{y}_t)$ *maximizes*

$$\sum_{t=1}^{T} u(x_t, y_t)$$

subject to

$$x_t \leqq y_{t-1} \qquad \ldots(5.3)$$

then there exist non-negative n-vectors $\bar{p}_1, \ldots, \bar{p}_T$, such that

$$\sum_{t=1}^{T} u(x_t, y_t) + \sum_{t=1}^{T} \bar{p}_t(y_{t-1} - x_t) \leqq \sum_{t=1}^{T} u(\bar{x}_t, \bar{y}_t). \qquad \ldots(5.4)$$

Proof. We consider the inequalities

$$\begin{aligned} x_1 &\leqq y_0 \\ x_2 - y_1 &\leqq z_1 \\ x_T - y_{T-1} &\leqq z_{T-1}, \end{aligned} \qquad \ldots(5.5)$$

and define

$$\mu_T(y_0, z_1, \ldots, z_{T-1}) = \max \sum_{t=1}^{T} u(x_t, y_t)$$

where (x_t, y_t) satisfy (5.5). From the result of [5] we must show that μ_T has bounded steepness. The proof is by induction on T. The fact that μ_1 has bounded steepness is the conclusion of Lemma 1. For the inductive step we note the recursion

$$\mu_T(y_0, z_1, \ldots, z_{T-1}) = \max_{x_1 \leqq y_0} \left[u(x_1, y_1) + \mu_{T-1}(z_1 + y_1, z_2, \ldots, z_{T-1})\right]$$

and since u and μ_{T-1} have bounded steepness so has μ_T, again by Lemma 1. Hence from Theorem 2 the Kuhn-Tucker Theorem (5.4) holds.

Theorem 3 has a very important

Corollary. For $\bar{p}_t$ and $(\bar{x}_t, \bar{y}_t)$ as above we have

$$u(x_t, y_t) + \bar{p}_{t+1} \cdot y_t - \bar{p}_t \cdot x_t \text{ is maximized at } (\bar{x}_t, \bar{y}_t), \qquad \ldots(5.6)$$

and

$$\bar{p}_t \cdot (\bar{y}_{t-1} - \bar{x}_t) = 0 \text{ for all } t < T. \qquad \ldots(5.7)$$

Proof. Rewrite (5.4) as

$$\bar{p}_1 \cdot y_0 + \sum_{t=1}^{T-1} (u(x_t, y_t) + \bar{p}_{t+1} \cdot y_t - \bar{p}_t \cdot x_t) + u(x_T, y_T) - \bar{p}_T \cdot x_T \leqq \sum_{t=1}^{T} u(\bar{x}_t, \bar{y}_t). \quad \ldots(5.8)$$

Since the sum (5.8) is maximized at $(\bar{x}_t, \bar{y}_t)$ and the terms under the summation sign are *independent*, the sum will be a maximum exactly when each term is a maximum, which proves (5.6), and (5.7) follows at once from (5.4) and (5.3).

The economic interpretation of (5.6) is important. If the $\bar{p}_t$ are thought of as prices then the expression $\bar{p}_{t+1} \cdot y_t - \bar{p}_t \cdot x_t$ is exactly the profit derived from choosing the pair (x_t, y_t) since $p_t \cdot x_t$ is the cost of the input x_t today and $p_{t+1} \cdot y_t$ is the return from y_t tomorrow. The corollary then states that in an optimum programme the pairs (x_t, y_t) are chosen so as to maximize the sum of profit and utility at each time t.

Note that condition (5.6) makes sense for any programme finite or infinite. This leads us to the following important

Definition. A programme (x_t, y_t) will be called *competitive* if there is a sequence of non-negative n-vectors $(\bar{p}_t)$ such that (5.6) holds for all t.

Henceforth when we speak of optimal T-period programmes we shall include the price variable $\bar{p}_t$ as well as the technological variables $(\bar{x}_t, \bar{y}_t)$, and we will denote such optimal programmes by a triple $(\bar{x}_t, \bar{y}_t; \bar{p}_t)$.

The following simple result will be used later on

Lemma 2. *Let $(\bar{x}_t, \bar{y}_t; \bar{p}_t)$ be a T-period optimal programme from y_0, where $\bar{p}_1 = (\bar{\pi}_{11}, \bar{\pi}_{12}, \ldots, \bar{\pi}_{1n})$, and let $\mu_T(z)$ be the value of the T-period optimal programme starting from z. Then the steepness of μ_t at y_0 is at most $\sum_{j=1}^{n} \bar{\pi}_{1j}$.*

Proof. Let (x'_t, y'_t) be an optimal T-period programme starting from y'_0. Then from (5.4)

$$\sum_{t=1}^{T}(u(x'_t, y'_t))+\bar{p}_1 \cdot (y_0-x'_1)+\sum_{t=1}^{T-1}\bar{p}_{t+1}\cdot(y'_t-x'_{t+1}) \leqq \sum_{t=1}^{T} u(\bar{x}_t, \bar{y}_t)$$

and since $x'_{t+1} \leqq y'_t$ we have, recalling the notation of the previous section

$$\mu(y'_0)-\mu(y_0) = \sum_{t=1}^{T}(u'_t-\bar{u}_t) \leqq \bar{p}_1 \cdot (x'_1-y_0) \leqq \bar{p}_1 \cdot (y'_0-y_0) \text{ since } x'_1 \leqq y'_0.$$

but $\bar{p}_1 \cdot (y'_0-y_0) \leqq \sum_j^n \pi_{1j} \| y'_0-y_0 \|$, completing the proof.

6. STATIONARY PROGRAMMES

From this point on we shall assume that the technology $\mathscr{T}$ contains the origin (0, 0) and also that *disposal* is possible, meaning

Assumption 1. If $(x, y) \in \mathscr{T}$ and $y' \leqq y$ then $(x, y') \in \mathscr{T}$.

We shall also assume that the technology is *productive*, meaning

Assumption 2. There exists $(x, y) \in \mathscr{T}$ such that $x<y$.

The disposal assumption may not always be realistic but the assumption of productivity is surely satisfied in the technologies one usually deals with.

A final assumption will concern the initial vector y_0 which is assumed to be *producible*, meaning

Assumption 3. There exists $x \geqq 0$ such that $(x, y_0) \in \mathscr{T}$.

Definition. A programme (x_t, y_t) is called *stationary* if (x_t, y_t) is constant (independent of t).

Clearly for a stationary programme we must have $x_t \leqq y_t$ and conversely for any (x, y) in $\mathscr{T}$ with $x \leqq y$ the sequence (x_t, y_t) is a stationary programme where $x_t = x, y_t = y$.

Definition. The pair $(\bar{x}, \bar{y})$ generates an *optimal stationary* programme if $(\bar{x}, \bar{y})$ maximizes $u(x, y)$ subject to the condition $x \leqq y$. We denote this maximum value of u by $\bar{u}$.

Optimal stationary programmes play a central role in what follows for it turns out that all " good " programmes must asymptotically approach the optimal stationary ones. At this point we will show that no programme can overtake the optimal stationary programme by more than a finite amount. We first need the important

Lemma 3. *There exists a (price) n-vector $\bar{p} \geqq 0$ such that*

$$u(x, y)+\bar{p} \cdot (y-x) \leqq \bar{u} \textit{ for all } (x, y) \textit{ in } \mathscr{T}. \qquad ...(6.1)$$

Proof. This is precisely the Kuhn-Tucker Theorem for the problem of maximizing $u(x, y)$ subject to the constraint $x \leqq y$. Since $\mathscr{T}$ is productive the constraints can be satisfied strictly and this is sufficient (see e.g. [6], page 201) for the validity of the Kuhn-Tucker Theorem.

Theorem 4. *There exists a number M such that for any programme (x_t, y_t) starting from any initial vector y_0*

$$\sum_{t=1}^{T}(u_t-\bar{u}) \leqq M \textit{ for all } T. \qquad ...(6.2)$$

Proof. From (6.1)

$$u(x_t, y_t)-u(\bar{x}, \bar{y}) \leqq \bar{p} \cdot (x_t-y_t) \qquad ...(6.3)$$

and summing (6.3) from 1 to T gives

$$\sum_{t=1}^{T}(u_t-\bar{u}) \leqq \bar{p} \cdot \sum_{t=1}^{T}(x_t-y_t)$$

$$= \bar{p} \cdot y_0 + \bar{p} \cdot \sum_{t=1}^{T}(x_t-y_{t-1}) - \bar{p} \cdot y_t$$

$$\leqq \bar{p} \cdot (y_0 - y_T) \leqq \bar{p} \cdot y_0$$

since $\bar{p} \geqq 0$ and $x_t \leqq y_{t-1}$. By boundedness of $\mathscr{T}$ there exists $M \geqq \bar{p} \cdot y_0$ for all y_0 by Assumption 3.

In view of Theorem 4 we can introduce a great notational convenience by choosing the zero of utility to be $\bar{u}$ so that (6.2) becomes simply $\sum_{t=1}^{T} u_t \leqq M$ for all T. From here on we shall assume therefore that $\bar{u} = 0$.

7. GOOD PROGRAMMES

We have seen that no programme can be infinitely better than an optimal stationary programme. A programme can, however, be infinitely worse. For example any non-optimal stationary programme has this property.

Definition. A programme (x_t, y_t) is called *good* if there is a number N such that

$$N \leqq \sum_{t=1}^{T} u_t \text{ for all } T.$$

Combining this definition with Theorem 4 we see that for good programmes the partial sums $\sum_{t=1}^{T} u_t$ form a bounded set. The following fact will be used in the subsequent development.

Theorem 5. *If the programme* (x_t, y_t) *is not good then* $\sum_{t=1}^{\infty} u_t = -\infty$.

Proof. We must show that for any N there is a T_N such that

$$\sum_{\tau=1}^{t} u_\tau \leqq N \text{ for } t > T_N. \qquad \text{...(7.1)}$$

Since (x_t, y_t) is not good there is a T_N such that

$$\sum_{\tau=1}^{T_N} u_\tau \leqq N - M \qquad \text{...(7.2)}$$

where M is the number whose existence was proved in Theorem 4, but we know from Theorem 4 that

$$\sum_{\tau=T_N}^{t} u_\tau \leqq M \text{ for all } t \qquad \text{...(7.3)}$$

and adding (7.2) and (7.3) gives (7.1).

From what has been said so far it is not clear that there need exist any good programmes. Indeed, whether or not such programmes exist will depend on the initial vector y_0. For example, if $y_0 = 0$ and the technology contains no pair $(0, y)$, $y \geqq 0$ then the only possible programme would be the zero programme which in general would not be good. This suggests the following:

Definition. The vector y_0 is called *sufficient* if there exists a programme (x_t, y_t) starting from y_0 such that $y_t > 0$ for some time t.

In words, y_0 is sufficient if eventually every other good can be produced from it directly or indirectly. The assumption that y_0 is sufficient is really no assumption at all, for if there were goods which could never be produced starting from y_0 one would not have included them in the technology in the first place.

Theorem 6. *If y_0 is sufficient there exists a good programme.*

Proof. Since y_0 is sufficient we can, after a finite time, obtain a vector y which is positive, so we may as well suppose that y_0 was positive to begin with, since what happens during any finite time interval does not affect whether a programme is good or not.

Since $\mathscr{T}$ is productive there is a pair (x_p, y_p) in $\mathscr{T}$ such that $x_p < y_p$ and we may also choose this pair so that $x_p < y_0$ (multiplying (x_p, y_p) by a small constant if necessary), using the assumption that $(0, 0) \in \mathscr{T}$.

Since $x_p < y_0$ there exists $0 \leqq \lambda < 1$ such that

$$(1-\lambda)\bar{x} + \lambda x_p \leqq y_0. \qquad \text{...(7.4)}$$

We now define the sequence (x_t, y_t) by the rule

$$\begin{aligned}(x_t, y_t) &= (1-\lambda^t)(\bar{x}, \bar{y}) + \lambda^t(x_p, y_p) \\ &= (\bar{x}, \bar{y}) + \lambda^t(x_p - \bar{x}, y_p - \bar{y}) \qquad \text{...(7.5)}\end{aligned}$$

and we will show that this gives the desired good programme. We first note the recursion

$$(x_t, y_t) = (1-\lambda)(\bar{x}, \bar{y}) + \lambda(x_{t-1}, y_{t-1}) \qquad \text{...(7.6)}$$

since

$$\begin{aligned}(1-\lambda)(\bar{x}, \bar{y}) + \lambda(x_{t-1}, y_{t-1}) &= (1-\lambda)(\bar{x}, \bar{y}) + \lambda[(1-\lambda^{t-1})(\bar{x}, \bar{y}) + \lambda^{t-1}(x_p, y_p)] \\ &= (1-\lambda^t)(\bar{x}, \bar{y}) + \lambda^t(x_p, y_p) = (x_t, y_t).\end{aligned}$$

We must show

$$x_t \leqq y_{t-1} \qquad \text{...(7.7)}$$

which follows from (7.4) and (7.5) for the case $t = 1$. Now by induction on t

$$x_{t+1} = (1-\lambda)\bar{x} + \lambda x_t \leqq (1-\lambda)\bar{y} + \lambda y_{t-1} = y_t$$

using (7.7). Thus (x_t, y_t) is a programme.

To show that the programme is good we have

$$\begin{aligned}u_t = u((\bar{x}, \bar{y}) + \lambda^t(x_p - \bar{x}, y_p - \bar{y})) &= u((\bar{x}, \bar{y}) + \lambda^t(x_p - \bar{x}, y_p - \bar{y})) - u(\bar{x}, \bar{y}) \\ &\leqq \sigma\lambda^t \, \| x_p - \bar{x}, y_p - \bar{y} \| \qquad \text{...(7.8)}\end{aligned}$$

where σ is the steepness of u at (x, y). But the inequalities (7.8) can be summed for all t giving

$$\sum_{t=1}^{\infty} u_t \leqq \frac{\sigma}{1-\lambda} \| x_p - \bar{x}, y_p - \bar{y} \|$$

where we use the fact that $\lambda < 1$. It follows that the partial sums $\sum_{t=1}^{T} u_t$ are bounded and so (x_t, y_t) is a good programme.

Example 4. It might be thought that in a productive technology one could always, after a finite number of time periods, arrive at the optimal stationary programme. That this need not be so is shown by the following example. There is a constant supply of one unit of labour and there are two activities. From one unit of labour one unit of capital can be produced and from one unit of labour combined with two units of capital one unit of utility (say, consumption) and the two units of capital can be produced. It is easy to see that the optimal stationary programme involves operating only the second activity. Given 2 units of capital one simply employs them repeatedly to produce utility. However, if initially one has less than 2 units of capital it is impossible to accumulate the two units despite the fact that the model is productive, for suppose there are c units of capital where $c<2$. Let x and y be the labour allocations to the first and second activities respectively then

$$x \leqq 1-y$$

$$y \leqq c/2 \qquad \ldots(6.9)$$

and the output of capital is

$$x+2y \leqq 1-y+2y = y+1 \leqq c/2+1<2.$$

For technical reasons in the next section we shall need a strengthened form of Theorem 6. For this purpose some new terminology is needed.

Definitions. The *goodness* G of a good programme (x_t, y_t) is defined by

$$G = \sup \left\{ N \mid \sum_{t=1}^{T} u_t \geqq N \text{ for all } T \right\}.$$

If y_0 is a sufficient vector we call the *lag* t_0 of y_0 the smallest t such that there is a t-period programme from y_0 with $y_{t-1}>0$. Thus if y_0 is positive, then $t_0 = 1$.

The *excess* q_t of a programme (x_t, y_t) in period t is defined by,

$$q_t = y_{t-1}-x_t.$$

A programme has *positive excess* at period t if $q_t>0$.

Clearly if y_0 has lag t_0 then there is a programme from y_0 with positive excess in period t_0. It is not hard to see that there is a good programme with positive excess in period t_0. Namely, one constructs a good programme starting from y_{t_0}. We shall need a somewhat stronger result for which the following assumption is needed.

Assumption 4. There exists an optimal stationary programme $(\bar{x}, \bar{y})$ where $\bar{y}$ is sufficient.

What we need to show is that there exists a uniformly good set of programmes from y_0 having a specified excess q for any given period t sufficiently large. More precisely

Lemma 4. *There exists a number N, a time $\bar{T}$ and a positive vector q such that for any $T' \geqq \bar{T}$ there is a programme $(x_t^{T'}, y_t^{T'})$ of goodness greater than N having an excess of q in period T'.*

Proof. Consider first a good programme (x_t, y_t) approaching the optimal stationary programme $(\bar{x}, \bar{y})$ of Assumption 4, given by Theorem 6. Since $\bar{y}$ is sufficient and $y_t \to \bar{y}$ there exists a sufficient vector y' and time t_1, such that $y' \leqq y_t$ for all $t \geqq t_1$. Let t' be the lag of this sufficient vector y' and let q be the positive excess that can be achieved in period t' by a good programme (x_t', y_t') starting from y'. Let G be the goodness of (x_t, y_t) and G' the goodness of (x_t', y_t'). Let $\bar{T} = t_1+t'$ and let $N = G+G'$ (note that generally speaking G and G' will be negative so N is less than G and G').

We now define the programme $(x_t^{T'}, y_t^{T'})$ as follows:

$$(x_t^{T'}, y_t^{T'}) = (x_t, y_t) \text{ for } t \leqq T'-t'$$

$$= (x'_{t+t'-T'} y_{t+t'-T'}) \text{ for } t>T'-t'.$$

To show that this is a programme it is only necessary to show that $x_{T'-t'+1} \leqq y_{T'-t'}$, but since $T' \geqq \bar{T} = t_1+t'$ it follows that $T'-t' \geqq t_1$ so by definition of t_1, $y_{T'-t'} \geqq y'$ and $x_{T'-t'+1} = x_1' \leqq y'$, so $(x_t^{T'}, y_t^{T'})$ is a programme. To estimate its goodness write

$$\sum_{\tau=1}^{t} u_\tau^{T'} = \sum_{\tau=1}^{T'-t} u_\tau^{T'} + \sum_{T'-t+1}^{t} u_\tau^{T'}$$

and note that the first term on the right is greater than G and the second greater than G' so the total is greater than N. Of course, the programme was constructed to yield excess q in period T' so the proof is complete.

8. INFINITE COMPETITIVE PROGRAMMES

In section 5 we defined competitive programmes as sequences $(x_t, y_t; p_t)$ which satisfy (see 5.6)

$$u(x_t, y_t)+\bar{p}_{t+1}\cdot y_t-\bar{p}_t\cdot x_t \leqq u(\bar{x}_t, \bar{y}_t)+\bar{p}_{t+1}\cdot \bar{y}_t-\bar{p}_t\cdot \bar{x}_t \text{ for all } (x_t, y_t) \text{ in } \mathscr{T} \quad \ldots(8.1)$$

and

$$\bar{p}_t\cdot(\bar{y}_{t-1}-\bar{x}_t)=0 \text{ for all } t. \quad \ldots(8.2)$$

We know that for regular technologies there exist T-period competitive programmes, namely those programmes which are T-period optimal. We will prove the existence of infinite competitive programmes by constructing them as limits of T-period optimal programmes. For this purpose we first introduce some notation. Let $(\bar{x}_t^T, \bar{y}_t^T; \bar{p}_t^T)$ be a T-period optimal programme. Essential for what follows is the following boundedness lemma.

Lemma 5. *There exists a positive constant β such that for any T there is a T-period optimal programme $(\bar{x}_t^T, \bar{y}_t^T; \bar{p}_t^T)$ with $\sum_{i=1}^{n} \bar{\pi}_{ti}^T \leqq \beta$ for all t, where $\bar{p}_t^T=(\bar{\pi}_{t1}^T, \ldots, \bar{\pi}_{tn}^T)$.*

We postpone for the moment the proof of this lemma which is the only mathematically difficult part of the present exposition.

Definition. The infinite sequence $(\bar{x}_t, \bar{y}_t; \bar{p}_t)$ is a *limit sequence* of the set F of finite programmes $(\bar{x}_t^T, \bar{y}_t^T; \bar{p}_t^T)$ if for any $\varepsilon>0$ and T there exists $T' \geqq T$ such that

$$\|(\bar{x}_t, \bar{y}_t; \bar{p}_t)-(\bar{x}_t^{T'}, \bar{y}_t^{T'}; \bar{p}_t^{T'})\| \leqq \varepsilon \text{ for all } t \leqq T.$$

Lemma 6. *There exists a limit programme.*

Proof. From Lemma 5 we may consider F to consist only of finite programmes for which $\| \bar{p}_t^T \| \leqq \beta$. Since the triples $(\bar{x}_1^T, \bar{y}_1^T; \bar{p}_1^T)$ are in a bounded set, there is a sequence (n_1) such that $(\bar{x}^{n_1}, \bar{y}_1^{n_1}; \bar{p}_1^{n_1})$ converges to some point $(\bar{x}_1, \bar{y}_1; \bar{p}_1)$. Similarly there is a subsequence $(n_2)\subset(n_1)$ such that $(\bar{x}_2^{n_2}, \bar{y}_2^{n_2}; \bar{p}_2^{n_2})$ converges to a point $(\bar{x}_2, \bar{y}_2; \bar{p}_2)$. Continuing in this way we construct the infinite sequence $(\bar{x}_t, \bar{y}_t; \bar{p}_t)$. This sequence has the desired property, for given any T we have a sequence (n_T) such that $(\bar{x}_t^{n_T}, \bar{y}_t^{n_T}; \bar{p}_t^{n_T})$ converges to $(\bar{x}_t, \bar{y}_t; \bar{p}_t)$ for all $t \leqq T$.

Theorem 7. *The limit sequence $(\bar{x}_t, \bar{y}_t; \bar{p}_t)$ is a good competitive programme.*

Proof. To show that $(\bar{x}_t, \bar{y}_t; \bar{p}_t)$ is a programme note first that $\bar{x}_1 \leqq y_0$ since $\bar{x}_1^T \leqq y_0$ for all T. Also there exists T such that $\bar{x}_t \leqq \bar{x}_t^T+\frac{\varepsilon}{2}e$ and $y_{t-1}^T \leqq \bar{y}_{t-1}+\frac{\varepsilon}{2}e$ where ε is any positive number and e is the n-vector with all coordinates unity. Hence

$$\bar{x}_t \leqq \bar{x}_t^T+\frac{\varepsilon}{2}e \leqq \bar{y}_{t-1}^T+\frac{\varepsilon}{2}e \leqq \bar{y}_{t-1}+\varepsilon e$$

and since this holds for all ε it follows that

$$\bar{x}_t \leqq \bar{y}_{t-1}.$$

To show that the programme is competitive, let $L(x, y; p, q)=u(x, y)+p\cdot y-q\cdot x$ and choose δ so that if $\|(x, y; p, q)-(x', y'; p', q')\| \leqq \delta$ then

$$|L(x, y; p, q)-L(x', y'; p', q')| \leqq \varepsilon.$$

Then choose T so that $\|(\bar{x}_t, \bar{y}_t; \bar{p}_t, \bar{p}_{t+1})-(\bar{x}_t^T, \bar{y}_t^T; \bar{p}_t^T, \bar{p}_{t+1}^T)\| \leqq \delta$ and we have

$$u(x_t, y_t)+\bar{p}_{t+1}^T \cdot y_t - \bar{p}_t^T \cdot x_t \leqq L(\bar{x}_t^T, \bar{y}_t^T; \bar{p}_t^T, \bar{p}_{t+1}^T) \leqq L(\bar{x}_t, \bar{y}_t; \bar{p}_t, \bar{p}_{t+1})+\varepsilon$$

and since this holds for all $\varepsilon>0$ we get (8.1). The proof of (8.2) is similar.

To show that the programme is good we recall that there exists a good programme $(\tilde{x}_t, \tilde{y}_t)$, hence a number N such that

$$\sum_{t=1}^{T} u(\tilde{x}_t, \tilde{y}_t) \geqq N \text{ for all } T. \qquad \ldots(8.3)$$

Now since each programme $(\bar{x}_t^T, \bar{y}_t^T)$ is T-period optimal it follows that

$$\sum_{t=1}^{T} u(\bar{x}_t^T, \bar{y}_t^T) \geqq N.$$

But now recall that for any programme at all with any initial y_0, $\sum_{t=1}^{T} u(x_t, y_t) \leqq M$ where M is given in Theorem 3. It follows that for $T'<T$

$$\sum_{t=1}^{T'} u(\bar{x}_t^T, \bar{y}_t^T) \geqq N-M \qquad \ldots(8.4)$$

since otherwise (8.3) would require $\sum_{t=T'}^{T} u(\bar{x}_t^T, \bar{y}_t^T)>M$. But (8.4) shows that

$$\sum_{t=1}^{T'} u(\bar{x}_t, \bar{y}_t) \geqq N-M \text{ for all } T'$$

since $(\bar{x}_t, \bar{y}_t)$ is a limit of the programmes $(\bar{x}_t^T, \bar{y}_t^T)$. This completes the proof.

Proof of Lemma 5. Let $\bar{T}$ be the constant given in Lemma 4. We first show that there is a constant β' such that $\| \bar{p}_{T'}^T \| \leqq \beta'$ for $T_t \geqq \bar{T}$. Let $(x_t^{T'}, y_t^{T'})$ be the programme of Lemma 4. From the Kuhn-Tucker Theorem (5.4) we have

$$\sum_{\tau=1}^{t} (u_\tau^{T'}+\bar{p}_\tau^T \cdot (y_{\tau-1}^{T'}-x_\tau^{T'})) \leqq \sum_{\tau=1}^{t} \bar{u}_\tau^T \leqq M \qquad \ldots(8.5)$$

where M is the constant of Theorem 4.

Also from Lemma 4 we have

$$\sum_{\tau=1}^{t} u_\tau^{T'} \geqq N \qquad \ldots(8.6)$$

where N is the constant of the Lemma.

Subtracting (8.6) from (8.5) gives

$$\sum_{\tau=1}^{t} \bar{p}_\tau^T \cdot (y_{\tau-1}^{T'}-x_\tau^{T'}) \geqq M-N$$

and since all terms in the sum above are non-negative we have in particular

$$\bar{p}_{T'}^T \cdot (y_{T'-1}^{T'}-x_{T'}^{T'}) = \bar{p}_{T'}^T \cdot q \leqq M-N$$

and since $q>0$ this gives a bound β' to $\| \bar{p}_{T'}^T \|$ which is independent of T and T' provided $T' \geqq \bar{T}$.

It remains to establish a bound on the prices p_t^T for $t<\bar{T}$. In view of Theorem 2 it will be sufficient to show that the function $\mu_T(y_0, z_1, \ldots, z_{T-1})$ has finite steepness at $(y_0, 0, \ldots, 0)$, where we recall that

$$\mu_T(y_0, z_1, \ldots, z_{T-1}) = \max \sum_{t=1}^{T} u(x_t, y_t)$$

subject to

$$x_1 \leqq y_0$$
$$x_2 - y_1 \leqq z_1$$
$$x_T - y_{T-1} \leqq z_{T-1}$$
$$x_{T+1} - y_T \leqq 0.$$

Now note that

$$\mu_T(y_0, z_1, \ldots, z_{T-1}) = \max \left[\sum_{t=1}^{T} u(x_t, y_t) + \mu_{T-T}(y_T) \right]$$

subject to

$$x_1 \leqq y_0$$
$$x_2 - y_1 \leqq z_1$$
$$\cdot \quad \cdot \quad \cdot \quad \cdot \quad \cdot \quad \cdot$$
$$x_T - y_{T-1} \leqq z_{T-1}.$$

But also from the corollary to Lemma 1 the steepness of μ_{T-T} at $\bar{y}_T^T$ is bounded by $\| \bar{p}_T^T \|$ which is at most β' independent of T. Also the function $\sum_{t=1}^{T-1} u(x_t, y_t)$ has bounded steepness and does not depend on T at all. It follows from Theorem 3 (since the technology is regular) that $\mu_T(y_0, z_1, \ldots, z_{T-1})$ has the desired bounded steepness, and hence the lemma follows from Theorem 2.

9. ASYMPTOTIC PROPERTIES OF GOOD PROGRAMMES

In this section we will prove a certain " turn-pike " property of good programmes which will be the final tool needed to prove existence of optimal programmes.

Definition. A function on a convex set X is called *strictly concave* at $\bar{x}$ in X if

$$f(\lambda\bar{x} + (1-\lambda)x) > \lambda f(\bar{x}) + (1-\lambda)f(x) \text{ for all } x \neq \bar{x} \text{ in } X \text{ and } 0 < \lambda < 1.$$

We note that strict concavity at $\bar{x}$ need not imply strict concavity in any neighbourhood of $\bar{x}$. As an example, if $f(x, y) = -(x+y)^2$ on the positive orthant, then f is strictly concave at (0, 0) for

$$f(\lambda(0, 0) + (1-\lambda)(x, y)) = -(1-\lambda)^2(x+y)^2$$
$$> -(1-\lambda)(x+y)^2 = \lambda f(0, 0) + (1-\lambda)f(x, y) \text{ for } 0 < \lambda < 1.$$

But

$$\tfrac{1}{2}(f(\varepsilon, 0) + f(0, \varepsilon)) = -\tfrac{1}{2}(2\varepsilon^2) = -\varepsilon^2$$

and

$$f(\tfrac{1}{2}(\varepsilon, 0) + \tfrac{1}{2}(0, \varepsilon)) = f\left(\frac{\varepsilon}{2}, \frac{\varepsilon}{2}\right) = -\varepsilon^2$$

so f is not strictly concave in any neighbourhood of (0, 0).

Assumption 5. The function u is strictly concave at some optimal stationary programme $(\bar{x}, \bar{y})$. (This implies, of course, that $(\bar{x}, \bar{y})$ is the only optimal stationary programme.)

Recall that $u(x, y)$ measures the satisfaction to society from engaging in the activities which create y out of x. The strict concavity of u implies that by " mixing " activities society derives a satisfaction strictly greater than the corresponding mixture of utilities. (We avoid here, as throughout the paper, asking whether social satisfaction really behaves in this way. From our point of view the function u serves as some sort of reasonable guide for making production decisions. If one is prepared to accept such a function at all, one should not object too violently to perturbing it slightly if necessary to obtain the desired strictness.)

Theorem 8. *Under Assumption* 5, *if* (x_t, y_t) *is a good programme then*

$$\lim_{t\to\infty} (x_t, y_t) = (\bar{x}, \bar{y}).$$

Proof. Let (x_t, y_t) be a good programme. We may rewrite Lemma 3 as

$$u(x_t, y_t) = \bar{p}(x_t - y_t) - \delta_t \text{ where } \delta_t \geqq 0. \qquad \text{...(9.1)}$$

Summing (9.1) on t and using the fact that (x_t, y_t) is good we know there is a number N such that

$$N \leqq \sum_{t=1}^{T} u_t = \sum_{t=1}^{T} \bar{p}(x_t - y_t) - \sum_{t=1}^{T} \delta_t$$

$$= \bar{p} \cdot y_0 + \sum_{t=1}^{T} \bar{p}(x_t - y_{t-1}) - \bar{p} \cdot y_T - \sum_{t=1}^{T} \delta_t$$

$$\leqq \bar{p} \cdot y_0 - \sum_{t=1}^{T} \delta_t \qquad \text{...(9.2)}$$

so that

$$\sum_{t=1}^{T} \delta_t \leqq \bar{p} \cdot y_0 - N$$

and hence $\sum_{t=1}^{T} \delta_t$ is bounded and therefore the infinite series $\sum_{t=1}^{\infty} \delta_t$ converges. In particular $\lim_{t\to\infty} \delta_t = 0$. Now defining

$$\phi(x, y) = u(x, y) + \bar{p}(y - x)$$

we know that ϕ is maximized at $(\bar{x}, \bar{y})$ and also that ϕ is strictly concave at $(\bar{x}, \bar{y})$. Hence $(\bar{x}, \bar{y})$ is the only maximum point of ϕ and $\phi(\bar{x}, \bar{y}) = 0$ since $u(\bar{x}, \bar{y}) = 0$.

But from (9.1)

$$\phi(x_t, y_t) = \delta_t,$$

and since $\delta_t \to 0$ it follows from continuity of ϕ that $(x_t, y_t) \to (\bar{x}, \bar{y})$.

Corollary. Under Assumption 5, the series $\sum_{t=1}^{\infty} u_t$ of any programme is convergent.

Proof. We have already seen (Theorem 4) that if the programme is not good it converges to $-\infty$. If the programme is good then from (9.2) we see that $\sum_{t=1}^{\infty} \bar{p}(x_t - y_{t-1})$ converges since all terms in the series are non-positive and the series is bounded below by $N - \bar{p} \cdot y_0$. Hence all terms on the right hand side of (9.2) approach limits because $\bar{p} \cdot y_T \to \bar{p} \cdot \bar{y}$, and therefore $\sum_{t=1}^{\infty} u_t$ is convergent.

This corollary is an analogue of a theorem proved by Koopmans [3] for a one sector model.

10. OPTIMAL PROGRAMMES

We can now pull together the results of all the preceding sections to obtain our main existence theorem.

Theorem 9. *Under Assumptions* 1-5, *the limit programme of Section* 7 *is optimal. If in addition we assume u to be strictly concave then the programme is unique and strongly optimal.*

B

Proof. Let $(\bar{x}_t, \bar{y}_t; \bar{p}_t)$ be the limit programme and let (x_t, y_t) be any other good programme. From the competitive conditions we know that

$$u(x_t, y_t)+\bar{p}_{t+1}\cdot y_t-\bar{p}_t\cdot x_t \leqq u(\bar{x}_t, \bar{y}_t)+\bar{p}_{t+1}\cdot \bar{y}_t-\bar{p}_t\cdot \bar{x}_t \text{ for all } t. \qquad \text{...(10.1)}$$

Treating first the case where u is strictly concave we see that unless $(x_t, y_t) = (\bar{x}_t, \bar{y}_t)$ for all t, there will be at least one t for which there is a difference of $\varepsilon>0$ between the two sides of (10.1). Summing them on t we get

$$\begin{aligned}\sum_{t=1}^{T} (u_t+(\bar{p}_{t+1}\cdot y_t-\bar{p}_t\cdot x_t))\\
&= \sum_{t=1}^{T} u_t-\bar{p}_1\cdot y_0+\sum_{t=1}^{T} \bar{p}_t\cdot(y_{t-1}-x_t)+\bar{p}_{T+1}\cdot y_T\\
&\leqq \sum_{t=1}^{T} \bar{u}_t-\bar{p}_1\cdot y_0+\sum_{t=1}^{T} \bar{p}_t\cdot(\bar{y}_{t-1}-\bar{x}_t)+\bar{p}_{T+1}\cdot \bar{y}_T-\varepsilon\\
&= \sum_{t=1}^{T} \bar{u}_t-\bar{p}_1\cdot y_0+\bar{p}_{T+1}\cdot \bar{y}_T-\varepsilon \text{ (because of the second competitive condition).}\end{aligned}$$

Rearranging gives

$$\sum_{t=1}^{T} (u_t-\bar{u}_t) \leqq \bar{p}_{T+1}\cdot(y_{T+1}-\bar{y}_T)-\varepsilon \qquad \text{...(10.2)}$$

but since both programmes are good, y_{T+1} and $\bar{y}_{T+1}$ approach $\bar{y}$ so the right-hand side of (10.2) becomes and remains negative for T sufficiently large which proves the strong optimality of and uniqueness of $(\bar{x}_t, \bar{y}_t)$.

In case u is not strictly concave, the ε in (10.2) becomes zero and the argument shows only that $\bar{u}_t$ catches up to u_t and is therefore optimal in the weaker sense.

University of California, Berkeley DAVID GALE.

REFERENCES

[1] Ramsey, F. P. " A Mathematical Theory of Savings ", *Economic Journal*, **38** (1928), 543-559.

[2] Samuelson, P. A. and Solow, R. " A Complete Capital Model Involving Heterogeneous Capital Goods ", *Quarterly Journal of Economics*, **70** (1956), 537-562.

[3] Koopmans, T. C. *On the Concept of Optimal Growth*, Pontificia Academia Scientiarum (Vatican City, 1965), 225-288.

[4] von Weizsäcker, C. C. " Existence of Optimal Programmes of Accumulation for an Infinite Time Horizon ", *Review of Economic Studies*, **32** (1965), 85-104.

[5] Gale, D. " A Geometric Duality Theorem with Economic Applications ", *Review of Economic Studies*, **34**, (1967), 19-24.

[6] Karlin, S. *Mathematical Methods and Theory in Games, Programming and Economics*, Vol. I, pp. 200-201, Addison-Wesley, Reading, Mass., 1959.

BIBLIOGRAPHY

Abbreviations

AEP	Australian Economic Papers
AER	American Economic Review
CJE	Canadian Journal of Economics and Political Science
EDCC	Economic Development and Cultural Change
EI	Economia Internazionale
EJ	Economic Journal
ER	Economic Record
Ec	Economica, New Series
Em	Econometrica
IER	International Economic Review
JB	Journal of Business
JPE	Journal of Political Economy
Kyk	Kyklos
Met	Metroeconomica
MS	Manchester School of Economics and Social Studies
OEP	Oxford Economic Papers
OIS	Oxford University Institute of Statistics Bulletin
OsEP	Osaka Economic Papers
QJE	Quarterly Journal of Economics
REStat	Review of Economics and Statistics
REStud	Review of Economic Studies
RISE	Revista Internazionale di Scienze Economiche e Commerciali
WA	Weltwirtschaftliches Archiv
YB	Yorkshire Bulletin of Economic and Social Research

Abramovitz, M. "Economics of Growth," *A Survey of Contemporary Economics*, Vol. 2, edited by B. F. Haley (Homewood, Ill.: Irwin, for American Economic Association, 1952).

Abramovitz, M. "Resources and Output Trends in the United States since 1870," *AER Papers and Proceedings*, Vol. 46, May 1956.

Abramovitz, M. "Economic Growth in the United States," *AER*, Vol. 52, September 1962.

Adelman, I. *Theories of Economic Growth and Development* (Stanford: Stanford University Press, 1961).

Adelman, I., and Lobo, O. "Some Observations on Full Employment versus Full Capacity," *AER*, Vol. 46, June 1956.

Adelman, I., and Thorbecke, E. (eds.). *The Theory and Design of Economic Development* (Baltimore: The Johns Hopkins Press, 1966).

Ahmad, S. "Harrod on Domar's Theory of Growth," *EJ*, Vol. 71, June 1961.

Alexander, S. S. "The Accelerator as a Generator of Steady Growth," *QJE*, Vol. 48, May 1949.

Alexander, S. S. "Mr. Harrod's Dynamic Model," *EJ*, Vol. 60, December 1950.

Allais, M. "The Influence of the Capital-Output Ratio on Real National Income," *Em*, Vol. 30, October 1962; "Errata," *Em*, Vol. 31, October 1963.

Allen, R. G. D. "The Structure of Macroeconomic Models," *EJ*, Vol. 70, March 1960.

Amano, A. "Biased Technical Progress and a Neoclassical Theory of Economic Growth," *QJE*, Vol. 78, February 1964.

Amano, A. "A Further Note on Professor .Uzawa's Two-Sector Model of Economic Growth," *REStud*, Vol. 31, April 1964.

Amano, A. "International Capital Movements and Economic Growth," *Kyk*, Vol. 58, fasc. 4, 1966.

Ames, E., and Rosenberg, N. "Changing Technological Leadership and Industrial Growth," *EJ*, Vol. 73, March 1963.

Anderson, L. C. "The Incidence of Monetary and Fiscal Measures on the Structure of Output," *REStat*, Vol. 46, August 1964.

Anderson, P. A. "The Apparent Decline in Capital-Output Ratios," *QJE*, Vol. 75, November 1961.

Anderson, P. S. "Relative Economic Growth Rates and Fiscal-Monetary Policies: A Comment" (followed by B. W. Sprinkel's reply), *JPE*, Vol. 73, February 1965.

Anderson, W. H. L., and Cornwall, J. "Problems of Growth Policy," *REStat*, Vol. 43, May 1961.

Ando, A., and Fisher, F. M. "Near-decomposability, Partition and Aggregation, and the Relevance of Stability Discussions," *IER*, Vol. 4, January 1963.

Ando, A., Fisher, F. M., and Simon, H. A. *Essays on the Structure of Social Science Models* (Cambridge, Mass.: M.I.T. Press, 1963).

Ando, A., and Simon, H. A. "Aggregation of Variables in Dynamic Systems," *Em*, Vol. 29, April 1961.

Ara, K. "Capital Theory and Economic Growth," *EJ*, Vol. 68, September 1958.

Arndt, H. W. "External Economies in Economic Growth," *ER*, Vol. 31, November 1955.

Arrow, K. J. "Alternative Proof of the Substitution Theorem for Leontief Models in the General Case," *Activity Analysis of Production and Allocation*, edited by T. C. Koopmans (New York: Wiley, 1951).

Arrow, K. J. "The Economic Implications of Learning by Doing," *REStud*, Vol. 29, June 1962.

Arrow, K. J., Chenery, H. B., Minhas, B., and Solow, R. M. "Capital-Labor Substitution and Economic Efficiency," *REStat*, Vol. 43, August 1961.

Asimakopulos, A. "Findlay's Robinsonian Model of Accumulation: A Note," *Ec*, N.S., Vol. 32, April 1965.

Asimakopulos, A., and Weldon, J. C. "The Classification of Technical Progress in Models of Economic Growth," *Ec*, Vol. 30, November 1963.

Asimakopulos, A., and Weldon, J. C. "Sir Roy Harrod's Equation of Supply," *OEP*, N.S., Vol. 15, November 1963.

Asimakopulos, A., and Weldon, J. C. "The Definition of Neutral Inventions," *EJ*, Vol. 73, December 1963.

Atsumi, H. "Neoclassical Growth and the Efficient Program of Capital Accumulation," *REStud*, Vol. 32, April 1965.

Avramovic, D. *Economic Growth and External Debt* (Baltimore: The Johns Hopkins Press, 1964).

Bagchi, A. K. "The Choice of the Optimum Technique," *EJ*, Vol. 72, September 1962.

Balassa, B. "Some Observations on Mr. Beckerman's 'Export-Propelled' Growth Model" (followed by W. Beckerman's reply), *EJ*, Vol. 73, December 1963.

Balassa, B. "Some Observations on Mr. Beckerman's 'Export-Propelled' Growth Model: A Rejoinder," *EJ*, Vol. 74, March 1964.

Balassa, B. "The Capital Needs of the Developing Countries," *Kyk*, Vol. 17, fasc. 2, 1964.

Ball, R. J. "The Cambridge Model of Economic Growth," *Ec*, N.S., Vol. 30, May 1963.

Balogh, T. "Equity and Efficiency: The Problem of Optimal Efficiency in a Framework of Underdevelopment," *OEP*, February 1962.

Baran, P. A. "The Political Economy of Growth" (New York: Monthly Review Press, 1957).

Baran, P. A., and Hobsbawm, E. J. "The Stages of Economic Growth," *Kyk*, Vol. 14, fasc. 2, 1961.

Barber, C. L. "Population Growth and the Demand for Capital," *AER*, Vol. 43, March 1953.

Bardhan, P. "International Differences in Production Functions, Trade and Factor Prices," *EJ*, Vol. 75, March 1965.

Bardhan, P. "Optimum Accumulation and International Trade," *REStud*, Vol. 32, July 1965.

Bardhan, P. "Equilibrium Growth in the International Economy," *QJE*, Vol. 74, August 1965.

Bator, F. M. "Capital Productivity, Input Allocation, and Growth," *QJE*, Vol. 71, February 1957.

Bauer, P. T., and Wilson, C. "The Stages of Growth," *Ec*, N.S., Vol. 29, May 1962.

Baumol, W. J. "Formalization of Mr. Harrod's Model," *EJ*, Vol. 59, December 1949.

Baumol, W. J. "Yet Another Note on the Harrod-Domar Model," *EJ*, Vol. 62, June 1952.

Baumol, W. J., and Quandt, R. E. "Investment and Discount Rates under Capital Rationing—A Programming Approach," *EJ*, Vol. 75, June 1965.

Bear, D. V. T. "A Multi-Sector Model of Balanced Growth," *REStat*, Vol. 43, May 1961.

Beckerman, W. "Projecting Europe's Growth," *EJ*, Vol. 72, December 1962.

Beckerman, W. "Professor Balassa's Comments on My 'Export-Propelled' Growth Model: A Rebuttal" (followed by B. Balassa's further note), *EJ*, Vol. 74, September 1964.

Beckman, M. J. "A Wicksellian Model of Growth," *RISE*, Vol. 12, March 1965.

Bensusan-Butt, D. M. "Some Elementary Theory about Accumulation," *OEP*, N.S., Vol. 6, September 1954.

Bensusan-Butt, D. M. *On Economic Growth: An Essay in Pure Theory* (Oxford: Clarendon Press, 1960).

Berglas, E. "Investment and Technological Change," *JPE*, Vol. 73, April 1965.

Bhagwati, J. "Immiserizing Growth: A Geometrical Note," *REStud*, Vol, 25, June 1958.

Bhagwati, J. "The Pure Theory of International Trade," *EJ*, Vol. 74, March 1964.

Bhati, R. J. "Disguised Unemployment and Saving Potential," *IER*, Vol. 4, August 1958.

Bhatt, V. V. "Techniques, Employment and Rate of Growth," *EJ*, Vol. 68, September 1958.

Bhatt, V. V. "Some Notes on Balanced and Unbalanced Growth," *EJ*, Vol. 75, March 1965.

Bicanic, R. "The Threshold of Economic Growth," *Kyk*, Vol. 15, fasc. 1, 1962.
Bierwag, G. O. "Balanced Growth and Technological Progress," *OEP*, N.S., Vol. 16, March 1964.
Bilkey, W. J. "A Note Regarding the *e* in Harrod's Second Fundamental Equation" (followed by R. F. Harrod's reply), *EJ*, Vol. 72, December 1962.
Birmingham, W. B., and Ford A. G. (eds.). *Planning and Growth in Rich and Poor Countries* (New York: Praeger, 1966).
Black, J. "Inflation and Long-Run Growth," *Ec*, N.S., Vol. 26, May 1959.
Black, J. "The Technical Progress Function and the Production Function," *Ec*, Vol. 29, May 1962.
Black, J. "Optimum Savings Reconsidered, or Ramsey without Tears," *EJ*, Vol. 72, June 1962.
Black, J. "Technical Progress and Optimal Savings," *REStud*, Vol. 29, June 1962.
Blaug, M. "A Survey of the Theory of Process Innovations," *Ec*, Vol. 30, February 1963.
Blitz, R. C. "Capital Longevity and Economic Development," *AER*, Vol. 46, June 1958.
Blyth, C. A. "Towards a More General Theory of Capital," *Ec*, N.S. Vol. 27, May 1960.
Bodenhorn, D. "The Stability of Growth Models," *AER*, Vol. 46, September 1956.
Bonner, J., and Lees, D. S. "Consumption and Investment," *JPE*, Vol. 71, February 1963.
Borts, G. H. "Professor Meade on Economic Growth," *Ec*, N.S., Vol. 29, February 1962.
Borts, G. H., and Stein, J. L. *Economic Growth in a Free Market* (New York: Columbia University Press, 1964).
Borukhov, E. "The Capital-Output Ratio, Factors and the Input of Capital," *EI*, Vol. 19, May 1966.
Bose, S. "Economic Growth in a Two-Sector Planning Model," *EI*, Vol. 18, August 1965.
Boulding, K. "Toward a General Theory of Growth," *CJE*, Vol. 19, August 1953.
Boulding, K. "The Malthusian Model as a General System," *Social and Economic Studies*, Vol. 4, September 1955.
Brems, H. "Stability and Growth," *EJ*, Vol. 65, December 1955.
Brems, H. "The Foreign Trade Accelerator and the International Transmission of Growth," *Em*, Vol. 24, July 1956.
Brems, H. "Constancy of the Proportionate Equilibrium Rate of Growth: Result or Assumption?," *REStud*, Vol. 24, February 1957.
Brems, H. "Growth Rates of Output, Labor Force Hours and Productivity," *REStat*, Vol. 39, November 1957.
Brockie, M. D. "Full Employment, Growth and Price Stabilization," *WA*, Vol. 94, Hft. 1, 1965.
Brody, A. "A Simplified Growth Model," *QJE*, Vol. 80, February 1966.
Bronfenbrenner, M. "A Simplified Mahalanobis Development Model," *EDCC*, Vol. 9, October 1960.
Bronfenbrenner, M. "Formalizing the Shimomura Growth Model," *EDCC*, Vol. 14, October 1965.
Brown, E. H. P., and Ozga, S. A. "Economic Growth and the Price Level," *EJ*, Vol. 65, March 1955.

Brown, J. A. C., and Stone, J. R. N. "Output and Investment for Exponential Growth in Consumption," *REStud*, Vol. 29, June 1962.

Brown, M. *On the Theory and Measurement of Technological Change* (Cambridge University Press, 1966).

Brown, M., and DeCani, J. S. "A Measure of Technological Employment," *REStat*, Vol. 43, November 1963.

Bruno, M., Burmeister, E., and Sheshinski, E. "Nature and Implications of the Reswitching of Techniques," *QJE*, Vol. 80, November 1966.

Bruton, H. J. "Growth Models and Underdeveloped Economies," *JPE*, Vol. 63, August 1955.

Bruton, H. J. "Innovations and Equilibrium Growth," *EJ*, Vol. 66, September 1956.

Bruton, H. J. *A Survey of Recent Contributions to the Theory of Economic Growth* (Cambridge, Mass.: Center for International Studies, 1956).

Burmeister, E. "The Existence of Golden Ages and Stability in the Two-Sector Model," *QJE*, Vol. 81, February 1967.

Buttrick, J. "A Note on Professor Solow's Growth Model," *QJE*, Vol. 72, November 1958.

Buttrick, J. "A Note on Growth Theory," *EDCC*, Vol. 9, October 1960.

Caff, J. T. "A Generalisation of the Multiplier-Accelerator Model," *EJ*, Vol. 71, March 1961.

Cairncross, A. K. "The Place of Capital in Economic Progress,"*Economic Progress*, Proceedings of International Economic Association Conference, edited by L. H. Dupriez (Louvain: Institut de Recherches Economiques et Sociales, 1955).

Cairncross, A. K. "International Trade and Economic Development," *Kyk*, Vol. 13, fasc. 4, 1960.

Carter, C. F., and Williams, B. R. *Industry and Technical Progress* (London: Oxford University Press, 1957).

Carter, C. F., and Williams, B. R. *Investment in Innovation* (London: Oxford University Press, 1958).

Carter, C. F., and Williams, B. R. *Science in Industry* (London: Oxford University Press, 1959).

Cartter, A. M. "Comment on Hans Brem's 'Stability and Growth,'" *EJ*, Vol. 66, December 1956.

Cass, D. "Optimum Growth in an Aggregative Model of Capital Accumulation," *REStud*, Vol. 32, 1965.

Chakravarty, S. "The Existence of an Optimum Savings Program," *Em*, Vol. 30, January 1962.

Chakravarty, S. "Programming Techniques for Economic Development," *EDCC*, Vol. 10, July, 1962.

Chakravarty, S. "Optimal Savings with Finite Planning Horizon," *IER*, Vol. 3, September 1962.

Chakravarty, S. "Optimal Investment and Technical Progress," *REStud*, Vol. 31, June 1964.

Chakravarty, S. "Optimal Programme of Capital Accumulation in a Multi-Sector Economy," *Em*, Vol. 33, July 1965.

Champernowne, D. G. "A Note on J. von Neumann's Article on 'A Model of Economic Equilibrium,'" *REStud*, Vol. 13, No. 1, 1945.

Champernowne, D. G. "Capital Accumulation and the Maintenance of Full Employment," *EJ*, Vol. 58, June 1958.

Champernowne, D. G. "A Dynamic Growth Model Involving a Production Function," *The Theory of Capital*, Proceedings of International Association Conference, edited by F. A. Lutz and D. C. Hague (London: Macmillan, 1961).

Champernowne, D. G. "Some Implications of Golden Age Conditions When Savings Equal Profits," *REStud*, Vol. 29, June 1962.

Champernowne, D. G., and Kahn, R. F. "The Value of Invested Capital; A Mathematical Addendum to Mrs. Robinson's Article," *REStud*, Vol. 21, 1962.

Chandavarkar, A. G. "The Saving Potential of Disguised Unemployment," *EJ*, Vol. 67, June 1957.

Chang, P. P. "Rate of Profit and Income Distribution in Relation to the Rate of Economic Growth: A Comment" (followed by L. L. Pasinetti's reply), *REStud*, Vol. 31, April 1964.

Chenery, H. B. "Patterns of Industrial Growth," *AER*, Vol. 50, September 1960.

Chenery, H. B. "Comparative Advantage and Development Policy, (A Survey)," *AER*, Vol. 51, March 1961.

Chenery, H. B., and Strout, A. M. "Foreign Assistance and Economic Development," *AER*, Vol. 56, No. 4, September 1966.

Clark, C. "Theory of Economic Growth," *Em*, Vol. 17, supplement, July 1949.

Clark, C. "The Fundamental Problems of Economic Growth," *WA*, Vol. 94, Hft. 1, 1965.

Colm, G. "Fiscal Policy Innovations in Relation to Economic Growth," *Kyk*, Vol. 19, fasc. 4, 1966.

Conlisk, J. "Unemployment in a Neoclassical Growth Model: The Effect on Speed of Adjustment," *EJ*, Vol. 76, September 1966.

Coombs, H. C. "Economic Development and Financial Stability," *ER*, Vol. 3, November 1955.

Corden, W. M. "The Two Sector Growth Model with Fixed Coefficients," *REStud*, Vol. 33, July 1966.

Cozzi, T. "A Comment—Balanced and Unbalanced Growth" (followed by V. V. Bhatt: A Reply), *EJ*, Vol. 76, September 1966.

Cragg, J. G. "Technological Progress, Investment and Full-employment Growth," *CJE*, Vol. 29, August 1963.

Dagnino-Pastore, J. M. "Balanced Growth: An Interpretation," *OEP*, N.S., Vol. 15, July 1963.

Dasgupta, A. K. "Decision Criteria and Balanced Growth," *REStud*, Vol. 31, April 1964.

Dasgupta, A. K. "A Note on Optimum Savings," *Em*, Vol. 32, July 1964.

Datta, U. "An Attempt at Application of Linear Programming to Planning," *IER*, Vol. 5, August 1960.

Davis, R. M. "Income Distribution in a Two-sector Economy," *OEP*, N.S., Vol. 13, October 1961.

Debreu, G. "Numerical Representations of Technological Change," *Met*, Vol. 6, August 1954.

Dehem, R. "The Economics of Stunted Growth," *CJE*, Vol. 28, November 1962.

Denison, E. F. "How to Raise the High-employment Growth Rate by One Percentage Point," *AER/S*, Vol. 52, May 1962.

Denison, E. F. *The Sources of Economic Growth in the United States and the Alternatives before Us* (New York: Committee for Economic Development, 1962).

Denison, E. F. "The Unimportance of the Embodied Question," *AER*, Vol. 54, March 1964.

Denison, E. F. "Capital Theory and the Rate of Return," *AER*, Vol. 54, September 1964.

Desrousseaux, J. "Expansion stable et taux d'intérêt optimal," *Annales des Mines*, November 1961.

Dhrymes, P. J. "A Multisectoral Model of Growth," *QJE*, Vol 76, May 1962.

Dhrymes, P. J. "Some Extensions and Tests for the CES Class of Production Functions," *REStat*, Vol. 47, November 1965.

Diamond, P. A. "Optimal Growth in a Model of Srinivasan," *Yale Economic Essays*, Vol. 4, Spring 1964.

Diamond, P. A. "Disembodied Technical Change in a Two-Sector Model," *REStud*, Vol. 32, April 1965.

Diamond, P. A. "Technical Change and the Measurement of Capital and Output," *REStud*, Vol. 32, October 1965.

Diamond, P. A. "National Debt in a Neoclassical Growth Model," *AER*, Vol. 55, December 1965.

Dickinson, H. D. "A Note on Dynamic Economics," *REStud*, Vol. 22, 1955.

Dobb, M. H. "Second Thoughts on Capital Intensity of Investment," *REStud*, Vol. 24, No. 1, 1956.

Dobb, M. H. "An Essay on Economic Growth and Planning" (New York: Monthly Review Press, 1960).

Dobb, M. H. "Some Problems in the Theory of Growth and Planning Policy," *Kyk*, Vol. 14, fasc. 2, 1961.

Dobb, M. H. *Economic Growth and Underdeveloped Countries* (New York: International Publishers, 1963).

Domar, E. D. "The Burden of the Debt and the National Income," *AER*, Vol. 34, December 1944.

Domar, E. D. "Capital Expansion, Rate of Growth and Employment," *Em*, Vol. 14, April 1946.

Domar, E. D. "Expansion and Employment," *AER*, Vol. 37, March 1947.

Domar, E. D. "The Problem of Capital Accumulation," *AER*, Vol. 38, December 1948.

Domar, E. D. "Economic Growth: An Econometric Approach," *AER/S*, Vol. 42, May 1952.

Domar, E. D. "Depreciation, Replacement and Growth," *EJ*, Vol. 63, March 1953.

Domar, E. D. *Essays in the Theory of Growth* (London: Oxford University Press, 1957).

Domar, E. D. "Depreciation, Replacement and Growth, and Fluctuations," *EJ*, Vol. 67, December 1957.

Domar, E. D. "On the Measurement of Technological Change," *EJ*, Vol. 71, December 1961.

Domar, E. D. "On Total Productivity and All That," *EJ*, Vol. 72, September 1962.

Domar, E. D. "Total Productivity and the Quality of Capital," *JPE*, Vol. 71, December 1963.

Dorfman, R. "Mathematical, or 'Linear,' Programming: A Nonmathematical Exposition," *AER*, Vol. 43, December 1953.

Dorfman, R. "A Graphical Exposition of Böhm-Bawerk's Interest Theory," *REStud*, Vol. 26, February 1959.

Dorfman, R. "Regional Allocation of Investment," *QJE*, Vol. 77, February 1963.

Dorfman, R., Samuelson, P. A., and Solow, R. M. *Linear Programming and Economic Analysis* (New York: McGraw Hill, 1958).

Drandanakis, E. M. "Factor Substitution in the Two-sector Growth Model," *REStud*, Vol. 30, October 1963.

Drandanakis, E. M. "On Efficient Accumulation Paths in the Closed Production Model," *Em*, Vol. 34, April 1966.

Drandanakis, E. M., and Phelps, E. S. "A Model of Induced Invention, Growth and Distribution," *EJ*, Vol. 76, December 1966.

Duesenberry, J. S. *Income, Saving and the Theory of Consumer Behaviour* (Cambridge, Mass.: Harvard University Press, 1949).

Duesenberry, J. S. "Innovation and Growth," *AER/S*, Vol. 46, May 1956.

Duesenberry, J. S. *Business Cycles and Economic Growth* (New York: McGraw Hill, 1958).

Easterlin, R. A. "Economic-Demographic Interactions and Long Swings in Economic Growth," *AER*, Vol. 56, December 1966.

Eckaus, R. S., and Lefeber, L. "Capital Formation: A Theoretical and Empirical Analysis," *REStud*, Vol. 44, May 1962.

Eckstein, O. "Investment Criteria for Economic Development and the Theory of Intertemporal Welfare Economics," *QJE*, Vol. 71, February 1957.

Eckstein, O. (Chief author), Staff Report on Employment, Growth and Price Levels, prepared for consideration by the Joint Economic Committee, Congress of the United States, December 24, 1959.

Eckstein, O. "Capital Theory and Some Theoretical Problems in Development Planning," *AER/S*, Vol. 51, May 1961.

Eisner, R. "Underemployment Equilibrium Rates of Growth," *AER*, Vol. 42, March 1952.

Eisner, R. "Depreciation Allowances, Replacement Requirements and Growth," *AER*, Vol. 42, December 1952.

Eisner, R. "Guaranteed Growth of Income," *Em*, Vol. 21, January 1953.

Eisner, R. "Technological Obsolescence and Aggregate Demand," *AER*, Vol. 46, March 1956.

Eisner, R. "Technological Change, Obsolescence and Aggregate Demand: A Reformulation," *AER*, Vol. 46, September 1956.

Eisner, R. "On Growth Models and the Neo-Classical Resurgence," *EJ*, Vol. 68, December 1958.

Eisner, R. "Capacity, Investment and Profits," *Quarterly Review of Economics and Business*, Vol. 4, No. 3, 1964.

Ellis, H. S. "Accelerated Investment as a Force in Economic Development," *QJE*, Vol. 72, November 1958.

Eltis, W. A. "Investment, Technical Progress, and Economic Growth," *OEP*, N.S., Vol. 15, March 1963.

Eltis, W. A. "A Theory of Investment, Distribution, and Employment," *OEP*, N.S., Vol. 17, March 1965.

Encarnación, J., Jr. "Overdeterminateness in Kaldor's Growth Model" (followed by N. Kaldor's comment), *EJ*, Vol. 72, September 1962.

Encarnación, J., Jr. "On Instability in the Sense of Harrod," *Ec*, Vol. 32, No. 127, August 1965 (followed by J. W. Nevile's reply, Vol. 33, August 1966).

Enzer, H. "On a Useful Capital Growth Matrix," *Em*, Vol. 34, January 1966.

Evans, W. D. "The Production Economics of Growth," *AER/S*, Vol. 46, May 1956.

Ezekiel, M. "Distribution of Gains From Rising Technical Efficiency in Progressing Economies," *AER/S*, Vol. 47, May 1957.

Fei, J. C. H. "Per Capita Consumption and Growth," *QJE*, Vol. 79, No. 1, February 1965.

Fei, J. C. H., and Ranis, G. "Innovation, Capital Accumulation and Economic Development," *AER*, Vol, 53, June 1963.

Fei, J. C. H., and Ranis, G. *Development of the Labor Surplus Economy: Theory and Policy* (Homewood, Ill.: R. D. Irwin, 1963).

Fei, J. C. H., and Ranis, G. "Innovational Intensity and Factor Bias in the Theory of Growth," *IER*, Vol. 6, No. 2, May 1965.

Fellner, W. J. *Trends and Cycles in Economic Activity* (New York: Holt and Co., 1956).

Fellner, W. J. "Automatic Market Clearance and Innovations in the Theory of Employment and Growth," *OEP*, Vol. 10, June 1958.

Fellner, W. J. "Rapid Growth as an Objective of Economic Policy," *AER/S*, Vol. 50, May 1960.

Fellner, W. J. "Appraisal of the Labour-saving and Capital-saving Character of Innovations," *The Theory of Capital*, Proceedings of International Economic Association Conference, edited by F. A. Lutz and D. C. Hague (London: Macmillan, 1961).

Fellner, W. J. "Does the Market Direct the Relative Factor-saving Effects of Technological Progress," Universities—National Bureau Committee for Economic Research, *The Rate and Directions of Inventive Activity* (Princeton: Princeton University Press, 1962).

Ferguson, C. E. "On the Theories of Acceleration and Growth," *QJE*, Vol. 74, February 1960.

Ferguson, C. E. "Theories of Growth and the Rate of Growth Hypothesis," *WA*, Vol. 89, Hft. 2, 1962.

Ferguson, C. E. "Substitution, Technical Progress, and Returns to Scale," *AER/S*, Vol. 55, May 1965.

Ferguson, C. E. "Saving and the Capital-Output Ratio in the Neoclassical Theory of Growth," *Quarterly Review of Economics and Business*, Vol. 5, No. 2, 1965.

Ferguson, C. E. "The Elasticity of Substitution and the Savings Ratio in the Neoclassical Theory of Growth," *QJE*, Vol. 79, August 1965.

Findlay, R. "International Specialization and the Concept of Balanced Growth: Comment" (followed by J. Sheahan's reply), *QJE*, Vol. 73, May 1959.

Findlay, R. "Economic Growth and the Distributive Shares" (followed by N. Kaldor's rejoinder), *REStud*, Vol. 27, June 1960.

Findlay, R. "Capital Theory and Development Planning," *REStud*, Vol. 29, February 1962.

Findlay, R. "The Robinsonian Model of Accumulation," *Ec*, Vol. 30, February 1963.

Findlay, R. "A Reply (to Robinson, J., 'Findlay's Robinsonian Model of Accumulation: A Comment')," *EC*, Vol. 30, November 1963.

Findlay, R. "Optimal Investment Allocation between Consumer Goods and Capital Goods," *EJ*, Vol. 76, March 1966.

Findlay, R. "Neutral Technical Progress and the Relative Stability of Two-Sector Growth Models," *IER*, Vol. 8, No. 1, February 1967.

Fisher, F. M. "Decomposability, Near Decomposability, and Balanced Price Change under Constant Returns to Scale," *Em*, Vol. 31, January-April 1963.

Fisher, F. M. "Balanced Growth and Intertemporal Efficiency in Capital Accumulation: A Comment," *IER*, Vol. 4, May 1963.

Fisher, F. M. "Embodied Technical Change and the Existence of an Aggregate Capital Stock," *REStud*, Vol. 32, October 1965.

Fisher, F. M., and Ando, A. "Near-Decomposability, Partition and Aggregation, and the Relevance of Stability Discussions," *IER*, Vol. 4, January 1963.

Fisher, F. M., Ando, A., and Simon, H. A. *Essays on the Structure of Social Science Models* (Cambridge, Mass.: M.I.T. Press, 1963).

Fleming, M. "External Economies and the Doctrine of Balanced Growth," *EJ*, Vol. 65, June 1955.

Frankel, M. "Obsolescence and Technological Change in a Maturing Economy," *AER*, Vol. 45, June 1955.

Frankel, M. "Producer Goods, Consumer Goods and Acceleration of Growth," *EJ*, Vol. 71, March 1961.

Frankel, M. "Recent Capital and Production Theory: Discussion," *AER/S*, Vol. 55, May 1965.

Frearson, K. S. "Recent Developments in the Theory of Economic Growth," *AEP*, Vol. 3, June-December 1964.

Frisch, R. "A Reconsideration of Domar's Theory of Economic Growth," *Em*, Vol. 29, July 1961.

Furuno, Y. "The Period of Production in Two-Sector Models of Economic Growth," *IER*, Vol. 6, No. 2, May 1965.

Furuya, H., and Inada, K. "Balanced Growth and Intertemporal Efficiency in Capital Efficiency," *IER*, Vol. 3, January 1962.

Gale, D. "The Closed Linear Model of Production," *Linear Inequalities and Related Systems*, edited by H. W. Kuhn and A. W. Tucker (Princeton: Princeton University Press, 1956).

Gale, D. *The Theory of Linear Economic Models* (New York: McGraw-Hill, 1960).

Gale, D. "On Equilibrium for a Multi-Sector Model of Income Propagation," *IER*, Vol. 5, No. 2, May 1964.

Gale, D. "On Optimal Development in a Multi-Sector Economy" (Symposium on Optimal Infinite Programmes), *REStud*, Vol. 34, No. 97, January 1967.

Gale, D. "Geometric Duality Theorem with Economic Applications" (Symposium on Optimal Infinite Programmes), *REStud*, Vol. 34, No. 97, January 1967.

Garegnani, P. "Switching of Techniques," *QJE*, Vol. 80, No. 4, November 1966.

Gehrels, F. "Factor Substitution, Consumer Wealth and Growth Stability," *AER*, Vol. 47, September 1957.

Gehrels, F. "Full Employment Growth in an Advanced Economy with Two Sectors," *WA*, Vol. 92, 1964.

Georgescu-Roegen, N. "The Aggregate Linear Production Function and Its Applications to von Neumann's Economic Model," *Activity Analysis of Production and Allocation*, edited by T. C. Koopmans (New York: Wiley, 1951).

Georgescu-Roegen, N. "Some Thoughts on Growth Models: A Reply" [followed by G. Bernard's réplique (in French) and Goergescu-Roegen's rejoinder], *Em*, Vol. 31, January-April 1963.

Georgescu-Roegen, N. *Analytical Economics: Issues and Problems* (Cambridge: Harvard University Press, 1966).

Gilbert, J. C. "Changes in Productivity and the Price Level in a Closed Economy," *YB*, Vol. 8, November 1956.

Goodwin, R. M. "The Problem of Trend and Cycle," *YB*, Vol. 5, August 1953.

Goodwin, R. M. "A Model of Cyclical Growth," *The Business Cycle in the*

Postwar World, proceedings of International Economic Association Conference, edited by E. Lundberg (London: Macmillan, 1955).

Goodwin, R. M. "The Optimal Growth Plan for an Underdeveloped Economy," *EJ*, Vol. 71, December 1961.

Gordon, D. F. "Obsolescence and Technological Change: A Comment" (followed by M. Frankel's reply), *AER*, Vol. 46, September, 1956.

Gordon, R. A. "Population Growth, Housing and the Capital Coefficient," *AER*, Vol. 46, June 1956.

Gordon, R. A. "Differential Changes in the Prices of Consumers' and Capital Goods," *AER*, Vol. 51, December 1961.

Gould, D. L. "Case of Unbalanced Growth," *ER*, Vol. 42, June 1966.

Graaff, J. de V. "Sir Roy Harrod's Second Essay" (followed by Harrod's comment), *EJ*, Vol. 70, December 1960.

Green, H. A. J. "Growth Models, Capital and Stability," *EJ*, Vol. 70, March 1960.

Green, H. A. J. "Dynamic Equilibrium and Instability in the Sense of Harrod," *Ec*, N.S., Vol. 29, February 1962.

Green, H. A. J. "Recent Contributions to the Theory of Economic Growth," *CJE*, Vol. 29, August 1963.

Green, H. A. J. "Embodied Progress, Investment and Growth," *AER*, Vol. 56, No. 1, March 1966.

Griliches, Z. "The Sources of Measured Productivity Growth: U.S. Agriculture 1940–60," *JPE*, Vol. 71, August 1963.

Griliches, Z., and Jorgenson, D. W. "Sources of Measured Productivity Change," *Papers and Proceedings, AER*, Vol. 56, No. 2, May 1966.

Grosse, R. N. "A Note on Capital-Output Ratios," *REStat*, Vol. 37, August 1955.

Guha, A. "Factor and Commodity Prices in an Expanding Economy," *QJE*, Vol. 77, February 1963.

Guha, A. "Scarcity of Specific Resources as a Limit to Output," *REStud*, Vol. 30, February 1963.

Gurley, J. G. "Fiscal Policy in a Growing Economy," *JPE*, Vol. 61, December 1953.

Haavelmo, T. *A Study in the Theory of Economic Evolution* (Amsterdam: North-Holland Publishing Co., 1954).

Haavelmo, T. *A Study in the Theory of Investment* (Chicago: University of Chicago Press, 1960.

Habakkuk, H. J. *American and British Technology in the Nineteenth Century* (London: Cambridge University Press, 1962).

Haberler, G. "Nurkse on Patterns of Trade and Development," *REStud*, Vol. 42, February 1960.

Haga, H., and Otsuki, M. "On a Generalized von Neumann Model," *IER*, Vol. 6, January 1965.

Hagen, E. E. "Population and Economic Growth," *AER*, Vol. 49, June 1959.

Hagger, A. "Planned Saving and Investment Under Conditions of Steady Growth," *REStat*, Vol. 38, November 1956.

Hahn, F. H. "The Share of Wages in the Trade Cycle," *EJ*, Vol. 60, September 1950.

Hahn, F. H. "The Share of Wages in the National Income," *OEP*, Vol. 3, June 1951.

Hahn, F. H. "The Stability of Growth Equilibrium," *QJE*, Vol. 74, May 1960.

Hahn, F. H. "Money, Dynamic Stability and Growth," *Met*, Vol. 8, 1961.

Hahn, F. H. "The Stability of Growth Equilibrium: Reply," *QJE*, Vol. 76, August 1962.
Hahn, F. H. "On the Disequilibrium Behaviour of a Multi-sectoral Growth Model," *EJ*, Vol. 73, September 1963.
Hahn, F. H. "On Two Sector Growth Models," *REStud*, Vol. 32, October 1965.
Hahn, F. H. "Equilibrium Dynamics with Heterogeneous Capital Goods," *QJE*, Vol. 80. No. 4, November 1966.
Hahn, F. H., and Matthews, R. C. O. "The Theory of Economic Growth: A Survey," *EJ*, Vol. 74, December 1964.
Hamberg, D. "Full Capacity vs Full Employment Growth," *QJE*, Vol. 66, August 1952.
Hamberg, D. "Underemployment Equilibrium Rates of Growth: Comment" (followed by H. M. Wagner's further comment and R. Eisner's rejoinder), *AER*, Vol. 43, June 1953.
Hamberg, D. "Income Growth in Secular Stagnation and Inflation," *EJ*, Vol. 63, September 1953.
Hamberg, D. "Steady Growth and Theories of Cyclical Crisis," Pt. I–II, *Met*, Vol. 6, April, August 1954.
Hamberg D. "Full Capacity vs Full Employment Growth: Some Further Remarks," *QJE*, Vol. 68, November 1954.
Hamberg, D. "Investment and Saving in a Growing Economy," *REStat*, Vol. 37, May 1955.
Hamberg, D. *Economic Growth and Instability; A Study in the Problem of Capital Accumulation, Employment and the Business Cycle* (New York: Norton, 1956).
Hamberg, D. "Production Functions, Innovations and Economic Growth," *JPE*, Vol. 67, June 1959.
Hamberg, D., and Schultze, C. L. "Autonomous Versus Induced Investment: The Interrelatedness of Parameters in Growth Models," *EJ*, Vol. 71, March 1961.
Hamberg, D., and Schultze, C. L. "Investment and Economic Growth," *Met*, Vol. 15, April 1963.
Hansen A. H. "Extensive Expansion and Population Growth," *JPE*, Vol. 48, August 1940.
Haque, W. "Balanced Growth in a Modified von Neumann Model," *Zeitschrift für Nationalökonomie*, Vol. 24, November 1964.
Haque, W. "A Pseudo-Classical Dynamic Programming Model of Capital Accumulation," *IER*, Vol. 6, No. 1, January 1965.
Haque, W. "Capital Accumulation Under Cobb-Douglas Production Functions," *Zeitschrift für Nationalökonomie*, Vol. 24, April 1964; "Correction and Comments," Vol. 25, June 1965.
Haque, W. "Intertemporal Optimality and Von Neumann Equilibrium in Non-Linear Activity Analysis," *Met*, Vol. 16, January-April 1964; "Corrections," Vol. 17, June–August 1965.
Haque, W. "Dynamic Programming in a Multi-Product Model of Economic Development," *IER*, Vol. 7, January 1966.
Harcourt, G. C. "Productivity and Technical Change," *ER*, Vol. 38, September 1962.
Harcourt, G. C. "A Simple Joan Robinson Model of Accumulation with One Technique: A Comment," *OsEP*, Vol. 11, No. 2, January 1963.
Harrod, R. F. *The Trade Cycle* (London: Oxford University Press, 1936).
Harrod, R. F. "An Essay in Dynamic Theory," *EJ*, Vol. 49, March 1939.

Harrod, R. F. *Towards A Dynamic Economics* (London: Macmillan, 1948).
Harrod, R. F. "Professor Fellner on Growth and Unemployment," *Kyk*, Vol. 10, 1957.
Harrod, R. F. "Domar and Dynamic Economics," *EJ*, Vol. 69, September 1959.
Harrod, R. F. "Second Essay in Dynamic Theory," *EJ*, Vol, 70, June 1960.
Harrod, R. F. "The 'Neutrality' of Improvements," *EJ*, Vol. 71, June 1961.
Harrod, R. F. "Dynamic Theory and Planning," *Kyk*, Vol. 15, fasc. 1, 1962.
Harrod, R. F. "Themes in Dynamic Theory," *EJ*, Vol. 73, September 1963.
Harwitz, M. "On the Invariance of the Stability of Dynamic Equilibrium" (followed by R. J. Van Noorden's note), *OEP*, N.S., Vol. 16, March 1964.
Hawkins, D., and Simon, H. A. "Some Conditions of Macroeconomic Stability," *Em*, Vol. 17, October 1949.
Henderson, P. D. "Retrospect and Prospect: The Economic Survey," *OIS*, Vol. 16, May–June 1954.
Hickman, B. G. "Investment Demand and U. S. Economic Growth" (Washington, D.C.: Brookings Institute, 1965).
Hicks, J. R. *The Theory of Wages* (London: Macmillan, 1st edition 1932, 2nd edition 1963).
Hicks, J. R. "Mr. Harrod's Dynamic Theory," *Ec*, N.S., Vol. 16, May 1949.
Hicks, J. R. *A Contribution to the Theory of the Trade Cycle* (Oxford: Oxford University Press, 1st edition 1950; Clarendon Press, 2nd edition 1961).
Hicks, J. R. "A Value and Capital Growth Model," *REStud*, Vol. 26, June 1959.
Hicks, J. R. "Thoughts on the Theory of Capital: The Corfu Conference," *OEP*, Vol. 12, June 1960.
Hicks, J. R. "Prices and the Turnpike—the Story of a Mare's Nest," *REStud*, Vol. 28, February 1961.
Hicks, J. R. *Capital and Growth* (New York: Oxford University Press, 1965).
Hicks, J. R. "Growth and Anti-Growth," *OEP*, Vol. 18, November 1966.
Hieser, R. "Another Look at the Acceleration Relationship and Equilibrium Growth," *ER*, Vol. 34, August 1958.
Hirschman, A. O. "Primary Products and Substitutes: Should Technological Progress be Policed?," *Kyk*, Vol. 12, fasc. 3, 1959.
Hogan, W. P. "Technological Progress and Production Functions" (followed by R. M. Solow's reply), *REStat*, Vol. 40, November 1958.
Holland, E. P. *Experiments on a Simulated Under-Developed Economy: Development Plans and Balance of Payments Policies* (Cambridge, Mass.: M.I.T. Press, 1963).
Hooley, R. W. "Saving, Investment, and the Analysis of Growth: A Comment," *EDCC*, Vol. 13, January 1965.
Hoover, E. M. "Capital Accumulation and Progress," *AER/S*, Vol. 40, May 1950.
Horvat, B. "The Optimum Rate of Investment Reconsidered," *EJ*, Vol. 55, September 1965.
Horwell, D. J. "Optimum Tariffs and Tariff Policy," *REStud*, Vol. 33, No. 94, April 1966.
Hoselitz, B. F. "Patterns of Economic Growth," *CJE*, Vol. 21, November 1955.
Howe, C. W. "An Alternative Proof of the Existence of General Equilibrium in a Von Neumann Model," *Em*, Vol. 28, July 1960.
Howrey, E. P. "A Note on Depreciation, Replacement, and Regular Growth," *EJ*, Vol. 75, March 1965.

Howrey, E. P. "Technical Change, Capital Longevity, and Economic Growth," *AER/S*, Vol. 55, May 1965.

Ilchman, W. F., and Bhargava, R. C. "Balanced Thought and Economic Growth," *EDCC*, Vol. 14, July 1966.

Inada, K. "On a Two-sector Model of Economic Growth: Comments and a Generalisation," *REStud*, Vol. 30, June 1963.

Inada, K. "Some Structural Characteristics of Turnpike Theorems," *REStud*, Vol. 31, January 1964.

Inada, K. "Economic Growth Under Neutral Technical Progress," *Em*, Vol. 32, January–April 1964.

Inada, K. "On the Stability of Growth Equilibria in Two-Sector Models," *REStud*, Vol. 31, April 1964.

Inada, K. "Economic Growth and Factor Substitution," *IER*, Vol. 5, September 1964.

Inada, K. "On Neoclassical Models of Economic Growth," *REStud*, Vol. 32, April 1965.

Inada, K. "The Mathematical Formulation of Harrod's Growth Model: A Comment" (followed by J. W. Nevile's reply), *EJ*, Vol. 75, September 1965.

Inada, K. "Investment in Fixed Capital and the Stability of Growth Equilibrium," *REStud*, Vol. 33, January 1966.

Inada, K., and Furuya, H. "Balanced Growth and Intertemporal Efficiency in Capital Accumulation," *IER*, Vol. 3, January 1962.

Intriligator, M. D. "Regional Allocation of Investment: Comment," *QJE*, Vol. 78, November 1964.

Intriligator, M. D. "Embodied Technical Change and Productivity in the United States 1929–1958," *REStat*, Vol. 47, February 1965.

Johansen, L. "Substitution versus Fixed Production Coefficients in The Theory of Economic Growth: A Synthesis," *Em*, Vol. 27, April 1959.

Johansen, L. "Rules of Thumb for the Expansion of Industries in a Process of Economic Growth," *Em*, Vol. 28, April 1960.

Johansen, L. *A Multi-Sectoral Study of Economic Growth* (Amsterdam: North-Holland Pub. Co., 1960).

Johansen, L. "Durability of Capital and Rate of Growth of National Product," *IER*, Vol. 2, September 1961.

Johansen, L. "A Method of Separating the Effects of Capital Accumulation and Shifts in Production Functions upon Growth in Labor Productivity," *EJ*, Vol. 71, December 1961.

Johansen, L. "A Multi-Sectoral Study of Economic Growth: Some Comments" (followed by E. Zabel's reply), *Ec*, N.S., Vol. 30, May 1963.

Johansen, L. "Some Theoretical Properties of aTwo-Sector Model of Optimal Growth" (Symposium on Optimal Infinite Programmes), *REStud*, Vol. 34, No. 97, January 1967.

Johnson, H. G. "Equilibrium Growth in an International Economy," *CJE*, Vol. 19, November 1953.

Johnson, H. G. "Economic Expansion and the Balance of Payments," *OIS*, Vol. 17, February 1955.

Johnson, H. G. "Economic Expansion and International Trade," *MS*, Vol. 23, May 1955.

Johnson, H. G. "A Further Note on Dynamic Economics," *REStud*, Vol. 23, No. 3, 1956.

Johnson, H. G. "Notes on Economic Development and the Maximum Rate of Growth," *Malayan Economic Review*, Vol. 2, No. 1, April 1957.

Johnson, H. G. "Factor Mobility and Rates of Technical Progress: A Critical Note on *Output, Labor and Capital in the Canadian Economy*" (followed by W. C. Hood's rejoinder), *CJE*, Vol. 27, February 1961.

Johnson, H. G. "A Simple Joan Robinson Model of Accumulation with One Technique," *OsEP*, Vol. 10, Nos. 1–2, February 1962.

Johnson, H. G. *Money, Trade and Economic Growth: Survey Lectures in Economic Theory* (Cambridge, Mass.: Harvard University Press, 1962).

Johnson, H. G. "Is Inflation the Inevitable Price of Rapid Development or a Retarding Factor in Economic Growth?," *Malayan Economic Review*, Vol. 11, April 1966.

Johnson, H. G. "The Neo-Classical One Sector Growth Model: A Geometrical Exposition and Extension to a Monetary Economy," *Ec*, Vol. 33, No. 131, August 1966.

Johnson, M. B. "Balanced Growth and the Two-Good, Two-Factor General Equilibrium Model," *QJE*, Vol. 75, August 1961.

Johnston, R. E. "Technical Progress and Innovation," *OEP*, Vol. 18, July 1966.

Jones, R. W. " 'Neutral' Technological Change and the Isoquant Map," *AER*, Vol. 55, September 1965.

Jorgenson, D. W. "On Stability in the Sense of Harrod," *Ec*, Vol. 27, August 1960.

Jorgenson, D. W. "A Dual Stability Theorem," *Em*, Vol. 28, October 1960.

Jorgenson, D. W. "Stability of a Dynamic Input-Output System," *REStud*, Vol. 28, February 1961.

Jorgenson, D. W. "The Development of a Dual Economy," *EJ*, Vol. 71, June 1961.

Jorgenson, D. W. "The Structure of Multi-sector Dynamic Models," *IER*, Vol. 2, September 1961.

Jorgenson, D. W. "The Structure of Multi-sector Dynamic Models: Some Further Examples," *IER*, Vol. 4, January 1963.

Kahn, A. E. "Investment Criteria in Development Programs," *QJE*, Vol. 65, February 1951.

Kahn, R. F. "Exercises in the Analysis of Growth," *OEP*, Vol. 2, June 1959.

Kahn, R. F., and Champernowne, D. G. "The Value of Invested Capital: A Mathematical Addendum to Mrs. Robinson's Articles," *REStud*, Vol. 21, No. 2, 1954.

Kaldor, N. "The Relation of Economic Growth and Cyclical Fluctuations," *EJ*, Vol. 64, March 1954.

Kaldor, N. "Alternative Theories of Distribution," *REStud*, Vol. 23, No. 2, 1956.

Kaldor, N. "A Model of Economic Growth," *EJ*, Vol. 67, December 1957.

Kaldor, N. "Economic Growth and the Problem of Inflation, Part I–II," *Ec*, Vol. 26, August, November 1959.

Kaldor, N. "A Rejoinder to Mr. Atsumi and Professor Tobin," *REStud*, Vol. 27, February 1960.

Kaldor, N. *Essays on Economic Stability and Growth* (London: G. Duckworth, 1960 and 1963).

Kaldor, N. "Capital Accumulation and Economic Growth," *The Theory of Capital*, Proceedings of International Economic Association Conference, edited by L. A. Lutz and D. C. Hague (London: Macmillan, 1961).

Kaldor, N. "Comment (in Symposium on Production Functions and Economic Growth)," *REStud*, Vol. 29, June 1962.

Kaldor, N. "Marginal Productivity and the Macro-Economic Theories of Distribution," *REStud*, Vol. 33, October 1966.

Kaldor, N., and Mirrlees, J. A. "A New Model of Economic Growth," *REStud*, Vol. 29, June 1962.
Kalecki, M. *Essays in the Theory of Economic Fluctuations* (London: Allen and Unwin, 1939).
Kalecki, M. *Studies in Economic Dynamics* (London: Allen and Unwin, 1943).
Kalecki, M. *Theory of Economic Dynamics* (London: Allen and Unwin, 1954).
Kalecki, M. "Observations on the Theory of Growth," *EJ*, Vol. 72, March 1962.
Kaneko, Y., and Morishima, M. "On the Speed of Establishing Multi-Sectoral Equilibrium," *Em*, Vol. 30, October 1962.
Karlin, S. *Mathematical Methods and Theory in Games, Programming and Economics, Vol. I* (Reading, Mass.: Addison-Wesley Publishing Co., Inc., 1959).
Karmel, P. H. "Some Reflections on Inflation, Productivity and Growth," *ER*, Vol. 35, December 1959.
Katano, K. "Some Characteristics of Professor Mahalanobis' Growth Model," *The Developing Economies*, Vol. 3, March 1965.
Kemeny, J. G., Morgenstern, O., and Thompson, G. L. "A Generalisation of the Von Neumann Model of an Expanding Economy," *Em*, Vol. 24, April 1956.
Kemp, A. (and others). "Economics and Changing Technology: Discussion," *AER/S*, Vol. 47, May 1957.
Kemp, M. C., and Thanh, P. C. "On a Class of Growth Models," *Em*, Vol. 34, April 1966.
Kendrick, J. W. *Productivity Trends in the United States*, National Bureau of Economic Research (Princeton: Princeton University Press, 1961).
Kendrick, J. W., and Sato, R. "Factor Prices, Productivity and Economic Growth," *AER*, Vol. 53, December 1963.
Kennedy, C. "A Static Interpretation of Some Recent Theories of Growth and Distribution," *OEP*, N.S., Vol. 12, June 1960.
Kennedy, C. "Technical Progress and Investment," *EJ*, Vol. 71, June 1961.
Kennedy, C. "Harrod on 'Neutrality,'" *EJ*, Vol. 72, March 1962.
Kennedy, C. "The Character of Improvements and of Technical Progress," *EJ*, Vol. 72, December 1962.
Kennedy, C. "Induced Bias in Innovation and the Theory of Distribution," *EJ*, Vol. 74, September 1964.
Kennedy, C. "Keynesian Theory in an Open Economy," *Social and Economic Studies*, Vol. 15, March 1966.
Kennedy, C. "Domar-Type Theory in an Open Economy," *Social and Economic Studies*, Vol. 15, September 1966.
Kervyn, A. "A Note on the Accelerator and Constant Growth," *REStud*, Vol. 22, No. 1, 1954.
Kindleberger, C. P. "Obsolescence and Technical Change," *OIS*, Vol. 23, August 1961.
Kindleberger, C. P. "Emigration and Economic Growth," *Banca Nazionale del Lavoro Review*, Vol. 18, September 1965.
Kitamura, H., and Yang, S. C. "Domestic Stability and Development: A Critique of Nurkse's Scheme," *Kyk*, Vol. 12, fasc. 3, 1959.
Kleiman, E., and Ophir, T. "The Durability of Durable Goods," *REStud*, Vol. 33, April 1966.
Klein, L. R., and Kosobud, R. F. "Some Econometrics of Growth: Great Ratios of Economics," *QJE*, Vol. 75, May 1961.
Konijn, H. S. "Findlay's Robinsonian Model of Accumulation: A Note," *Ec*, N.S., Vol. 32, August 1965.

Koopmans, T. C. "Analysis of Production as an Efficient Combination of Activities," *Activity Analysis of Production and Allocation*, edited by T. C. Koopmans (New York: Wiley, 1951).
Koopmans, T. C. *Three Essays on the State of Economic Science* (New York: McGraw-Hill, 1957).
Koopmans, T. C. "Stationary Ordinal Utility and Impatience," *Em*, Vol. 28, April 1960.
Koopmans, T. C. "Economic Growth at a Maximal Rate," *QJE*, Vol. 78, August 1964.
Koopmans, T. C. "On the Concept of Optimal Economic Growth," *The Econometric Approach to Development Planning*, by Salviucci, and others (Amsterdam and Chicago: North-Holland Publishing Co. and Rand-McNally & Co., 1966, a reissue of *Pontificiae Academiae Scientiarium Scripta Varia*, Vol. 28, 1965).
Koopmans, T. C. "Objectives, Constraints and Outcomes in Optimal Growth Models," *Em*, Vol. 35, January 1967.
Koopmans, T. C., and Bausch, A. F. "Selected Topics in Economics Involving Mathematical Reasoning," *SIAM Review*, Vol. 1, No. 2, July 1959.
Koopmans, T. C., Diamond, P. A., and Williamson, R. E. "Stationary Utility and Time Perspective," *Em*, Vol. 32, January–April 1964.
Krueger, A. O. "The Implications of a Backward-Bending Labor Supply Curve," *REStud*, Vol. 29, October 1962.
Kurz, M. "A Two-sector Extension of Swan's Model of Economic Growth: The Case of No Technical Change," *IER*, Vol. 4, January 1963.
Kurz, M. "Substitution versus Fixed Production Coefficients: A Comment," *Em*, Vol. 31, January–April 1963.
Kurz, M. "Optimal Paths of Capital Accumulation Under the Minimum Time Objective," *Em*, Vol. 33, January 1965.
Kuznets, S. "Proportion of Capital Formation to National Product," *AER/S*, Vol. 42, May 1952.
Kuznets, S. "Economic Growth and Income Equality," *AER*, Vol. 45, March 1955.
Kuznets, S. In *Economic Growth: Brazil, India, Japan*, edited by S. Kuznets, W. E. Moore, and J. J. Spengler (Durham, N. C.: Duke University Press, 1955).
Kuznets, S. *Quantitative Aspects of the Economic Growth of Nations* (Chicago: The University of Chicago Press, 1956).
Kuznets, S. "Quantitative Aspects of the Economic Growth of Nations" (Parts I–IX), *EDCC*, Vols. 5, 6, 7, 8, 9, 10, 11 and 13, October 1956–October 1964.
Kuznets, S. *Six Lectures on Economic Growth* (New York: Glencoe, 1959).
Kuznets, S. *Postwar Economic Growth, Four Lectures* (Cambridge, Mass.: Belknap Press of Harvard University Press, 1964).
Kuznets, S. *Economic Growth and Structure: Selected Essays* (New York: Norton, 1965).
Kuznets, S. *Modern Economic Growth, Rate, Structure and Spread* (New Haven: Yale University Press, 1966).
Laing, N. F. "A Geometrical Analysis of Some Theorems on Steady Growth," *JPE*, Vol. 72, October 1964.
Lamfalussy, A. *The United Kingdom and the Six, An Essay on Economic Growth in Western Europe* (New York: St. Martin's Press, 1963).
Lancaster, K. "Mrs. Robinson's Dynamics," *Ec*, N.S., Vol. 27, February 1960.
Lange, O. "The Output-Investment Ratio and Input-Output Analysis," *Em*, Vol. 28, April 1960.

Lange, O. *Economic Development, Planning and International Cooperation,* lectures (Cairo: Central Bank of Egypt, 1961).
Lange, O. "A Model of Economic Growth," *Mathematical Studies in Economics and Statistics in the U.S.S.R. and Eastern Europe,* Vol. 1, No. 3, 1965.
Langley, K. M. "Economic Growth in the West: A Comment," *Ec,* Vol. 32, No. 128, November 1965.
La Tourette, J. E. "Technological Change and Equilibrium Growth in the Harrod-Domar Model," *Kyk,* Vol. 17, fasc. 2, 1964.
Laumas, P. S. "Doctrine of Balanced Growth and the Theory of International Specialization," *EI,* Vol. 17, November 1964.
Lefeber, L., and Chakravarty, S. "Wages, Employment and Growth," *Kyk,* Vol. 19, fasc. 4, 1966.
Leibenstein, H. *Economic Backwardness and Economic Growth* (New York: Wiley, 1957).
Leibenstein, H. "Incremental Capital-Output Ratios and Growth Rates in the Short-Run," *REStat,* Vol. 47, February 1965.
Leontief, W. W. *The Structure of American Economy: 1919–1939* (New York: Oxford University Press, 1941, 2nd edition, 1951).
Leontief, W. W. *Studies in the Structure of the American Economy* (New York: Oxford University Press, 1953).
Leontief, W. W. "Theoretical Note on Time-Preference Productivity of Capital, Stagnation and Economic Growth,"*AER,* Vol. 48, March 1958.
Leontief, W. W. "Lags and the Stability of Dynamic Systems: A Rejoinder," *Em,* Vol. 29, October 1961.
Leontief, W. W. *Input-Output Economics* (New York: Oxford University Press, 1966).
Lerner, A. P. "On Some Recent Developments in Capital Theory," *AER/S,* Vol. 55, May 1965.
Letiche, J. M. "The Relevance of Classical and Contemporary Theories of Growth to Economic Development," *AER/S,* Vol. 49, May 1959.
Letiche, J. M. *Balance of Payments and Economic Growth* (New York: Harper, 1959).
Levhari, D. "A Nonsubstitution Theorem and Switching of Techniques," *QJE,* Vol. 79, No. 1, February 1965.
Levhari, D. "Further Implications of Learning by Doing," *REStud,* Vol. 33, January 1966.
Levhari, D. "Extensions of Arrow's 'Learning by Doing,'" *REStud,* Vol. 33, April 1966.
Levhari, D., and Samuelson, P. A. "The Nonswitching Theorem is False" (Paradoxes in Capital Theory: A Symposium), *QJE,* Vol. 70, November 1966.
Lewis, W. A. "Economic Development with Unlimited Supplies of Labour," *MS,* Vol. 22, May 1954.
Lewis, W. A. "Unlimited Labour: Further Notes," *MS,* Vol. 26. January 1958.
Little, I. M. D. "Classical Growth," *OEP,* Vol. 9, June 1957.
Little, I. M. D. "The Real Cost of Labor and the Choice between Consumption and Investment," *QJE,* Vol. 75, February 1961.
Liviatan, N. "The Concept of Capital in Professor Solow's Model," *Em,* Vol. 34, January 1966.
Lovell, M. C. "A Comment on the Viability of Multi-Sector Dynamic Models," *IER,* Vol. 4, January 1963.
Lundberg, E. "A Bridge between Classical Analysis and Modern Dynamic

Theories of Growth," *WA*, Vol. 92, Hft. 1, 1964.
McCarthy, M. D. "Embodied and Disembodied Technological Progress in the Constant Elasticity of Substitution Production Function," *REStat*, Vol. 47, No. 1, February 1965.
McFadden, D. M. "Further Results on C.E.S. Production Functions," *REStud*, Vol. 30, June 1963.
McFadden, D. M. "The Evaluation of Development Programmes" (Symposium on Optimal Infinite Programmes), *REStud*, Vol. 34, No. 97, January 1967.
McKenzie, L. W. "An Elementary Analysis of the Leontief System," *Em*, Vol. 25, July 1957.
McKenzie, L. W. "The Dorfman-Samuelson-Solow Turnpike Theorem," *IER*, Vol. 4, January 1963.
McKenzie, L. W. "Turnpike Theorems for a Generalized Leontief Model," *Em*, Vol. 31, January–April 1963.
McKenzie, L. W. "The Turnpike Theorem of Morishima," *REStud*, Vol. 30, October 1963.
Maclaurin, W. R. "The Sequence from Invention to Innovation and its Relation to Economic Growth," *QJE*, Vol. 67, February 1953.
McManus, M. "Self-contradiction in Leontief's Dynamic Model," *YB*, Vol. 9, May 1957.
McManus, M. "Process Switching in the Theory of Capital," *Ec*, N.S., Vol. 30, May 1963.
McManus, M. "Notes on Jorgenson's Model" (followed by D. W. Jorgenson's reply), *REStud*, Vol. 30, June 1963.
Malinvaud, E. "Capital Accumulation and Efficient Allocation of Resources," *Em*, Vol. 21, April 1953.
Malinvaud, E. "Programmes d'expansion et taux d'intérêt," *Em*, Vol. 27, April 1959.
Malinvaud, E. "The Analogy between Atemporal and Intertemporal Theories of Resource Allocation," *REStud*, Vol. 28, June 1961.
Malinvaud, E. "Efficient Capital Accumulation, a Corrigendum," *Em*, Vol. 30, July 1962.
Malmgren, H. B. "Balance, Imbalance and External Economies," *OEP*, N.S., Vol. 15, March 1963.
Maneschi, A. "Optimal Savings with Finite Planning Horizon: A Note" (followed by S. Chakravarty's reply and A. Maneschi's rejoinder), *IER*, Vol. 7, January 1966.
Mansfield, E. "Technical Change and the Rate of Imitation," *Em*, Vol. 29, October 1961.
Marty, A. L. "The Neoclassical Theorem," *AER*, Vol. 54, December 1964.
Massell, B. F. "Investment, Innovation and Growth," *Em*, Vol. 30, April 1962.
Massell, B. F. "Another Small Problem in the Analysis of Growth," *REStat*, Vol. 44, August 1962.
Massell, B. F. "Aggregation and Multiplicative Production Functions," *EJ*, Vol. 74, March 1964; "Correction," September 1964.
Mathur, A. "Balanced versus Unbalanced Growth—A Reconciliatory View," *OEP*, Vol. 18, No. 2, July 1966.
Mathur, G. "Thriftiness and Consumption in Steady Growth," *OIS*, Vol. 24, August 1962.
Mathur, G. *Planning for Steady Growth* (Oxford: Blackwell, 1965).
Mathur, P. N. "Output and Investment for Exponential Growth in Con-

sumption: An Alternative Formulation and Derivation of their Technological Upper Limits," *REStud*, Vol. 31, January 1964.

Matthews, R. C. O. "The Saving Function and the Problem of Trend and Cycle," *REStud*, Vol. 22, No. 2, 1955.

Matthews, R. C. O. "A Note on Crawling Along the Ceiling," *REStud*, Vol. 27, October 1959.

Matthews, R. C. O. *The Business Cycle* (Chicago: University of Chicago Press, 1959).

Matthews, R. C. O. "Duesenberry on Growth and Fluctuations," *EJ*, Vol. 69, December 1959.

Matthews, R. C. O. "The Rate of Interest in Growth Models," *OEP*, Vol. 12, October 1960.

Matthews, R. C. O. "The New View of Investment: Comment," *QJE*, Vol. 78, February 1964.

Mazumdar, D. "The Marginal Productivity, Theory of Wages and Disguised Unemployment," *REStud*, Vol. 26, June 1959.

Mead, D. C. "Saving, Investment and the Analysis of Growth," *EDCC*, Vol. 12, October 1963.

Meade, J. E. *A Neo-Classical Theory of Economic Growth* (London: Allen and Unwin, 1961; 2nd edition revised 1964).

Meade, J. E. "The Effect of Saving on Consumption in a State of Steady Growth," *REStud*, Vol. 29, June 1962.

Meade, J. E. "The Adjustment of Saving to Investment in a Growing Economy," *REStud*, Vol. 30, October 1963.

Meade, J. E. "The Rate of Profit in a Growing Economy," *EJ*, Vol. 73, December 1963.

Meade, J. E. "Life-Cycle Savings, Inheritance and Economic Growth," *REStud*, Vol. 33, January 1966.

Meade, J. E., and Hahn, F. H. "The Rate of Profit in a Growing Economy," *EJ*, Vol. 75, June 1965.

Minabe, N. "Economic Growth and International Trade in a Simple Dynamic Leontief Model," *CJE*, Vol. 32, February 1966.

Minabe, N. "The Heckscher-Ohlin Theorem, the Leontief Paradox and Patterns of Economic Growth," *AER*, Vol. 56, No. 5, December 1966.

Minami, R. "Economic Growth and Labor Supply," *OEP*, N.S., Vol. 16, July 1964.

Mirrlees, J. A. "Optimum Growth When Technology is Changing" (Symposium on Optimal Infinite Programmes), *REStud*, Vol. 34, No. 97, January 1967.

Mirrlees, J. A., and Kaldor, N. "A New Model of Economic Growth," *REStud*, Vol. 29, June 1962.

Mishan, E. J. "International Factor Price Determination with Neutral Technical Progress," *Ec*, Vol. 33, August 1966.

Montias, J. M. "Balanced Growth and International Specialization: A Diagramatic Analysis," *OEP*, N.S., Vol. 13, June 1961.

Morishima, M. "An Analysis of the Capitalist Process of Reproduction," *Met*, Vol. 8, December 1956.

Morishima, M. "A Dynamic Analysis of Structural Change in a Leontief Model," *Ec*, N.S., Vol. 25, May 1958.

Morishima, M. "Prices, Interest and Profits in a Dynamic Leontief System," *Em*, Vol. 26, July 1958.

Morishima, M. "Some Properties of a Dynamic Leontief System with a Spectrum of Techniques," *Em*, Vol. 27, October 1959.

Morishima, M. "Economic Expansion and the Interest Rate in Generalized Von Neumann Models," *Em*, Vol. 28, April 1960.
Morishima, M. "Prices and Turnpike II: Proof of a Turnpike Theorem; The 'No Joint Production Case,'" *REStud*, Vol. 28, February 1961.
Morishima, M. *Equilibrium, Stability and Growth; A Multi-sectoral Analysis* (Oxford: Clarendon Press, 1964).
Morishima, M. "On the Two Theorems of Growth Economics: A Mathematical Exercise," *Em*, Vol. 33, October 1965.
Morishima, M. "Refutation of the Nonswitching Theorem" (Paradoxes in Capital Theory: A Symposium), *QJE*, Vol. 80, November 1966.
Morishima, M., and Kaneko, Y. "On the Speed of Establishing Multi-sectoral Equilibrium," *Em*, Vol. 30, October 1962.
Morishima, M., and Seton, F. "Aggregation in Leontief Matrices and the Labour Theory of Value," *Em*, Vol. 29, April 1961.
Mukerji, V. "Output and Investment for Exponential Growth in Consumption: the General Solution and Some Comments," *REStud*, Vol. 31, January 1964.
Mundell, R. A. "Growth, Stability and Inflationary Finance," *JPE*, Vol. 73, April 1965.
Nath, S. K. "The Theory of Balanced Growth," *OEP*, N.S., Vol. 14, June 1962.
National Bureau of Economic Research. *The Rate and Direction of Inventive Activity,* Universities-National Bureau Committee for Economic Research (Princeton: Princeton University Press, 1962).
Neale, A. B. "Investment Allocation in a Full Employment Economy," *Met*, Vol. 7, April 1955.
Neisser, H. "Balanced Growth Under Constant Returns to Scale: Some Comments," *Em*, Vol. 22, October 1954.
Neisser, H. "Depreciation, Replacement and Regular Growth," *EJ*, Vol. 65, March 1955.
Neisser, H. "Equilibrium Dynamics, Behavior Dynamics, Stability of Movement," *Met*, Vol. 13, April 1961.
Neisser, H. "On Equilibrium Growth of Capital and Labor" (followed by Y. Shinkai's reply), *IER*, Vol. 3, January 1962.
Nelson, R. R. "The Economics of Invention: A Survey of the Literature," *JB*, Vol. 32, April 1959.
Nelson, R. R. "A Note on Stability and the Behavior Assumptions of Harrod-type Models," *EJ*, Vol. 71, June 1961.
Nelson, R. R. "Aggregate Production Functions and Medium-Range Growth Projections," *AER*, Vol. 54, September 1964.
Nelson, R. R. "The CES Production Function and Economic Growth Projections," *REStud*, Vol. 47, August 1965.
Nelson, R. R. "Full Employment Policy and Economic Growth," *AER*, Vol. 56, No. 5, December 1966.
Nelson, R. R., and Phelps, E. S. "Investment in Humans, Technological Diffusion, and Economic Growth," *AER Papers and Proceedings*, Vol. 56, No. 2, May 1966.
Nevile, J. W. "The Stability of Warranted Growth," *ER*, Vol. 36, December 1960.
Nevile, J. W. "The Mathematical Formulation of Harrod's Growth Model," *EJ*, Vol. 72, June 1962.
Newman, P. "A Property of Mr. Harrod's Dynamic Model," *REStud*, Vol. 22, No. 1, 1954.

Newman, P. "Production of Commodities by means of Commodities," *Schweizerische Zeitschrift für Volkswirtschaft und Statistik,* 98th year, 1962.

Nicholson, M. "The Growth of Capital Stock," *EJ,* Vol. 75, June 1965.

Niehans, J. "Economic Growth with Two Endogenous Factors," *QJE,* Vol. 77, August 1963.

Niehans, J. "Interest Rates, Forced Saving, and Prices in the Long Run," *REStud,* Vol. 32, October 1965.

Nikaidô, H. "Some Dynamic Phenomena in the Leontief Model of Reversely Lagged Type," *REStud,* Vol. 29, October 1962.

Nikaidô, H. "Persistence of Continual Growth near the Von Neumann Ray—A Strong Version of the Radner Turnpike Theorem," *Em,* Vol. 32, January–April, 1964.

Nikaidô, H. "Balanced Growth in Multi-Sectoral Income Propagation under Autonomous Expenditure Schemes," *REStud,* Vol. 31, January 1964.

Nowlan, D. M. "A Robinsonian Growth Model," *CJE,* Vol. 32, November 1966.

Nurkse, R. "Balanced Growth on Static Assumptions," *EJ,* Vol. 66, June 1956.

Nurkse, R. "Notes on 'Unbalanced Growth,'" *OEP,* N.S., Vol. 11, October 1959.

Nurkse, R. *Equilibrium and Growth in the World Economy; Economic Essays,* edited by G. Haberler and R. M. Stern (Cambridge, Mass.: Harvard University Press, 1961).

Okamoto, T., and Inada, K. "A Note on the Theory of Economic Growth," *QJE,* Vol. 76, August 1962.

Oshima, H. T. "Income Originating in the Models of Harrod and Domar," *EJ,* Vol. 69, September 1959.

Oshima, H. T. "The Ranis-Fei Model of Economic Development: Comment" (followed by G. Ranis and J. C. H. Fei's reply), *AER,* Vol. 53, June 1963.

Ott, A. E. "The Relation Between the Accelerator and the Capital Output Ratio," *REStud,* Vol. 25, June 1958.

Ozga, S. A. "Capital Resources, Equilibrium and Growth," *Ec,* N.S., Vol. 29, November 1962.

Ozga, S. A. "The Propensity to Save, the Capital-Output Ratio, and the Equilibrium Rate of Growth," *Ec,* N.S., Vol. 31, November 1964.

Paige, D. "Economic Growth: The Last Hundred Years," *National Institute Economic Review,* No. 16, July 1961.

Pasinetti, L. L. "On Concepts and Measures of Changes in Productivity" (followed by R. M. Solow's comment and Pasinetti's reply), *REStat,* Vol. 41, August 1959.

Pasinetti, L. L. "A Mathematical Formulation of the Ricardian System," *REStud, Vol.* 27, February 1960.

Pasinetti, L. L. "Rate of Profit and Income Distribution in Relation to the Rate of Economic Growth," *REStud,* Vol. 29, October 1962.

Pasinetti, L. L. "A Comment on Professor Meade's 'Rate of Profit in a Growing Economy,'" *EJ,* Vol. 74, June 1964.

Pasinetti, L. L. "Changes in the Rate of Profit and Switches of Techniques" (Paradoxes in Capital Theory: A Symposium), *QJE,* Vol. 80, November 1966.

Patel, S. J. "Savings, Investment and Economic Growth: A Dynamic Approach," *ER,* Vol. 4, No. 4, August 1959.

Pearce, I. F. "The End of the Golden Age in Solovia: A Further Fable for Growthmen Hoping to be 'One Up' on Oiko" (followed by E. S. Phelps' comment), *AER*, Vol. 52, December 1962.

Pesek, B. P. "Kuznets' Incremental Capital-Output Ratios," *EDCC*, Vol. 12, October 1963.

Peterson, W. C. "Investment and the Threshold of Economic Growth," *Kyk*, Vol. 18, fasc. 1, 1965.

Pfouts, R. W. "Recent Capital and Production Theory: Discussion," *AER/S*, Vol. 55, May 1965.

Phelps, E. S. "The Golden Rule of Accumulation: A Fable for Growthmen," *AER*, Vol. 51, September 1961.

Phelps, E. S. "The New View of Investment; A Neo-Classical Analysis," *QJE*, Vol. 76, November 1962.

Phelps, E. S. "Substitution, Fixed Proportions, Growth and Distribution," *IER*, Vol. 4, September 1963.

Phelps, E. S. "Second Essay on the Golden Rule of Accumulation," *AER*, Vol. 55, September 1965.

Phelps, E. S. "Models of Technical Progress and the Golden Rule of Research," *REStud*, Vol. 33, No. 94, April 1966.

Phelps, E. S. *Golden Rules of Economic Growth* (New York: W. W. Norton, 1966).

Phillips, A. W. "Stabilization Policy in a Closed Economy," *EJ*, Vol. 64, June 1954.

Phillips, A. W. "A Simple Model of Employment, Money and Prices in a Growing Economy," *Ec*, Vol. 28, November 1961.

Phillips, A. W. "Employment, Inflation and Growth," *Ec*, Vol. 29, February 1962.

Pilvin, H. "Full Capacity versus Full Employment Growth" (followed by R. F. Harrod's comment and E. D. Domar's further comment), *QJE*, Vol. 67, November 1953.

Pitchford, J. D. "Growth and the Elasticity of Factor Substitution," *ER*, Vol. 36, December 1960.

Power, J. H. "Capital Intensity and Economic Growth," *AER/S*, Vol, 45, May 1955.

Power, J. H. "The Economic Framework of a Theory of Growth," *EJ*, Vol. 68, March 1958.

Power, J. H. "Laborsaving in Economic Growth," *AER/S*, Vol. 52, May 1962.

Prasad, P. H. "Business Cycle Phenomena in the Harrod-Domar Model," *IER*, Vol. 6, No. 1, January 1965.

Pryor, F. L. "Economic Growth and the Terms of Trade," *OEP*, Vol. 18, March 1966.

Pyatt, G. "A Measure of Capital," *REStud*, Vol. 30, October 1963.

Qayum, A. "Theory of Income Generation and Economic Growth," *EJ*, Vol. 70, December 1960.

Qayum, A. "Accumulation of Capital," *Met*, Vol. 15, April 1963.

Radner, R. "Paths of Economic Growth that are Optimal with Regard Only to Final States, A Turnpike Theorem," *REStud*, Vol. 28, February 1961.

Radner, R. *Notes on the Theory of Economic Planning* (Athens, 1963).

Radner, R. "On Intertemporal Efficiency," *Met*, Vol. 17, September–December 1965.

Radner, R. "Optimal Growth in a Linear-Logarithmic Economy," *IER*, Vol. 7, January 1966.

Radner, R. "Efficiency Prices for Infinite Horizon Production Programmes"

(Symposium on Optimal Infinite Programmes), *REStud*, Vol. 34, No. 97, January 1967.

Rahman, M. A. "Regional Allocation of Investment: An Aggregate Study in the Theory of Development Programming," *QJE*, Vol. 77, February 1963.

Ramaswami, V. K. "The Effects of Accumulation on the Terms of Trade," *EJ*, Vol. 70, September 1960.

Ranis, G. "Allocation Criteria and Population Growth," *AER/S*, Vol. 53, May 1963.

Ranis, G., and Fei, J. C. H. "A Theory of Economic Development," *AER*, Vol. 51, September 1961.

Ratchford, B. U. "Mr. Domar's 'Burden of the Debt,'" *AER*, Vol. 35, June 1945.

Reddaway, W. B., and Smith, A. D. "Progress in British Manufacturing Industries in the Period 1948–54," *EJ*, Vol. 70, March 1960.

Reiter, S. "Choosing an Investment Program Among Interdependent Projects," *REStud*, February 1963.

Resek, R. W. "Neutrality of Technical Progress," *REStat*, Vol. 45, February 1963.

Reubens, E. P. "Capital-Labor Ratios in Theory and in History: Comment" (followed by J. C. H. Fei and G. Ranis' reply), *AER*, Vol. 54, December 1964.

Robertson, D. H. *Growth, Wages and Money* (London: Cambridge University Press, 1961).

Robinson, J. "The Classification of Inventions," *REStud*, Vol. 5, February 1938.

Robinson, J. "Mr. Harrod's Dynamics," *EJ*, Vol. 59, March 1949.

Robinson, J. "The Model of an Expanding Economy," *EJ*, Vol. 62, March 1952.

Robinson, J. *The Rate of Interest and Other Essays* (London: Macmillan, 1952).

Robinson, J. *The Accumulation of Capital* (London: Macmillan, 1956).

Robinson, J. "Economic Growth and Capital Accumulation," *ER*, Vol. 33, April 1957.

Robinson, J. *Collected Economic Papers*, Vols. I, II, and III (Oxford: Blackwell, 1960).

Robinson, J. *Exercises in Economic Analysis* (London: Macmillan, 1960).

Robinson, J. "Equilibrium Growth Models," *AER*, Vol. 51, June 1961.

Robinson, J. "A Neo-Classical Theorem," *REStud*, Vol. 29, June 1962.

Robinson, J. *Essays in the Theory of Economic Growth* (New York: St. Martin's Press, 1962).

Robinson, J. "Learning by Doing: A Further Note," *REStud*, Vol. 30, October 1963.

Robinson, J. "Findlay's Robinsonian Model of Accumulation: A Comment," *Ec*, Vol. 30, November 1963.

Robinson, J. "Pre-Keynesian Theory After Keynes," *Australian Economic Papers*, Vol. 3, June–December 1964.

Robinson, J. "Comment on Samuelson and Modigliani" (followed by P. A. Samuelson and F. Modigliani's reply), *REStud*, Vol. 33, October 1966.

Robinson, R. "Employment, Growth and Price Levels: The Joint Economic Committee Report," *AER*, Vol. 50, December 1960.

Robson, R. "Note on the Output-Capital Ratio and the Return on Capital in Developing Countries," *OEP*, Vol. 17, July 1965.

Rose, H. "The Possibility of Warranted Growth," *EJ*, Vol. 69, June 1959.
Rose, H. "Expectations and Stability in Neo-Keynesian Growth Theory," *QJE*, Vol. 77, February 1963.
Rose, H. "Unemployment in a Theory of Growth," *IER*, Vol. 7, September 1966.
Rosenberg, N. "Capital Goods, Technology and Economic Growth," *OEP*, N.S., Vol. 15, November 1963.
Rosenberg, N. "Neglected Dimensions in the Analysis of Economic Change," *OIS*, Vol. 26, February 1964.
Rosenberg, N. "Economic Instruction for Economic Growth," *EDCC*, Vol. 13, October 1964.
Rosenberg, N., and Ames, E. "Changing Technological Leadership and Industrial Growth," *EJ*, Vol. 73, March 1963.
Rothbarth, E. "Causes of the Superior Efficiency of U.S.A. Industry as Compared with British Industry," *EJ*, Vol. 56, September 1946.
Rothschild, K. W. "The Limitations of Economic Growth Models: Critical Remarks on Some Aspects of Mr. Kaldor's Model," *Kyk*, Vol. 12, fasc. 4, 1959.
Salant, W. A. "Savings, Investment and Stability," *AER/S*, Vol. 46, May 1956.
Salter, W. E. G. *Productivity and Technical Change* (London: Cambridge University Press, 1960).
Salter, W. E. G. "Productivity Growth and Accumulation as Historical Processes," paper presented to International Economic Association Congress on Problems in Economic Development, Vienna, 1962.
Salviucci (and others). *The Econometric Approach to Development Planning* (Amsterdam and Chicago: North-Holland Publishing Co. and Rand-McNally & Co., 1966, a reissue of *Pontificiae Academiae Scientiarium Scripta Varia*, Vol. 28, 1965).
Samuelson, P. A. *Foundations of Economic Analysis* (Cambridge, Mass.: Harvard University Press, 1947).
Samuelson, P. A. "Abstract of a Model Concerning Substitutability in Open Leontief Models," *Activity Analysis of Production and Allocation*, edited by T. C. Koopmans (New York: Wiley, 1951).
Samuelson, P. A. "Prices of Factors and Goods in General Equilibrium," *REStud*, Vol. 21, No. 1, 1953.
Samuelson, P. A. "An Exact Consumption-loan Model of Interest with or without the Social Contrivance of Money," *JPE*, Vol. 66, December 1958.
Samuelson, P. A. "A Modern Treatment of the Ricardian Economy: I. The Pricing of Goods and of Labor and Land Services. II. Capital and Interest of the Pricing Process," *QJE*, Vol. 73, February–May 1959.
Samuelson, P. A. "Efficient Paths of Capital Accumulation in Terms of the Calculus of Variations," *Mathematical Methods in the Social Sciences*, edited by K. J. Arrow, S. Karlin, and P. Suppes (Stanford: Stanford University Press, 1960).
Samuelson, P. A. "Parable and Realism in Capital Theory: The Surrogate Production Function," *REStud*, Vol. 29, June 1962.
Samuelson, P. A. "A Catenary Turnpike Theorem Involving Consumption and the Golden Rule," *AER*, Vol. 55, June 1965.
Samuelson, P. A. "A Theory of Induced Innovation Along Kennedy-Weizsacker Lines," *REStat*, Vol. 47, November 1965.
Samuelson, P. A. *The Collected Scientific Papers of Paul A. Samuelson*, Vols. I and II, edited by J. E. Stiglitz (Cambridge, Mass.: M.I.T. Press, 1966).

Samuelson, P. A., and Modigliani, F. "The Pasinetti Paradox in Neoclassical and More General Models," *REStud*, Vol. 33, October 1966.

Samuelson, P. A., and Solow, R. M. "Balanced Growth under Constant Returns to Scale," *Em*, Vol. 21, July 1953.

Samuelson P. A., and Solow, R. M. "A Complete Capital Model Involving Heterogeneous Capital Goods," *QJE*, Vol. 70, November 1956.

Sargan, J. D. "Mrs. Robinson's Warranted Rate of Growth," *YB*, Vol. 10, June 1958.

Sargan, J. D. "The Instability of the Leontief Dynamic Model," *Em*, Vol. 26, July 1958.

Sargent, J. R. "The Stability of Growth Equilibrium: Comment," *QJE*, Vol. 76, August 1962.

Sato, K. "On the Adjustment Time in Neo-classical Growth Models," *REStud*, Vol. 33, July 1966.

Sato, K. "The Neo-classical Theorem and Distribution of Income and Wealth," *REStud*, Vol. 33, October 1966.

Sato, R. "Fiscal Policy in a Neo-classical Growth Model: An Analysis of Time Required for Equilibrating Adjustment," *REStud*, Vol. 30, February 1963.

Sato, R. "The Harrod-Domar Model vs the Neo-classical Growth Model," *EJ*, Vol. 74, June 1964.

Sato, R., and Kendrick, J. W. "Factor Prices, Productivity and Economic Growth," *AER*, Vol. 53, December 1963.

Sau, R. K. "Rules of the Game in the Solow Model with Cobb-Douglas Production Function," *Met*, Vol. 14, April–August–December 1962.

Sau, R. K. "Intertemporal Efficiency of Capital Accumulation and the von Neumann Ray," *QJE*, Vol. 79, November 1965.

Schmookler, J. "Technological Change and Economic Theory," *AER/S*, Vol. 55, March 1965.

Schmookler, J. *Invention and Economic Growth* (Cambridge Mass.: Harvard University Press, 1964).

Schneider, E. "Income and Income Distribution in Macro-Economic Theory," *International Economic Papers*, No. 8, 1958.

Schumpeter, J. A. *Business Cycles* (New York: McGraw Hill, 1939).

Schwartz, E. "On Relative Rates of Economic Growth," *WA*, Vol. 92, Hft. 2, 1964.

Schwartz, J. T. *Lectures on the Mathematical Method in Analytical Economics* (New York: Gordon and Breach, 1961).

Scitovsky, T. *Papers on Welfare and Growth* (Stanford: Stanford University Press, 1964).

Seers, D. "A Model of Comparative Rates of Growth in the World Economy," *EJ*, Vol. 72, March 1962.

Seers, D. "Normal Growth and Distortions: Some Techniques of Structural Analysis," *OEP*, N.S., Vol. 16, March 1964.

Sen, A. K. "Unemployment, Relative Prices and the Saving Potential," *IER*, Vol. 3, No. 4, August 1957.

Sen, A. K. "A Note on Tinbergen on the Optimum Rate of Saving," *EJ*, Vol. 67, December 1957.

Sen, A. K. "On Optimizing the Rate of Saving" *EJ*, Vol. 71, September 1961.

Sen, A. K. "On the Usefulness of Used Machines," *REStat*, Vol. 44, August 1962.

Sen, P. K. "Use of Capital-output Ratio in Economic Planning," *IER*, Vol. 5, February 1960.

Sengupta, J. K. "On the Relative Stability and Optimality of Consumption in Aggregative Growth Models," *Ec,* N.S., Vol. 31, February 1964.
Sengupta, J. K. "Policy Criteria for Stabilization and Growth," *OEP,* N.S., Vol. 16, November 1964.
Sengupta, J. K. "Equilibrium, Stability and Growth," *Kyk,* Vol. 18, fasc. 2, 1965.
Sengupta, J. K. "Truncated Decision Rules and Optimal Economic Growth with a Fixed Horizon," *IER,* Vol. 7, January 1966.
Sengupta, J. K., and Tintner, G. "On Some Aspects of Trend in the Aggregative Models of Economic Growth," *Kyk,* Vol. 16, fasc. 1, 1963.
Sengupta, J. K., and Tintner, G. "The Flexibility and Optimality of Domar-Type Growth Models," *Met,* Vol. 17, January–August 1965.
Sengupta, J. K., and Walker, D. A. "On the Empirical Specification of Optimal Economic Policy for Growth and Stabilization under a Macro-Dynamic Model," *MS,* Vol. 32, September 1964.
Shearer, R. A. "The Concept of Economic Growth," *Kyk,* Vol. 14, fasc. 4, 1961.
Shell, K. "Toward a Theory of Inventive Activity and Capital Accumulation," *AER,* Vol. 56, May 1966.
Shell, K. (ed.). *Essays on the Theory of Optimal Economic Growth* (Cambridge, Mass.: M.I.T. Press, 1967).
Shinkai, Y. "On Equilibrium Growth of Capital and Labor," *IER,* Vol. 1, May 1960.
Shinkai, Y. "An Effect of Price Changes in the Harrod–Domar Model," *QJE,* Vol. 77, August 1963.
Shone, R. "Problems of Planning for Economic Growth in a Mixed Economy," *EJ,* Vol. 75, March 1965.
Simon, H. A., and Ando, A. "Aggregation of Variables in Dynamic Systems," *Em,* Vol. 29, April 1961.
Singer, H. W. *International Development: Growth and Change* (New York: McGraw Hill, 1964).
Singer, M. "Theories of Economic Growth," *Kyk,* Vol. 15, fasc. 4, 1962.
Sirkin, G. "Professor Dobb on Investment Criteria," *Kyk,* Vol. 17, fasc. 3, 1964.
Smith, P. E. "A Note on Comparative Advantage, Trade and the Turnpike," *Journal of Regional Science,* Vol. 5, No. 2, 1964.
Smith, W. L. "Monetary-fiscal Policy and Economic Growth," *QJE,* Vol. 71, February 1957.
Smithies, A. "Economic Fluctuations and Growth," *Em,* Vol. 25, January 1957.
Smithies, A. "Productivity, Real Wages and Economic Growth," *QJE,* Vol. 74, May 1960.
Solow, R. M. "A Contribution to the Theory of Economic Growth," *QJE,* Vol. 70, February 1956.
Solow, R. M. "Technical Change and the Aggregate Production Function," *REStat,* Vol. 39, August 1957.
Solow, R. M. "Competitive Valuation in a Dynamic Input-Output System," *Em,* Vol. 27, January 1959.
Solow, R. M. "Is Factor Substitution a Crime, and if so, How Bad? Reply to Professor Eisner," *EJ,* Vol. 69, September 1959.
Solow, R. M. "Investment and Technical Progress," *Mathematical Methods in the Social Sciences,* edited by K. J. Arrow, S. Karlin, and P. Suppes (Stanford: Stanford University Press, 1960).

Solow, R. M. "Note on Uzawa's Two Sector Model of Economic Growth," *REStud*, Vol. 29, October 1961.

Solow, R. M. "Technical Progress, Capital Formation and Economic Growth," *AER Papers and Proceedings*, Vol. 52, May 1962.

Solow, R. M. "Substitution and Fixed Proportions in the Theory of Capital," *REStud*, Vol. 29, June 1962.

Solow, R. M. *Capital Theory and the Rate of Return* (Amsterdam: North Holland Publishing Co., 1963).

Solow, R. M. "Heterogeneous Capital and Smooth Production Functions: an Experimental Study," *Em*, Vol. 31, October 1963.

Solow, R. M., and Samuelson, P. A. "Balanced Growth under Constant Returns to Scale," *Em*, Vol. 21, July 1953.

Solow, R. M., and Samuelson, P. A. "A Note on the Price Level and Interest Rate in a Growth Model," *REStud*, Vol. 21, No. 1, 1953.

Solow, R. M., Tobin, J., von Weizsäcker, C. C., and Yaari, M. "Neoclassical Growth with Fixed Factor Proportions," *REStud*, Vol. 33, April 1966.

Soper, C. S. "Jorgenson on Stability in the Sense of Harrod," *Ec*, N.S., Vol. 31, November 1964.

Soper, C. S. "The Elasticity of Substitution," *ER*, Vol. 41, December 1965.

Sprinkel, B. W. "Relative Economic Growth Rates and Fiscal-monetary Policies," *JPE*, Vol. 71, April 1963.

Sraffa, P. *Production of Commodities by Means of Commodities* (London: Cambridge University Press, 1960).

Srinivasan, T. N. "Optimal Savings in a Two-sector Model of Growth," *Em*, Vol. 32, July 1964; "Errata," *Em*, Vol. 33, April 1965.

Stein, J. L. "Economic Growth in the West," *EC*, Vol. 32, February 1965.

Stein, J. L. "Money and Capacity Growth," *JPE*, Vol. 74, October 1966.

Stern, E. H. "Capital Requirements in Progressive Economies," *Ec*, N.S., Vol. 12, August 1945.

Stern, E. H. "The Problem of Capital Accumulation" (followed by E. D. Domar's rejoinder), *AER*, Vol. 39, December 1949.

Stoleru, L. G. "An Optimal Policy for Economic Growth," *Em*, Vol. 33, April 1965.

Stone, J. R. N., and Brown, J. A. C. "Output and Investment for Exponential Growth in Consumption," *REStud*, Vol. 29, June 1962.

Straussman, W. P. "Economic Growth and Income Distribution," *QJE*, Vol. 70, August 1956.

Straussman, W. P. "Interrelated Industries and the Rate of Technological Change," *REStud*, Vol. 27, October 1959.

Streeten, P. "Unbalanced Growth," *OEP*, Vol. 11, June 1959.

Streissler, E. "Population Change and Economic Growth," *Zeitschrift für Nationalökonomie*, Vol. 17, July 1957.

Suits, D. B. "Dynamic Growth under Diminishing Returns to Scale," *Em*, Vol. 22, October 1954.

Sutcliffe, R. B. "Balanced and Unbalanced Growth," *QJE*, Vol. 78, November 1964.

Swan, T. W. "Economic Growth and Capital Accumulation," *ER*, Vol. 32, November 1956.

Swan, T. W. "Growth Models of Golden Ages and Production Functions," *Economic Development with Special Reference to East Asia*, edited by K. E. Berrill (London: Macmillan, 1963).

Sweezy, A. R. "Population Growth and Investment Opportunity," *QJE*, Vol. 55, November 1940.

Takayama, A. "On a Two-Sector Model of Economic Growth: A Comparative Statics Analysis, I," *REStud*, Vol. 30, June 1963.
Takayama, A. "On a Two-Sector Model of Economic Growth with Technological Progress: A Comparative Statics Analysis," *REStud*, Vol. 32, July 1965.
Takayama, A. "A Reconsideration of the Nurkse Balanced Growth Thesis," *IER*, Vol. 8, No. 1, February 1967.
Tinbergen, J. "The Optimum Rate of Saving," *EJ*, Vol. 66, December 1956.
Tinbergen, J. "Optimum Savings and Utility Maximization Over Time," *Em*, Vol. 28, April 1960.
Tinbergen, J., and Bos, H. C. *Mathematical Models of Economic Growth* (New York: McGraw-Hill, 1962).
Tobin, J. "A Dynamic Aggregative Model," *JPE*, Vol. 63, April 1955.
Tobin, J. "On Growth Models and the Neo-Classical Resurgence" (Reply to Professor Eisner), *EJ*, Vol. 69, September 1959.
Tobin, J. "Towards a General Kaldorian Theory of Distribution," *REStud*, Vol. 27, February 1960.
Tobin, J. "Economic Growth as an Objective of Government Policy" (with discussion by H. G. Johnson and H. Stein), *AER/S*, Vol. 54, May 1964.
Tobin, J. "Money and Economic Growth," *Em*, Vol. 33, October 1965.
Trezza, B. "Stability of Harrod's Model: A Comment on Hahn and Matthews" (followed by F. H. Hahn and R. C. O. Matthews' reply), *EJ*, Vol. 76, December 1966.
Tsiang, S. C. "A Model of Economic Growth in Rostovian Stages," *Em*, Vol. 32, October 1964.
Tsukui, J. "On a Theorem of Relative Stability," *IER*, Vol. 2, May 1961.
Tsukui, J. "The Consumption and the Output Turnpike Theorems in a von Neumann Type of Model: A Finite Term Problem" (Symposium on Optimal Infinite Programmes), *REStud*, Vol. 34, No. 97, January 1967.
Urquhart, M. C. "Capital Accumulation, Technological Change and Economic Growth," *CJE*, Vol. 25, November 1959.
Uzawa, H. "Neutral Inventions and the Stability of Growth Equilibrium," *REStud*, Vol. 28, February 1961.
Uzawa, H. "On a Two-sector Model of Economic Growth: I," *REStud*, Vol. 29, October 1961.
Uzawa, H. "Production Functions with Constant Elasticities of Substitution," *REStud*, Vol. 29, October 1962.
Uzawa, H. "On a Two-sector Model of Economic Growth: II," *REStud*, Vol. 30, June 1963.
Uzawa, H. "Optimal Growth in a Two-sector Model of Capital Accumulation," *REStud*, Vol. 31, January 1964.
Uzawa, H. "Optimum Technical Change in a Aggregative Model of Economic Growth," *IER*, Vol. 6, No. 1, January 1965.
Uzawa, H. "On a Neo-classical Model of Economic Growth," *Economic Studies Quarterly*, Vol. 17, 1966.
Vanek, J. "Toward a More General Theory of Growth with Technological Change," *EJ*, Vol. 76, December 1966.
Vanek, J. "A Theory of Growth with Technological Change," *AER*, Vol. 57, March 1967.
van Rijckeghem, W. "Some Further Properties of Cobb-Douglas Growth Models," *Southern Economic Journal*, Vol. 31, July 1964.
Verdoorn, P. J. "Complementarity and Long-range Projections," *Em*, Vol. 24, October 1956.

von Neumann, J. "Uber ein okonomisches Gleichungsystem und eine Verallgemeinerung des Brouwerschen Fixpunktsatzes," *Ergebnisse eines Mathematischen Seminars* (Vienna, 1938). Translated by G. Morgenstern as "A Model of General Equilibrium," *REStud*, Vol. 13, 1945–46.

von Weizsäcker, C. C. "Existence of Optimal Programs of Accumulation for an Infinite Time Horizon," *REStud*, Vol. 32, April 1965.

von Weizsäcker, C. C. "Tentative Notes on a Two-sector Model with Induced Technical Progress," *REStud*, Vol. 33, July 1966.

von Weizsäcker, C. C. "Lemmas for a Theory of Approximate Optimal Growth" (Symposium on Optimal Infinite Programmes), *REStud*, Vol. 34, No. 97, January 1967.

Walters, A. A. "The Accelerator and Technical Progress," *REStud*, Vol. 30, February 1963.

Walters, A. A. "Production and Cost Functions: An Econometric Survey," *Em*, Vol. 31, January–April 1963.

Walters, A. A. "Incremental Capital–Output Ratios," *EJ*, Vol. 76, December 1966.

Wan, H. Y., Jr. "Intertemporal Optimization with Systematically Shifting Cost and Revenue Functions," *IER*, Vol. 7, May 1966.

Weil, R. L., Jr. "An Algorithm for the Von Neumann Economy," *Zeitschrift für Nationalökonomie*, Vol. 24, November 1964.

Weintraub, S. *Approach to the Theory of Income Distribution* (Chilton, 1958).

Weldon, J. C., and Asimakopulos, A. "The Classification of Technical Progress in Models of Economic Growth," *Ec*, Vol. 30, November 1963.

Westfield, F. M. "A Mathematical Note on Optimum Longevity," *AER*, Vol. 48, June 1958.

Westfield, F. M. "Time-preference and Economic Growth: Comment" (followed by W. Leontief's reply), *AER*, Vol. 49, December 1959.

Whittlesey, C. R. "Relation of Money to Economic Growth," *AER*, Vol. 46, May 1956.

Winter, S. G., Jr. "A Boundedness Property of the Closed Linear Model of Production," *Review* P–2, 3, and 4, July 1961.

Winter, S. G., Jr. "Some Properties of the Closed Linear Model of Production," *IER*, Vol. 6, May 1965.

Winter, S. G., Jr. "The Norm of a Closed Technology and the Straight-Down-the-Turnpike Theorem" (Symposium on Optimal Infinite Programmes), *REStud*, Vol. 34, No. 97, January 1967.

Worswick, G. D. N. "Mrs. Robinson on Simple Accumulation: a Comment with Algebra" (followed by J. Robinson's comment), *OEP*, N.S., Vol. 11, June 1959.

Wurtele, Z. S. "Equilibrium in a Uniformly Expanding Closed Leontief-type System," *REStud*, Vol. 28, October 1960.

Yeager, L. B. "Some Questions about Growth Economics," *AER*, Vol. 44, March 1954.

Zabel, E. "A Multi-sectoral Study of Economic Growth," *Ec*, N.S., Vol. 29, August 1962.

Zauberman, A. "A Few Remarks on Kalecki's Theory of Economic Growth under Socialism," *Kyk*, Vol. [illegible], fasc. 3, 1966.